MW00624067

# SOLAR HEATING AND COOLING

# SOLAR HEATING AND COOLING

## Recent Advances

J.K. Paul

NOYES DATA CORPORATION

Park Ridge, New Jersey, U.S.A.

Copyright © 1977 by Noyes Data Corporation
    No part of this book may be reproduced in any form
    without permission in writing from the Publisher.
Library of Congress Catalog Card Number: 77-89630
ISBN: 0-8155-0674-0
Printed in the United States

Published in the United States of America by
Noyes Data Corporation
Noyes Building, Park Ridge, New Jersey 07656

# FOREWORD

The detailed, descriptive information in this book is based on U.S. patents issued since 1970 that deal with solar heating and cooling.

This book serves a double purpose in that it supplies detailed technical information and can be used as a guide to the U.S. patent literature in this field. By indicating all the information that is significant, and eliminating legal jargon and juristic phraseology, this book presents an advanced, technically oriented review of solar heating and cooling.

The U.S. patent literature is the largest and most comprehensive collection of technical information in the world. There is more practical, commercial, timely process information assembled here than is available from any other source. The technical information obtained from a patent is extremely reliable and comprehensive; sufficient information must be included to avoid rejection for "insufficient disclosure." These patents include practically all of those issued on the subject in the United States during the period under review; there has been no bias in the selection of patents for inclusion.

The patent literature covers a substantial amount of information not available in the journal literature. The patent literature is a prime source of basic commercially useful information. This information is overlooked by those who rely primarily on the periodical journal literature. It is realized that there is a lag between a patent application on a new process development and the granting of a patent, but it is felt that this may roughly parallel or even anticipate the lag in putting that development into commercial practice.

Many of these patents are being utilized commercially. Whether used or not, they offer opportunities for technological transfer. Also, a major purpose of this book is to describe the number of technical possibilities available, which may open up profitable areas of research and development. The information contained in this book will allow you to establish a sound background before launching into research in this field.

Advance composition and production methods developed by Noyes Data are employed to bring our durably bound books to you in a minimum of time. Special techniques are used to close the gap between "manuscript" and "completed book." Industrial technology is progressing so rapidly that time-honored, conventional typesetting, binding and shipping methods are no longer suitable. We have bypassed the delays in the conventional book publishing cycle and provide the user with an effective and convenient means of reviewing up-to-date information in depth.

The Table of Contents is organized in such a way as to serve as a subject index. Other indexes by company, inventor and patent number help in providing easy access to the information contained in this book.

**15 Reasons Why the U.S. Patent Office Literature Is Important to You —**

1. The U.S. patent literature is the largest and most comprehensive collection of technical information in the world. There is more practical commercial process information assembled here than is available from any other source.

2. The technical information obtained from the patent literature is extremely comprehensive; sufficient information must be included to avoid rejection for "insufficient disclosure."

3. The patent literature is a prime source of basic commercially utilizable information. This information is overlooked by those who rely primarily on the periodical journal literature.

4. An important feature of the patent literature is that it can serve to avoid duplication of research and development.

5. Patents, unlike periodical literature, are bound by definition to contain new information, data and ideas.

6. It can serve as a source of new ideas in a different but related field, and may be outside the patent protection offered the original invention.

7. Since claims are narrowly defined, much valuable information is included that may be outside the legal protection afforded by the claims.

8. Patents discuss the difficulties associated with previous research, development or production techniques, and offer a specific method of overcoming problems. This gives clues to current process information that has not been published in periodicals or books.

9. Can aid in process design by providing a selection of alternate techniques. A powerful research and engineering tool.

10. Obtain licenses — many U.S. chemical patents have not been developed commercially.

11. Patents provide an excellent starting point for the next investigator.

12. Frequently, innovations derived from research are first disclosed in the patent literature, prior to coverage in the periodical literature.

13. Patents offer a most valuable method of keeping abreast of latest technologies, serving an individual's own "current awareness" program.

14. Copies of U.S. patents are easily obtained from the U.S. Patent Office at 50¢ a copy.

15. It is a creative source of ideas for those with imagination.

# CONTENTS AND SUBJECT INDEX

# INTRODUCTION

Solar energy is a vast and relatively untapped energy source, available to all but, as yet, used by only a few. Since more than 25% of the total energy consumed in this country is used for the heating and cooling of buildings and the provision of hot water, the diversion of this energy demand from fossil fuels to an alternate source such as solar energy would result in a substantial reduction in the nation's dependence on fossil fuels. It has been projected that by the year 2020 as much as 50% of the thermal energy needed for heating and cooling of buildings could be provided by the sun. While the initial installation cost of either a new or retrofitted solar system may seem high to the prospective buyer, the fact that in most locations a great percentage of future operating costs would be saved may be incentive enough to induce him to invest in such a system, especially as the costs of other natural resources continue to increase.

The technology for solar energy utilization is becoming increasingly available, as indicated by the large number of patents issued in the past several years. Recent developments encompass a number of areas, two of which will be treated in this book—low temperature solar collector construction and heating and cooling systems which utilize these low temperature collectors. The material discussed is based on 175 patents, issued since 1970, which illustrate 157 processes.

Collectors can be categorized into three basic classes: (1) flat plate collectors which collect but do not concentrate the sun's radiant energy, (2) medium performance focusing collectors which utilize a curved surface to focus the sun's rays on a heat exchange means such as a collecting pipe or plate-type collector and are adapted for slightly higher temperatures than the flat plate-type and (3) concentrating collectors which utilize large, curved surface concentrators or concentrators composed of multiple mirrors to reach high temperatures for use in operating steam generators, turbines and the like. The first two types have application to direct heating and cooling of buildings and these in various forms are covered here. A flat plate collector is relatively simple to assemble, but a large number of collectors may be necessary to achieve the desired heat capacity. Alternatively, the focusing collector, while somewhat more complex, may supply more heat per unit area and thus effect a more efficient collection of solar energy. Obviously, the choice of collector will depend on the needs of the individual user.

1

In its simplest form a flat plate collector consists of a sheet of glass or transparent material situated above a "flat" plate so constructed that it acts as a black body to absorb heat. The sun's rays pass through the glass and are trapped in the space between the cover and plate or are absorbed by the black body. The heat may then be utilized by passing a fluid through a conduit system located between the cover and absorber plate, the heated fluid subsequently being used to heat a home, water supply, or swimming pool. Flat plate collectors, the majority of which are intended for rooftop installation, may be modified to improve their absorbing properties and a number of such modifications are presented in the first chapter as are various insulation means, conduit dispositions and a few miscellaneous applications.

The second chapter deals with focusing collectors which use curved or combinations of flat devices to reflect solar rays onto an absorber surface to achieve a greater concentration of energy (higher temperature) than is possible with the flat plate collector. Included under focusing collectors are parabolic and other curved reflectors, as well as a few lens configurations.

Information has been included describing several coatings used to improve absorption properties and detailing a number of devices which employ liquids, crushed rock or other media for the storage of absorbed energy for use at times when the weather is cloudy or hazy, or at night. A chapter on upright collectors covers window and wall installations which cannot strictly be considered flat plate collectors.

The heating and cooling systems described, while suitable for single building units, can be scaled up and a few large scale systems are noted. These systems essentially employ a liquid or gaseous circulation medium, pumps, and temperature sensing devices to condition the air in an individual building structure. To date relatively little has been done on cooling ("air conditioning") systems per se; however, several systems which can operate in both heating and cooling modes are included as well as those systems used only for heating. Some of the systems have storage facilities, some do not; many rely on auxiliary, conventional systems to supply additional heat when necessary.

The use of solar energy for the heating of water for personal consumption has been popular in Australia, Israel and Japan for many years. It is expected that a market for hot water heating systems will emerge in the U.S. soon also. Several units are described in the chapter on domestic hot water systems and many others can be envisioned by extension, using information available in other sections of the book.

Finally, it is estimated that there are in excess of 500,000 swimming pools in this country, many of which burn fossil fuels. Some states have already passed legislation prohibiting the use of fossil fuels for pool heating, thereby almost requiring that pools be heated by solar energy. Other states will no doubt follow suit. Therefore, a chapter has been included on applications for use with swimming pools, another simple and basic system readily adaptable for conversion to solar heating.

# FLAT PLATE COLLECTORS

## ABSORBER ARRANGEMENTS

### Heat Trap Formed by Elongated Diverging Channels

The process of *R.D. Cummings; U.S. Patent 4,019,496; April 26, 1977; assigned to Daystar Corporation* makes possible highly efficient solar-to-thermal energy conversion by providing for highly effective inhibition of radiation and convection losses of thermal energy, while maximizing transmission of solar energy to the absorber. A heat trap is provided which is durable, reliable, dimensionally stable at operating temperatures and easily and inexpensively manufactured.

In general the process features, in a solar-to-thermal energy converter comprising an insulated frame, a solar energy absorber mounted in the frame, fluid flow heat exchanger means thermally coupled to the absorber to carry away as thermal energy the absorbed solar energy, and a window transmissive to solar energy mounted in the frame and spaced from the absorber, that improvement consisting of a heat loss suppressor comprising a multiplicity of walls extending between the window and the absorber, adjacent walls being at least in part nonparallel to each other to define a first set of elongated channels generally diverging and opening toward the window interleaved with a second set of elongated channels generally diverging and opening toward the absorber, the walls being of material transmissive to solar energy and absorptive of thermal energy, the channels being narrow enough to reduce convection heat loss and deep enough to reduce radiation heat loss.

In preferred examples the suppressor is a sheet of the material folded in zigzag form to form the channels between adjacent folds, the depth of the channels is at least three times (and most preferably at least ten times) and no more than twenty times their maximum width, the maximum channel width is no more than $\frac{3}{8}$ inch, the sheet has peripheral flanges connected to the frame and the fold lines at the closed ends of the channels of the second set contact the window, and the frame has internal side walls which converge along the direction from the window toward the absorber. The process is applicable to all temperature ranges.

3

Referring to Figure 1.1, rectangular 4 x 7 foot frame **10** has an insulated bottom **12** and insulated sides **14**, **16** with sloping interior side walls **18**, **20** to provide a window area **22** larger than the exposed bottom area **24**, increasing efficiency. Heat absorber **25** is mounted on bottom **12**, with its periphery retained in frame recess **26**. Transparent window **28**, with channel supports **30**, **32** along its edges, is mounted on top of the frame over window area **22**. Pleated trap **34** is mounted between the window and the absorber.

Absorber **25** has black surfaces to absorb the solar energy passing through window **28**. Channels **40** are connected to manifolds **42** and **44** which in turn feed inlet and outlet conduits **46** and **48** to permit liquid circulation through the absorber to transfer heat absorbed to a point of use.

Trap **34** is of plastic material highly transmissive of light energy and highly absorptive of heat energy. It is pleated to form one set of wedge-shaped channels **50** which diverge and open toward window **28** and a second set of wedge-shaped channels **52** which are interleaved with channels **50** and which diverge and open toward absorber **25**. The end pleats **54** are shallower than the rest, lie along walls **20** and have flaps **56** sandwiched between the frame and channels **32**. Similar flaps **58** are attached to the long sides of the trap near its top and are sandwiched between the frame and channels **30**. In this way the upper vertices **60** of the trap are held against the window **28**.

Slots **62** are provided in channels **30** to receive vertices **60**. Spacers **64** are mounted on walls **18** and have lugs **66** to fit between adjacent pleats. The spacers cooperate with slots **62** to maintain the pleated geometry of the trap. Lower vertices **68** of the trap are spaced sufficiently above the absorber to allow for temperature-induced expansion during use.

The example shown is designed to operate as a flat plate collector in the low temperature (e.g., below 400°F) region. It is preferably installed so that channels **50** extend generally parallel to the east-west arc **70** swept by the sun's rays during the day. In operation, most incoming rays **72** will strike a surface **73** of trap **34** at a small acute angle A.

The major component of the ray will be transmitted toward the absorber. The small reflected components **72a** will also head toward the absorber because of the small value of A, which is also the angle of reflection. Ray **72a** will hit the opposite wall **74** at another small acute angle B, and, again, most of that ray will be transmitted to the absorber with a small component **72b** being reflected back to surface **73**. Such successive interactions occur in each converging channel **50**, until virtually the entire energy in the incoming rays reaches the absorber.

As a fraction of the absorbed heat is radiated back from the absorber into channels **52** along lines **80**, it is absorbed by the channel walls, e.g., at **82**. A fraction of that heat absorbed at **82** is symmetrically reradiated along lines **84**, again to be absorbed by the trap walls. In this way, the spectrally selective transmissive-absorptive qualities of the trap material, along with the geometry of the interleaved channels, provide for retention in the collector of a very high percentage of the incoming light. The efficiency of the collector is even further increased by the convection suppression function of trap **34**. In the first place, because the trap is formed from a continuous sheet of material it forms a virtually complete convection barrier across the collector between the window and the absorber. In this sense it offers the advantages of a second window without its disadvantages. In the second place, the narrow width of channels **52** provides insufficient space for generation of natural convection cells.

## FIGURE 1.1: HEAT TRAP FORMED BY ELONGATED DIVERGING CHANNELS

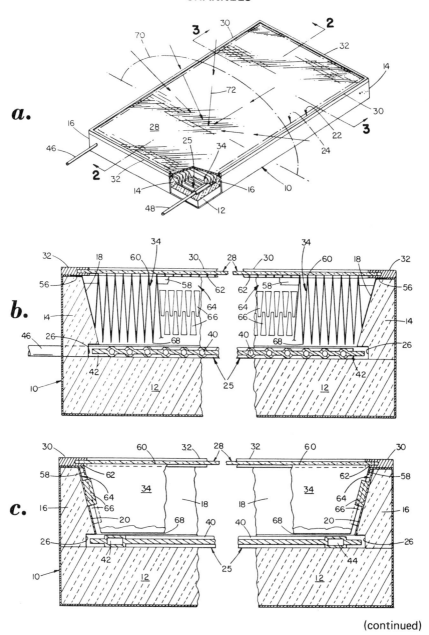

(continued)

**FIGURE 1.1:** (continued)

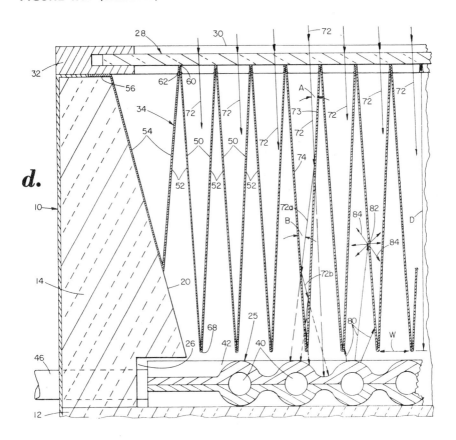

(a)   A perspective view of flat plate collector
(b)(c)  Sectional views partially broken away taken respectively
        along lines **2—2** and **3—3** of Figure 1.1a
(d)   Enlarged view of fragment of Figure 1.1b

Source:  U.S. Patent 4,019,496

**Finned Heat Transfer Plate**

*Y.B. Safdari; U.S. Patent 4,019,494; April 26, 1977* provides a solar heat generator which incorporates a finned heat-absorbing and transfer plate which employs
upstanding fins of relatively small length which are arranged in uniformly spaced
rows across the direction of gas flow, with the fins in each row laterally displaced a constant, relatively short distance from the position of the fins in the
upstream adjacent row.

As shown in Figures 1.2a and 1.2b, the apparatus comprises a heat exchange
plate **10** having a flat base plate **11**, to one surface of which are affixed a plu-

rality of upstanding fins **12**. Both base plate and fins are made of a thin, heat-conductive material, such as aluminum or other metal, the surface of which is adapted (e.g., polished) to aid in the transfer of heat from the plate to a stream of gas in contact therewith, in accordance with principles known to those skilled in the art. In the example shown, each of the fins is square or rectangular, although it is also within the scope of the process to use fins having other shapes, e.g., trapezoidal or arcuate. It should be understood when any dimension of a fin, such as its length, is referred to herein, the average dimension is intended.

The fins are arranged in rows extending transversely and preferably perpendicularly to the direction of air flow. While it is preferred that each of the fins be perpendicular to the base plate, i.e., that the fin form an angle of about $90°$ with the base plate, it is also within the contemplation of the process to use angles of attachment which differ from $90°$. All of the fins in a row are generally parallel to the direction of air flow and equidistantly spaced along the row. The fins in any given row (e.g., **12**) are laterally displaced a constant distance **D** from the fins (e.g., **12a**) in the adjacent upstream row. The direction of displacement (i.e., right or left) is constant throughout the plate.

While the actual dimensions of the fins used in a specific heat exchange plate of the process depend on the particular requirements, e.g., the heat load, the desired quantity of air to be heated and the temperature to be achieved in the air stream, the relative dimensions of the fins and the spacing of the fins in the plate can be specified.

For an arrangement in which the spacing between adjacent fins **12** is **S**, the length **L** of the fins is about 0.75 **S** to 5.0 **S**, and preferably about 1.0 **S** to 3.0 **S** and the height **H** of the fins is about 1.0 **S** to 5.0 **S** and preferably about 1.375 **S** to 4.13 **S**, while the lateral displacement **D** between the fins in one row and the fins in the next adjacent row in the direction of air travel is about 0.1 **S** to 0.5 **S** and preferably within the range of about 0.125 **S** to 0.375 **S**.

In the preferred form shown in the figures, it will be seen that there is no overlap, in the direction of air travel, between the end of the fins in one row and the beginning of the fins in the downstream row, i.e., the projected ends of the fins in adjacent rows fall on a line.

As seen in Figure 1.2a, two adjoining edges of base plate **11** are provided with offset lips **13** and **14**, which permits a plurality of individual heat exchange plates **10** to be assembled with a free edge of base plate **11** resting on and supported by the lips of adjacent plate assemblies. In this manner, a composite heat exchange surface can be made to any desired size by the use of individual plates such as that shown in Figure 1.2a. A portion of such an assembly is shown in Figure 1.2b, with each plate in turn supporting and being supported by the lips **13** and **14** on the individual plates. In such a construction, any suitable means of attachment between adjacent plates can be used, such as rivets, soldering, welding and the like.

A typical solar heat generator in accordance with the process which is suitable for use in space heating and cooling of homes is illustrated in Figures 1.2c and 1.2d. As shown, the generator comprises a frame consisting of side walls **21** and bottom **22**, attached to side support members **23**, all of which are suitably made of wood or other heat insulating material.

## FIGURE 1.2:  FINNED HEAT TRANSFER PLATE

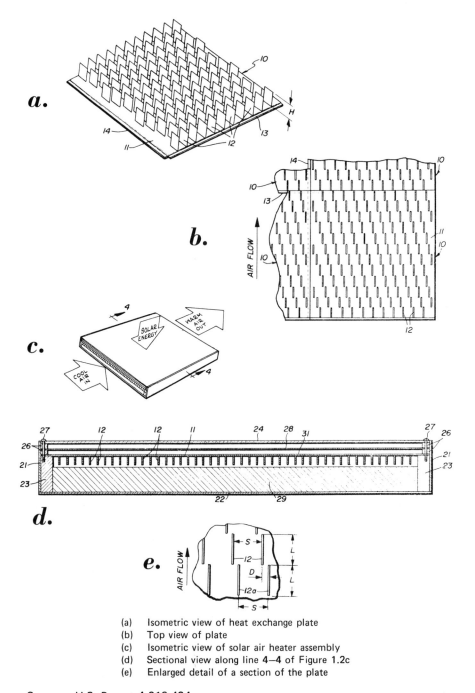

(a)    Isometric view of heat exchange plate
(b)    Top view of plate
(c)    Isometric view of solar air heater assembly
(d)    Sectional view along line 4—4 of Figure 1.2c
(e)    Enlarged detail of a section of the plate

Source:  U.S. Patent 4,019,494

At the top of the structure and spanning the distance between side walls **21** is a sheet **24** of glass, plastic, or other material which is transparent to solar energy. Sheet **24** is supported at its outer edges by insulating spacers **26** and held by conventional fasteners **27**. As an optional feature which may be desirable for use of the process in relatively cold climates, a second sheet **28** of transparent glass or plastic can be mounted a short distance below glass sheet **24**. The layer of air between sheets **24** and **28** acts as an insulating zone to prevent the escape of heat from within the heat generator.

Mounted a short distance below sheet **28** is a heat exchange assembly such as that shown in Figure 1.2b, with the base plate **11** uppermost and fins **21** depending therefrom. The upper surface **31** of the assembly, i.e., the surface on which radiant energy passing through plates **24** and **28** will impinge, is preferably treated to facilitate the absorption of the radiant energy, as by coating with a flat black paint or other suitable material in a manner which is known to those skilled in the art. Disposed immediately below the lower edges of fins **21** is a layer **29** of a suitable heat-insulating material, such as glass fiber mats, used to prevent the escape of heat from the generator.

The assembly of Figure 1.2d provides a conduit for air flow bounded on the top by sheet **24** (or, optionally, by sheet **28**), on the bottom by the upper surface of insulation **29** and on opposite sides by insulating supports **23** and spacers **26**. The conduit is suitably equipped with conventional inlet and outlet flow control means (not shown) for controlling the air flow. The air to be heated is introduced into the conduit in any appropriate manner and in passing therethrough comes into contact with the heat exchange plate assembly, which transfers the heat generated by absorption of the solar radiant energy to the stream of air, as indicated schematically in Figure 1.2c.

A typical assembly of the type illustrated in Figures 1.2c and 1.2d has a dimension of about 7 inches between glass plate **24** and the bottom **22** of the assembly; a spacing of about ¾ inch between plates **24** and **28** and between plate **28** and the top surface of heat exchange plate **10**; fins **21** having a length and width of about 1 inch; a displacement distance between rows of fins of about ¼ inch; the width of the assembly being about 4 feet and the length about 8 feet. In the operation of such a heat generator, the efficiency of heat transfer from the plate to the stream of air is such that the bulk of air passing therethrough is heated to a temperature which approaches within about $10°F$ the temperature of the heat transfer plate.

By comparison, under essentially the same conditions, but without the use of the fins in the heat exchange plate, the differential between the temperature of the plate and the air exceeds about $40°F$. This increase in efficiency of heat transfer is achieved without any significant increase in power requirement.

### Collector with Tabbed Plates

The solar collector of *M.F. Taylor; U.S. Patent 4,016,861; April 12, 1977* is formed by a unitary top plate having spaced apart downwardly extending tabs, a unitary bottom plate having spaced apart upwardly extending tabs, a frame holding the plates together in spaced apart relationship with the tabs intermeshed, and a backing plate held in the frame under the bottom plate. The upper surfaces of all plates and tabs are painted black to better absorb solar heat. Air is circulated between the heat collector and a porous heat storage unit to transfer heat from the collector to the storage unit, the tabs of the heat collector serving both as heat absorbent surfaces and as baffles to maximize heat transfer from the heat collector to the air stream. The tabs can be formed by making a plurality of H-shaped cuts in the top and bottom plates and then bending the inner margins of each H-shaped cut away from the plane of the corresponding plate to form two tabs. A looped water conduit can be mounted on staggered supporting panels within the heat storage unit, the staggered supporting panels acting as baffles to maximize air stream contact with the looped conduit to thus maximize heat transfer to the water therein.

Figure 1.3a shows the major portions of a solar heating system utilizing the solar heat collector and water conduit support of this process. The solar heat collector **10** is contained in a hollow rectangular frame. Solar heat collector **10** is mounted on the front of a porch **12** in such position, and at such angle, as to be exposed to the sun in winter to effectively absorb heat therefrom. A reflecting cover **14** which has a reflecting surface on its inner side and is covered with siding on its outer side is hinged at its bottom edge to solar heat collector **10**. When the solar heating system is not in use, reflecting cover **14** is swung to its closed position, indicated by the dashed lines in Figure 1.3a, and provides a decorative cover for solar heat collector **10**. In its open position, indicated by the solid lines in Figure 1.3a, reflecting cover **14** is supported by a block **16** at such an angle as to reflect sunlight onto solar heat collector **10** as indicated by arrows **18** to increase the intensity of illumination thereof.

A heat storage unit **20** is formed underneath porch **12** by a bin **22** full of relatively small rocks **24**. A blower motor **26** is coupled to the top of solar heat collector **10** and to the top of bin **22** by conduit **28**. The bottom of solar heat collector **10** is coupled to the bottom of bin **22** by conduit **30**. Blower motor **26** causes air to circulate between solar collector **10** and heat storage unit **20** to transfer heat from collector **10** to storage unit **20**. A second blower motor **32** is coupled between heat storage bin **22** and the various rooms of house **34** to circulate heated air from bin **22** to the house. Air returns to bin **22** through air return duct **33**. In this arrangement, it will be understood that the heat storage capacity of rocks **24** will tend to retain the temperature of the air circulating through the house at a constant level even when the sun goes under the clouds.

To provide hot water for the house, a water conduit **36** is mounted in heat storage bin **22** on staggered supporting panels **38, 40** and **42**, which can be plywood panels. Water conduit **36** is arranged in loops on the sides of panels **38-42**, facing solar heat collector **10** to intercept the hot air stream entering through air conduit **30** from solar heat collector **10**. The staggered location of panels **38-42** causes the panels to act as baffles to maximize air stream contact with the looped water conduit **36** to thus maximize heat transfer to the water therein. Fins **44** can be added to the looped portion of water conduit **36** to further enhance heat absorption and the surface of panels **38-42** facing conduit **36** can be lined with a reflective coating for the same purpose.

Figures 1.3b and 1.3c show the construction of the solar heat collector. In Figure 1.3b, each section of solar heat collector **10** includes a unitary top plate **46** having spaced apart downwardly extending tabs **48**, a unitary bottom plate **50** having spaced apart upwardly extending tabs **52**, and a back plate **54** underneath bottom plate **50**. Circulation openings **56** are formed in tabs **52** in this example, although they are not essential to the process.

## FIGURE 1.3: COLLECTOR WITH TABBED PLATES

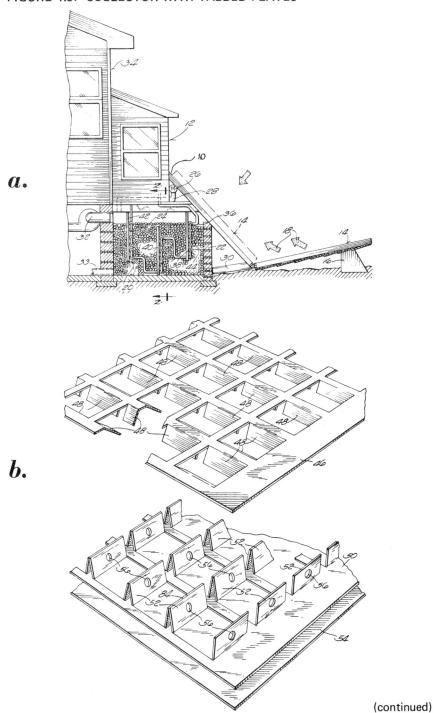

*a.*

*b.*

(continued)

FIGURE 1.3: (continued)

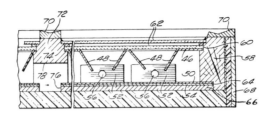

**c.**

(a) Side elevational view, partially cut away, showing the
    major portions of solar heating system
(b) Perspective view of collector
(c) Cross-sectional view of collector

Source:  U.S. Patent 4,016,861

The solar heat collector also includes frame means for holding plates **46** and **50** together in spaced apart relationship with tabs **48** intermeshed with tabs **52** and with backing plate **54** under bottom plate **50**. A typical frame is illustrated in Figure 1.3c. The frame includes wooden 2 x 4 side framing members **58** which are recessed at **60** to receive the edges of top plate **46** and a double pane glass top **62** which provides a transparent air-tight cover for the solar heat collector. Framing member **58** is recessed at **64** to receive the edges of bottom plate **50** and backing plate **54** which are supported by a plywood bottom panel **56**.

Plates **46** and **50** are held in spaced apart relationship with tabs **48** intermeshed with tabs **52** to create a plurality of rectangular heating chambers each defined by an adjacent pair of tabs **48** and an adjacent pair of tabs **52**. The upper surfaces of plates **46, 50** and **54**, and tabs **48** and **52**, are preferably painted black to better absorb solar heat. An insulation pad **66** on the bottom of the frame retards loss of heat therethrough.

The exterior edges of framing members **58** are covered by a decorative trim of redwood panels **68**, and redwood molding **70** covers the top of framing members **58**. The interior edges of plates **46, 50** and **54** are supported by wooden 2 x 4 framing members **72** which are recessed at **74** to receive glass top **62** and top plate **46** and are recessed at **76** to receive bottom plate **50**, backing plate **54** and panel **56**. The lower section of framing members **72** is cut away at **78** to provide air circulation between the adjacent panels of solar heat collector **10**. Air enters solar heat collector **10** at an air inlet opening in one corner of heat collector **10** and exits through an air outlet in the diagonally opposite corner of heat collector. As the air passes through the solar heat collector, the airstream is repeatedly baffled by the intermeshed tabs **48** and **52**, which act both as heat absorbing surfaces and as baffles to maximize the transfer of heat to the airstream flowing through heat collector **10**.

**Panel with Tapered Reflector Body**

*P. Guba; U.S. Patent 4,007,728; February 15, 1977* describes apparatus for collecting heat of radiation comprising a hollow member having a panel with a substantially flat exterior surface, the panel being capable of absorbing radiation incident to the surface and transferring the heat therefrom to a fluid passing through the member. A reflector body extends away from the flat surface, the reflector body adapted to reflect radiation incident thereto toward the flat surface of the panel.

In a preferred example, the reflector body has a hollow interior communicating with the interior of the hollow member, such that fluid circulating through the hollow member likewise circulates through the interior of the reflector body. Further, each reflector body is tapered in a direction away from the flat surface of the panel, the extremity of each tapered reflector body distal to the flat surface being defined by a level surface which is likewise absorptive of radiation in the same manner as the flat surface of the panel.

The collector illustrated in Figures 1.4a and 1.4b, referred to generally as **10**, comprises a member **12** having a hollow interior therein. The hollow member **12** includes a panel **13** having an exterior flat surface **14** which is preferably coated with a heat-absorbing material, such as a flat, black paint, so as to render that surface relatively heat absorbing with respect to the reflective surfaces **22** of the reflector body **20**, as is described in greater detail below.

The hollow member **12** further includes an input and output **16** and **18**, respectively, both of which communicate with the hollow interior of the member **12** such that a fluid flowing through the input is capable of circulating through the member **12** and then through the output **18** (note arrows in Figure 1.4b).

In accordance with the process, a plurality of hollow reflector bodies **20** are provided, each reflector body having a hollow interior communicating with the hollow interior of the member **12** and tapering inward in a direction away from the flat surface **14**. As shown in Figure 1.4a, each reflector body may comprise a trianguloid; however, it will be understood that a variety of other geometric shapes may be employed. The extremity of each reflector body comprises a plane surface **26** which is preferably substantially parallel with the flat surface **14**, and includes a heat-absorbing material, such as a layer of flat, black paint, so as to heat water circulating therein. As shown in Figure 1.4b, each reflector body includes a hollow interior which communicates with the hollow interior of the member **12**. The panel **13** and reflector bodies **20** may be formed from an integral sheet by conventional stamping or molding processes.

The collector further includes a base **28** which carries the hollow member **12**, and through which extends the input and output **18** and **20**, respectively. The base includes supporting sides **30**, the base and sides being formed of a material which is relatively heat resistant with respect to the member in order that little or no heat is lost through this material.

The collector further includes a cover **32** which is transparent to solar radiation, in order that the heat of radiation falls onto the reflector surfaces **22** of the reflector bodies **20** and the flat surface **14**. The cover **32** is supported by the sides **30**, as is shown in Figure 1.4b. The collector **10** is provided with brackets **40**, each of which extends through the hollow interior of the member along a column of the reflector bodies. Each bracket includes a plurality of apertures **42**, each aperture being positioned at the front of the corresponding reflector body so as to direct fluid upward into the hollow interior of the reflector body.

## FIGURE 1.4: PANEL WITH TAPERED REFLECTOR BODY

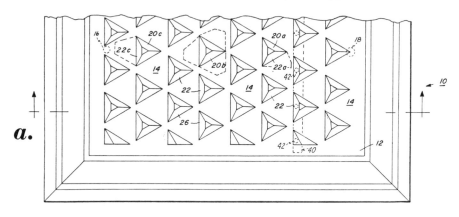

*a.*

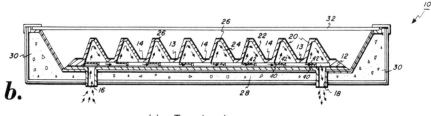

*b.*

(a)    Top plan view
(b)    Cross-sectional view

Source: U.S. Patent 4,007,728

The manner in which the collector functions is described below. The collector is positioned on a roof, or against the wall of a building so as to be exposed to solar radiation during the course of the day. The collector may be permanently emplaced in conjunction with the building. The black-coated flat surface **14** absorbs incident solar radiation, the heat of which passes through the panel to heat water, or any other fluid, passing through the hollow interior of the member. During those periods when the angle of incidence of the sun's rays is relatively shallow, one of the reflecting surfaces **22a** reflects the low-angle solar radiation onto the flat surface **14** in order to achieve the desired heat absorption (reflected radiation is defined by dotted lines).

During those periods when solar radiation is substantially perpendicular to the flat surface **14**, a substantial portion of all of the reflective surfaces of the reflector body **20b** reflect the solar radiation onto the flat surface **14**. As the rotation of the earth changes the relative position of the sun during any given day, another reflective surface **22b** receives the solar radiation at low angles of incidence on the opposite side of the collector, and reflects this radiation onto the flat surface in order to heat the water passing through the member **12**. In this way, the reflector bodies serve to increase the efficiency of a flat collector,

by increasing the amount of solar energy during periods of low angles of incidence of solar radiation. The relatively high heat resistive base **28** prevents heat
transfer from the water, during periods when the water is circulating through the
member. The cover **32** assists in providing a greenhouse effect, by trapping
heated air between the member and the cover, to further increase the efficiency
of heat absorption at the flat surface and through the panel. As the water leaves
the output **18**, it may be pumped into a water storage tank. Alternatively, other
fluids may be heated as described above for utilizing that heat for performing
other work functions.

### Triangular Finned Absorber

In the system of *C.E. Balkus, Jr.; U.S. Patent 4,003,364; January 18, 1977* one
or more heat absorbing panels are arranged on a generally flat area provided
over an underground fluid storage reservoir, and the fluid is pumped from the
reservoir through finned tubes in each panel and then back to the reservoir or
is pumped through a distribution system to heat one or more houses or the like.
Each panel has reflective surfaces associated with each tube to efficiently capture the sun's rays, and each tube has projecting fins so oriented as to absorb
both direct sunlight and also any rays reflected from these surfaces.

Figure 1.5a shows two houses **A** and **B** representing a community of residential
dwellings which are to be supplied with heat from a single source located in the
immediate neighborhood. Each house has a thermostat **10** providing an input
signal to a controller **12** of conventional configuration whereby the controller
**12** is adapted to produce an output signal in lines **14** and **16** when any one of
the houses **A, B** and so forth are calling for heat. More particularly, a reservoir
**18** adapted to store a relatively large quantity of heated fluid, such as water, is
provided with a valve **20** such that warm fluid is adapted to be withdrawn
through line **22** and to be pumped by pump number 2 indicated generally by
reference numeral **24** so as to be pumped through a loop defined by line **26**.

Each house is adapted to withdraw fluid from this line **26** as indicated generally
at reference numeral **28** and **30** for house **A** and **32, 34** for house **B**. Thermostat **10** in each of the houses **A** and **B** controls a valve **29** and **35** in lines **28** and
**34** to allow heat to enter only that house, **A** or **B**. The lines **28** and **34** are input lines to each of the houses **A** and **B** respectively, whereas the lines **30** and
**32** return fluid from these houses back to the loop **26**. These return lines **30**
and **32** associated with each house, **A** and **B**, include a balance valve (not shown)
such that houses more remote from the source of heated fluid are adapted to
receive a higher fluid flow rate than those arranged in closer relationship to such
heated fluid source. The general configuration for such valves is known in the
art.

Turning next to a detailed description of the mode of operation for the reservoir,
and more particularly for heating the fluid within the reservoir it will be seen
from Figure 1.5a that such reservoir **18** comprises a generally rectangular tank
having a bottom wall or floor well below grade level and indicated generally at
**36**. The sidewalls of the tank indicated generally at **38** and **40** are also located,
throughout a major portion of their depth, underground as indicated generally
by the grade level **G**. These walls may be provided with an insulating layer of
Styrofoam material so as to reduce the heat loss from the fluid in the reservoir
to the adjacent ground **G**.

# FIGURE 1.5: TRIANGULAR FINNED ABSORBER

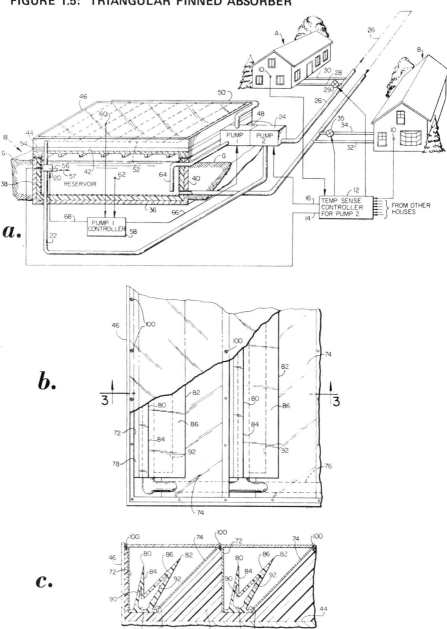

(a)    Schematic illustrating the overall configuration of the solar heating system
(b)    Fragmentary view showing one corner of panel
(c)    Vertical sectional view taken generally on line 3—3 of Figure 1.5b

Source:   U.S. Patent 4,003,364

The roof **42** of the tank may be provided of reinforced concrete, and may also include a layer of insulating material **44** which material may comprise Styrofoam or the like. A rectangular frame is provided around the periphery of the paneled area as indicated generally at **46**, and a plurality of heat collecting panels are arranged on the top of the reservoir **42** and more particularly on the Styrofoam insulating layer **44** in a manner to be described in greater detail with reference to Figures 1.5b and 1.5c. As mentioned previously, the area of layer **44** will be dictated by the heating requirements of the loop or loops **26, 26,** and more particularly by the area of the heat absorbing or collecting panels required.

The heat collecting panels are depicted in Figures 1.5b and 1.5c. The peripheral boundary of the structure is indicated in Figure 1.5b as comprising a sidewall **46** which sidewall extends downwardly to protect the heat collecting panel itself, and also to protect the underlying layer of Styrofoam **44** provided thereunder. The Styrofoam layer is preferably covered with a layer of aluminum foil or the like and the heat collecting panels of the process are provided above such layer.

Each panel comprises a Styrofoam base **70**, which base is precut to define upwardly open, generally trapezoidally shaped, cavities two of which are illustrated. These cavities are preferably wider at their open tops than at the bottom, and each includes a generally vertically extending sidewall to which is attached a reflective surface such as indicated generally at **72**. The opposite sidewall of each of these cavities preferably includes an inclined reflective surface also attached to the Styrofoam base, such inclined reflective surface **74** being arranged at approximately 45° to the horizontal.

Means is provided for introducing fluid to be heated to tubes within the cavities defined for this purpose in the base **70**, and such means includes the feed tube **50** and also the return tube or pipe indicated generally at **76**. The return pipe **76** communicates with the pipe **54** and thus a plurality of generally parallel paths are provided to circulate fluid from the reservoir through the heat collecting tubes and then to return the fluid either to the reservoir or to send heated fluid directly to one or more houses calling for heat.

Figure 1.5c shows the tubes in vertical section, and each tube can be seen to include a base portion **78** which is adapted to occupy the shorter side of the generally trapezoidally shaped cavity and is preferably cemented thereto. The tube is fabricated from a plastic material by an extrusion process, and the preferred material for extruding these tubes is reinforced polyvinyl chloride having a black color such that the solar energy from the sun can be readily absorbed by the tube and more particularly by upwardly projecting fins, each fin being oriented at an appropriate angle such that the reflective surfaces **72** and **74** are adapted to reflect energy back to the fins and more significantly to avoid reflecting any solar energy outwardly of the cavity itself. Two such projecting fins are preferably provided and each of these fins can be seen to have a generally triangular cross section such that one of the fin surfaces on each fin is oriented parallel to one of the two reflective surfaces **72** and **74**.

The tube configuration provides a very efficient shape from the point of view of the absorption of solar energy, and also from a practical point of view the tube shown is capable of withstanding extremes of temperature. The heat collecting panel further includes a transparent cover of acrylic plastic or glass, which cover is supported by the upper edges of the Styrofoam base, and which cover may be attached to the base by means of fasteners as indicated generally at **100, 100**. This cover keeps dust and rainwater off the solar panel's fins and reflecting surfaces.

### Absorber Plate with Hill and Valley Configuration

In the collector of *E.J. O'Hanlon; U.S. Patent 3,986,491; October 19, 1976* the heat absorbing liquid is confined to a narrow unobstructed path, with wide flaring wings exposed directly to the sun. The need for painted heat absorbing surfaces is largely eliminated. A transparent or translucent corrugated cover is easily removable and replaceable.

With reference to Figures 1.6a, 1.6b and 1.6c, collector **1** has its exterior corrugated plastic surface **2** covering heat collecting plate **3**, resting on plastic foam **4** in heat collector tray **5**. The heat collector plate is provided with wide flaring hill portions **6** at an angle upward from each side of valley portion **7**, these hill and valley indentations running lengthwise the heat collecting and transmitting plate from its upper portion **9** to its lower portion **10**.

At **10** this heat collector plate is turned upward to comprise a reservoir for solar heated liquid which has run down the valleys and is to exit through pipe **11**. Numeral **12** in all figures of the drawing represents the liquid distributing manifold through which the solar heat pickup liquid enters the collector. The numerals **13** are the holes in this uppermost positioned liquid entering manifold (or tube) by which each valley in the heat collecting metal sheet or plate **3** receive the liquid needed to acquire the incoming solar heat.

It will be noted that the corrugations in the transparent or translucent corrugated sheet **2** are so arranged to focus the rays of the sun in the morning on one side of the hill indentations **6**, and on the other side of the hill indentations in the afternoon. Since the corrugated sheet has circular cross sectioned surfaces, these same surfaces tend to act somewhat as a magnifying glass in assembling the solar rays and causing them to impact the valleys and the flared hill portions of the sheet metal heat collecting plate below. These upward surfaces in the corrugated sheet are designated by **14** in the drawings. The heat absorbing liquid can contain black powder.

At numerals **16** are shown longitudinal strips of sponge rubber positioned to make fairly heat-leak-tight the space between the corrugated sheet and the metallic solar heat collector plate. These are glued in place by a suitable adhesive material and the corrugated sheet is held down in position by a holding angle metal strip **17** along each of the two sides of the solar heat collector.

Across the two ends of the corrugated sheet, numeral **18** shows the upper strip of sponge rubber glued along its uncorrugated bottom surface to a flat strip of elongated sheet metal **19** welded to the metallic solar heat collector plate. In similar manner along the width of the solar heat collector sheet is welded a similar strip of sheet metal **20** to which the noncorrugated bottom of sponge rubber strip **21** is suitably glued. The upper surfaces of sponge rubber cross strips are properly corrugated to conform with the corrugations in the corrugated plastic plate into which they fit. At the low points in the corrugated plastic sheet, holding screws are inserted to hold the corrugated plastic sheet firmly to each end of the solar heat collector **1**.

## FIGURE 1.6: ABSORBER PLATE—HILL AND VALLEY CONFIGURATION

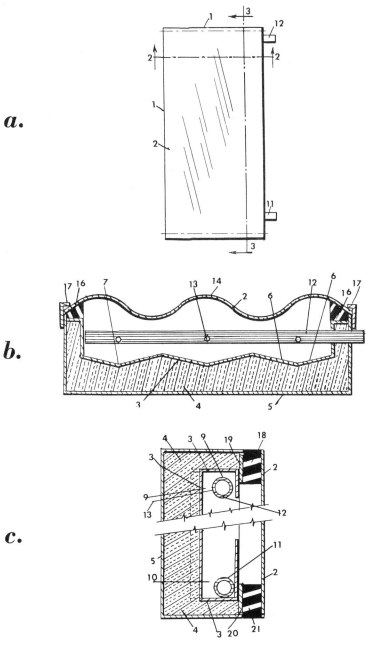

(a)    Plan view of collector
(b)    Sectional view along line **2—2** in Figure 1.6a
(c)    Sectional view along line **3—3** in Figure 1.6a

Source:  U.S. Patent 3,986,491

## Double Tiered Collector-Heat Exchanger

*M.N. Worthington; U.S. Patent 3,957,109; May 18, 1976* describes a system comprising a double tiered solar collector and heat exchanger that is mounted on a roof at an angle ranging from 30° to 45° with respect to the horizontal, with its upper surface being blackened. Each tier of the heat exchanger includes a series of longitudinal channels, there being upper and lower manifolds communicating with all of the channels. A duct depends from the middle of the upper channel and is connected to an air blower that takes air from the premises being heated or cooled. Another pair of ducts depend from the lower manifold at the opposite end thereof and discharge heated air into the premises. A heat trap in the form of a transparent plastic sheet is removably mounted above the collector and heat exchanger in close proximity thereto.

With reference to Figures 1.7a and 1.7b, mounted on roof **11** is a solar collector and heat exchanger which is identified in its entirety by the reference character **14**. Exchanger **14** is rectangular in shape and purely for exemplary purposes, it is noted it may have a transverse dimension of 12 feet and a longitudinal dimension of 10 feet. The latter has a vertical component caused by the slope of the roof. It also may have a thickness of about 4 inches.

Referring to Figure 1.7c, heat exchanger **14** comprises side walls **15** and **16** between which extend an upper corrugated metallic sheet **17**, the exposed top surface of which is blackened; an intermediate flat sheet **18** and a lower corrugated metal sheet **19**. The bottoms or bends of the corrugations in sheets **17** and **19** are secured to intermediate sheet **18** in any preferred manner as by the spot welds indicated at **20**. Corrugated sheets **17** and **19** are preferred examples of metallic sheets that are formed with longitudinal grooves which open onto intermediate sheet **18**. Sheets **17** and **18** cooperate to define an upper tier of channels **21** while sheets **18** and **19** define a lower tier of channels **22**.

A heat trap which is removably mounted over heat exchanger **14** comprises a flat transparent sheet **23**, of which plastic is an example, and side bars **24** and end bars (not illustrated). The latter overlap side pieces **15** and **16** when the heat trap is in effective position with sheet **23** in close proximity to outer bends of corrugated sheet **17**. An upper manifold is designated generally **25** and is mounted transversely on the upper end of exchanger **14** so as to communicate with the channels **21** and **22**. Depending from the center of manifold **25** is a duct **26** which is connected at its lower end to an air blower **27** as shown in Figure 1.7b. Blower **27** is mounted on a joist **12** and has an inlet at **28** which withdraws air from premises **10**.

Extending across the lower ends of channels **21** and **22** is a lower manifold depicted diagrammatically in Figure 1.7e at **29**. A duct **30** depends from each end of lower manifold **29** and extends into premises **10** into which it discharges heated air. The structures so far described are the elements which are essential to use of the system for heating. Certain additional structure and mechanism is required to adapt the system to cooling. These are described below.

A water sump **31** is shown in Figures 1.7b and 1.7d as mounted on roof **11** immediately below and at one end of exchanger **14**. A pipe **32** enters sump **31** from the bottom and is connected to an appropriate water supply. A valve **33** is mounted on the upper discharge end of pipe **32** and is controlled by a float **34** to maintain the water in sump **31** at a desired constant level.

## FIGURE 1.7: DOUBLE TIERED COLLECTOR-HEAT EXCHANGER

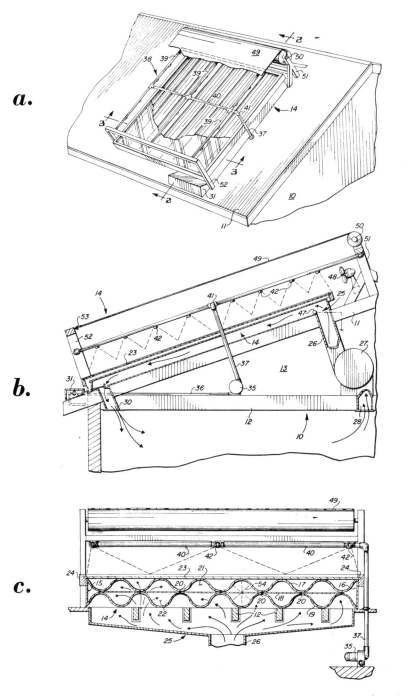

(continued)

FIGURE 1.7: (continued)

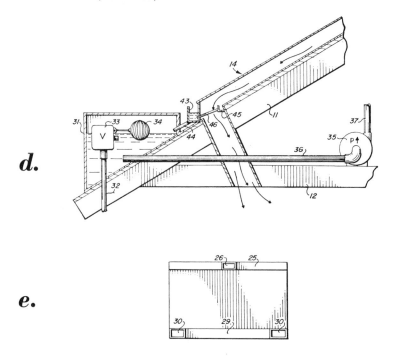

(a)　Perspective of roof
(b)　Side view, partially in section and partially in elevation,
　　　taken on line 2—2 of Figure 1.7a
(c)　Transverse section taken on plane of line 3—3 of Figure 1.7a
(d)　Fragmentary view, enlarged and depicting the lower end of
　　　the heat exchanger
(e)　Bottom plan view of heat exchanger and manifolds

Source:　U.S. Patent 3,957,109

A water pump **35** is mounted on a joist **12** and is connected to sump **31** by a pipe **36**. Another pipe **37** extends upwardly to an arrangement of spray pipes referred to in its entirety at **38**. Pipe arrangement **38** comprises 3 longitudinal pipes **39** and a cross pipe **40** which is connected to and communicates with pipes **39** midway thereof with one end of pipe **40** being connected to the upper end of pipe **37** at **41**. All of pipes **39** are formed with small apertures on their undersides to provide nozzles as indicated at **42**. This water is sprayed onto upper corrugated sheet **17** of the heat exchanger when the heat trap is removed as it is during cooling.

A main trough or gutter **43** is mounted transversely of exchanger **14** immediately below its lower end in which position water sprayed onto the top surface of corrugated sheet **17** runs down into gutter **43**. A short conduit **44** extends from the bottom of gutter **43** to sump **31** whereby water in trough **43** is drained into sump **31**. A small trough or gutter **45** is mounted in lower manifold **29** close to the top corner where this manifold meets the lower tier of channels **22**. This trough **45** has a raised center (not illustrated) and slopes towards its opposite ends at small angles to the horizontal. A pair of tubes **46** at opposite ends of trough **45** drain water from the latter and pass such water into main trough **43**.

It is recognized that under certain climatic conditions it may be desirable to humidify air that passes through heat exchanger **14**. A small transverse tube **47** is mounted in upper manifold **25** at the corner where channels **22** meet duct **26**. Tube **47** is perforated to provide a series of small openings (not illustrated) through which water drips into the upper ends of the channels **22**. Tube **47** is connected to a source of water under pressure in any well-known manner.

When the system is used for cooling, water evaporated from contact with upper sheet **17** will cool the air immediately above this sheet. Being cooled it will exhibit a tendency to flow downwardly towards the lower end of the exchanger **14**. However, to ensure such a draft of air, a motor driven fan **48** may be mounted on roof **11** above the upper end of exchanger **14**.

A flexible sunshade **49** is assembled in roll form on a shaft **50** which is spring-biased to retract sunshade **49**. Shaft **50** is mounted on structure designated generally **51** which upstands from roof **11** above heat exchanger **14**. After being pulled downwardly, sunshade **49** is secured in protective position in any well-known manner such as by being secured to an inverted U-shaped member **52** upstanding from roof **11** at the lower end of exchanger **14**. This anchorage is indicated at **53**. The top surface of sunshade **49** is white or silvered so as to reflect sun rays and maintain the temperature of air therebeneath at a low degree.

### Triangular Shaped Tubular Absorber Surface

*L.W. Brantley, Jr.; U.S. Patent 3,951,129; April 20, 1976; assigned to U.S. National Aeronautics and Space Administration* has an effective solar energy absorber which reduces heat loss from the absorber surface. The apparatus includes a tubular absorber with a triangular surface which has a surface coating thereon having a high radiation absorption factor ($\alpha$) for absorbing the visible sectrum of the electromagnetic energy emitted by the sun and a low thermal factor ($\epsilon$). Positioned between the outside atmosphere and the tubular absorber is a plurality of spaced glass plates for transmitting the visible spectrum to the absorber and for trapping between the spaces of the glass plates heat or thermal energy from the infrared radiation which is reradiated from the tubular absorber. Between the first and second plates of glass a fluid is circulated for removing the heat from the glass plates so as to reduce the heat loss from the absorber. Either a separate fluid or the same fluid is conveyed in heat exchange relationship with the tubular absorber for absorbing thermal energy therefrom.

Referring to Figure 1.8, there is illustrated an absorber surface constructed of a triangular shaped tubular member **18**. The tubular absorber is shown schematically and the adjacent layers thereof communicate with each other, and the overall configuration whether circular, rectangular, etc., depends on the desired application of the device. A coating **20** is provided on the tubular absorbent surface for absorbing the visible spectrum of electromagnetic waves generated by the sun. The coating is characterized by having a high $\alpha$ value (absorption factor) for the visible spectrum of electromagnetic radiation and a low $\epsilon$ value (emittance factor) making it a poor thermal emitter. Positioned directly above the tubular absorber is a glass plate **22**. Interposed between the glass plate **22** and the absorber is a vacuum or air. Directly above the glass plate **22** is another glass plate **24**. The ends of the glass plates **22** and **24** are sealed to provide a sealed conduit **26** therebetween. A clear liquid such as pure water is fed into an inlet port **28** carried adjacent one end of the conduit **26** and exits out of an outlet port **30** carried adjacent the other end of the conduit **26** for removing thermal energy contained in the plates **22** and **24**. While water may be utilized as the fluid for removing the thermal energy from the plates **22** and **24** in some applications it may be desirable to utilize a clear liquid having a higher or lower boiling point. A gas (air, helium, hydrogen, etc.) could also be utilized for removing the heat from the plates **22** and **24**.

### FIGURE 1.8: TRIANGULAR SHAPED TUBULAR ABSORBER SURFACE

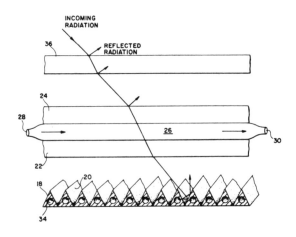

Source: U.S. Patent 3,951,129

A source of fluid may be provided which employs two separate fluid reservoirs so that the sealed conduit **26** may be supplied with a fluid or a gas separate from the fluid conveyed to a bore **34** located in tubular absorber **18**. In this case, any conventional pumping means may be used to convey the two separate fluids to the inlet **28** and to the bore **34** respectively. In the case where the same fluid is used in both **26** and **34** a source of fluid with a single reservoir may be provided using conventional pumping means to convey the fluid separately to inlet **28** and the bore **34**. It may also be desirable to convey the fluid passing from the outlet **30** directly through the bore **34** of tubular absorber **18** instead of conveying the fluid separately to each one.

Superimposed above the glass plate **24** is an exterior glass plate **36**. The ends of all of the glass plates **22, 24** and **36** are generally sealed with a vacuum or air being interposed between glass plates **24** and **36**. While the plates **22, 24** and **36** have been described as being glass, it is to be understood that depending on the temperature requirements, such could be made of other materials such as clear, transparent plastic. In operation, as the visible spectrum of electro-magnetic radiation is emitted from the sun, such is first passed through the outer plate **36**. A portion of the incoming radiation is reflected upon engaging the outer surface of the plate **36**. The remaining passes through the plate **36** towards the absorber surface. Additional reflection takes place as the incoming radiation engages the lower surface of the plate **36**. As the radiation continues down-wardly it then passes through the glass plate **24** the fluid in conduit **26** and glass plate **22** to strike the inclined surfaces of the absorber. Similar reflection as de-scribed in connection with plate **36** takes place as the radiation passes through plates **22** and **24**. The waves engaging the inclined surfaces **20** of the absorber heat the fluid passing through the central bore **34** extending therethrough.

Depending on the temperature difference between the surface of the absorber and the lower surface of the glass plate **22** infrared radiation will be transferred therebetween heating the glass plate **22**. This infrared radiation is absorbed by the plate **22** and is transferred by conduction to the working fluid in conduit **26** flowing therethrough. Since the working fluid entering the inlet **28** is at a low temperature, such will reduce the temperature of the glass plates **22** and **24**. As the fluid passes through the conduit **26**, its temperature is raised and exits out of the outlet **30** for subsequent use as a preheated fluid. Since the tempera-ture of the glass plate **24** has been reduced, a lesser amount of radiation than normal would radiate from glass **24** to the outer glass **36**. Therefore, the over-all thermal energy loss of the system is reduced.

### Honeycomb Sandwich Panel

A structural solar energy collection and transfer arrangement is provided by *I.R. Barr; U.S. Patent 4,018,211; April 19, 1977; assigned to AAI Corporation* which includes an insulating light-transmitting honeycomb sandwich array and a lateral fluid flow solar energy collection and heat transfer honeycomb sand-wich array, the lateral fluid flow honeycomb sandwich array having dark, pref-erably nongloss or dull surfaced, honeycomb walls and bottom surface for solar energy absorption and transfer to a fluid, preferably a liquid, passed laterally through fluid passageway openings formed in the honeycomb walls. Solar energy is absorbed and transferred to a flowing fluid, by passing solar light rays through the insulating honeycomb sandwich array and into contact with the dark walls and base of the facially interconnected heat transfer honeycomb sandwich array, and passing the heat transfer fluid through the lateral openings formed in the honeycomb cell walls and thereby flowing such fluid through adjacent honey-comb cells.

Referring to Figures 1.9a, 1.9b and 1.9c, a solar radiation energy collection and transfer structural panel assembly **11**, hereinafter generally referred to as a struc-tural solar panel assembly **11** is shown utilizing an interconnected multilayer honeycomb sandwich construction, including a solar light-transmitting insulating honeycomb sandwich array, generally indicated at **IH**, and a lateral fluid flow solar energy collection and transfer honeycomb sandwich array generally indi-cated at **HTH**, with a suitable insulating protective enclosure **E**, which may suit-ably be made of rubber, and an insulating backing **47** and protective back cover plate **49**, mounted on a stand or support **S** at a suitable angle of inclination for desired passage and collection therein of solar energy rays. The insulating honey-comb sandwich array **IH** includes an outer sheet, plate or panel **21**, an inner sheet, panel or plate **31**, and an interconnecting honeycomb array section **25**;

and the energy collection and transfer honeycomb sandwich array HTH includes a honeycomb section 35 and bottom plate, sheet, or panel 41, the honeycomb section 35 being facially interconnected along its top and bottom edges to the faces of bottom plate or sheet 41 and mid sheet or plate 31 of the sandwich array IH.

The outer and inner sheets 21, 31 are suitably secured to the honeycomb section 25, preferably through the medium of a cured adhesive or cement along the intersection of respective edges of the honeycomb at the zones of intersection thereof with the respective two sheets 21 and 31. The outer and mid sheets 21 and 31 may be suitably formed of glass, plastic or other sheet material which is preferably efficiently transparent to the major available radiant solar energy spectrum.

The honeycomb section 25 may be formed of opaque, transparent, translucent and/or reflective-surfaced honeycomb material. The honeycomb material may be itself constructed in various cell configurations and may have various cell cross sections and constructions, and transmit solar energy, either directly or by reflection or both, through the joining mid panel or sheet 31, to the base or energy collection and transfer honeycomb sandwich array HTH, within which energy collection and transfer is effected, with both impinging ray heat and accumulated heat in the array HTH being transferred therein to a fluid F which is flowed therethrough, by passage through inlet conduit 51 and outlet conduit 61.

To this end, the inlet conduit 51 may suitably be provided with a lateral header conduit 55 connecting therewith in fluid flow relation, and having spaced fluid distribution orifices 55a disposed in general alignment with fluid flow passageway orifices 35h formed in the forward and rear lateral walls 35f, 35r or honeycomb cells HTHC of the honeycomb section 35 of the solar energy collection and transfer honeycomb sandwich array HTH.

The honeycomb 25 in the insulating honeycomb sandwich array IH may, in various embodiments, be formed of various sheet or strip materials, such as metal, reflective-covered (e.g., metal or plastic-coated or covered, as by painting or vacuum deposition or lamination of layers) plastic or paper, and may be of transparent or translucent material, such as various plastic resins, coated or uncoated fiber materials such as paper, or other suitable honeycomb material.

As an aid to minimizing return flow convection losses through the insulation honeycomb sandwich array, the insulating honeycomb sandwich array may be and is preferably evacuated to an effective extent for most effective return convection and conduction barrier action with respect to heat transmission in the outward direction, although partial or no evacuation may be and is readily accommodated with some decrease in overall efficiency.

The honeycomb 35 of the energy collection and transfer honeycomb sandwich array HTH may be of plastic, metal or plastic-coated or metal coated fiber or other composition material such as paper, or other fluid compatible heat transfer material, being preferably dark or dark coated on its surface (e.g., black, etc.), and has, as heretofore mentioned, lateral fluid flow passageway orifices 35h formed in the walls 35f, 35r of the respective honeycomb cells HTHC, thereby connecting the cells in lateral fluid flow relation for the desired flow of a heat transfer fluid F therethrough, preferably in the form of a liquid, although other flowable heat transfer media such as air or other gas may be utilized, the heat transfer fluid **F** being heated as a result of heat transfer thereto, during passage through the lateral fluid flow orifices **35h** and in contact with the walls of the cells **HTHC** and the upper surfaces of the bottom wall **41** of the energy collection and transfer honeycomb sandwich array. In the preferred embodiment, the lateral fluid flow passageway openings **35h** are formed by generally longitudinally aligned openings in the front and rear honeycomb cell walls **35f, 35r** of respective cells **HTHC**, although such may be offset or staggered, and may be single or multiple in various ones of the walls of respective cells **HTHC**, for a desired quantity and/or path of fluid flow therethrough.

For liquid fluids, these lateral wall fluid flow orifices or openings **35h** are preferably formed on the lower edges of the honeycomb cell walls as by slots, grooves or other holes or openings and preferably interface with the lower panel or sheet **41** of the honeycomb sandwich array **HTH**. The bottom panel or sheet **41** of the honeycomb sandwich array **HTH** is preferably opaque and may be formed of metal, plastic, glass, or other suitable material, being desirably dark, (e.g., black, etc.) on the upper or outward facing surface and is preferably of a material providing good heat transfer to the particular fluid **F** being passed through the honeycomb cell passageway openings **35h**. Water is a suitable inexpensive liquid fluid, although other liquid fluids **F** may be employed for a given embodiment or utilization, it being understood that various liquids and other fluids, including gasses, have different heat transfer, viscosity, volatility, and other characteristics, which may be useful in a given embodiment or instance of use.

An insulation backing layer or layers **47** is preferably provided beneath the base or energy collection and transfer honeycomb sandwich array or layer **HTH**, as heretofore noted, and may be either a further insulated honeycomb array or layer, and/or other suitable insulation material, such as insulated foam plastic, glass fiber matting, etc.

Each of the insulating honeycomb sandwich array **IH**, and the solar energy collection and transfer honeycomb sandwich array **HTH**, includes a perimeter sealing wall in the form of a plurality of foam insulation strips **27, 37**, which are suitably adhesively secured together and to the respective sheets or panels **21, 31, 41** of the two arrays **IH** and **HTH**. Thus, the insulating honeycomb sandwich array is desirably hermetically sealed from the outside atmosphere, and each of the cells **IHC** is in turn sealed from one another along their oppositely extending wall edges at the juncture line thereof with the outer and mid panels or sheets **21** and **31**.

In addition, the energy collection transfer honeycomb sandwich array **HTH** is sealed from the upper or outer insulating honeycomb sandwich array **IH** and its internal cells **IHC**, while also being fluid sealed around its perimeter by strips **37** in order to enable the passage of fluid **F** therethrough from the inlet conduit **51** and header **55** through the lateral wall passageway openings **35h**, and out therefrom through the outlet conduit **61** after collection at and along the base of the honeycomb sandwich array **HTH**, as generally indicated in Figures 1.9b and 1.9c.

The fluid inlet conduit **51**, as well as the fluid outlet conduit **61** may be suitably secured and sealed in place as through the medium of reinforcing and securing plates **52, 62** and sealing adhesive **53, 63**, and these inlet and outlet conduits may, if desired, be suitably formed of metal, and/or rubber, and/or other desired material.  Additional diagrams showing other views of the panels and various methods of assembling the panels are to be found in the patent.

### FIGURE 1.9:  HONEYCOMB SANDWICH PANEL

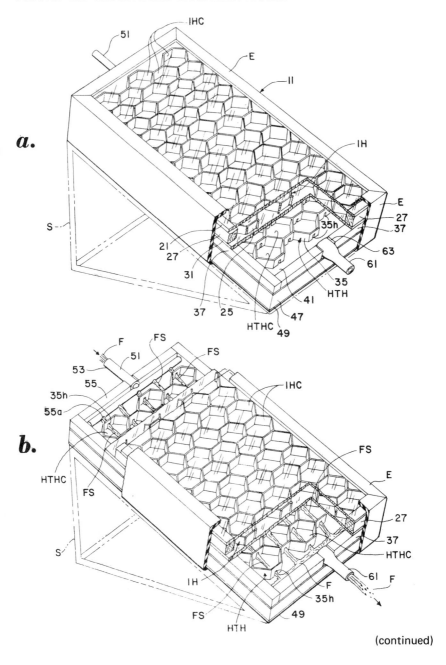

(continued)

**FIGURE 1.9:** (continued)

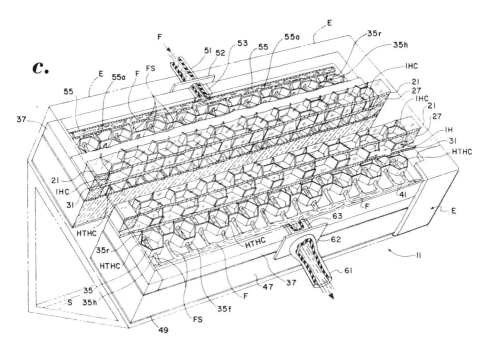

*c.*

(a)    Orthographic view of panel
(b)    View similar to Figure 1.9a showing passage of heat transfer fluid
(c)    Enlarged view, in fragmental sections, of panel

Source:   U.S. Patent 4,018,211

**Tapered Honeycomb Shaped Absorber**

*N.S. Kapany; U.S. Patent 3,985,116; October 12, 1976; assigned to Kaptron, Inc.*
describes a solar panel in which a window portion is interposed between the incident light and a heat absorbing portion and at least one of the heat absorbing
and window portions has a plurality of spaced apart reflecting surfaces, separate
ones of which face each other and transmit the incident light by multiple reflec-
tions to the heat absorbing portion. In at least one embodiment, these opposed
reflecting surfaces converge in the direction of light travel from the window portion to the heat absorbing portion and infrared reflecting means are interposed
between the window portion and the heat absorbing portion to return infrared
light emitted by the heat absorbing portion back to the heat absorbing portion.

Referring to Figure 1.10, the combined solar panel of the process includes a window panel portion **10** and a heat absorbing portion **12**. The heat absorbing portion further includes a fluid heat exchanging chamber **14** and an insulating back
**16** for the heat exchanging chamber. The heat exchanging fluid, such as water
or air, is continuously admitted to the chamber through an inlet pipe **15** and is
exhausted from the chamber by an outlet pipe (not shown). In operation, inci-

dent solar radiation **18** passes through the window portion to strike the heat absorbing portion. The heat generated in the heat absorbing portion by the solar radiation is transferred to fluid passing through the heat exchanging portion. This transfer of solar generated heat into the fluid raises its temperature.

**FIGURE 1.10:  TAPERED HONEYCOMB SHAPED ABSORBER**

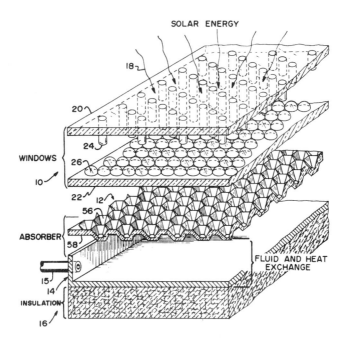

Source:  U.S. Patent 3,985,116

The window portion must be designed to accept solar radiation over as wide an angle of incidence as possible. It also must be designed to prevent heat loss through reradiation from the heat absorbing portion and heat loss due to convection currents above the heat absorbing portion. The window panel includes a pair of thin, transparent sheets **20** and **22** which are spaced apart by a plurality of upstanding columns or ribs **24** which are also made of lightweight, transparent material and preferably of a material which has high optical transmission qualities. In practice, the material chosen for the sheets and the ribs may be lightweight plastic. In other embodients, the top sheet may be glass for ruggedness.

Means are provided for segmenting the air space between the sheets to reduce heat loss due to convection currents which would otherwise develop between the two sheets. In the embodiment depicted in Figure 1.10, the means for segmenting the space comprises a plurality of transparent bubbles **26** on the upper surface of the sheet **22**. The bubbles may be made of a transparent material such as plastic. The bubbles can be pressed flat against the flat sheets **20** and **22** to reduce reflection losses at the spherical surface.

The ideal absorber has a high absorptivity in the wavelength range of 0.3 to 2 microns and a low emissivity in the wavelength range of approximately 10 microns (the far infrared). In the embodiment depicted in Figure 1.10, the absorbing portion has a tapered honeycomb structure **56** embossed directly on the upper face of the top panel **58** of the heat exchanger. The embossed honeycomb structure provides multiple bounce absorption of the incident light ray transmitted through the window portion. Multiple bounce absorption is the incident light passing through the window which is reflected a multiple number of times within the hollows of the honeycomb structure **56** until it strikes the upper surface of the heat exchanger **14** where the incident light is converted into thermal energy.

The honeycomb structure **56** gives good contact between the heat exchanger **14** and the fluid to be heated and it is inexpensive to manufacture in large quantities. In other less advantageous embodiments, the honeycomb structure **56** is not tapered downwardly towards the heat exchanging portion **14** and has a substantially uniform cross section. The advantage of having a multiple bounce absorption structure is that it provides high absorption with low emissivity of infrared. Several other panel modifications are also included in the patent.

**Collector with Series of Spaced Members Above Flat Plate**

*K.A. Alkasab; U.S. Patent 3,929,122; December 30, 1975; assigned to Universal Oil Products Company* describes an improved type of flat plate solar energy collector which will not only collect more energy per unit of collector area than conventional collectors but will do so at less cost per unit of energy collected.

The apparatus comprises a single flat plate lower collector member mounted in an insulated housing covered by a pair of glass plates and a plurality of upper collector members mounted above the lower collector but below the glass plates. The lower collector is preferably formed of a highly conductive metal such as copper or aluminum which has its upper surface painted or otherwise blackened to increase its absorbency. A series of parallel tubes are brazed or otherwise attached to the flat plate and connected at their ends to inlet and outlet manifold to carry the heat away from the flat plate.

The spacing of the tubing, the sizing of the tubing and the manifolds, and the flow rate of the fluid therein are derermined in accordance with the desired temperature of the outlet fluid. Although higher flow rates result in greater total heat transfer, it is usually more desirable to control the fluid flow so as to provide fluid temperatures in the range of about 77° to 93°C.

An upper absorption means comprising a plurality of extruded aluminum channel members is positioned above the flat plate. The channel members are preferably spaced from each other so as to overlie the flat plate in areas between the lower parallel tubes, thus giving solar energy rays direct access to the lower tubes. The channels have relatively wide, flat, elongated top portions which are blackened on their upper surface to improve energy absorption and which have a tube brazed or otherwise attached to their lower surface. The upper tubes are connected at their ends to manifolds similar to those used with the lower tubes. The side walls of the channels extend downwardly and inwardly and have an outwardly facing concave surface which, in one embodiment, defines an approximately 60° sector of a circle. The concave side walls are preferably left as shiny as possible since they serve to reflect and focus the solar rays on the lower tubes and flat plate. The concave side walls serve to concentrate the solar rays and increase the incident energy on the lower tubes when the sun is at low angles. The lower edges of the side walls of each channel are spaced from each other by a distance greater than the width of the tube mounted on the underside of the top surface of the channel.

The aforesaid spacing of the channel side walls permits the undersides of the channel top portions to be in nonobstructed communication with portions of the underlying flat plate collector member. Thus, portions of the energy which would normally be reradiated into space from the lower flat plate will be trapped by the channel members and utilized to heat the fluid in the channel mounted tubes. The side walls of the channels should not touch the lower flat plate so as to avoid conducting heat from the plate. However, they should be positioned quite close to it, and preferably at a distance less than the diameter of the tubes, so as to block the flow of air which takes place in a conventional flat plate collector due to convection caused by the hot lower plate and the cool upper glass. The particular spacing of the channel members and the shape and location of the concave curved surfaces can be varied to change the operational characteristics of the collector.

Referring to Figure 1.11a, the solar collector is indicated generally at **10**. The collector includes a base plate **12** of metal or other suitable material to which a support layer **14** of insulating material, such as rigid polystyrene or polyurethane foam, is applied. The side portions **16** and end portions **17** of the collector are also preferably formed of insulating material. A pair of glass plates **18, 20** are positioned near the top of the collector in slots **22** formed in the side and end members **16, 17** to further insulate and protect the collector.

Positioned on top of the insulating member **14** is a flat conductive plate **24** formed of copper, aluminum or other conductive material. The plate preferably includes a coating **26** of black paint or other material which is efficient in absorbing solar energy. A plurality of tubes **28** are attached to the plate such as by brazing. The tubes are connected in parallel at their opposite ends to an inlet manifold (not shown) and to an outlet manifold **30** and an outlet connector member **34** for the purpose of circulating fluid such as water through the collector in order to carry away the solar energy which reaches the tubes directly or by reflection, or by conduction from the plate.

The upper absorption means indicated generally at **38** comprises generally channel-shaped extruded aluminum side members **40** and channel-shaped intermediate members **42**. The side members include a flat side portion **44** which may be attached to the collector side members **16** by means of fasteners **46**. The side channel members further include a generally flat portion **50** which is coated on its top surface with a black energy absorbent coating **52** similar to the coating **26** on the plate **24**. The channel member also includes a downwardly and inwardly extending concave-curved shiny side surface **54** which serves as a reflector for reflecting solar rays onto the most closely adjacent tube **28** and the portions of plate **24** near the tube. A tube **58** attached to the lower surface of flat portion **50** such as by brazing serves to carry fluid to and from the collector in a manner similar to the lower tubes. The intermediate channel members **42** include an upper flat channel portion **60** having a black coating **62** and concave side portions **64, 65** similar to the corresponding portions **54** of channel member **40**. The lower edges **66, 67** of the side portions **64, 65** respectively, are preferably positioned quite close to the flat plate **24** in order that they might serve to block a large portion of the movement of air between the flat plate and glass plate **20** which would take place by convection in the absence of an obstruction such as side surfaces **64, 65**.

In addition to blocking air movements, the side surfaces further act to trap energy radiated upwardly between edges **66, 67** from the flat plate and permit it to be partially absorbed by the fluid passing through tube **68**. The tubes **68** and **58** are attached at their ends to inlet and outlet manifolds **70, 72** respectively. The manifolds **70, 72** are attached to inlet and outlet connector members **74, 34** which carry fluid to and from the collector. The connectors **74, 34** are also joined to the lower inlet manifold (not shown) and the lower outlet manifold **30**, respectively.

Although the improved collector is probably not significantly more efficient than an ordinary flat plate reflector when the sun's rays are directly above the unit, the collector is believed to be significantly more efficient when the sun is at low angles in the early morning or late afternoon since the angled rays are reflected from side surfaces **64, 65** and **54** directly onto the adjacent tubes **28** or the adjoining portions of plate **24**. This is illustrated by dotted lines **A** and **B** which represent low angle solar rays which are caused to impinge directly on tube **28** by virtue of being reflected from curved surface **64**.

FIGURE 1.11: COLLECTOR WITH SERIES OF SPACED MEMBERS ABOVE FLAT PLATE

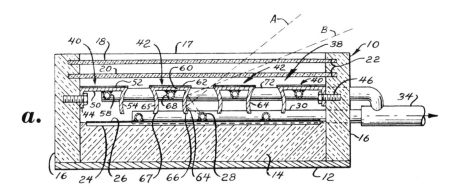

(continued)

FIGURE 1.11: (continued)

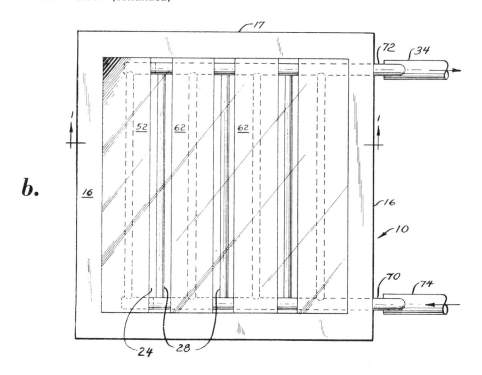

(a)     End sectional view taken on line **1—1** of Figure 1.11b
(b)     Top view

Source:  U.S. Patent 3,929,122

**Heat Absorbing Porous Wicking Membrane**

A solar energy collector panel including a housing having a solar window therein and which contains a loop of tubing through which a fluid is pumped for heating of the fluid is described by *J.M. Cutchaw; U.S. Patent 3,923,038; Dec. 2, 1975.* A heat absorbing porous wicking membrane containing a vaporizable working liquid is positioned within the housing for collecting solar heat and transferring that heat to the fluid within the tubing.

The working liquid is vaporized by solar energy and the vapor which contains latent heat will move toward and condense proximate the tubing to release the latent heat and thus transfer that heat to the fluid in the tubing. The condensed vapor, or working liquid is reabsorbed by the wicking membrane and is returned by wicking action to the vicinity of the solar window so that a continuous cycle of vaporization, condensation and liquid pumping takes place to efficiently collect and transfer heat. Referring to Figure 1.12a, a solar energy collector panel is indicated generally by the reference numeral **10**. The panel **10** includes a housing **12** having a solar window **14** and an enclosed cavity **16** formed therein.

FIGURE 1.12: HEAT ABSORBING POROUS WICKING MEMBRANE

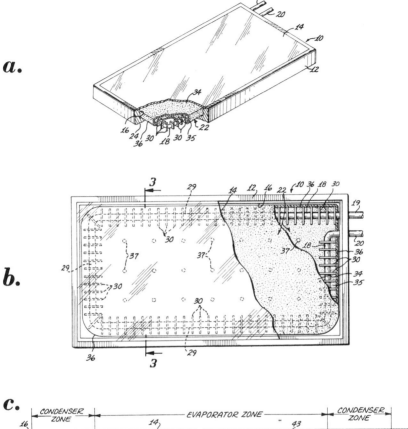

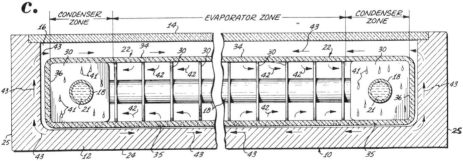

(a) Isometric view of collector panel
(b) Plan view
(c) Sectional view taken on line 3–3 of
    Figure 1.12b

Source: U.S. Patent 3,923,038

A tube **18** is positioned within the cavity of the housing and is provided with an inlet **19** and an outlet **20** communicating exteriorly of the housing so that a suitable heat absorbing fluid **21**, Figure 1.12c, such as air or water, can be pumped through the cavity of the housing for absorbing the heat collected by the panel. A wicking membrane **22** containing a vaporizable working liquid is positioned within the cavity of the housing adjacent the solar window and extends into the vicinity of the fluid carrying tube **18**. The wicking membrane and the vaporizable liquid provide means for collecting the solar energy and transferring the heat produced thereby to the fluid **21** contained within the tubing **18**.

The housing **12** is fabricated of suitable thermally insulative material and includes a bottom **24** with upstanding walls **25** configured so as to form the housing into a flat upwardly opening box shaped structure, having the cavity **16** therein. The upwardly extending ends of the side walls **25** of the housing are adapted to sealingly retain the peripheral edges of the solar window **14** so as to close the upwardly opening housing thus enclosing the cavity thereof. The solar window may be formed of any suitable transparent material, such as glass, plastic or the like.

As is well-known in the art, the solar window **14** may be formed of a single sheet of transparent material as shown in Figure 1.12c. It should be noted that the inwardly facing surface of the transparent material forming the solar window is ideally a wettable surface to prevent formation of condensation which could result in much heat loss due to reflective scattering of the incoming solar heat energy. In any event, the housing is hermetically sealed and may be at least partially evacuated.

The tubing, through which the heat absorbing fluid is pumped, is disposed within the cavity of the housing in a single loop so that each leg **29** (Figure 1.12b) of the loop is positioned adjacent a different one of the side walls **25** of the housing. The tubing may be of conventional materials and design, however, it is preferred that the material be copper, aluminum or other suitable thermally conductive material, and that the tubing be provided with a plurality of incrementally spaced transverse fins **30** of any convenient shape such as square. Other suitable heat transfer elements may also be employed. The fins **30** are employed for efficient conduction of heat to the heat absorbing fluid **21** moving through the tubing as will hereinafter be described in detail.

As seen best in Figures 1.12b and 1.12c, the wicking membrane **22** in the preferred embodiment is an envelope-like structure which substantially encloses that portion of the tubing which is disposed within the cavity of the housing. The wicking membrane is formed of a unitary sheet of material formed to provide an upper surface **34**, a lower surface **35** which is spaced from and substantially parallel to the upper surface **34**, and an endless side wall **36** that extends between the peripheral edges of the surfaces **34** and **35**. The wicking membrane is positioned within the cavity so that the upper surface and the lower surface are substantially parallel with respect to the solar window **14** of the housing and are coextensive therewith.

The loop of tubing is positioned within the wicking membrane so that the side wall **36** and the peripheral edges of the upper and lower surfaces **34** and **35** are in engaging contact with the fins **30** of the tubing **18**. The wicking membrane **22** is fabricated of a porous material such as a screen, cloth, felt, sintered powder and the like. A preferred form of wicking membrane is fabricated from a compressed sheet of shredded metal such as steel wool, copper wool, or aluminum wool. In the event that the wicking membrane 22 is formed of a pliable, or nonrigid material, means for supporting the membrane will be needed to prevent sagging thereof between the loop of tubing 18. Figure 1.12b illustrates a plurality of spaced standards 37, such as of plastic, extending between the upper and lower surfaces 34 and 35 of the membrane 22 to prevent sagging thereof.

Since one function of the wicking membrane is to collect solar heat energy, it is desirable that the outwardly facing surface of the membrane be colored black for efficient absorption of heat. The wicking membrane may have its inwardly facing surfaces colored silver or white for heat reflecting purposes. A vaporizable working liquid 41, shown as droplets on the fins of the tubing, is contained within the wicking membrane. The operating temperature of the solar energy collector panel is determined largely by the type of working liquid employed.

In operation, the working liquid 41 is present within the wicking membrane 22, and the upper surface 34 thereof acts as an evaporator zone due to impingement of solar heat energy thereon. The impinging solar heat energy will vaporize the working liquid 41 present in the evaporator zone which causes a pressure differential to be created between the evaporator zone and the area proximate the tubing 18. The area proximate the tubing 18 acts as a condenser zone due to the relatively lower temperature maintained in that zone by the movement of the heat absorbing fluid 21 through the tubing. The vapor produced in the evaporator zone will exit from the wicking membrane 22 and will move, as indicated by arrows 42 in Figure 1.12c, toward the condenser zone due to the pressure differential existing between the two zones.

The vapor will be condensed in the condenser zone due to the lower temperature and will thus release the latent heat of vaporization. The heat thus transferred to the condenser zone will be picked up by the fins 30 of the tubing which in turn conducts the heat to the fluid 21 within the tubing. The vapor condensed in the condenser zone is reabsorbed by the wicking membrane 22 and will move by surface tension pumping, or wicking action, back to the evaporator zone as indicated by arrows 43. In some climates, the intensity of the incoming solar heat energy will be sufficient to cause evaporation of the working liquid 41 to take place in the lower surface 35 of the wicking membrane which would cause both the upper and lower surfaces 34 and 35 to act as the evaporator zone.

It may be seen that if the incoming solar energy is intense enough to cause the working liquid to boil, a continuous cycle of vaporization, condensation and surface tension pumping will occur. Thus, the working liquid can be selected to suit a particular climate. For example, ethyl chloride ($CH_3CH_2Cl$) will boil at approximately 54°F and would be suitable in relatively cold climates, while water, which of course, boils at 212°F, would be ideal for use in mild and warm climates.

### Cylindrical Double-Walled Finned Metallic Absorber

The solar energy conversion device of *A.D. Beauchaine; U.S. Patent 3,983,861; October 5, 1976; assigned to Westman Manufacturing Company* has spaced, concentric outer and inner tubes of high conductivity metal, the outer tube having a blackened outside surface and a reflective inside surface. A core rod of low heat conductivity extends concentrically inside the inner tube and water flows around this core rod in a shallow cylindrical stream inside the inner tube to absorb heat efficiently from the inner tube. The inner tube may have fins on the outside to enhance the heat transfer.

The solar energy conversion device has a shallow base tray with a flat, rectangular, broad area bottom wall, short upstanding front and back walls and short up-standing end walls **13** and **14** (Figure 1.13a). This base tray may be of wood, metal or a suitable rigid plastic. Preferably, the inside of the tray is covered with a suitable heat insulation material, such as fiber glass or Styrofoam. The top of this tray is covered by a flat, rectangular sheet of glass or other suitable material which is transparent to the sun's rays and has low heat conductivity.

The energy conversion device has an inner tube **16** for conducting water or other fluid to be heated. This inner tube enters the support tray through an opening at **17** formed in the end wall **14** near the back wall **12** and below the glass cover. From there the inner tube extends parallel to the back wall **12** for most of the latter's length and then it curves through a 180° turn **18** near the opposite end wall **13**. From there it extends back toward the end wall **14** parallel to the back wall **12** until it makes another 180° turn **19** close to end wall **14**. From this point the inner tube continues back and forth in serpentine fashion, presenting elongated straight segments which are spaced apart in succession from the back wall **12** toward the front wall **11** and 180° turn segments between the successive elongated straight segments. Tube **16** passes out through an opening at **20** in the end wall **14** close to the front wall of the support tray. At each successive turn **18** or **19** the inner tube **16** is supported by a rigid metal bracket **21** extending up from the tray bottom.

Each elongated straight segment of the inner tube **16** is encircled by an outer tube **22**. As best seen in Figure 1.13b, at the opposite ends of each outer tube **22** a flat, transverse, annular wall **23** extends radially inward toward the inner tube. An annular grommet or sleeve **24** of suitable heat insulation material is engaged between the outside of the inner tube **16** and the inside edge of each corresponding end wall **23** of the outer tube to prevent the conduction of heat between them. Preferably, both the inner tube **16** and the outer tube **22** are of circular cross section and they are concentric with one another.

In accordance with one aspect of this process, the outer tube **22** is of high heat conductivity metal, such as aluminum, the outside of which is coated with a flat black paint which is very efficient in absorbing the sun's rays, and the inside of which has a bright finish for maximum reflectivity. The inner tube **16** is of high conductivity metal, such as copper or aluminum.

Each elongated straight segment of the inner tube **16** receives a core **25** of suitable low heat conductivity material. This core extends inside the inner tube for substantially the entire length of the corresponding outer tube **22**. Preferably, as shown, the core is a solid rod of suitable heat insulation, plastic or wood, circular in cross section and located concentrically inside the corresponding straight segment of the inner tube **16**, so that a shallow cylindrical passageway **P** is formed between the outside of this rod and the inside of the inner tube.

FIGURE 1.13: CYLINDRICAL DOUBLE-WALLED FINNED METALLIC ABSORBER

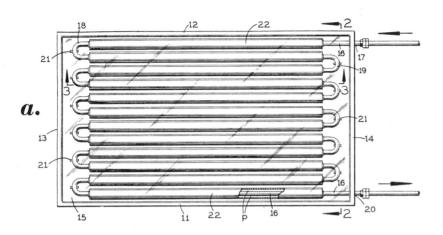

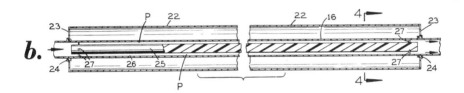

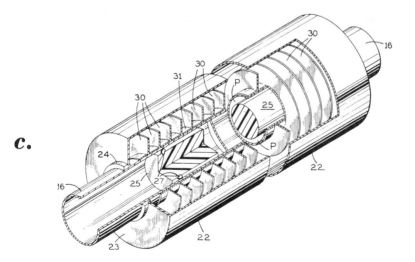

(a) Top plan view of solar energy conversion device
(b) Longitudinal section taken along line 3—3 in Figure 1.13a
(c) Fragmentary perspective view of finned absorber

Source: U.S. Patent 3,983,861

The core **25** carries small, radially-protruding projections **27** near its opposite ends for centering it inside the inner tube **16**.

Figure 1.13c shows an alternative embodiment which is the same as in Figures 1.13a and 1.13b except that the inner tube **16** is provided with radial fins to enhance the heat transfer effect. In this embodiment, a plurality of flat, annular, radially-disposed fins **30** are attached to the outside of a cylindrical metal sleeve **31** which snugly engages the outside of the inner tube **16**. The fins **30** are spaced apart in succession along the length of the outer tube **22**. The outer edge of each fin is spaced from the inside of the outer tube to avoid the conduction of heat between them. The purpose of these fins is to increase the rate at which heat is transferred by convection from the outer tube **22** to the inner tube **16**.

### Absorber Plate Supported by Spaced Posts

The process of *E.J. Hojnowski; U.S. Patent 3,995,615; December 7, 1976* deals with a relatively thin panel having a flat energy absorbing metal plate which is insulated from the panel base and its transparent cover by an evacuated space.

A molded plastic base has longitudinally extended channels, with the channel walls being relieved at laterally spaced locations to define closely spaced posts which support a transparent cover. A flat metal heat absorbing plate is provided just below the cover and has holes for loosely receiving the posts. A corrugated plate is welded to the underside of the heat absorbing plate to define fluid passageways, which passageways are located in the channels of the base. The plate assembly is supported at one end of the base by inlet and outlet pipes for circulation fluid to be heated and at the opposite end the plate assembly is supported by a gas adsorbing device which operates from the expansion and contraction of the plate assembly in order to preserve the vacuum in the area surrounding the heat absorbing plate.

With reference to Figure 1.14, the heat collector panel preferably includes a transparent glass cover **10**. It should be noted that other materials might also be used, as for example, methacrylate plastic material such as Lucite and Plexiglas. The solar heat collector panel (Figure 1.14a) also includes a base **12** which is preferably fabricated from a molded plastic material having thermal expansion and conductivity characteristics similar to that of the glass cover. The coefficient of thermal expansion should be significantly less than that of the internal components.

The plastic material chosen for the base should also have a relatively low coefficient of thermal conductivity as well, this to enhance the efficiency of the panel from the point of view of heat lost to the surrounding atmosphere. It is important that the heat loss of the components within the panel is effectively minimized not so much as a result of the materials chosen for the cover and base, but rather due to the high degree of vacuum achieved within the panel, not only initially upon assembly of the panel, but also during extended periods of use as a result of the supporting device for the panel to be described hereinafter.

Still with reference to the base **12** and referring more particularly to Figure 1.14b, the base can be seen to define an upwardly open cavity having a corrugated floor **14** which defines a plurality of side-by-side longitudinally extending channels. Each of these channels is defined by longitudinally extending channel walls **16, 16,** which walls include upper end portions **18, 18** for supporting the glass cover. The channel walls **16, 16** are preferably cut away or grooved either during the molding process of the base, or afterwards, so that the uppermost ends **18, 18** of these channel walls define relatively small diameter circular posts. The posts **18, 18** are arranged in a closely-spaced generally rectangular, square pattern shown in Figure 1.14a, the posts being spaced both longitudinally and laterally in the panel for efficiently counteracting the atmospheric pressure exerted upon the glass cover.

The perimeter of the base can be seen to include a peripherally extending flange **20** which is adapted to receive the glass cover and to be sealed in the area of the recess **22** by a suitable adhesive such that the cavity defined between the cover and the base can be conveniently evacuated through a port following assembly of the panel. It may further be necessary to bake the panel in an oven in order to reduce the vapor pressure of the plastic materials from which the base is fabricated. This can be done following assembly and prior to actually evacuating the cavity.

Turning next to a more detailed consideration of the components provided within the panel cavity for absorbing the solar energy, the means preferably comprises a generally flat metallic heat collector plate **30** which plate is provided with a plurality of openings for loosely receiving the posts **18, 18.** The plate has a front face which is blackened with a coating of material well adapted to absorb solar radiation. The rear face of the plate **30** is provided with means defining longitudinally extending fluid passageways which are best shown in Figure 1.14b. Preferably, the passageway comprises a corrugated plate **40** having corrugations adapted to fit within the channels defined by the base **12** and having area between the fluid passageway defining portions **42, 42** suitable for welding the corrugated plate to the underside of the heat absorbing plate.

These areas or lands are indicated generally at **44** and such areas include the hole defining portions of the heat absorbing plate. More particularly, holes are also provided in the corrugated plate so as to receive the posts **18, 18** utilized to support the glass cover as mentioned previously. The holes in the plate assembly **30** and **40** are preferably large enough, as compared to the cross sectional size of posts **18, 18** so that no interference occurs during expansion and contraction of the plate assembly.

It should be noted that, while a corrugated plate is illustrated in Figure 1.14b, the fluid passageway defining means carried by the underside of the heat collector plate could also be provided in the form of individual strips defining each of the individual longitudinal passageways **42, 42.** Furthermore, the opposite longitudinal end portions of the corrugated plate require further fabrication in order to provide communication between the laterally spaced longitudinally extending passageways **42, 42** for the fluid to be heated.

The inlet pipe **50** includes a flange which serves to support the corrugated plate **40** from the base **12** and a similar pipe (not shown) is provided immediately below the pipe **50** of Figure 1.14a, so as to provide a convenient means for withdrawing heated fluid from the panel. An inlet header is illustrated generally at **54** such that communication is provided between approximately one-half of the longitudinally extending fluid passageways **42, 42** at their respective inlet ends. A similar header **56** is provided at the opposite end of the panel and it serves to provide communication between at least a portion of the outlet ends of each of the longitudinally extending passageways **42, 42.** Although not shown, the outlet pipe also includes an outlet header similar to the header **54** and arranged opposite thereto in the Figure 1.14a panel such that the corresponding ends of the other half of the longitudinally extending passageways **42, 42** communicate with one another and at their respective outlet ends. Furthermore, a header **58** provides communication between the remaining number of longitudinally extending fluid passageways such that fluid can be circulated through the panel as indicated generally by the broken line arrows.

### FIGURE 1.14: ABSORBER PLATE SUPPORTED BY SPACED POSTS

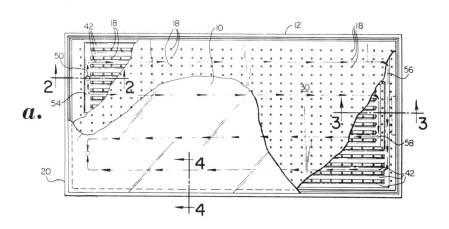

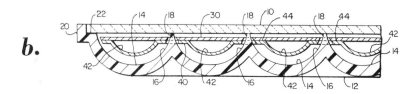

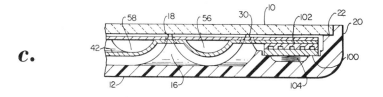

(a) Plan view of heat collector plate
(b) Sectional view taken on line **4—4** of Figure 1.14a
(c) Sectional view taken on line **3—3** of Figure 1.14a

Source: U.S. Patent 3,995,615

Obviously, some of the fluid will utilize the header **56** associated with the right hand end of the panel of Figure 1.14a and another portion of the fluid will utilize the header **58** also provided in the panel for this purpose. Two such headers are provided at the right hand of the panel but one header might be provided for this purpose, two being preferred in order to assure the proper rate of flow in each of the various passageways.

The plate assembly comprising the heat collecting flat plate **30** together with its associated fluid passageway defining plate **40** is mounted in the base at the left hand end as a result of the fluid inlet and outlet pipes such as depicted at **50** and is supported at its right hand end as illustrated in Figure 1.14c.

Figure 1.14c illustrates an expansion joint device whereby advantage is taken of the expansion and contraction of the metallic plate assembly. As a result of this motion caused by daily variations in the incident solar energy, a bar of titanium, provided in the base **12** and a file member **102** is provided on the underside of the lower plate **40** such that movement of the plate assembly with respect to the base **12** causes the titanium bar **100** to be continually abraded and any gases within the evacuation space are absorbed by the titanium bar **100**. This action preserves the vacuum within the cavity.

The titanium bar may be spring biased upwardly as a result of the spring **104** provided between the base and the member **100** and the file member **102** is preferably carried by the underside of the plate assembly but the locations for these members might be reversed, with the titanium bar being carried by the plate assembly and the file member being provided in a suitable receptacle defined in the base **12**. Any suitable gas adsorptive material can be used in place of the titanium bar **100**.

### Collector with Moisture Control Means

Although there are many solar heat collector designs in the prior art, each of the designs has drawbacks. For example, during the day, solar energy rays are incident on the absorber of the solar heat collector. Solar energy is absorbed and the collector is heated. Then, in the evening, the temperature of the solar heat collector decreases. Any moisture trapped in the space between the cover plate and absorber during fabrication and/or moisture that moves into the space during use of the collector condenses on the surface of the cover plate and the absorber.

The moisture acts as a barrier to the solar radiation decreasing the absorptivity coefficient of the absorber and the transmittance coefficient of the cover plate, thereby requiring a longer time for the heat collector to be heated by solar radiation. As the solar heat collector is heated by solar radiation and infrared energy, the moisture evaporates and in some instances, leaves spots on the cover plate and/or absorber. These spots further reduce the efficiency of the solar heat collector by decreasing the transmittance coefficient of the cover plate and the absorptivity coefficient of the absorber.

A solar heat collector is disclosed by *P.G. Patil; U.S. Patent 3,974,822; Aug. 17, 1976; assigned to PPG Industries, Inc.* having an outer cover plate, an intermediate cover plate and a solar radiation absorber mounted in spaced relation to each other by edge packing. The edge packing removes moisture from the air space between the cover plates and absorber and prevents moisture from entering the air space between the cover plates and the absorber.

With reference to Figure 1.15a, solar heat collector unit **20** of this process, in general, includes a solar heat collector **22** mounted in an insulated box **24**. The solar heat collector includes a solar radiation and infrared energy absorber and, intermediate and outer cover plates **28** and **30** respectively, mounted in spaced relation to the absorber. The cover plates 28 and 30 pass solar radiation to the absorber, reflect infrared energy back toward the absorber, trap infrared energy between the cover plate and absorber and reduce convection heat losses.

The absorber **26** and cover plates **28** and **30**, respectively, are held in spaced relation by edge packing **32**, which edge packing absorbs moisture trapped between the cover plates and the absorber during fabrication of the collector and prevents moisture from moving into the space between the cover plates and the absorber during use of the heat collector unit. The heat collector is preferably mounted in the insulated box **24** to minimize conduction and convection heat losses.

With reference to Figures 1.15a and 1.15b, the absorber **26** includes a plate **34** having a conduit **36** mounted on surface **38** of the plate. The plate and conduit are made of a heat conductive material such as aluminum, steel or copper. The conduit is advantageously mounted on surface **38** of the plate **34** such that ends **40** and **42** of the conduit extend beyond the insulated box to provide external access to the conduit for moving a heat absorbing medium through the conduit (shown better in Figure 1.15c). The heat absorbing medium, e.g., water or ethylene glycol mixed with water, is moved through the end **40** of the conduit **36** and out of end **42** of the conduit **36** in any conventional manner. As the absorber **26** is heated by solar radiation and infrared energy, the heat absorbing medium moving through the conduit is heated by conduction and convection.

The cover plates **28** and **30** are selected to pass solar radiation and to reflect and/or trap infrared energy. The cover plates **28** and **30** may be made of com-mercial-soda-lime glass or borosilicate glass. To improve the reflectance coeffi-cient of the plates while passing sufficient solar energy to the absorber, the cover plate **28** and/or cover plate **30** may be coated as described in U.S. Patent 3,981,293.

With reference to Figure 1.15b, the discussion will be directed to the edge pack-ing **32** for the solar heat collector. The edge packing preferably is of the type that absorbs moisture from between the cover plates **28** and **30** and from be-tween the cover plate **28** and absorber **26**, which moisture is trapped therebe-tween during fabrication, and prevents moisture from moving between the cover plates **28** and **30** and from moving between the cover plate **28** and absorber **26** during the use of the solar heat collector.

It has been found that when edge packing having the above characteristics is used in the construction of solar heat collectors, the efficiency of the heat col-lector is increased. The efficiency is increased because there will be no moisture to condense on the outer and intermediate cover plates and absorber when the solar heat collector cools. In the prior art, no provisions are made for prevent-ing moisture from moving between the cover plates and absorber or for remov-ing moisture trapped therebetween during fabrication. When prior art solar heat collectors are cooled, the moisture between the cover plates and absorber condenses on the plates and absorber thereby decreasing the transmittance and reflectance coefficients of the cover plates and the absorptivity coefficient of the absorber. When this occurs, the time required for the solar heat collector to heat up increases. Removing and preventing moisture from moving between the cover plates and the absorber, the efficiency of the solar heat collector is increased because there is no condensation which can obstruct the passing of solar radiation to the absorber, there is no reduction in the amount of infrared energy and solar radiation reflected back to the absorber and there is no reduction in the amount of solar radiation and infrared energy absorbed by the absorber.

With reference to Figure 1.15b, the cover plates **28** and **30** and the absorber **26** are separated at their marginal edges by a metal spacer element **100** such as disclosed in U.S. Patent 2,684,266. The discussion will be directed to the edge packing between cover plates **28** and **30** with the understanding that the discussion is applicable to the edge packing between intermediate cover plate **28** and absorber **26** unless indicated otherwise.

The spacer element **100** includes a tubular portion of generally rectangular cross section that is filled with a desiccant material **102**, such as granular or powdered silica gel. Communication between the air spaces between cover plates **30** and **28** and the desiccant **102** is provided through a plurality of channels or passages **104** in spacer element **100**. The spacer **100** extends completely around and between the marginal edges of the cover plates **28** and **30**.

**FIGURE 1.15: COLLECTOR WITH MOISTURE CONTROL MEANS**

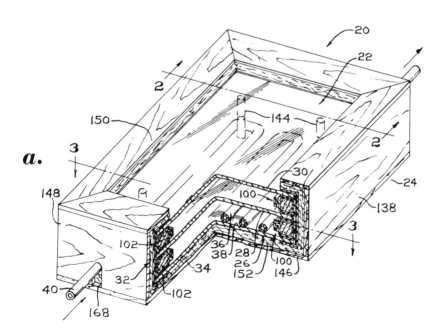

(continued)

**FIGURE 1.15:** (continued)

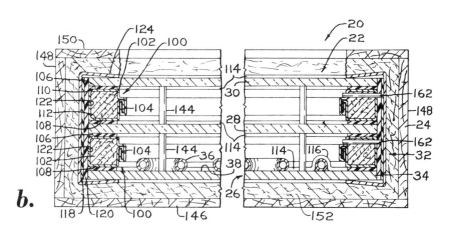

**b.**

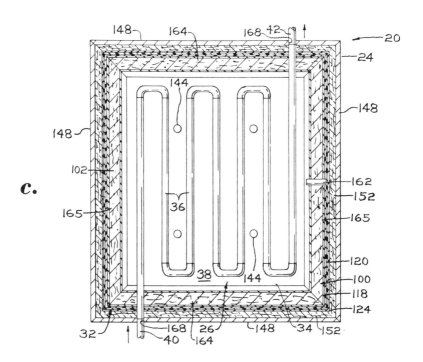

**c.**

(a)     Isometric view of collector unit
(b)     Cross-sectional view of collector unit taken
        along line **2—2** of Figure 1.15a
(c)     Cross-sectional view of collector unit taken
        along line **3—3** of Figure 1.15a

Source:   U.S. Patent 3,974,822

Opposed surfaces 106 and 108 of the spacer element 100 are adhered to marginal surfaces 110 and 112 of the cover plates 28 and 30 respectively, by a thin continuous film of a moisture-resistant adhesive 114. The moisture-resistant adhesives 114 which may be used are materials that are capable of flow at room temperature and include precured materials such as disclosed in U.S. Patent 2,974,377, as well as room temperature-curable materials such as disclosed in U.S. Patent 3,791,910.

With reference to the spacer element 100 between the cover plate 28 and absorber 26, a portion of the spacer at 116 is removed to receive inlet end 40 and similarly a portion of the spacer (not shown) is removed to receive outlet end 42 of the conduit 36 which ends extend beyond the solar heat collector (see Figure 1.15c also).

A resilient moisture-resistant strip 118 with a layer of mastic 120 adhered thereto, such as disclosed in U.S. Patent 2,974,377, is bonded to the peripheral edge, e.g., flat side 122 of the metal spacer element 100 and the peripheral edges of the absorber and cover plates 26, 28 and 30, respectively. A channel member 124 of essentially U-shaped cross section also extends completely around the perimeter of the window to protect its edges. The channel member 124 generally includes several sections of channeling that are joined or butted together at their ends.

The moisture resistant strip 118 having the layer of adhesive 120 is adhesively bonded to peripheral edges of the cover plates 28 and 30, absorber 26 and the flat side of the metal spacer channel 162. The channel member 124 as shown completely surrounds the collector.

A vacuum can be provided between the cover plates and the absorber to reduce heat losses due to convection. In the instance where vacuum is to be employed between the plates and the absorber it is recommended that the metal spacer element 100 or the metal spacer channel 162 as shown in Figure 1.15b, be used. This is because the atmospheric pressure urges the cover plates and absorber toward each other. By providing a rigid metal spacer, the sheets are maintained in spaced relation. Further, if the sheets are of large dimension, for example, greater than about 2 feet by 2 feet, it is recommended that spacer blocks 144 made of cork or plastic be selectively positioned between the cover plates 30 and 28 and between the absorber 26 and cover plate 28 to prevent the plates from contacting one another and the absorber.

Further, the glass sheets may be prestressed, for example, provided with a radius so as to act against positive pressure of the atmosphere thereby eliminating the need for spacer blocks. Further, it is recommended that approximately the same amount of vacuum be provided between the cover plates 28 and 30 and between cover plate 28 and absorber 26. In this manner, the plate 28 will be maintained in spaced relationship to both the plate 30 and absorber 26. Still further, it is recommended that the glass sheets be tempered.

The solar heat collector is preferably mounted in the insulated box 24 to reduce convection heat losses. The insulated box 24 includes a solid bottom 146 and sides 148. The top portion of the box as viewed in Figure 1.15a is provided with a ledge 150 to maintain the collector in the box. The inlet and outlet ends 40 and 42, respectively, of the conduit 36 pass through sides of the box to provide external access to the conduit so as to move the heat-absorbing medium through the conduit. Insulating material 152 such as fiber glas or glass wool or urethane foam is provided between the solar heat collector and inside surfaces of the box to minimize convection heat losses of the heat collector.

The cork packing for this collector is further described by *P.G. Patil; U.S. Patent 3,974,823; August 17, 1976; assigned to PPG Industries, Inc.* The layer of cork is provided between the second spacer assembly and the marginal edge portions of the absorber to minimize conduction heat losses from the absorber to the spacer assembly.

*F.H. Gillery; U.S. Patent 3,981,293; September 21, 1976; assigned to PPG Industries, Inc.* provides a description of the cover plate which may be coated with tin oxide and/or indium oxide. The cover plate has a transmittance coefficient (t) for solar radiation, e.g., in the wavelength range of about 0.3 to 2.1 microns, and a reflectance coefficient (r) for infrared energy in the wavelength range of about 2 to 15 microns. The transmittance coefficient and reflectance coefficient of the cover plate are selected such that the product of (r) and (t) is equal to or greater than about 0.25 to increase the saturation temperature of the solar heat collector.

As described further by *R.J. Mazzoni and L.F. Schutrum; U.S. Patent 3,990,431; November 9, 1976; assigned to PPG Industries, Inc.* the vapor barrier seal for the collector includes: (1) a moisture-impervious adhesive to prevent moisture from moving between the glass sheets and absorber, and (2) a vapor-impervious strip, e.g., an aluminum strip mounted between the adhesive and peripheral edge portions of the glass sheets and absorber to prevent solvent vapors of the adhesive from moving between the glass sheets and absorber.

According to *R.J. Mazzoni and L.F. Schutrum; U.S. Patent 3,990,429; Nov. 9, 1976; assigned to PPG Industries, Inc.* the collector is equipped with a breather arrangement to provide communication between the ambient air and air in the airspace of the collector through desiccant material. In this manner, the air pressure in the airspace is equalized to the ambient air pressure without moisture moving into the airspace and the desiccant material is regenerated.

A breather tube for the absorber plate is described by *W.R. Bauer and L.F. Schutrum; U.S. Patent 3,999,536; December 28, 1976; assigned to PPG Industries, Inc.*

The U-shaped channel member used for the collector frame is further described by *P.G. Patil; U.S. Patent 3,995,613; December 7, 1976; assigned to PPG Industries, Inc.* The legs of the channel member engage the outer cover plate of the collector and the protective sheet to urge the collector and the protective sheet together about the thermal-insulating material.

In a modification of the collector described above the absorber of *O.J. Cerra and P.G. Patil; U.S. Patent 3,995,614; December 7, 1976; assigned to PPG Industries, Inc.* has a pan-shaped configuration. The side walls of the absorber support the cover plate in spaced relation to the base of the absorber, thereby eliminating the need of a spacer frame.

## Absorber Supported Within Evacuated Chamber

The collector of *J.M. Estes, E.E. Kerlin and H.A. Blum; U.S. Patents 3,961,619; June 8, 1976; assigned to Solarsystems Incorporated; and 3,916,871; Nov. 4, 1975* has a housing with an evacuated chamber defined therein. A transparent planar wall forms one side of the chamber and a radiant energy absorber with flow passages therein is supported within the chamber thermally insulated from the housing. Heat exchanger flow conduits extend from the absorber and through the housing without contacting the walls of the housing to allow circulation of heat exchange fluid through the absorber with minimal conduction heat losses.

In Figures 1.16a through 1.16e the details of the construction of the improved flat plate solar collector module **30** are illustrated. The module has a housing which is assembled with a pair of parallel spaced planar endwalls **60** which are connected to a pair of parallel spaced sidewalls **62** to form a quadrilateral shaped member. In the preferred embodiment, the endwalls are approximately 1.3 meters long and sidewalls are approximately 2.6 meters long to form an elongated shaped member as illustrated. A planar upper cover **64** is attached to the quadrilateral shaped member formed by the walls. This cover is constructed from radiation transmission material to allow radiant energy to enter the chamber formed in the module.

A bottom wall **66** is attached to walls **60** and **62**. This wall with walls **60, 62** and the cover defines a chamber **68**. A material **70** insulates the outside surface of wall **66** and can be formed from any suitable heat insulating material.

In Figures 1.16a through 1.16d a heat absorber assembly **80** is shown positioned within the chamber. The absorber is of the flat plate type and has planar portions **81** for receipt of the incident solar radiation with a plurality of fluid flow paths therein for circulating heat exchange fluid through the absorber. In operation the portions are heated by solar radiation and heat is transferred to and carried away by the circulation of the heat exchange fluid.

## FIGURE 1.16: ABSORBER SUPPORTED WITHIN EVACUATED CHAMBER

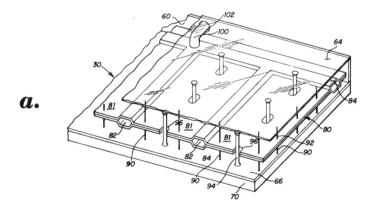

*a.*

(continued)

FIGURE 1.16: (continued)

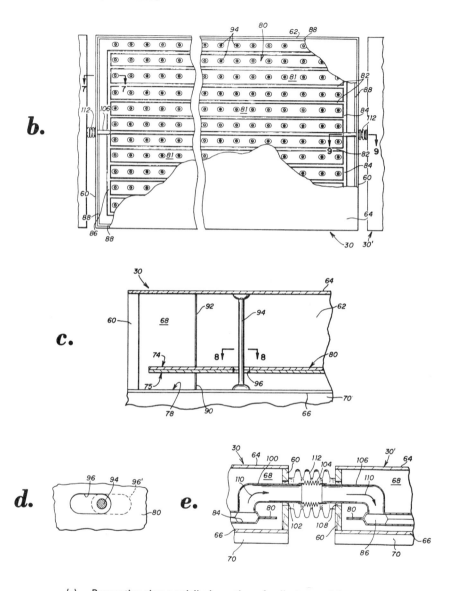

(a)    Perspective view partially in section of collector module
(b)    Plan view with a portion of the cover removed
(c)    Enlarged section of the module taken on line **7—7** of
        Figure 1.16b looking in the direction of the arrows
(d)    A partial enlarged sectional view taken on line **8—8** of
        Figure 1.16c looking in the direction of the arrows
(e)    Enlarged section taken on line **9—9** of Figure 1.16b
        looking in the direction of the arrows

Source: U.S. Patent 3,961,619

The absorber assembly **80** can be formed from two sheets of material which are laminated as illustrated to form a plurality of parallel conduits **82** which extend along the length therof. Each of the conduits is connected at opposite ends to manifolds **84** and **86** formed in the absorber. As will be hereinafter described in more detail, manifold **86** is appropriately connected to a supply of heat exchange fluid to receive and distribute the fluid to the conduits. Manifold **84** is positioned at the opposite end of the conduits to receive the heat exchange fluid flowing therefrom and convey them from module **30**.

It is important to note that the absorber is smaller than chamber **68** and a small clearance **88** is provided between the absorber and the housing. This clearance prevents contact between the absorber and walls **60** and **62** to prevent conduction heat treansfer and losses from the absorber to the housing and prevents the absorber from imposing stresses in the housing due to thermal expansion. Other constructions of the absorber could be utilized which do not require the lamination of two sheets of material.

The module can be constructed from any suitable material which is structurally sound and sufficiently impermeable to hold a vacuum in the chamber for a reasonable period of time. In the present embodiment moldable opaque plastic material was used for walls **60, 62** and **66**. A transparent plastic material which adequately transmits solar radiation was used for cover **64**. The three walls and the cover are attached together in any suitable manner to provide a seal between the individual walls. In the preferred embodiment, it was envisioned that these walls could be integrally molded as a unitary piece with the cover removably attached to the unitary piece to allow assembly and maintenance of the interior of the modules.

The absorber can be constructed from any suitable material such as metal, plastic or the like, which can withstand the operating temperatures thereof; can efficiently conduct heat; and can have suitable heat transfer coatings thereon. In the preferred embodiment, aluminum was used for the construction of the absorber with a coating on upper surface **74** of high solar absorptivity and low radiation emissivity at the operating temperatures on the upper surface. The lower surface **75** has a coating or finish with a low radiation emissivity at the operating temperatures. Surface **78** of the wall **66** and the interior surfaces of walls **60** and **62** were provided with a highly reflective coating thereon.

The absorber is supported above the lower wall **66** by means of a plurality of lower support pins **90**. The pins are constructed with a very small diameter and have sufficient columnar strength to hold the absorber assembly supported in the position illustrated above the lower wall. If desired, upper support pins **92** can also be provided between the absorber assembly and upper wall **64** to assist in holding the absorber assembly in position during transport, installation and the like. It is envisioned that these upper pins could be removed at installation of the module to prevent any unnecessary conduction heat transfer therethrough to the upper wall.

The support pins in the present embodiment are constructed from metallic material which has a very small diameter in the range of 0.127 cm to restrict and inhibit conduction heat transfer between the absorber and the lower wall. It is important to note that the pins have a particular advantage in providing flexibility in directions transverse to their length to allow for relative thermal expansion between the housing and the absorber during operation without imparting substantial stresses to the housing itself.

Due to the fact that the chamber **68** is evacuated during use, a plurality of spaced compression supports **94** are mounted within the chamber to assist in resisting bending and deformation of the cover and lower wall **64** and **66**, respectively, due to the forces generated by differential pressure across the chamber walls. The lower wall **66** can be constructed as thick and as rigid as desirable but any thickening or bracing of the upper wall must be kept to a minimum to prevent blocking of incident radiation entering through the upper wall.

The compression members in the preferred embodiment were constructed from a plastic material or the like with a diameter in the range of 0.254 cm except at the top and bottom of the chamber where the diameter is larger to prevent stress concentrations. It is envisioned that the compression members could be integrally molded when forming the housing. The members **94** are attached to the lower wall but their upper ends are not attached to the cover to allow removal of the upper wall and to reduce the buildup of stresses. A plurality of elongated slots **96** are provided in absorber **80** to prevent contact between the compression members and the absorber. These slots eliminate conduction heat transfer and losses from the absorber to the relatively massive compression members.

As can be seen in Figure 1.16d elongated slot **96** allows for thermal expansion of the absorber. The slot outlines **96** and **96'** illustrate the extremes of movement of the absorber due to thermal expansion during normal operating temperatures. By designing the compression members such that they do not contact the absorber, conduction heat losses through these massive compression members are prevented. By combining this structure and support pins **90**, the efficiency of the module 80 is increased.

Interconnection of adjacent modules **30** and **30'** for circulation of the heat exchange fluid is illustrated in Figure 1.16e. In this figure manifold **80** of a first module **30** is illustrated with a conduit **100** in fluid communication with manifold **84**. The conduit extends through an enlarged port **102** in endwall **60** without contacting wall **60**. A bellows connection **104** is provided between the conduit and a second conduit **106**. Conduit **106** in turn extends through an enlarged port **108** in wall **60** of a second module **30'** without contacting wall **60**. This conduit **106** is in fluid communication with manifold **86** of the absorber assembly therein. By connecting the absorber **80** of modules **30** and **30'** in this manner heat exchange fluid can flow from manifold **84** of module **30** through conduit **100**, the bellows, conduit **106** and into this manifold of module **30'**.

The bellows allows for relative axial movement between the absorber assemblies due to variations in temperature thereof. In addition, some relative movement between the modules **30** and **30'** is allowed by this bellows configuration. A second bellows **112** is positioned concentrically around bellows **104** and the conduits and is sealed and attached between walls **60** of modules **30** and **30'**. In this manner the evacuated chambers of the modules are connected while some relative movement between the modules is permitted.

A similar configuration can be used to connect the modules to other pairs of manifolds. For example, a bellows could be provided for connection of the heat exchange fluid conduit to the appropriate manifold and a larger concentrically mounted bellows can be connected between the periphery of the port and the exterior of the conduit to seal the chamber **68**.

The collector of the process is designed to be operated normally between 250° and 300°F at a desirable efficiency with a normal operating load. It is also envisioned that during some periods of operation such as during no load conditions the absorber will reach temperatures in the neighborhood of 600°F. In the design of the absorber itself these wide temperature variations need to be taken into consideration in the selection of suitable material, but this is not necessary in the selection of materials in the construction of the housing.

This is due to the fact that the physical separation of the absorber and its associated fluid flow conduits from the housing as disclosed in the process prevents the housing from contacting the absorber. This physical isolation of the absorber in combination with the evacuation of the chamber insulates the housing from the absorber and allows the use of unsophisticated materials which need not have a temperature tolerance within the operation range of the absorber itself.

In addition to reducing conduction losses evacuation of the chamber tends to extend the life of the coating on the absorber and prevents chemical and weather deterioration of the absorber itself. It is also envisioned that the residual gases other than air could be inserted in the chamber to further reduce heat losses from and deterioration of the surface of the absorber.

### Structurally Integrated Steel Collector-Roof

*S.W. Moore; U.S. Patent 4,010,733; March 8, 1977;* assigned to the United States Energy Research and Development Administration describes a flat plate solar heat collector unit integrated as a structural unit so that the collector also functions as the building roof. The functions of efficient heat collection, liquid coolant flow passages, roof structural support and building insulation are combined into one unit.

Referring to Figure 1.17a a pair of rectangular steel plates **13** and **14** are seam welded around the periphery of the heat exchanger area. In addition, an array of intermittent spot welds hold the plates together over the central portion of the heat exchanger area. An inlet pipe and and outlet pipe are welded to suitable apertures in bottom plate **14** only. A compressed gas is introduced between upper plate **13** and lower plate **14** to force the plates apart where they are not welded together.

As a result a flow network of parallel flat flow passages from one end to the other are formed. The resulting surface has a quilted appearance, and is coated with a suitable anticorrosion protective coating. Sufficient steel is provided on either side of the steel plates to form the integrated structural unit of the process. The sides of the upper plate are bent upward at either side to form a generally I-shaped flange structure **21**. Additional strength is obtained by bending the flange back on itself to form a lip **22**.

Lower unit section **14** is bent downward, transversely, and up, to form a C-shaped structural channel similar to that employed in a conventional steel C-beam. It will be apparent that the two steel plates welded together form a structural unit strong enough to provide a self-supporting roof structure. Thermal insulation **18**, conveniently foam, is formed about the bottom of lower plate **14**.

## FIGURE 1.17: STRUCTURALLY INTEGRATED STEEL COLLECTOR-ROOF

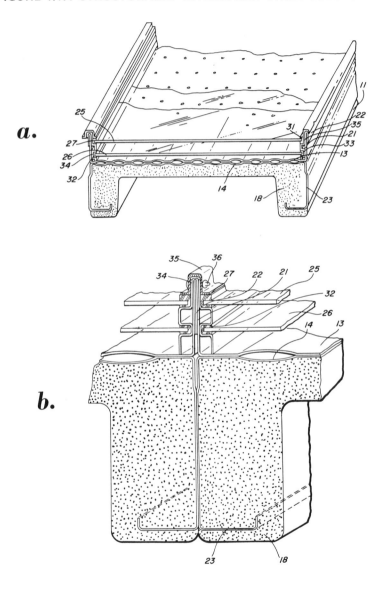

(a)   Cross section of solar collector panel
(b)   Cross section of solar collector unit connection

Source:   U.S. Patent 4,010,733

Efficiency of the collector is increased markedly by covering the collection surface with glass. Glass is opaque to reradiated infrared energy and thus traps reradiated energy, increasing heat collected by the panel. The air gas between the collector surface and the glass also serves to insulate the collector surface from the outside environment. Two panes of glass are an improvement over one in this regard. Therefore, means are provided for mounting two panes of glass 25 and 26 on the collector unit. Glass sheet 25 is retained by a pair of resilient strips 27 and 31. Glass sheet 26 is similarly retained by strips 32 and 33. The resilient strips, fabricated of a suitable weather resistant rubber or plastic, have a substantially U-shaped cross section enclosing the edges of the glass sheets. They are retained in proper relation to the heat exchanger surface by a pair of sheet metal retainer stampings 34 and 35.

As more clearly illustrated in Figure 1.17b, glass retainer 34 is placed in contact with the upstanding portions 21 on adjacent units. A cap strip 35 fastens adjacent elements of the two adjacent collector assemblies. A retaining fastener 36, passing through apertures in 27, 34 and 35, permanently secures the two adjacent collector assemblies and compresses elastic glass retaining strips 27 and 32.

In use the solar collector would be filled with a suitable nonfreezing heat exchanging liquid which is pumped through a heat exchanger wherein the collected heat is transferred to a suitable heat storage unit to be used for building heating and/or heating water. The collector units can be readily mass produced and factory assembled, resulting in large cost savings. The collector is completely self-supporting, providing a unitary roof structure. Its surface thereby serves a structural function, as well as energy collection, thus contributing to the overall section modulus of the roof. The collector glazing support means 27, 32 and 34 and the upper sheet 13 of the collector are integral, eliminating the possibility of leakage through the roof structure. The foam insulation not only is a basic insulator but increases panel rigidity to enhance the structural stability, and deadens sound.

### Laminated Absorber Member

Conventionally, the absorber member is a copper sheet of substantial thickness to which a series of liquid carrying tubes is soldered. The absorber member is generally painted black and mounted on an insulating surface such as wood or foam which is in turn mounted in a collector frame tightly covered with one or two panels of glass. The glass helps prevent reradiation of energy to the atmosphere and reduces losses by conduction and convection. Although such collectors are very simple, they are quite heavy and expensive due to the large amount of copper sheet and tubing they require. In view of the large amount of collector surface required in a typical solar heating installation, the expense of the installation has seldom been justified where alternate sources of energy have been available.

A flat plate absorber described by *R.G. Sarazin and L.D. Olson; U.S. Patent 3,996,092; December 7, 1976; assigned to Universal Oil Products Company* includes a flat heat absorbing sheet of a thin metal foil such as copper, or a thin plastic film such as polyvinyl fluoride, bonded to a channeled substrate, and particularly to a plastic laminate such as a glass epoxy laminate. The absorber member provides an energy collecting efficiency which is much greater than that of a much more expensive conventional collector having a series of copper tubes soldered to a copper sheet. The absorber is preferably made by the method of taking a base sheet of fully cured glass epoxy laminate and overlying it with a precut, patterned intermediate layer of semicured glass epoxy which defines the depth of the side walls of the channels. The cover sheet of metal foil or plastic film is then placed over the semicured glass epoxy intermediate layer and heat and pressure are applied to bond the semicured glass epoxy to the cover sheet and to the previously cured base sheet.

Referring to Figures 1.18a and 1.18b, the improved flat plate absorber indicated generally at **10** includes a base insulating and support layer **12**, a patterned intermediate layer **14** and a top layer **16**. The patterned layer may have any channel pattern desired but is shown as including a pair of channel portions **18, 20** defined by an outer rim portion **22** and an inner strip **24**. The channels are joined at their inlet and outlet ends by connecting portions **26, 28** respectively. Heat transfer fluid such as water or water and antifreeze solution enters the collector through an inlet fitting **32** and exits through an outlet fitting **34**. The fittings are attached to the upper layer **16** in surrounding relationship to the apertures **36, 38** (Figure 1.18e) and are fastened to this layer by any suitable means such as solder where this layer is a metal foil or adhesive where this layer is a plastic film.

FIGURE 1.18:  LAMINATED ABSORBER MEMBER

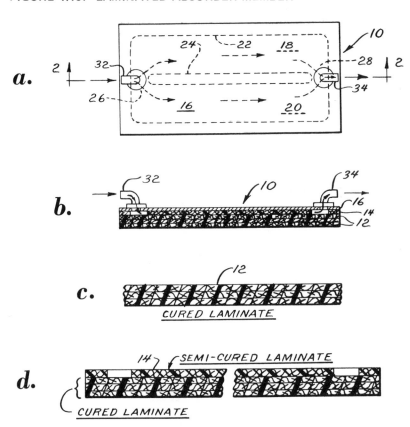

(continued)

FIGURE 1.18: (continued)

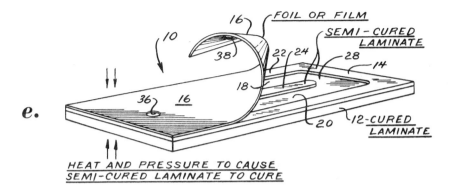

e.

(a)  Top view of absorber
(b)  Side sectional view of absorber taken on line 2—2
        of Figure 1.18a
(c)-(e)  Successive stages of building up the absorber member

Source:  U.S. Patent 3,996,092

In operation, the collector is preferably positioned at an angle to the horizontal so that the right side in Figure 1.18b will be higher than the left.  The angle is chosen depending on the particular location of the collector in order to maximize the collection of solar energy.  By placing the outlet **34** higher than the inlet **32** the channels will always be filled with heat transfer fluid.  Preferably, the upper layer **16** is painted black or is made of a black material to enhance its ability to absorb heat.

The layer **16** is extremely thin compared to prior art devices.  The thinness of the layer not only reduces the cost and weight of the collector substantially compared to thicker prior art collectors but provides faster and more efficient transfer of heat to the fluid flowing under it.  Since the thinness of the layer also reduces its ability to conduct heat sideways in the plane of the layer, it is desirable to minimize the width of spacer elements such as the strip **24** which it overlies and to maximize the width of the fluid channels.

The steps involved in assembling the collector are illustrated in Figures 1.18c through 1.18e.  Figure 1.18c shows the base cured laminate layer **12** to which the semicured laminate or prepreg layer **14** is assembled (Figure 1.18d).  Figure 1.18e illustrates the addition of the top heat absorbing sheet **16**.  After the three layers are assembled, heat and pressure are applied to the entire stack to cure the prepreg layer and cause it to bond to the layers **12** and **16** which are positioned beneath and above it.  The fittings **32, 34** are then attached.  Although not shown, the collector is preferably covered during use by a transparent cover which allows the solar rays to reach the absorbent surface **16**, but restricts re-radiation, protects the cover **16**, and reduces convection losses.

## Transition from Irregular to Planar Collector Sheet

Open-flow solar heat collectors have been described in U.S. Patents 3,145,707 and 3,215,134. Improvements were needed to avoid heat loss, vapor loss, and condensation, near the top and bottom of the corrugated solar heat collector sheet.

In the improvement of *H.E. Thomason and H.J.L. Thomason, Jr; U.S. Patent 3,989,031; November 2, 1976* a transition area or transition section is used to change the collector sheet from an irregular or nonplanar configuration to a substantially planar configuration. At the bottom, the irregular, nonplanar sheet may be formed to a planar configuration and then shaped to form a collector trough with an outlet for warm water flowing therefrom. At the top, the irregular, nonplanar collector sheet may be changed, at the transition area or section, to a substantially planar configuration and substantially sealed to, or adjacent to, the collector glazing material to reduce heat and vapor loss at the top.

Referring to Figure 1.19, solar heat collector **1** may be constructed as a large unit. It may cover a major part of the roof of a home. It preferably faces slightly west of south to collect solar energy to heat a home. Or, the solar heat collector may be built as a panel to be installed on a roof, or as a free-standing unit, or otherwise. Several panels may be connected in parallel to heat larger volumes of water, or in series to achieve higher temperatures, or both.

## FIGURE 1.19:  TRANSITION FROM IRREGULAR TO PLANAR COLLECTOR SHEET

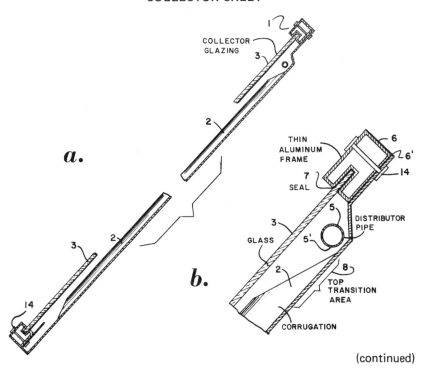

(continued)

FIGURE 1.19: (continued)

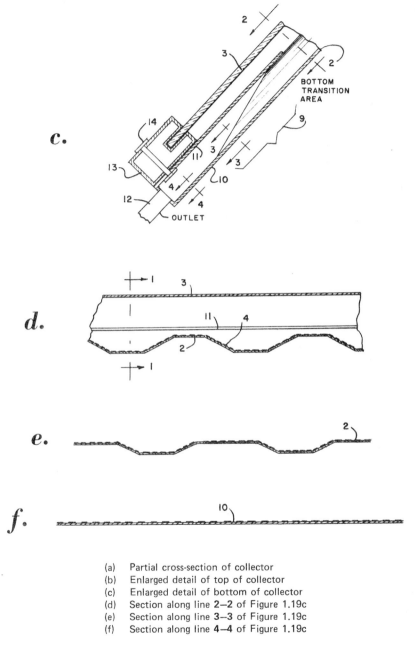

(a) Partial cross-section of collector
(b) Enlarged detail of top of collector
(c) Enlarged detail of bottom of collector
(d) Section along line 2—2 of Figure 1.19c
(e) Section along line 3—3 of Figure 1.19c
(f) Section along line 4—4 of Figure 1.19c

Source: U.S. Patent 3,989,031

Glass, or other transparent material **3**, admits solar energy to collector sheet **2** to warm it. The collector sheet preferably has embossing to help spread liquids flowing thereover, to increase heat transfer to the liquid flowing thereover, to strengthen the thin sheet, and to provide a better surface for a black solar-absorbing coating, helping keep the paint intact as the years go by.

A distributor pipe **5** has a small outlet hole **5′** for each valley in the collector sheet. The collector sheet may be corrugated, V-crimped, or otherwise formed to channel fluid flowing down thereover, as taught in U.S. Patents 3,145,707 and 3,215,134. For purposes of this process the various patterns are referred to as irregular, or nonplanar. One of the best available is a corrugated, embossed, aluminum sheet having flat valleys and flat hill-tops. The liquid spreads wide across the flat valleys, and even climbs the sides of the valleys. That important and unusual action is assisted by the embossing. That yields better heat pickup because the liquid spreads over more of the warm surface.

A thin aluminum frame **6** with sealant **7**, such as neoprene or vinyl, supports the top edge of the glass. If desired sealant material **6′** may also be used between the thin frame and the heat collector sheet to seal against vapor and warm air loss and to reduce heat loss by conduction from the collector sheet to the thin aluminum frame. That sealant may be calking sealant such as silicone seal, or neoprene, or vinyl, or other.

A transition area or section **8** adjacent to the top of the collector changes the collector sheet configuration from irregular, nonplanar to substantially planar, and may be curved or otherwise shaped as needed to fit or match other parts of the collector. The transition area or section at the top is similar to that at the bottom and will be better understood by reference to the bottom transition area or section, as illustrated in Figures 1.19c, 1.19d, 1.19e and 1.19f, more particularly described as follows.

Bottom transition area or section **9** changes from the full height corrugations, illustrated in Figure 1.19d; to partial height corrugations, illustrated in Figure 1.19e; to substantially planar, illustrated in Figure 1.19f. The planar section may be formed, as at **10, 11**, to provide a collector trough, with an outlet **12**. The lower transition area or section, or an extension, may be formed to mate with a glass supporting section **13** somewhat as at the top of the collector. Gaskets or sealants may be used to reduce heat and vapor loss, or heat conductivity from the warm collector sheet to the glass supporting member, or otherwise as needed.

### Lightweight Absorber Panel

*J.A. Godrick; U.S. Patent 3,987,784; October 26, 1976; assigned to Kennecott Copper Corporation* describes an absorber panel comprising a heat absorbing and conducting sheet and an array of fluid conduits in thermal contact with the sheet. For a given efficiency, the weight of the panel is minimized by providing a sheet thickness of between about 0.001" and 0.006" and a conduit density of between about 3 and 7 conduits per foot. To precisely accomplish the weight minimization, for given operating parameters (i.e., effective insolation level per unit area, $S_{eff}$, and sheet internal temperature difference, $T_L - T_0$), the sheet thickness, $t_s$, is chosen to minimize the panel weight per unit area, WA (shown on the following page),

$$WA = p_s t_s + \frac{w_t}{L + W}$$

where $p_s$ is the sheet material's density, $w_t$ is the weight per unit length of conduit, and W is the conduit width in contact with the sheet. For the value of $t_s$ that is thus determined, the conduit spacing, defined as L, is determined as $L = [8(T_L - T_0)k_s t_s/S_{eff}]^{0.5}$, where $k_s$ is the sheet's thermal conductivity.

Figure 1.20a illustrates a solar absorber unit **10** sized to be supported between rafters **12** of a roof. The unit comprises a solar absorber panel **14** supported in a frame **16** intermediate an overlying glass plate **18** and underlying insulation **20**, both of which are employed, as is conventional, to reduce heat loss from the panel back to the ambient. Plumbing fittings **22**, **24** deliver an energy transfer fluid (e.g., water) to, and remove it from, conduits **26** provided on the undersurface of a sheet **27**, which, together with the conduits, defines the panel. The conduits are arranged in a parallel array extending the length of the panel. Manifolds or headers **29** connect each conduit to the fittings.

**FIGURE 1.20: LIGHTWEIGHT ABSORBER PANEL**

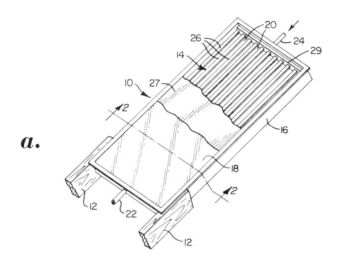

*a.*

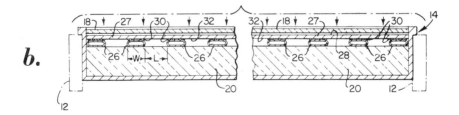

*b.*

(continued)

FIGURE 1.20: (continued)

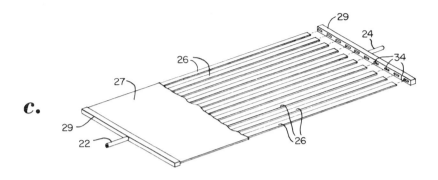

**c.**

    (a)   Partially broken away perspective view
    (b)   Enlarged view taken at **2–2** of Figure 1.20a
    (c)   Perspective view of a tube assembly of a panel of the process

Source: U.S. Patent 3,987,784

Referring to Figure 1.20b, radiant solar energy (indicated by arrows) incident upon the exposed upper surface **28** (which is typically painted black) of sheet **27**, is absorbed, causing the temperature of the sheet to rise. Heat is transferred to the fluid, flowing in the conduits **26**, by passing through the sheet, through a bond **30** at the conduit-sheet interface (or any other thermal contact between the conduit and sheet), through the tube wall, and ultimately into the fluid.

In the preferred embodiment the sheet is a thin (e.g., 0.0027") copper sheet and the conduits are thin walled (e.g., 0.008") rectangular copper radiator tubes having a width of about ½" (and since the full width is in contact with sheet **27, W** = ½") and spacing, **L**, of about 1.5". Each tube has a flat side bonded with minimum thermal resistance (e.g., soldered) to the undersurface **32** of the sheet. While both the sheet and the conduits can be formed from other materials, copper base materials are preferred because of their compatibility with existing home heating systems, their ease of formability and their high corrosion resistance (which together allow the manufacture and use of thin walled tubing), and their high thermal conductivity.

Because heat is withdrawn from the sheet through bonds **30**, a temperature differential, $T_L - T_0$, exists in the sheet itself between the midpoint between tubes ($T_L$) and a sheet location aligned with a tube ($T_0$). A temperature differential $T_0 - T_f$, also exists between the sheet above a tube location and the working fluid in the tube. To a first approximation, for a given ambient temperature, solar absorber unit energy losses increase in proportion to the average absorber panel temperature. Thus, in order to enhance collector performance, the temperature differences described above, which necessarily cause the average panel temperature to be above the fluid working temperature, should be kept to small levels, (e.g., $T_L - T_0 = 10°F$).

For any given application of a solar absorber unit, an allowable temperature difference, $T_L - T_0$, and an effective insolation level, $S_{eff}$, which accounts for probable energy losses from the unit, can be specified. $S_{eff}$ is simply the net thermal energy gain of the panel per unit time and panel area (i.e., Btu/hr-ft$^2$). Typical values of $S_{eff}$ for insulated glass enclosed panels used in temperate zones range up to 250 Btu/hr-ft$^2$.

According to the process and using the equation given above for a particular sheet material, tubing material and tube size, an optimum sheet thickness ($t_0$) and an optimum tube spacing (L) can be derived, to provide an absorber panel of minimum weight.

Panels **14** may be constructed in the following manner. Two headers **29** (see Figure 1.20c) are laid out on a table. The headers are square in cross section and are provided with prepunched holes **34** for receiving conduits **26**. The conduits are then inserted into the prepunched holes and are soldered in place. A strip of soldering tape is then applied along the length of flat surface of each rectangular conduit.

A sheet **27** is then placed over the tubes and the soldering tape. The assembly is then heated to a temperature at which the solder flows. It has been found convenient to heat the assembly to the appropriate temperature by placing heating blankets (not shown) above and beneath the assembly. When cooled, the upper surface **28** of the sheet is then sprayed with black paint or otherwise coated to more efficiently absorb radiation. The assembly is then placed in frame **16** which has been backed with insulation **20** (see Figures 1.20a and 1.20b).

### Absorber Cells at Different Temperatures

The solar heat absorber of *G.W. Laird; U.S. Patent 4,013,062; March 22, 1977* includes a frame and a plurality of clear panels respectively overlying a plurality of arcuate shaped heat collecting plates supported by the frame and compartmented each from the next by separators forming dead air spaces or cells. At least one continuous fluid passage tube is soldered to each plate and provides a cool tube inlet and a feedback hot tube outlet section for each plate whereby some of the heat in the hot tube section is transferred through the cell to its cool tube section within each cell prior to discharge of the fluid out the hot tube section. Each of the cells is at a temperature different than the temperature of an adjacent cell and a heat sink is provided in contact with each panel to substantially equalize the temperature of the panels.

This process is based on the concept that heat is fed back from the hotter tube section into a cell or chamber which contains a cooler tube section and some of the heat from the hotter tube section is transferred into the cooler tube section and provides an ultimately hotter output from the collector.

Referring to Figures 1.21a–1.21d, the collector is generally designated by numeral **20** and includes an enclosure or closed box frame **21** formed by two wood side walls **22** and **23**, two wood end walls **24** and **25** and a formed metal pan bottom **26**, with pairs of wood corner posts **27** and **28**, suitably attached by adhesive and screws, including screw **30**, to the side walls and end walls. A plurality of foot members **32** are spacedly mounted by screws **33** throughout the bottom for supporting the collector on a roof, as hereinafter more fully described.

FIGURE 1.21:  ABSORBER CELLS AT DIFFERENT TEMPERATURES

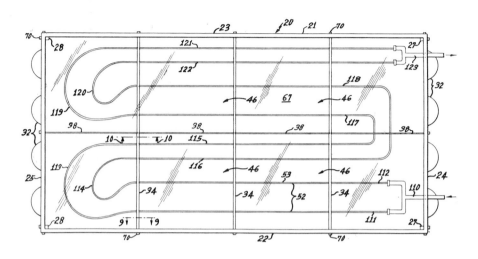

*a.*

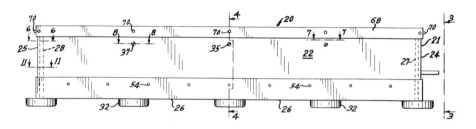

**b.**

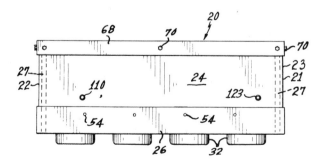

**c.**

(continued)

FIGURE 1.21: (continued)

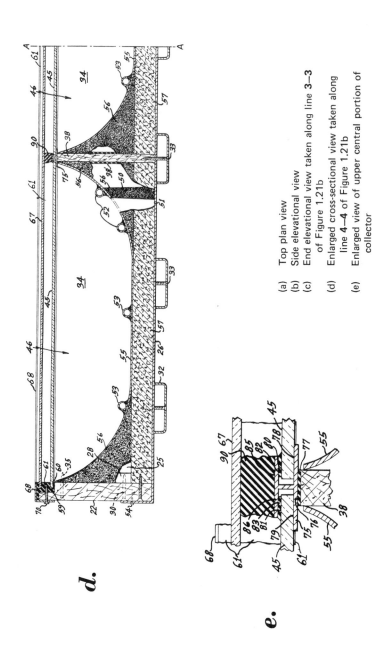

*d.*

*e.*

(a) Top plan view
(b) Side elevational view
(c) End elevational view taken along line 3—3 of Figure 1.21b
(d) Enlarged cross-sectional view taken along line 4—4 of Figure 1.21b
(e) Enlarged view of upper central portion of collector

Source: U.S. Patent 4,013,062

Compartmental or separation means in the form of transverse wood members **34** extend parallel to the end walls **24** and **25** and are connected by adhesive and screws, including screws **35** and **37**, to side walls **22** and **23**. The separation means includes longitudinal wood members glued by silicon rubber glue. Longitudinal members **38** adjacent to the end walls are also glued within vertical grooves by a plurality of elongated pins. Each of the transverse and longitudinal members extend to the bottom **26**, and the screws **33** securing the foot members **32** extend through the bottom and into members **34** and **38**, as clearly seen in Figure 1.21d, and terminate substantially adjacent the glass cover **45**, the cover comprising a plurality of glass panels overlying respective dead air spaces or cells **46**.

Each of the wood members **34** is provided with a plurality of slots, including slot **50**, which extend from edges, including edge **51**, and terminate in predetermined locations upwardly therefrom through which the fluid passage means **52**, in the form of copper tubing **53**, extends. Prior to attaching the bottom to the wood side and end walls by rivets **54** the tubing, is passed through the slots, including slot **50**, and is passed into the upper ends of the slots which retain the tubing in the proper location illustrated in Figure 1.21d.

The arcuate copper plates **55** are then positioned in contact with the tubing and soldered thereto in a manner obvious to a skilled person in the art. Thereafter, soft loose fiberglass insulation **56** is closely packed under absorbing plates **55** and into the slots, including slot **50**. Hard pressed fiberglass insulation panels **57** are respectively positioned beneath each of the copper plates within respective spaces or cells and then the bottom is attached, the foot members are connected by the screws which extend through the bottom and terminate in respective wood members **34** and **38** thereby completing the assembly of the bottom portion of the collector **20**.

Each glass panel **45** is supported along edge **59** by a ledge **60** of side wall **22**, or side wall **23**, and sealed thereto by silicone rubber adhesive **61**. Sealed within the adhesive is an elongated single cover plate **67** of Plexiflas or like transparent material which overlies all of the glass panels and provides a protective shield therefor as well as additional insulation for the collector to retain the infrared energy within the collector by reducing reradiation losses. L-shaped caps **68** are also positioned along the side and end walls and are sealed thereto by the adhesive to provide protection to the collector from the weather elements. A plurality of screws **70** affix caps **68** to respective side and end walls.

Heat sink means, in the form of an I-shaped extrusion **75**, is attached along the upper surfaces **76** of longitudinal separator members **38**, and the intersection of cross members **34**, by adhesive **77**. Within each of the channels **78** and **79** are disposed glass edge portions **80** and **81** which are sealed therein by silicone rubber adhesive **82** and **83** between the upper flanges **85**, **86** and respective transparent glass panels **45**. An insulative spacer **90** formed of a mound of silicone rubber or any other suitable material supports and affixes the uppermost transparent cover plate **67** to extrusion **75** spacedly above and overlying all of the glass panels, the cover plate being of a clear plastic, like Plexiglas, glass or any other appropriate clear or transparent material. The heat sink means provides a certain amount of surface temperature equalization between the various glass panels and tends to reduce the occurrence of hot spots and cold spots.

As may be seen from Figures 1.21a and 1.21d, the fluid passage means **52** in the form of copper tubing **53** includes an absorber inlet section **110** extending through and sealed to end wall **24**, inlet section **110** herein being shown bifurcated and connected to a pair of copper inlet conduits **111** and **112** which pass through each of the separators **34** and within the cell **46** adjacent the opposite end wall **25**; bent or curved conduit sections **113** and **114** are provided to return fluid passing from the inlet conduits through the curved sections back through the outlet conduits **115** and **116**.

When the outlet conduits return to the cell containing inlet section **110**, the outlet conduits pass through and are sealed to the separator **38** common with the adjacent cell and thus become inlet conduits **117** and **118**. Again these conduits have curved sections **119** and **120** communicating between the inlet conduits **117** and **118** and respective return or outlet conduits **121** and **122** which are fluidly attached to absorber outlet section **123** which extends through and is sealed to the end wall **24** of the absorber housing. An example of the spacing dimensions of the conduits as measured from lower side wall **22** towards upper side wall **23** is as follows

| Conduit | Centimeters |
|---------|-------------|
| 111 | 9 |
| 112 | 20 |
| 116 | 30 |
| 115 | 36 |
| 117 | 49 |
| 118 | 60 |
| 122 | 70 |
| 121 | 76 |

The bent tube sections **113, 114, 119** and **120** and other portions of the tubing means **52** are approximately as shown. The hotter portions of the tubes, i.e., conduits **115, 116, 121** and **122** are accordingly located toward the upper portions of the respective cells which are somewhat hotter than the lower portions thereof increasing the heat absorbed by such conduits from the metal plates **55**. Of course, the hotter conduits being fed back through the same cell containing the cooler inlet conduits **111, 112**, and **117, 118** causes some of the heat within the hotter conduits to be reintroduced into the cell and absorbed by the liquid in the cooler conduits.

It is intended that a small pump be used to circulate the fluid through the absorber, the rate of flow preferably being approximately ½ gpm, an extremely slow rate compared to the fast pumping of the prior art flat box collectors. In tropical or temperate areas which have a good amount of sunlight, the absorber may be used without a pump, i.e., draining the absorber under the 30 lb water pressure, which normally is present in the homes, through an outlet valve at the rate of about 0.5 gpm normally provides adequate heating of the water. The collector in accord with this process may be operated from about 0.01 to no more than 1.5 gpm.

Each of the cells is at differing temperatures and each cell acts as a series heater with respect to the fluid being passed therethrough, while simultaneously the hotter tube section has fed back some of its heat into the cell containing such hotter tube section and such heat is absorbed by the fluid within the cooler tube section in such cell.

## Semicylindrical Configurations of Foamed Plastic

*H.A. Clark; U.S. Patent 3,866,285; February 18, 1975; assigned to Dow Corning Corporation* describes a solar energy collector having a body of foamed plastic and a surface configuration of generally semicylindrical recesses in closely spaced parallel relationship, the surface of the recesses being covered with reflective or absorptive foil to reflect or transmit solar energy to receiving devices such as fluid conduits.

Referring to Figure 1.22a, there is shown a base **11** which may simply be a level piece of ground, a block of concrete or a sheet of plywood, for example. A frame **12**, preferably of rectangular configuration, extends upwardly from the base. The frame may be, for example, wood, metal, or plastic. There are laid on the base a plurality of generally semicylindrical male mold portions **13** in closely spaced parallel relationship. In their simplest form these mold portions may be metallic or plastic pipe which is simply sawed in half axially. The pipe, for example, can have an external diameter of 2" to 6".

There is now placed on top of the male mold portions a layer of foil **14** which may be either a metallized reflective plastic foil such as polyester film or a polished or light absorbent metallic foil such as aluminum or stainless steel. The foil is made to conform to the surface of the mold portions by tucking it into the crevices between adjacent mold portions. Desirably the foil is protected by a thin film of clear silicone resin on the surface which is put on the side facing the mold portions.

## FIGURE 1.22:  SEMICYLINDRICAL CONFIGURATIONS OF FOAMED PLASTIC

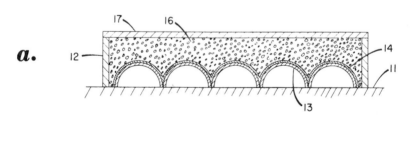

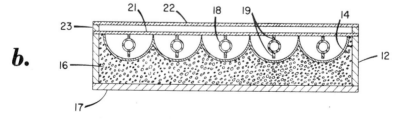

(continued)

**FIGURE 1.22:** (continued)

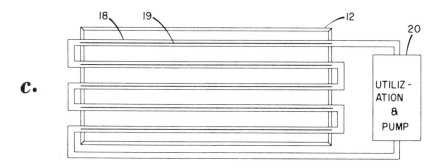

**c.**

(a)  Vertical cross sectional illustrating method of manufacturing collector
(b)  Vertical cross sectional of collector
(c)  Top plan view of heat exchanger application of process

Source:  U.S. Patent 3,866,285

Now a plastic mix, formulated to obtain the desired weight per cubic foot which may be, for example, in the 1 to 15 pcf range, is poured over the whole assembly and allowed to foam and cure.  Syntactic foams, of course, can also be used and would not require foaming.  Suitable foams are commercially available and are made from phenolic, polyester or polyurethane resins, for example.  Virtually any rigid foam material capable of withstanding temperatures generated in use of the device can be used satisfactorily.  It is preferred that the thermal conductivity for the cured foam be less than 0.25 Btu/hr/ft²/°F/in.

The surface of the foam is trimmed off, if necessary, level with the top of the frame **12**.  The foam is shown in the drawings by the numeral **16**.  If protection of the foam backing is desired, a layer of plastic, metallic foil, or rigid base material **17** can be cemented on the top surface of the foam and frame.  The composite is now lifted from the male mold portions **13** and turned over.  The foil **14** is, of course, laminated to the foam by virtue of having been in contact with the foam during curing, and does not adhere to the male mold portions.

The resulting composite can be seen in Figure 1.22b in which a plurality of pipes **18** which serve as solar energy receiving devices have been mounted within the recesses in the composite which were formed by the male mold portions.  The pipes should be colored or coated for maximum absorption of heat.  If desired, the pipes may have metallic fins **19** extending vertically therefrom to aid in collecting solar energy reflected by the metallic foil **14** supported on the foam.  The frame is preferably left on the panel and used to support the pipes.

It also serves to protect the edges of the foam from damage.  If desired, however, it can be removed.  A pair of glass sheets **21** and **22**, separated by blocks **23** are preferably placed over the panel to protect and insulate it.  The inner panel **21** can be extremely thin and lightweight if it is supported on the high points of the configuration as shown.  This arrangement has the added advantage that convection is eliminated in arrays which are tipped at an angle to the horizontal. In a preferred embodiment the spacing between the glass sheets is maintained at about ⅜".

In Figure 1.22c there is shown a top plan view showing diagrammically the interconnection of pipes **18** and the connection of the array of pipes with the utilization device and a circulating pump **20**. The utilization device may be, in its simplest form, a radiator in a dwelling. Alternatively, it can be any other means of extracting the thermal energy carried by fluid in the pipes which in turn was derived from solar radiation impinging upon the reflective foil **14** and the exterior of the pipes and fins **19**.

While the system of Figure 1.22c shows only a single panel interconnected in series obviously an array of panels may be interconnected with one another and the pipes may be connected in either series or parallel relationship as desired for maximum efficiency in the particular application in which the solar collector is to be used. The panels, due to their low density, are extremely low in weight and are cheap and simple to manufacture. If desired, they can be manufactured on site but due to their lightness can be easily transported. Arrays of virtually any size can be made by placing panels side-by-side and/or end-to-end on the ground or in any elevated configuration desired.

### Combination Flat Plate and Concentrating Collector

Solar collectors used in solar energy systems fall within two general categories: flat plate collectors and concentration collectors. The concentration collectors operate on the principle that the reflective element focuses the light to a central focal point so as to concentrate the heat at this focal point. The flat plate collectors tend to utilize flat surfaces which can receive light from a wide variety of angles, and which are exposed over a large cross-sectional area. The concentration type of collector tends to be more efficient than the flat plate type of collector on sunny days, while the flat plate collectors tend to be more effient on hazy days because they collect radiation from all angles. Concentration collectors also tend to work at a higher temperature and produce heat that can be used in more applications.

The collector of *F.R. Eshelman; U.S. Patent 4,011,855; March 15, 1977* provides concentration of radiant energy while at the same time collecting radiant energy from all angles. Thus it is superior to both types of collectors previously mentioned, giving higher temperatures than flat plate collectors while at the same time collecting energy on both bright and overcast days. In addition, the collector is designed to pick up solar rays from any angle and thus there is no need to provide power means to follow the movement of the sun.

The collector comprises a light collecting member mounted within a light reflecting member. The light reflecting member includes a surface having a curvature which causes all the light entering therein to be directed toward the light collecting member. In one modification of the device the reflecting member includes two circular surfaces, and in another modification the reflecting member includes a singular circular surface. The light collecting member may be a horizontal flat plate, an elongated member having a center and flanges radiating outwardly therefrom, an elongated circular member, or an elongated vertical plate.

Referring to Figures 1.23a and 1.23b, the solar collector of the process is referred to generally by the numeral **10**. It includes an outer box frame **12** having
lateral side walls **14** and **16**, end walls **18** and **20**, a bottom **21** and a transparent
top **22**. The top may be any transparent material such as glass and the like, but
the preferred material is a transparent form of Teflon. The top may be hinged
adjacent its edges to provide easy access into the interior of the box frame.

### FIGURE 1.23; COMBINATION FLAT PLATE AND CONCENTRATING COLLECTOR

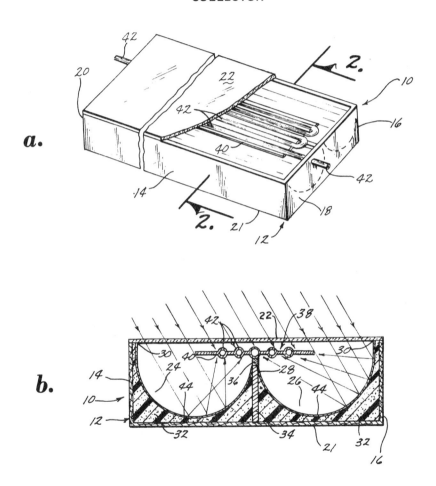

(a)  Perspective view of the process
(b)  Sectional view taken along line 2–2 of Figure 1.23a

Source:  U.S. Patent 4,011,855

Within box frame **12** are a pair of concave surfaces **24, 26** which are semicircular in shape and which intersect at an apex **28**. Each concave surface forms a circular surface, and extends upwardly to transparent top **22**. The apex is substantially below the top. The surfaces may be formed from any reflective material such as mirrors or the like. However, a preferred form for the surfaces is aluminized Mylar. The upper lateral margins of the surfaces are designated by the numeral **30**.

The curvature at the margins is such that all radiant energy passing through the transparent top **22** adjacent the margins will be reflected in the general direction of the apex. This is true regardless of the angle at which the light enters and strikes the margins. Underlying surfaces **24, 26** is a foamed plastic material **32** which has the properties of being able to withstand high temperatures. A preferred foamed plastic material is a urea-formaldehyde foam. It is preferred because it can withstand temperatures up to 210°F and is not flammable.

Extending upwardly from bottom **21** of the box frame is a vertical support member **34** made of wood or the like. The support member extends upwardly to the apex, and supports on its upper surface a pedestal member **36**. This member should be constructed of a material capable of withstanding high temperatures, and for this purpose it is preferred that Teflon be utilized. Resting on pedestal member **36** and being supported thereby is a light absorbing member **38** which is comprised of a horizontal plate **40** having one or more continuous fluid passageways **42** extending therethrough. As shown in the drawings, the passageway is a singular passageway which is coiled back and forth along the length of the plate and which exits at the opposite end of the box.

The width of the plate is substantially narrower than the distance between the upper margins of the concave surfaces. However, the plate is sufficiently wide to lie in covering relationship over the extreme lower portions **44** of the arcuate surfaces. Thus any light entering through the top will either strike plate **40**, or will strike the portions of the surfaces which are located laterally outside the lower portions. Thus, all light rays entering the top will either contact the absorbing member directly or will be reflected to the absorbing member by the arcuate surfaces. The absorbing member may be formed of any light absorbing material, but it is preferred that an aluminum material be used with a thin coating of black nickel being electroplated thereon. Other modifications of the reflector and absorber are described in the patent.

### Flat Plate-Focal Point Collector

*J.L. Schoenfelder; U.S. Patent 3,951,128; April 20, 1976; assigned to Sun Power, Inc.* describes a solar heat collector system which is comprised of a roof or wall structure element, a conduit for heat exchange fluid in the roof or wall structure element, and a focal point reflector plate behind the conduit and in the structure element. Preferably the conduit is of a flat elliptical cross section. The flat plate-focal point collector adds an advantage of reflecting sunlight directly onto the conduit for heat exchange fluid in order to insure more efficient heat exchange between the sun's rays and the fluid contained in the conduits; and the reflector directs reradiated heat from the conduit back to the conduit.

As seen in Figure 1.24c, the heat collector system is comprised of a first exteriorly exposed tansparent member **10**, and spaced apart therefrom and behind the first exterior transparent member **10** is a second or interiorly disposed transparent member **12**. Between the exterior transparent member and the interior transparent member is a first void space **14**. This space is filled with "dead air" or in other words, air which is not fluidly movable throughout the system.

### FIGURE 1.24:  FLAT PLATE-FOCAL POINT COLLECTOR

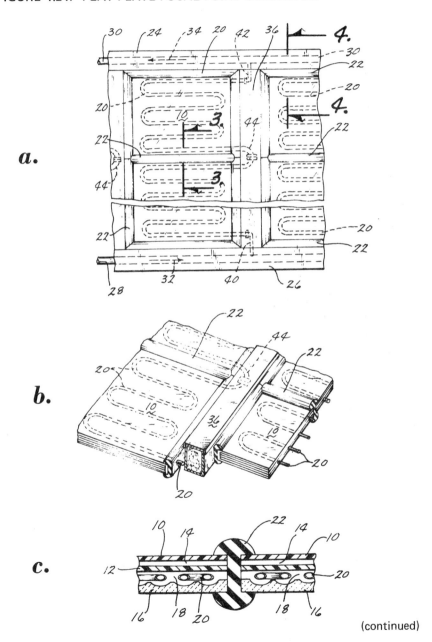

(continued)

FIGURE 1.24: (continued)

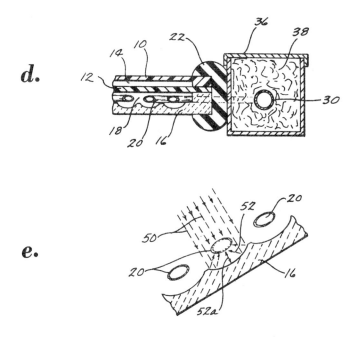

d.

e.

    (a)   Plan view, with certain parts broken away, of collector
    (b)   Elevated perspective view showing with more detail,
           of collector
    (c)   Sectional view of Figure 1.24a along line 3—3
    (d)   Sectional view of Figure 1.24a along line 4—4
    (e)   Schematic illustration of solar absorption

Source:  U.S. Patent 3,951,128

Space **14** and the air entrapped therein is provided in order to provide a dead
air space which acts as an insulating barrier to prevent, or at least minimize, conductive heat loss and the attendant efficiency loss which would accompany such
outward reradiation of solar energy.  Transparent members **10** and **12** can be
comprised of any suitable material which will readily allow solar rays to pass
therethrough.  Typically, the transparent members are comprised of a transparent plastic material of which a preferred one is plastic acrylic material resistant
to ultraviolet rays.  Spaced apart from and behind the most interior transparent
member **12** is a reflector plate **16**.

As seen in Figure 1.24c, the focal point reflector plate **16** is comprised of a
plurality of parabolic curved surfaces.  These parabolic curved surfaces provide
an ideal reflective surface for focusing and reflecting solar rays.  The reflector
plate can be comprised of any suitable metal material coated with a mirror reflecting surface, such as, for example, aluminum, steel, and other suitable alloys.
In addition, if desired, the focal point reflector can be comprised of a glass or
plastic material coated with a mirror reflecting surface.  However, since glass is

highly frangible, it is not desirable to utilize in most situations. The parabolic curvatures of focal point reflector **16** are shown in Figure 1.24c as a plurality of concave impressions on the surface of the collector plate most near interior transparent member **12**. However, it is to be understood that a focal point reflector can be utilized which employs convex parabolic impressions on the most interiorly disposed surface of focal point reflector **16** to provide the same effect. The reflector plate can also be a flat reflective surface, but this flat configuration would be less efficient.

A second dead air space **18** is defined by the interior transparent member and the spaced apart from and therebehind focal point reflector. Positioned within this space are fluid conveying conduits **20**. The conduits or pipes are typically made of copper, aluminum, steel or other heat absorbing alloys. It is preferred that the conduits be painted a dark solar ray absorbing color such as a flat black or the like. It is also preferred that the conduit be of a configuration which allows the conduits to substantially travel over the majority of the surface of the focal point reflector.

It is preferred that the conduit generally be folded back upon itself in what can be described as a serpentine configuration to cover a substantial part of the reflector plate surface for maximum heat transfer efficiency. For maximum heat transfer efficiency it is preferred that the conduit be a flat ellipse in cross section as opposed to the conventional circular cross section for most pipe or fluid conveying conduits.

The heat absorption fluid traveling through the conduit can be water, mineral oil, or any of the glycol heat-absorption materials such as ethylene glycol, propylene glycol, or mixtures thereof. The generally laminar construction of the solar heat collection system, or modules thereof as explained below, is held in position by glazing gasket **22**, comprised of conventional construction material, neoprene or the like.

Figure 1.24a shows one method of how the entire collector system, including the plumbing circuitry, might be employed in a typical operation. There a frame for the individual modular units is shown which is comprised of a gable or ceiling board frame member **24** and a bottom frame member **26**. Within the bottom frame member is a fluid inlet line **28** and correspondingly, within the gable or ceiling board frame member is a fluid outlet line **30**. Directional arrows **32** and **34** indicate the flow in the inlet line and the outlet line, respectively.

Periodically spaced in the solar heat collector system transverse to the gable or ceiling frame member and the base or bottom frame member and extending therebetween are channel frame members **36**. As seen in Figure 1.24d, glazing gasket **22**, is secured to the channel frame member. This can be accomplished by adhesive bonding, by mechanical linkage means, or by designing a groove or channel frame member **36** for the glazing gasket to fit therewithin.

The channel frame member is typically filled with insulation material **38** and as can be seen best in Figures 1.24a and 1.24b contains necessary conduit linkage to fluidly connect the conduit with the outlet line and the inlet line as depicted by linkage conduits **40** and **42**. In addition, as needed, the channel frame member will contain a plurality of U-shaped linkage members **44** which fluidly and in a sealing relationship connect the conduits of the solar heat collector system to allow heat absorption fluid to be pumped through a plurality of such units. The plumbing circuitry for the solar heat collector system can vary widely in terms of the precise arrangement thereof and the pattern of fluid flow therethrough. However, the important feature is that the conduits 20 be positioned in a solar heat collector system in front of a mirror reflecting focal point reflector plate 16. The conduits are held in position in the solar heat collector system by the glazing gasket 22, by the connecting linkages within channel frame member 36 at 40, 42 and 44. In addition, if desired, intermittent plastic or rubber spacers can be employed to more securely hold the conduit within the space between collector 16 and interiorly disposed transparent member 12.

As can be seen in Figure 1.24e, solar rays 50, after passing through transparent members 10 and 12, strike the concave parabolic surfaces of the focal point reflector or alternatively strike the conduits. Of course those rays that strike the conduits are immediately absorbed and converted into heat energy to heat the fluid flowing in the conduit. Those rays which do not strike the surface of the conduit hit the parabolic curves of the focal point reflector plate and are reradiated from the reflecting mirror surface thereof and directed to the back portion of the conduits as indicated at 52. In addition, heat energy radiated from the conduit is reradiated back thereto by the reflector as depicted at 52a.

### Absorber Plate Positioned Above Parabolic Reflector

A collector apparatus is disclosed by *J.M. Cohen and M.D. Cohen; U.S. Patent 4,022,188; May 10, 1977* which comprises a generally planar, horizontally extending absorber having a radiation-accepting aperture in the lower surface thereof, and a duct extending therethrough for receiving a heat transfer fluid. A stationary reflector is disposed directly beneath the absorber, the reflector exhibiting a cross-sectional configuration of a parabolic cylindrical nature.

Referring to Figures 1.25a and 1.25b, a solar energy collecting means is shown which comprises an absorption means 10 in combination with a reflecting element 12. The absorption means comprises an extended, horizontal element exhibiting a generally planar structure. The upper and outer surface of the absorption means, not visible in Figure 1.25a, may be flat and imperforate having no solar energy collection functions. Wood, sheet metal or any other substantially rigid material may be selected for use. Within the outer and upper surface or shell of the absorption means, generally denoted at 14, is a layer which may be formed from any appropriate insulating material.

The insulating material terminates about the lower edges of the absorption means to define an enlarged aperture 16 which extends across substantially all of the lower surface of the absorption means. The aperture is closed by a pair of parallel glass sheets, through which can be seen a convoluted length of tubing 18 within which a suitable heat transfer fluid is pumped. A series of vertically disposed, parallel black metal plates 20 are attached to the tube and extend across the surfaces of the tube to effectively enlarge the light-receiving surfaces of the duct. A horizontal black metal plate 39 is also attached to and resides just above the tube to enlarge the light-receiving surface of the tube.

The reflecting element is horizontally elongate, as is the absorption means. The transverse cross section of the reflecting means exhibits a generally parabolic configuration, and the reflecting means may be considered to be generated by the translation of a parabolic arc along a horizontal line parallel to the long axis of the absorption means to form a section of a parabolic cylinder. Such a reflective surface may be formed from aluminum, metalized plastic or any one of a number of appropriate materials. An inlet duct **22** and outlet duct **24** allow heat transfer fluid to be pumped through duct **18**, and to an appropriate reservoir or heat sink. In a preferred embodiment these ducts (tubes) should exit through the rear of the absorption means so as not to block any incident solar rays.

**FIGURE 1.24: ABSORBER PLATE POSITIONED ABOVE PARABOLIC REFLECTOR**

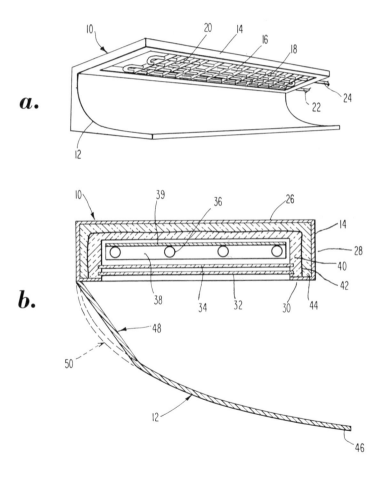

(a)   Oblique view of apparatus
(b)   Transverse cross section of apparatus

Source:  U.S. Patent 4,022,188

The absorption means generally indicated at **10** advantageously comprises a shell **14** of a thin, rigid material such as metal or the like. The shell forms an extended upper surface and side surfaces of relatively small depth, so that the overall form of the absorption means is an extended planar element. The shell includes lower portions **30** which define an aperture in the lower surface of the absorption means. The aperture is closed by a pair of glass plates **32, 34** which are disposed horizontally one above the other, and parallel to one another so as to define a narrow air space therebetween. The space between the glass sheets defines a pocket of stagnant air which effectively decreases heat losses due to conduction. Convective loss in the air is minimal because the hotter glass plate **34** is disposed above the colder glass plate **32**.

To reduce the reflection of impingent radiation, the outermost or lower glass plate may be coated with a material such as magnesium fluoride to reduce the reflectivity of the surface. Each glass plate acts as a filter which transmits the desired solar radiation entering the absorber and traps the infrared radiation generated within the absorption means. Appropriate insulation is provided about the periphery of the glass plates to avoid unwanted heat transfer to the shell which supports them.

Insulating means are provided within the shell, lining the upper and side surfaces thereof to define a cavity within the shell, above the glass plates. Extending within the cavity are a plurality of ducts **36** which may, for example, comprise convolutions of an elongate length of tubing. Appropriate heat transfer fluid is pumped through the tubing to collect heat absorbed thereby, then pumped to a remote utilization or storage means.

Black vertical plates **38** extend transversely across the duct means, and effectively serve to increase the surface thereof. Backing plate **39** extends horizontally behind the tubes and is heated by that radiation which bypasses the tubes **36** and plates **38**. The heat is then reradiated within the enclosed cavity and ultimately absorbed by the fluid within the tubes. Heat absorbed by plate **39** is also transferred to the tubes by conduction. In this manner a larger surface is presented to solar radiation entering the absorption means through glass plates **32, 34**.

In a preferred embodiment, the insulation comprises a plurality of layers of insulating material. In order to optimize the construction of the apparatus, and to minimize cost, the innermost layer of insulation **40** may be of a high-temperature insulating material. By this is meant an insulation which will withstand temperatures in excess of 600°F without noticeable deterioration. Glass wool, asbestos, and other similar materials may be used.

Surrounding the innermost layer of insulation is a separator **42** of aluminum foil. The separator serves to reflect impingent radiation to further reduce convection, and to act as a vapor barrier, aiding in the activity of the insulation layers. An outermost layer **46** of insulation is provided, and may be of a low-temperature material, that is, one which need not withstand temperatures in excess of 600°F. An inexpensive foam material such as urethane may be selected for this purpose in regions where the temperature is below approximately 250°F.

Extending beneath the absorption means is reflecting element **12**. As stated above, the reflecting element exhibits a cross-section configuration approximating that of a parabolic arc. The outermost lip **46** of the parabola may advantageously extend from under the absorption means. Further, the vertex portion of the reflecting means **48** may depart from the actual parabolic configuration shown as dotted line **50** to comprise a chord of the parabolic arc. In this vein it will be appreciated that the entire parabolic surface can be approximated by a series of flat chordal segments. Further details of the geometry of the parabolic surface are given in the patent.

### Parabolic Reflector Combined with Upright and Overhanging Absorbers

*A. Fattor; U.S. Patent 4,015,585; April 5, 1977* describes a solar radiation reflector, including a parabolic trough reflecting surface which transmits solar radiation in a general line reflection on an upright heat absorber during winter and early spring months of low to moderate sun angles. A juxtaposed overhanging heat absorber above the upright absorber during summer high-sun angle periods produces heated transfer medium from each absorber for domestic water supply and refrigeration.

As shown in Figure 1.26a a block or concrete wall building **20** with a flat roof **21** is provided with a solar heating unit shown in general by numeral **22** mounted on top of the flat roof.

In the form of the device shown in Figures 1.26b and 1.26c, a base frame **30** is arranged to support a parabolic trough reflector **31** which extends from a front edge **32** to a rear edge **33**. The parabolic trough reflector is planar in its width or horizontal extent, that is, its width lines are straight and horizontal while the vertical lines are parabolic. This forms a trough, with a horizontal bottom contiguous with the parabolic sides. The front end of the frame is sloped downwardly at an angle, usually about 60°, from the horizontal, and contains solar absorption panels **34a, 34b, 34c,** etc.

These panels may be typical solar absorption panels which are normally formed with a pair of spaced apart glazing elements (clear glass or plastic) arranged over a black solar absorber and arranged to heat either air passing over the solar absorber or to heat pipes containing flowing liquid which may be secured in the solar absorber and generally where the pipes are in front of the absorber, painted black similarly to the absorber. The solar radiation reflector **31** overlays a sinuous or serpentine array of a pipe **36** having an inlet **37** at one side and an outlet **38** at the outside; the purpose of this line is explained below.

### FIGURE 1.26: PARABOLIC REFLECTOR COMBINED WITH UPRIGHT AND OVERHANGING ABSORBERS

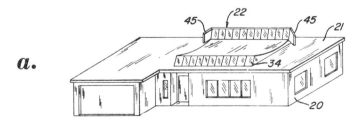

*a.*

(continued)

FIGURE 1.26: (continued)

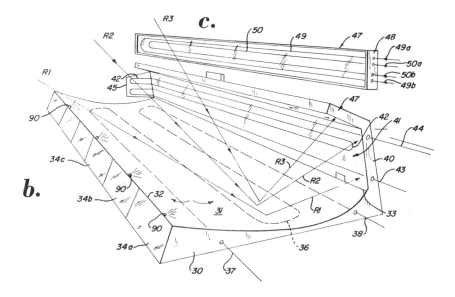

    (a)   Perspective, schematic view of a building utilizing a
            solar heating unit according to the process
    (b)   Perspective, schematic view of one form of solar
            reflector and heat absorber
    (c)   Plan view of a summer heat absorption panel

Source:  U.S. Patent 4,015,585

Extending upwardly from the reflector frame **30** is an upright frame **40** into
which is mounted a solar absorption panel, shown in general by numeral **41**.
This panel contains typically an inner and an outer glazing for the admission of
solar radiation and for the retention of heat resulting from the radiation.  Behind the glazing is the black absorption panel and a sinuous fluid line **42**
mounted on the absorption plate.  The array **42** includes an inlet **43** and an
outlet **44** for the purpose of conveying heat picked up in absorber **40**.

In one form of the process, a wing **45**, shown at the left end of the unit (it
may include a wing at each side) extends at an angle from the surface of the
absorber **41**, and it also includes portions of the surface of the absorber, and
it also includes portions of the piping **42**, which provides an additional absorber
arranged to pick up solar radiation from morning sun on the one side and the
evening sun on the other side.

Extended from the top of the frame is an overhang over the parabolic reflector
and over the absorber **40** forming another absorber shown in general by numeral **47**.  This is shown in detail in Figure 1.26c, wherein a framework **48** supports conventional inner and outer glazing and a pipe loop for fluid flow **49**
and an inner pipe loop **50**.  The loop **49** has an inlet **49a** and an outlet **49b**,

and the inner loop has its inlet **50a** and an outlet **50b**. The use of the overhang absorber and the double loop is explained below.

The parabolic-trough reflector is arranged to reflect sun's rays onto the upright absorbers and the position of the reflected ray is determined by the position of the sun in its seasonal movement, even when the whole unit is mounted station-ary on the roof of a building. During the winter time, the sun in northern latitudes, is at a low angle, and a ray **R1** is used to indicate the approximate angle of solar radiation during the months of December and January at the highest azimuth of the sun, usually noon.

This ray is reflected into a lower portion of the panel **40**, and the lower area of the absorber will receive the reflected sun rays during December through about February. At the lowest sun angle, the reflected area will be in the lowermost portion of the absorption panel, and as the sun rises, the reflected area also rises on the collector. Thus, with ray **R2**, the ray from the sun is depicted in about September, October and November and in February, March and April, producing a reflection in about the middle of the solar collector.

The ray **R3** depicts the angle of the sun's rays in about the period of May, June, July, and August with the rays reflected onto the panel **47**, which absorbs the heat from the sun's rays at the hottest period of the year. This panel is pro-vided with the two loops, normally one loop is of larger diameter than the other loop. The larger tubing loop **49a** and **49b** is used for domestic water purposes and is normally connected to the hot water heater. The smaller tubing loop **50a** and **50b** is used for absorption cooling for an air conditioning system. The fluid from the absorption panel **41** is generally passed to a heat storage unit and is used for heating water for domestic purposes in space heating, as well as do-mestic water for washing, etc.

### Flat Plate Panel Array with Complementary Reflectors

The solar energy collecting system of *F.N. Broberg; U.S. Patent 4,020,827; May 3, 1977,* which may be operated to provide usable energy throughout the year, comprises a plurality of rows of elongate radiant solar energy collecting panels, each having upper and lower edges, being mounted to form an angle to the horizon and to face the sun's position at solar noon.

An elongate reflector, also having upper and lower edges, complements each row of collector panels to reflect radiant solar energy to it. The upper edge of each row of collector panels is positioned adjacent the upper edge of a reflector to define a single, inverted, generally V-shaped peak. The lower edge of each col-lector which forms a part of one peak is spaced from the lower edge of the re-flector which forms a part of an adjacent peak to define a valley. A walkway is constructed in each valley to provide access to both the reflectors and collector panels for drainage and maintenance.

To achieve optimum year-long system operation, the height of the peaks as well as the horizontal distance between them is such that little or no shadow falls on the collector panels near noon on the winter solstice. Further, a plane tangent to each reflector at its upper edge makes an angle with the horizon less than one-half the solar altitude during the season when maximum system performance is desired to insure that most reflected solar radiation is incident on the col-lector during this season.

All components of this solar energy collecting system with the exception of a
fluid circulating system are mounted in fixed positions above the base and may
be easily reached from the access walkways. Accordingly, this system may be
more easily maintained than prior art systems which mount certain components
below the base surface or which provide no access at all to the components
mounted above the base surface. Further, since the collector panels and reflectors
are fixed, capital investment and continuing maintenance costs of more compli-
cated systems having moving components is avoided.

Referring first to Figure 1.27a, the solar energy collecting system of the process
is illustrated installed on the horizontal flat roof **10** of a building **12** which may,
for example, be a school, factory, or office building or which may be any other
type of residential, commercial, or industrial building; however, this system may
be installed on any flat base which is preferably horizontal. The system comprises a series of elongate rows **14** of a number of solar energy collecting panels
**16**, each mounted to face the sun's position at solar noon.

### FIGURE 1.27: FLAT PLATE PANEL ARRAY WITH COMPLEMENTARY REFLECTORS

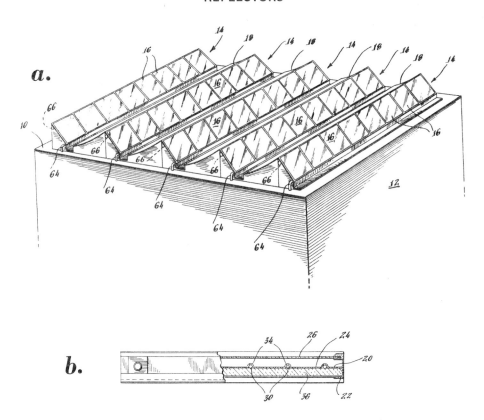

(continued)

FIGURE 1.27: (continued)

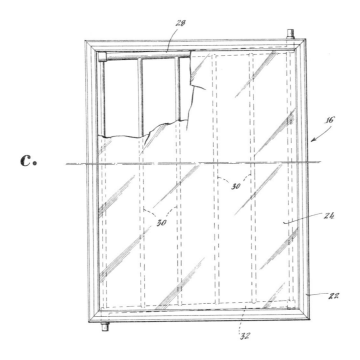

c.

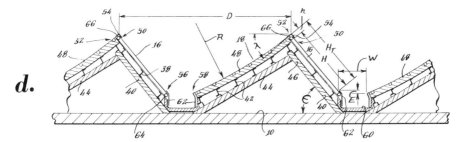

d.

(a)   Perspective view of system
(b)   Cross-sectional view of collecting panel
(c)   Top plan view of collecting panel
(d)   Vertical cross-sectional view of components of system

Source:   U.S. Patent 4,020,827

Complementing each row of the solar energy collecting panels is an elongate
solar energy concentrator or reflector **18** which focuses radiant solar energy on
the collector panels in a manner to be described in greater detail below.  Figures
1.27b and 1.27c illustrate a suitable solar energy collecting panel for use in the
process. This panel includes a main plate **20** that is mounted in a frame **22**

and that has a flat black or, preferably, a selective coating **24** which absorbs radiant solar energy and is thus heated.

The collector panel further includes one or more transparent windows **26** which transmit sunlight to the energy absorbing coating, tend to be opaque to infrared reradiation from the plate **20**, and also retard convective heat transfer from the plate. Accordingly, the plate is heated by the solar radiation. A system for circulating a fluid medium in heat conducting contact with the heated plate comprises an inlet manifold **32** that communicates in parallel with a series of vertically extending tubes **30** that ultimately lead to an outlet manifold **28**. As shown in Figure 1.27b, the tubes are continuously soldered into arcuate depressions **34** formed in the bottom of the main plate to improve the heat transferring contact between the tubes and plate.

A layer of insulation **36** is also mounted in frame **22** below the plate to retard heat transfer through the bottom of panel **16** and, thus, to improve the efficiency of the heat transfer from the plate to water circulated in the tubes.

As shown in Figure 1.27d, each of the solar energy collecting panels **16** is mounted on a series of purlins **38** carried on a rafter **40** which is fixed to building roof **10** at an angle $\epsilon$. Accordingly, this angle determines the angle at which the collector panels are mounted to face the sun. Each reflector **18** is also mounted on a number of purlins **42** which are carried on a rafter **44** that forms an interior peak **46** with one collector supporting rafter **40**. The reflectors may be parabolic or circular in cross section. It has been found, however, that the circular cross-section is most easily and economically fabricated. For example, stainless steel can be provided with relatively high reflectivity and easily formed to the circular curve to approximately focus solar radiation onto the collector panels.

A layer of insulation **48** underlies each reflector to retard building heat loss by conduction downwardly through it. The upper horizontal edge **50** of each row of collector panels is joined to the upper horizontal edge **52** of each row of reflectors by a flashing **54** to form an external peak. Accordingly, the bottom edge **56** of the collector panel row and the bottom edge **58** of an adjacent reflector may be spaced by a distance W to form a valley. A depressed walkway **60**, which may be built up roofing or other materials sufficiently durable to withstand the installation and maintenance of roof-mounted equipment, is positioned in each valley formed between respective collector-reflector peaks and is mounted on the roof. Suitable flashing **62** extends from the bottom edge **56** of the collector panel rows and from the bottom edge **58** of the reflectors into the walkway to prevent leakage.

The walkway provides a convenient access to both the reflectors and collectors for installation and maintenance. Thus, in the event that a malfunction occurs, a workman can easily reach the defective area and may also transport repair equipment with him in walkways **60**. Furthermore, these walkways provide drainage from the surfaces of the collectors and reflectors for rain and snow.

Accordingly, the walkways may be canted slightly from the center to the edges to form suitable gutters or may be provided with roof drains at their centers and be canted slightly theretoward. In either case, the system is essentially self-cleaning. If the reflectors are made from a corrosion-resistant material such as stainless steel and if the collectors are provided with an upper transparent pane of glass, the natural process of rain and snow will wash dirt and other debris from them. However, if further cleaning becomes necessary, walkway **60** provides easy access to the facing surfaces of the collectors and reflectors for doing so.

The system may be adapted to operate in conjunction with any form of device which utilizes the heated water produced in the collectors **16**. Accordingly, all collectors in a given row are connected in parallel to an inlet header **64** (Figure 1.27d) which runs along the bottom edge **56** of the collector and conducts water to each of the individual panels to be circulated through the circulation tubing **30**. Further, each panel in a row is connected to an outlet header **66** from which water that has now been heated is circulated by means of a pump (not shown) through a supply main (not shown) to a device (not shown) for utilizing the heated water. Details of the calculations for peak heights and the horizontal distance between peaks are included in the patent.

### Moving Belt Absorber

The collection device of *K.A. Alkasab; U.S. Patent 3,972,316; August 3, 1976; assigned to Universal Oil Products Company* uses a motor driven moving endless belt absorber member which is mounted in a glass covered collector housing so as to present a flat plate configuration to the solar rays. The moving belt progressively increases in temperature as it passes through the housing, and is guided, after it is heated, to a heat transfer chamber outside the main collector housing where its heat can be transferred to a suitable heat transfer fluid.

By mounting the moving belt absorber on a plurality of rollers and a driving shaft so that it continually carries heat out of the collector housing into a separated heat exchange compartment, the heat loss by reradiation to the atmosphere is considerably reduced.

In a preferred embodiment, the heat transfer fluid contacting the moving belt absorber within the heat exchange compartment is air. Although the air must be moved, the expense of doing so is considerably less than pumping a liquid. By using air, the problems of freezing, leaks, and moisture on the cover glass are eliminated. The belt is preferably made of reinforced rubber or other flexible heat absorbing material.

Although the belt can be driven at a constant speed, it is preferable that the speed be adjustable so that one can select an appropriate speed between the faster ones which would produce greater total heat transfer and slower ones which would produce heat transfer at higher temperatures. Controls are also provided to stop the movement of the belt when the temperature of the absorbing surface is less than a desired minimum. Appropriate seals between the belt and the heat exchange compartment serve to prevent excessive leakage of air into the collector housing.

In a modified form of collector, a liquid such as water can be used as the heat exchange compartment. The liquid contacts the moving belt and extracts heat therefrom, which heat can then be transferred to a finned, liquid containing tube immersed in the liquid which will carry it to a heat storage tank, for example.

Even though liquid is used as a heat transfer medium, it does not present the freezing problems associated with liquid passing through tubes on the surface of a conventional flat plate collector since it is contained within an insulated heat exchange compartment in association with a heat storage tank. By the use of appropriate seals and wipers the liquid can be substantially completely removed from the belt before it returns to the collector housing. However, some moisture might still be retained which could produce some condensation on the glass cover plate.

Referring to Figures 1.28a and 1.28b, the solar collector indicated at **10** comprises a housing **12** which may be formed of a suitable material such as wood or plastic covered with metal. The housing defines an energy collection chamber **13** which is closed on one side by a panel of glass **14** through which solar rays **16** enter the collector and impinge upon the surface of moving belt member **18**.

The moving belt is formed of fabric reinforced rubber or other suitable material and is preferably black to increase its absorptivity. The belt is guided around a plurality of guide rollers **20, 22, 24, 26** and **28** and a driving roller **30** which is driven by a motor **32** mounted on a support bracket **34** attached to the housing. A heat exchange compartment **36** is integrally attached to the housing and separated from the chamber by a partition member **38** having apertures **40, 42** which permit the moving belt to move in and out of the compartment.

Preferably, a plurality of units **10, 10'** are positioned side by side as indicated in Figure 1.28b so that the moving belts **18, 18'** can be rotated by a single drive roller. The heat exchange compartments **36, 36'** preferably include flange portions **38, 38'** which permit a plurality of collectors to be arranged in series so that the air may be circulated through the compartments as indicated by the arrows in Figure 1.28b.

## FIGURE 1.28:  COLLECTOR WITH MOVING BELT ABSORBER

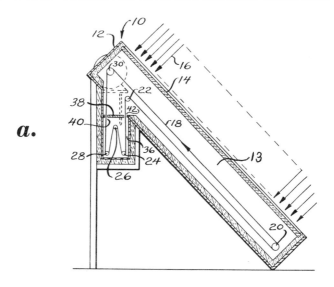

*a.*

(continued)

FIGURE 1.28: (continued)

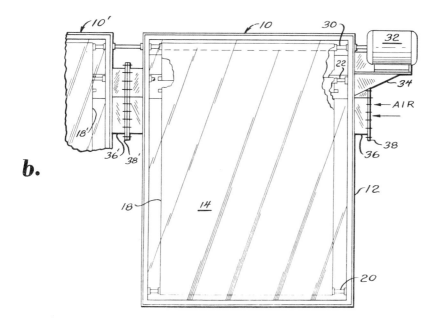

b.

(a)   Sectional side view of the collector
(b)   Top view

Source:   U.S. Patent 3,972,316

## Particulate Heat Absorber

*G.R. Gaydos, Jr.; U.S. Patent 3,853,114; December 10, 1974* describes a solar
heater having a helix of tubing contained within a transparent box, the box being contained within a second transparent box, forming an air gap between the
two boxes on all six sides. The cavity of the internal box around the tubing is
filled with a particulate heat absorbing material such as a mixture of magnetite,
perlite and lampblack.

The helix is connected to a heat exchange device by tubing sections which extend through walls of the boxes. In one embodiment the boxes are essentially
cubes. A further absorber is also disclosed in which a relatively tall, thin box
containing a sinuous tubular array is provided with means for mounting the box
on a roof of a house. The box is similarly filled with a particulate heat absorbing material and can be provided with double walls.

Referring to Figures 1.29a, there is shown an apparatus having an exterior box
indicated generally at **10** and an interior box indicated generally at **11**. The exterior box is composed of side walls **12**, an upper wall **13** and a lower wall **14**
and the interior box includes side walls **15**, an upper wall **16** and a lower wall
**17**. The upper wall of the interior box is provided with marginal extension

portions **20** which extend outwardly beyond side walls **15** and contact the interior surfaces of walls **12** to act as spacers, forming a gap **21** between walls **15** and walls **12** on all sides of the interior box.

## FIGURE 1.29: PARTICULATE HEAT ABSORBER

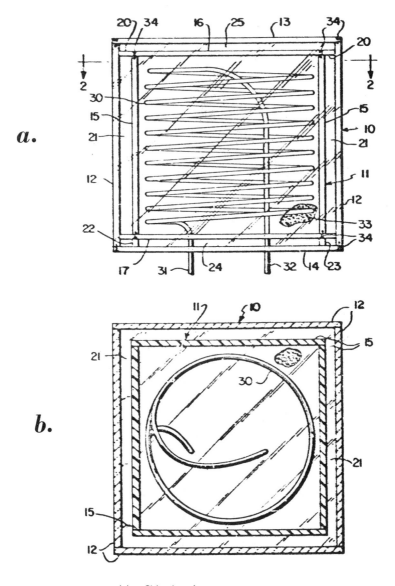

(a)    Side elevation
(b)    Plan view along line 2–2 of Figure 1.29a

Source:  U.S. Patent 3,853,114

These constitute dead air spaces for insulating purposes. Support spacers **22** and **23** are provided between lower walls **17** and **14** so that the interior box is upwardly spaced from the lower wall of the exterior box, providing an additional dead air spacer **24** between the box bottoms. Spacers **22** and **23** are dimensioned so that the upper walls **13** and **16** of the boxes are spaced apart, creating a dead air space **25**.

Walls **15** are preferably made of Plexiglas or a similar plastic material which has a relatively low coefficient of thermal conductivity and, in addition, is transparent to solar radiation. Walls **12** can be made of glass panels to better withstand the effects of exposure to the elements, but Plexiglas or the like can alternatively be used. While not all of the walls **12** and **15** need be transparent, it will be apparent that at least two walls thereof must be transparent and, additionally, they should be adjacent ones of the walls in the two boxes.

Contained within interior box **11** is a helical arrangement of tubing **30** having inlet and outlet connecting tubing portions **31** and **32** which pass through walls **17** and **14** of the two boxes. Surrounding helix **30** and substantially filling the interior of box **11** is an aggregation of loose particulate material **33** which is employed to absorb solar energy and retain the heat derived therefrom. For simplicity, most of the particulate material is omitted from Figures 1.29a and 1.29b so that the coil and wall structure will not be obscured.

As an example of the specific construction technique, the interior box can be constructed of sheets of ¼" Plexiglas, each approximately 3 ft², connected together as illustrated using threaded fasteners as shown at **34** or using a suitable adhesive. In any event, it is desirable to apply adhesive to all joints to prevent undesirable air circulation between cavities. The outer box can be formed from similar and slightly larger sheets of glass or Plexiglas and similarly fastened and adhered together so that the spaces **21, 24** and **25** are essentially sealed air spaces and, therefore, highly insulating. The spaces can conveniently be about ½" between parallel sheets.

The helix can be formed from ⅜" copper tubing and, in a box of the dimensions described about 160' of tubing can be employed, resulting in a substantial volume of fluid within the interior chamber at any single time. The tubing should, of course, be coiled with no kinks to impede fluid flow.

The particulate material perferably includes perlite, magnetite and lampblack, the proportions being approximately 8:1:1, respectively, by volume. This particular mixture of materials has been found to be quite suitable in that it absorbs energy from solar radiation and reaches an elevated temperature which effectively heats the liquid within helical conduit **30**. A more convenient measure is by weight, the proportions then being 100 lb of perlite mixed with 50 lb of magnetite and 25 lb of lampblack. This mixture has been found to be particularly effective in gathering and holding heat.

The apparatus is designed for use in conjunction with a remote heat exchanger of any conventional type and the system can employ a pump to circulate any fluid, such as water, through tubing **30** and to the exchanger. Thus, heat absorbed by particulate material **33** is transferred to the tubing and to the fluid contained therein, which fluid is pumped to the other exchanger to elevate the temperature at that location.

## INSULATION MEANS

### Flexibly Insulated Cover Plates

A highly efficient solar heat collector characterized by a layer of light transmitting insulating (i.e., convection and infrared radiation suppressing) material disposed between the outer surface of the collector and the heat absorptive layer thereof is described by *B.Y.H. Liu, R.C. Jordan and K. Willeke; U.S. Patent 4,015,582; April 5, 1977; assigned to The Regents of the University of Minnesota.* Glass fibers are a particularly effective lightweight insulating material which may be used. Through use of flexible polymeric films, lightweight, low-cost solar heat collectors may be fabricated for conversion of existing structures to partial or complete solar heating. Either gaseous or liquid heat transfer fluids may be used.

Referring now to Figure 1.30a, there is shown in transverse section a solar heat collector, indicated generally at **10**, utilizing air or other gas as the heat transfer fluid. The collector includes a heat insulative base **11** formed from conventional insulating materials.

## FIGURE 1.30: FLEXIBLY INSULATED COVER PLATES

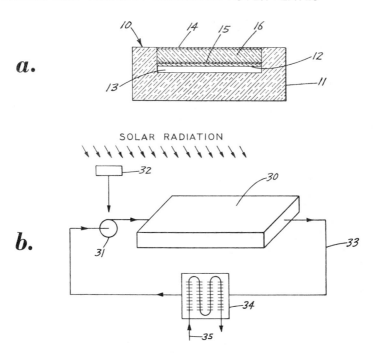

(a) Transverse section of one form of collector utilizing air as heat transfer fluid
(b) Schematic representation of a system for utilizing heat from collector

Source: U.S. Patent 4,015,582

A sheet or layer **12** of heat absorbing material overlies the insulative base spaced therefrom to define a channel **13** for gas flow. The heat absorbing surface may likewise be rigid or flexible in the form of a black or blackened plate or film such as a painted metal sheet or dyed or pigmented polymer rigid or semirigid sheet or flexible film. The heat absorbing surface can also be in the form of a porous medium such as dyed, pigmented or painted glass fibers, painted metal fibers or painted screens with high solar absorptance.

A protective cover overlies the heat absorbing surface. The protective cover is in the form of a sandwich comprising spaced apart sheets **14** and **15** composed of light transmitting material with the air space in between partially occupied by a light transmitting and insulating (i.e., convection and infrared radiation suppressing) packing **16**, such as randomly arrayed, loosely packed glass fibers in the form of a mat or batting. As is apparent, in order for the protective cover to function as an air buffer, it must be impervious to the passage of air through the cover and sheets **14** and **15** are formed from material which of necessity is nonporous and relatively impermeable to the passage of air.

Both sheets **14** and **15** may be rigid or flexible, or outer sheet **14** may be rigid and inner sheet **15** may be flexible, and made from light transmitting materials such as glass, glass fiber reinforced plastic sheeting, polymer films and the like. Where weight and cost are important factors, films are used. Tough durable films such as polyvinyl fluoride films such as "Tedlar" are capable of withstanding long usage and resistant to degradation from exposure to solar radiation.

The functions of heat absorbing layer **12** and inner protective cover sheet **15** may in some instances by combined in a single layer. For example, inner sheet **15** may be formed from black polymer film, in which event another heat absorbing layer is unnecessary. In some instances channel **13** may be located between the heat absorbing layer and the protective cover. Likewise, the heat absorbing surface may be located within channel **13** with gas flowing on both sides of the surface, or in the case of a porous heat absorbing medium such as pigmented, dyed or painted glass fibers or painted metal screens, the gas would flow partially or wholly through the medium. Although one air space is shown, it is understood that there can be more than one air space and that the insulating material can be separated by thin plastic or glass sheets or separated into individual pockets to further reduce convection.

While glass fiber is a desirable material for filling the air space to reduce heat loss, the material does not have to be glass, nor does it have to be in the form of fibers. Other natural and artificial fibers which are capable of transmitting light may be used, such as mineral fibers; polymeric fibers, such as polyacrylonitrile (Dynel, Orlon), nylon, polyester (Dacron), polyvinyl and the like; cellulosic fibers of artificial or plant origin, such as rayon, α-cellulose, cotton jute, sisal, flax and the like; fibers of animal origin, such as wool, silk, etc.

Any other material that is reasonably transparent to solar radiation can be used. The material can be in the form of solid or hollow particles of microscopic or macroscopic size. It can also be in the form of rigid or flexible foam with entrapped gas bubbles. Fused plastic films containing entrapped gas bubbles and plastic honeycomb or similar structures which partially or fully entrap the air, such as those commonly used for packaging, can also be used.

In general, these materials are not totally transparent. Their appearance can best be described as translucent. Perfect transparency is not required for flat-plate collector operation.

The collector can also be adapted for water as the heat transfer fluid and an inflatable collector configuration is also included in the patent.

Figure 1.30b shows a solar heat collector **30** with air or other gas as the heat transfer medium and the subsequent transfer of this heat into a liquid such as water for such purposes as water heating, refrigeration or heat storage. Blower **31** is activated when the sensor **32** indicates sufficient solar intensity for collector operation. As the gas passes through the collector, it is heated to a higher temperature. This heated gas then passes through suitable ducts along flow line **33** through the heat exchanger **34** where the heat is extracted by the liquid **35** flowing through the heat exchanger. The gas is then recirculated to the collector for further heating. The heated liquid may then be utilized in heat exchange and storage systems known in the prior art.

The use of gas as the heat transfer fluid and the use of the heat exchanger in this manner have two main advantages: (1) the weight of the collector can be much reduced, and (2) the heat exchanger can be located inside the house or in an enclosure to prevent the liquid from coming into direct contact with freezing temperatures during winter since the blower and the gas circulation through the heat exchanger may be stopped at night or during periods of low sunshine.

It is understood that the collectors are made in individual modules of a suitable size. The modules can be connected in series or in parallel, or in any combination thereof. The solar collectors can be applied to the roof of a house or to any vertical south-facing or nearly south-facing surface. For application in the northern United States, where snow buildup is expected to be a problem for roof collectors, the collectors should be mounted at a steep angle or on south-facing walls or on any free-standing vertical surface not too far away from the energy-consuming buildings.

### Use of Rigid and Soft Insulators

*A. Grossman; U.S. Patent 4,003,363; January 18, 1977* describes a solar panel construction comprising an elongated rectangular receptacle of sheet material provided with fiberglass insulation covering the bottom wall and the side walls of the receptacle. A solar energy absorber plate provided with fluid circulating tubes and a black coating is supported at its marginal edges upon the insulation material which is relatively rigid in structure while the interior portions of the plate are supported upon insulation material of relatively soft structure. The insulation material, both rigid and soft, is permeable.

Spaced above the solar absorber plate is a dual pane window to transmit radiant energy from the sun and yet reduce heat transfer from the air space and the solar panel beneath the window. The entire panel is hermetically sealed and so constructed that as the temperature increases within the receptacle and the air pressure becomes greater, the absorber plate and the receptacle can move and compensate for such changes in pressure and temperature. A method of assembling the solar panel construction is used such that the compensation stresses imposed upon the receptacle and panel during operation are reduced.

Referring to Figures 1.31a, 1.31b and 1.31c, solar panel construction **20** includes an elongated rectangular receptacle **22** within which a solar collector plate **23** is supported in spaced relation to a radiant energy transmitting means **24**. The solar collector plate and energy transmitting means are supported on permeable insulation mounting means generally indicated at **25** which enhances the operability of the solar panel. The solar collector plate is in conductive contact with a suitable array or pattern of fluid conducting tubes **26**. The solar panel construction is hermetically sealed, is arranged to be capable of expansion and contraction of its several component parts of different material and is adapted to withstand temperatures of materials used therein in the order of 450° to 550°F.

## FIGURE 1.31: USE OF RIGID AND SOFT INSULATORS

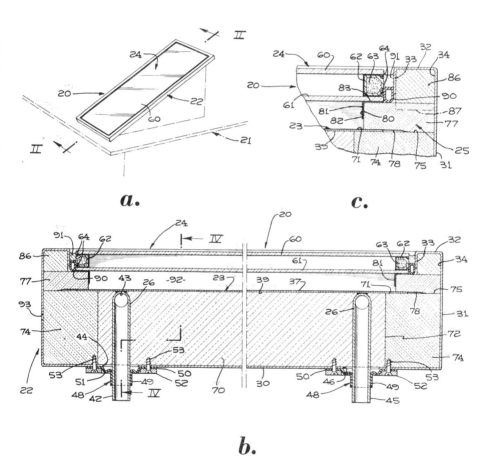

(a) Fragmentary perspective view
(b) Vertical section view along plane of line II—II of Figure 1.31a
(c) Enlarged cross-sectional view of upper right corner of Figure 1.31b

Source: U.S. Patent 4,003,363

In detail, solar panel construction 20 may comprise the receptacle, box or case 22 which may be formed from a single rectangular blank sheet of sheet metal material. The sheet metal may be galvanized on both surfaces and may be formed to provide an elongated rectangular bottom wall 30 and an upstanding peripheral wall 31 integral with the bottom wall. Along the top of the peripheral wall is an inwardly turned wall margin 32 terminating in a downwardly extending lip 33 forming with the wall margin 32 and the upper portion of peripheral wall 33 a peripheral downwardly facing recess 34.

In formation of the rectangular case, wall margins 32 and depending lips 33 are cut along a bias so that each corner is mitered. The corners formed by peripheral wall, edge margin and lips are welded or brazed along the length of the corner joint so that the receptacle 22 is fluid tight. An exemplary rectangular dimension of such a receptacle may be 2 feet wide and 7 feet long. The sheet metal material may comprise brake-formed 22-gauge galvanized steel. A butyl-based sealant may be applied at the welded corners to assure air tightness.

Solar collector plate 23 comprises a flat rectangular metal plate of slightly smaller dimension than the rectangular dimension of the case. The collector or absorber plate may be fabricated of aluminum, copper, stainless steel or other suitable metal materials. The collector plate is mounted within the receptacle 22 below the plane of the opening defined by wall margins 32 and depending lips 33 and is provided with an upwardly facing uninterrupted planar top surface 37 to receive radiant energy from the sun.

The top surface is preferably coated with a black coating having characteristics of maximum absorptivity and minimum reflectivity. The characteristic of minimum reflectivity is preferably one which closely approximates a true black body for which reflectivity is zero. Radiant energy which is reflected from the surface is not absorbed by the surface and therefore decreases the efficiency of the energy absorption. Such black coatings include coatings of black oxide, black anodizing for aluminum and its alloys, and a black sprayable paint of polyurethane.

Under temperatures greater than ambient, certain of such black coatings are subject to outgassing which results in the emission of gaseous vapors within the receptacle. Outgassing is undesirable because collection of such gas in the space between the collector plate and the radiant energy transmitting means results in fogging or clouding of such air space and interferes with unobstructed transmission of solar radiant energy to collector plate. A solar collector plate having a black coating which has minimum outgassing, minimum reflectivity and maximum absorptivity is preferred.

The bottom surface 39 of the collector plate may be uncoated. On the bottom surface may be secured as by welding or brazing, metal conduit or tubing suitably arranged in a winding serpentine path so that tubing sections lie in parallel relation and extend for substantially the entire length of the collector plate. The tubing is connected along its entire length by welding or brazing to the collector plate so that heat absorbed by the plate from the radiant energy falling thereupon is conducted by the plate directly to the tubing. The tubing may be of the same material as the plate. At one end of the plate an inlet tubing portion 42 is provided which joins the serpentine tubing at a transverse header portion 43. Inlet portion 42 extends through an opening 44 in bottom wall 30.

An outlet end portion 45 of the tubing may be provided at the opposite end of the collector plate from inlet portion 42 and at a bent U portion of the centrally located portions of tubing 40. Outlet tubing portion 45 also extends through an opening 46 in the bottom wall 30. In normal installation, the solar panel construction is inclined at an angle to the horizontal and when so inclined the inlet tubing portion 42 may be at the upper part of the inclined panel construction and the outlet portion at the lower panel portion.

Openings 44 and 46 for the inlet and outlet tubing portions are sealed in such a manner that the tubing portions 42 and 45 may move laterally and axially with respect to bottom wall 30 without impairing the sealed relationship of the inlet and outlet tubing portions with respect to the receptacle. Means for sealing the passage therethrough of the inlet and outlet portions may comprise an elastomeric fitting 48 of flexible impervious heat resistant material having a cylindrical outer sleeve 49 tightly receiving the tubing portion and secured thereon by suitable bonding or adhesive material.

Outer sleeve 49 terminates in a laterally extending annular flange 50 which is joined to the sleeve by an annular formed corrugation 51. Flange 50 is secured in tight sealing relation to the outer surface of bottom wall 30 by an annular retainer ring 52 secured by suitable sheet metal screws 53 to the bottom wall. The annular corrugation which joins the sleeve and the flange of the gasket fitting is flexible and yieldable and capable of permitting the tubing portion to move laterally of its axis, longitudinally of its axis, and also yields to any axial misalignment of the tubing with respect to the openings 44 or 46.

Within the top opening of receptacle 22 and in spaced relation above the collector plate is positioned energy transmitting means 24. Means 24 may comprise an insulating glass cover comprising a top glass pane 60 approximately ⅛ inch thick and a lower glass pane 61 approximately 3/32 thick. The glass panes may be spaced apart approximately ½ inch. The two panes are of identical rectangular configuration slightly smaller than the opening in the top of the receptacle. The panes are held in spaced relation by a hollow peripheral spacer member 62 of suitable elastomeric material such as vinyl. Within the hollow spacer member may be provided dehydrating crystals 63 for collection of and retention of any moisture or humidity present in the air space between glass panes. Spacers 62 are formed with peripheral recesses 64 which may be filled with a butyl sealant compound so that the air space between the panes is hermetically sealed.

Means for mounting and maintaining the solar collector plate and the energy transmitting means and the receptacle in proper assembled relationship and in hermetically sealed relationship while withstanding stresses caused by expansion and contraction due to changing heat conditions comprises an arrangement of insulation means of material capable of withstanding internal temperature in the order of 350° to 450°F and pressures resulting therefrom. Generally speaking, such mounting means includes an interior insulation member 70 comprising a pad or block of insulation material supporting substantially all of the solar collector plate 23 except for a peripheral edge margin 71 of the plate. Insulation member 70 may comprise a relatively soft yieldable permeable fiberglass insulation material.

In the space between the peripheral side walls 31 and the edge surfaces 72 of the relatively soft yieldable insulation member is provided a relatively rigid non-yieldable insulation member **74** having a depth corresponding to the depth of member **70** in unstressed condition and completely filling the marginal space around the interior insulation member **70**. Rigid outer peripheral insulation member **74** provides a flat top surface **75** coplanar with the top surface of insulation member **70** for supporting the edge margins of the collector plate with virtually no deformation of the upper interior configuration of the rigid insulation member **74**.

On top of peripheral rigid insulation member **74** may be provided a second outer peripheral rigid insulation member **77**, the member having a depth less than the space between the top surface **75** of member **74** and the bottom edge of depending lip **33**. Rigid insulation member **77** defines the space between the top surface **37** of the collector plate and the bottom surface of the glass pane **61** of the energy transmitting means **24**. The peripheral insulation member is provided with a bottom surface having a downwardly facing rabbeted recess or edge **78** within which may be received a portion of the edge margin **71** of the collector plate. Recess **78** extends sidewardly beyond the edge of edge margin **71** to provide space for lateral expansion of plate **23**. Rigid insulation member **77** may be made of the same material as member **74** and in this example may include permeable fiberglass insulation material capable of withstanding temperatures in the order of 350° to 450°F.

Rigid peripheral insulation member **77** at its interior upper edge portion **80** is provided with an angle section metal cover strip **81** having a depending leg **82** extending along the interior edge surface of member **77** and a top horizontal leg **83** lying on the top surface of member **77** and providing a seat for the bottom surface of the edge margin of the lower glass pane **61** of the dual pane insulation glass cover. The rigidity of member **77** thus supports the glass cover **24** in desired dimensional relationship with respect to the solar collector panel.

The outer rigid insulation members **77** and **74** may be held in assembled relation with the receptacle **22** by a third peripheral insulation member **86** of slightly less rigid characteristic than members **77** and **74** and which is dimensioned to fit laterally within the recess **34** beneath the receptacle edge margins **32** and within depending lip **33**. Third insulation member **86** has a depth normally greater than the distance between edge margin **32** and the top surface of insulation member **77**. Since insulation member **86** is somewhat yieldable when the insulation members are assembled, the insulation member will be placed under compression and will frictionally retain and hold second insulation member **77** in position and against any lateral movement thereof which might be caused by expansion and contraction of the solar panel construction.

In order to assemble the rigid insulation member **77** and the somewhat softer insulation member **86**, member **86** may be placed in position in recess **34**. An angle shaped lifting member may be placed with one leg of the angle beneath the bottom surface of member **86** and an upward force placed upon the angle shaped member so as to compress it within recess **34**. The second insulation member **77** may then be laterally slid between the horizontal leg of the lifting member and the top surface of first insulation member **74** so that member **77** may be properly positioned tightly against the peripheral wall **31**. The lifting member may be laterally withdrawn from beneath the member **86** and the depending lip **33** thus permitting the insulation member **86** to expand downwardly and into pressure contact against insulation member **77**.

Energy transmitting member 24 may then be positioned upon the angle shaped covers 81 on the second insulation member 77 and located in uniformly spaced relationship to the depending lips 33 on the receptacle. A suitable vinyl spacer 90 is placed at the bottom of the groove formed between the lip 33 and the edge of the dual pane cover, the spacer being seated upon top surface of rigid member 77. On top of the spacer may then be applied compound 91 suitable butyl-type sealant or caulking compound for sealing and retaining the insulated dual pane cover 24 in assembled relation with the receptacle.

The metal angle section cover 81 which may be painted black and which affords a seat for the edge margins of the glass cover, provides a means for transfer of heat between edge margins of the lower glass pane 61 and heated air in space 92 between pane 61 and plate 23 and also insulation member 77. Spacer member 62 between peripheral edge margins of glass panes 60 and 61 may also have its interior, top and bottom surfaces provided with a black coating or paint. The black coating on spacer member 62 and angle cover 81 serves to absorb heat from the sun's rays and increase the temperature of the edge margins of the glass panes.

Since the central portions of the glass panes are heated by the sun's rays and expand, the increased heating of the edge margins of the glass panes by use of the black coating substantially reduces any temperature gradient between the center and edges of the panes. Thus abnormal edge stresses, usually produced by differential temperatures between the center and edges of the glass panes are substantially relieved and minimized.

While the solar panel construction described above is capable of breathing, that is, yielding and compensating for stresses imparted thereto by the collection of solar radiant energy, the rigid tubing sections may move relative to the receptacle and such movement does not cause loss of the weather-tight sealed condition because of the flexibility and yieldability of the gasket mounting of the inlet and outlet tubing portions in either the bottom or peripheral wall of the receptacle. It should be noted that the breathing effect provided by this solar panel construction is the result of the absence of fixed fasteners or screws in the assembly of the receptacle, rigid and soft insulation material, support and retention of the collector plate between rigid insulation material, and yieldable positioning and retention of the dual pane glass cover by the butyl sealant.

## Provision for Close Contact Between Absorber and Conduit

The solar collector of *J.J. Medico, Jr.; U.S. Patent 3,898,979; August 12, 1975* comprises a collecting box having a layer of flexible insulating material, such as shredded asbestos, foam rubber or the like upon which is placed a thin sheet of metal of high thermal conductivity, such as copper, aluminum, etc. A fluid conducting coil formed of high thermal conducting metal, preferably of the same metal of which the sheet of metal on the insulation is formed. The coil is connected to a source of supply of water or other suitable fluid and either to a domestic item, such as a water heater for supplying hot water for domestic use, to a swimming pool or to a suitable insulated storage container from which it is drawn for subsequent use. The flexibility of the insulation and the flexibility of the metal sheet upon which the coil rests allows the weight of the coil to deform the sheet, i.e., to form a close firm contact between the thin sheet of metal and a portion of the tubes resting thereon, thus imparting solar heat

collected by a thin sheet of metal to the tubes augmenting their collection of
solar heat and providing increased heating of the fluid in the tubes.

Referring to Figure 1.32, the solar heat collector includes a tray or box **2**, the
upper open side of which is closed by a transparent clear window **1**. The tray
or box contains therein the elements of the solar or thermal heat units and will
hereinafter be called the container.

FIGURE 1.32:  CROSS SECTION OF PANEL

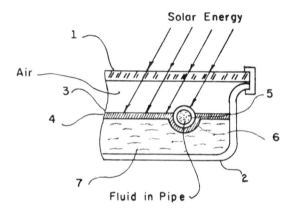

Source:  U.S. Patent 3,898,979

A layer of flexible insulating material **7** is placed in the container at the bottom thereof and may be formed of shredded asbestos, highly flexible rubber
or the like.

A thin sheet **3** of suitable metal having a high thermal conductivity, such as
copper, is placed over the layer of insulating material.  While copper is specifically mentioned herein, any metal having a high thermal conductivity may be
used.  The thin sheet of metal is highly flexible due to its thinness and may
have its upper surface coated with lampblack or other suitable black material
having a high heat absorptivity.

A coil of tubing **5** through which the water or other fluid to be heated passes
is placed in the container and has suitable inlet for cool water and a suitable
outlet for heated water to leave the container.  The coil is formed of suitable
metal having a high heat conductivity and it rests upon the thin metal sheet **3**.
The weight of the coil **5** will cause it to deform the thin metal sheet **3** due to
the flexibility of the insulating material upon which the thin sheet rests, thus
providing surface to surface contact between the entire length of the coil and
the thin sheet to provide heat conducting relationship between the sheet and
tubing coil.

If it is found desirable, the thin metal sheet and the tubing of the coil may be
bonded together by a thermal heat conducting material so as to insure complete

contact all along the coil with the metal sheet and thus enhance the transfer of absorbed solar heat from the metal sheet to the tube coil and provide increased heating to the fluid flowing through the coil.

The thin sheet and the coil tubing may be coated with a black coating of thermal heat absorbing material such as lampblack. Holding blocks hold the coil in its proper place within the container.

## Transparent Thermal Insulating System

The process of D. Chahroudi; U.S. Patent 3,953,110; April 27, 1976 provides a transparent thermal insulating system having controllable transmissivity to visible radiation comprising a first layer generally transparent to visible radiation; a second layer generally transparent to visible radiation and spaced from the first layer; partition means for separating the space between the layers into compartments; a thermal radiation suppression device for suppressing thermal radiation transmission; and a variable transparency thermal control device for controlling transmission of visible radiation as a function of temperature.

There is shown in Figure 1.33a a functional block diagram of a transparent thermal insulating system 10 having controllable transmissivity to visible radiation. Insulating system 10 includes means for suppressing convection, conduction and thermal radiation heat losses—convection suppressor 12, conduction suppressor 14 and thermal radiation suppressor 16. Each of the suppressors 12, 14 and 16 of thermal transport mechanisms extend over the whole system but are shown distinctly for convenience in explanation. Actually they are superimposed. Visible radiation control 18 adjusts the transmissivity of system 10 to visible radiation in accordance with the temperature of the area whose environment is to be controlled.

Conduction suppressor 14 may be provided through the use of two or more spaced layers with a gas, vacuum or other medium between them to prevent conduction.

Convection suppressor 12 may include compartmentalizing the space between the layers or providing therein a vacuum. The compartmentalizing may be accomplished by baffles or partitions which extend transversely between the layers and/or parallel to the layers to restrict convective heat transport.

Thermal radiation suppressor 16 may include a coating or layer of material which either reflects thermal radiation to prevent its transmission or absorbs and reemits thermal radiation one or more times reducing the intensity of the thermal radiation with each absorption and reemission.

Visible radiation control 18 may include a pressurizing system responsive to a thermostatic element for varying the pressure in the compartments to increase or decrease the transmission of visible radiation. Alternatively such control may be accomplished with a variable transmission layer including a material which becomes cloudy and opaque white to visible radiation above a certain temperature and remains clear to transmit visible radiation below that temperature.

# FIGURE 1.33: TRANSPARENT THERMAL INSULATING SYSTEM

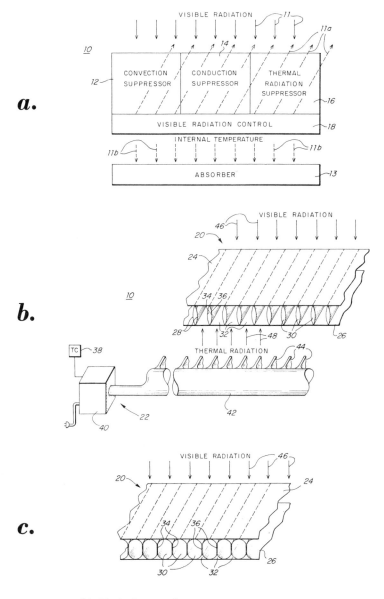

(a) Block diagram of system
(b) Schematic diagram with insulating member adjusted to transmit visible radiation
(c) Schematic diagram of insulating member of Figure 1.33b adjusted to block visible radiation

Source: U.S. Patent 3,953,110

In operation visible radiation, arrows **11**, e.g., sunlight incident on system **10** is either reflected, arrows **11a**, by variable transmission layer **18** in the opaque condition or transmitted, arrows **11b**, by variable transmission layer **18** in the transparent condition. Transmitted radiation **11b** strikes absorber **13**, causing its temperature to rise.

In one specific embodiment, Figure 1.33b, the system **10** includes a transparent insulating member **20** and a pressurizing system **22**. Insulating member **20** includes an outer layer **24** which may be formed of a plasticized vinyl with an ultraviolet absorber having a thickness of 16 mils and an inner layer **26** of similar 6 mil vinyl. Tubular webbing **28** extends transversely between layers **24** and **26** to form a first set of compartments **30** and a second set of interstitial compartments **32**. Webbing **28** is formed of Mylar with aluminized inner surfaces **34** and **36**. Pressurizing unit **22** includes a thermostatic control **38**, a vacuum or pressure pump **40** and a manifold **42** whose outputs **44** interconnect with compartments **30** or **32** or both.

As shown in Figure 1.33b, insulating member **20** provides good insulation against convection and conduction losses and permits good transmission of visible radiation, arrows **46**, through compartments **32** because of parallel mirrors **34** and **36**. In this condition there is some loss of thermal radiation **48** through the same compartments **32** which is tolerable in view of the heat which will be generated by the visible radiation which is transmitted by insulating member **20**.

Insulating member **20** may be made to block further transmission of visible radiation **46** and further heat losses due to transmission of thermal radiation **48** by increasing the pressure in compartments **30** relative to the pressure in compartments **32** so that insulating member **20** assumes the configuration shown in Figure 1.33c wherein the tubular webbing **28** of each of compartments **30** has expanded to contact the tubular webbing of the adjacent compartments. In this configuration, radiation **46** will be reflected by the aluminized surfaces **34** and **36** of compartments **30** to provide low emissivity surfaces to minimize thermal transport by radiation.

If substantial cooling is desired, both compartments **30** and **32** can be completely deflated so that there is good conduction between layers **24** and **26** through the collapsed webbings **28** of compartments **30** and **32** while the aluminized surfaces **34** and **36** maintain their opacity to visible radiation.

In operation, assuming system **10**, Figure 1.33b, is in the heating mode, insulating member **20** will assume a configuration similar to that shown in Figure 1.33b with compartments **30** at least partially deflated so that visible radiation may be transmitted through compartments **32** of insulating member **20** to heat the interior of the enclosure. As the interior absorbs the heat from visible radiation **46**, the temperature rises until at a predetermined level thermostatic control **38** actuates pumps **40** to increase the pressure in compartments **30** relative to that in compartments **32** to expand compartments **30** and obstruct or block at least a portion of the visible radiation **46**.

As the temperature continues to increase, the thermostatic control **38** will increase the pressure and therefore the expansion of compartments until eventually insulating member **20** will appear as shown in Figure 1.33c, where visible radiation is entirely blocked from entering the interior and thermal radiation from the interior is prevented from leaving so that the temperature in the interior remains stable. Alternative insulating systems are also included in the patent.


## CONDUIT DISPOSITION

### Conduits Positioned by Curvilinear Channels

*R.G. Gallagher; U.S. Patent 3,972,317; August 3, 1976; assigned to Energy Systems, Inc.* describes a solar heater for heating a fluid passing through a plurality of side by side positioned solar panels. The solar panels are formed of heat conducting material with an upper solar energy exposed surface covered with a radiant heat absorbing material with high heat absorbing characteristics. A V-shaped hinge groove is positioned along the upper longitudinal center line of the panel. The panel portions on each side of the hinge groove slope downward toward their outer edges.

Curvilinear channels are formed below the outer edges. The curvilinear channels are received by bottom surface supported conduits that have common headers at respective ends extending beyond the solar panels. One header delivers ambient fluid to the conduits and the other removes heated fluid. The panels, conduit and headers are confined within a sealed insulated housing having integral, rigid side walls and bottom and at least one transparent panel spaced above the solar panels and sealed to the atmosphere. Fasteners partially passing through the hinge groove and secured to the support members hinge downward at the groove biasing the curvilinear channels against the conduits.

Referring now to Figures 1.34a, 1.34b and 1.34c, each panel is confined between two conduits **14** at its outer curvilinear conforming edge **16**. The conduits are shown supported by support member **18**, four being used for a typical 4 x 8 foot assembly. Headers such as **20** for delivering ambient fluid to be heated and carrying away the heated liquid from the heater respectively are soldered, brazed or otherwise suitably connected to common ends of the conduit **14** to form a leakproof construction and thereby increase the efficiency of the heater. A bracket **24**, one end shown, confines the two outermost conduits in a fixed spaced relationship.

The basic solar heater **10** is confined within a container for the purpose of confining the heat collected from the sun and preventing cooling by the surrounding atmosphere. The side walls **28** and the integral bottom portion **30** are generally constructed from a single piece of sheet metal, tin or aluminum, but may be constructed of separate pieces of similar material or wood to successfully practice the process.

Support members **18** rest upon the bottom **30** of the container and are connected to the side walls **28** by any convenient means. Nails **32** passing through the side walls and securing into support member **18** are shown as typical. Any other similar means as well as glue may be used to satisfactorily practice the process.

A plurality of panels **12** are positioned in a side by side noncontacting relationship to make up a solar fluid heater of the process. These panels are spring biased between two adjacent conduits **14** with the curvilinear portion **16** pressed into physical contact with the conduit. The panels are bowed upward along the V hinge **42**, placed between the conduits and released allowing the elasticity of the panel material to return to its prebowed configuration wherein force is applied at the conduit contact areas. The panels can be formed of aluminum or like material having such characteristics. When additional pressure between the panel edges and conduit is required, an aperture **44** is provided selectively along the V hinge.

A securing means such as a screw **43** with its body portion passing through aperture **44** and secured into the support member **18** pulls the panel downward at its center transmitting force to the edges **16**. The V hinge permits the panel portions on each side of the hinge to move downward at their hinge connection without bowing their rectilinear surfaces. The securing means **43** additionally functions to hold the conduits positioned between the end conduits downward against bracket **24** and support member **18**.

The space between the support members between the lower surface of the panels and the bottom of the container is filled with a good insulation material **34** which may be glass wool, fiberglass, foam plastic, sawdust or the like.

Additional insulation material **36** is positioned between the outer confined conduits and the adjacent side walls **28**. Standard duct liner insulations enclosed in a smooth container are preferred but any suitable insulation material easily held in position may be used. As shown in Figure 1.34c, insulation **36** is biased toward the wall **28** at its lower portion by bracket **24** and at its upper portion by a metal clip **38** held in place by sealing tape **40** hereinafter described.

FIGURE 1.34:  CONDUITS POSITIONED BY CURVILINEAR CHANNELS

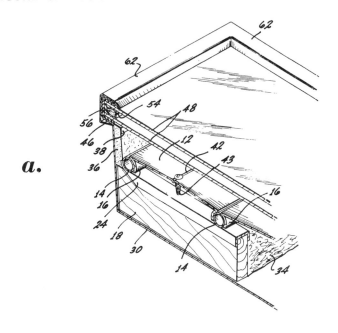

*a.*

(continued)

FIGURE 1.34: (continued)

**b.**

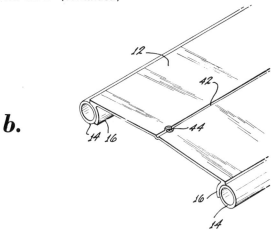

**c.**

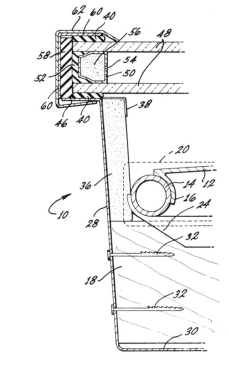

(a) Partial perspective detailed view of solar liquid heater
(b) Partial perspective view of a single panel
(c) Partial end view of solar liquid heater

Source: U.S. Patent 3,972,317

The side walls **28** include a lip **46** extending outwardly around the periphery of the container for supporting at least one transparent panel **40**. Two panels are shown in the various figures as most generally two would be utilized. A single panel application may be used in areas having extremely high temperatures. When one panel is used, the bottom panel **48** nearest the upper surface of the panels **12** would be removed and a spacer **40** of increased height would be used between the lip **46** and the spacing member **50**.

When both panels **48** are used, as shown, the spacer **50** is confined between the panels and a spacing member **52**. The spacer **50** has an opening **54** in its inner wall and is filled with a moisture absorbent material **56**. Any moisture trapped between the panels during assembly is absorbed thereby.

A second spacer **40** is positioned on the upper surface of the upper panel **48**. The spacers **40** continue along the entire periphery of the panels. The spacers are made from soft nonhardening material such as sealing tape well-known in the construction art. This tape is generally made from plastic and provides an airtight seal with the panels **48**. Spacers **52** are formed from thermosetting material and spacers **58** formed from neoprene or any like nonoutgassing material.

A metal angle bracket **60**, generally made from sheet metal or the like, forms a continuation of lip **46** and holds the various adjacent spacers in place. The angle bracket **60**, like the spacers and the outer channel **62**, hereinafter described, are continuous around the panels **48**.

The outer channel **62** is formed from stainless steel or like material having similar characteristics. The channel is formed having a space between its open ends smaller than the space between the lip **46** and the angle bracket **60**. This feature provides a positive bias between the lip and the angle bracket when installed thereby sealing the various components together within the inner portion of the solar fluid heater from the atmosphere.

In the preferred embodiment, the upper or solar energy exposed surface of the panel is coated with a radiant energy absorbent coating black in color and is either brushed, spray painted or electroplated on the panel surface.

**Tight-Fitting Circular Channel for Conduit**

The solar panels of *R.G. Gallagher; U.S. Patent 4,011,856; March 15, 1977; assigned to Energy Systems, Inc.* are formed of heat conducting material with an upper solar energy exposed surface covered with a radiant heat absorbing material having high heat absorbing characteristics. A conduit formed of heat conducting material is held in place by an open circular channel of a diameter less than the conduit and positioned below the longitudinal center line of the solar panel. The solar panel portions on each side of the center line slope downward away from the center. The respective ends of the conduits are connected to a separate common header. One header delivers ambient fluid to the conduits and the other removes heated fluid.

An insulated housing for containing the solar panel comprises a bottom, side panels, panel supports supported by the bottom panel, insulating material positioned between the bottom panel and the lower surface of the solar panels and at least one transparent panel spaced above the solar panels and sealed to the atmosphere. The solar panels are secured in a fixed side by side physical contacting relationship. The circular channel firmly secures the conduit therein at ambient temperature. When the heater is exposed to solar energy, the heat expands the solar panels and conduit thereby providing an increased pressure between the adjacent panels as well as between the channel and the conduit. Apertures are provided at selected positions along the solar panels near the longitudinal center. Fasteners partially passing through the panel apertures and secured to the panel supports may be provided to increase the physical pressures between the solar panels and the channel and conduit at ambient temperature.

Referring to Figures 1.35a, 1.35b and 1.35c, the solar liquid heater is shown in detail. The basic solar liquid heater 10 is confined within a container 24 for the purpose of confining the heat collected from the sun and prevent cooling by the surrounding atmosphere. The side walls 26 are generally constructed from extruded aluminum and are provided with various interior protrusions hereinafter described. It should be obvious that metal material, other than aluminum, can be utilized in the same manner as well as channeled wood.

A base panel 28 is contained by side wall protrusion 30, 32 and is positioned at the lower portion of side wall 26. The base panel 28 is typically constructed of masonite, plywood or similar stiff, flat material.

Supports 16 rest upon or are connected to the base panel 28 as shown and snugly nest between side wall protrusions 32 and 34. Notches 36 are formed along the supports 16 so as to allow the open circular channels 38 of panels 12 to fit freely therein.

The void provided between the base panel 28 and the lower surface 40 of the panels 12 is filled with a good insulating material 42 which may be fiberglass, foam plastic, sawdust or the like.

The panels 12 are positioned along supports 16 in a manner shown by the various figures. Each panel has a firm, physical contact with each adjacent panel and is secured in that position by fastener means 22, such as screws as shown in Figures 1.35b and 1.35c. The fasteners pass partially through semicircular apertures 44 cut into the outer edge of the panels. The abutting apertures form a circular opening between adjacent panels of a sufficient diameter to allow the fastener to pass through while the panels continue to maintain a firm physical contact between their edges. The semicircular openings in the two outermost panels by necessity must ride against their associated fastener means 22 to prevent movement of the endmost panels. The endmost panels 12 are positioned so as to have a space 46 between the panel edge and protrusion 34 of the side wall 26 so as to prevent an undesirable transfer of heat from the panels to the side walls.

Two transparent panels 48 and 50 are utilized in the preferred embodiment. Panel 48 is positioned above and spaced from the uppermost surface of the panels 12 so as to provide a dead air space therebetween. The space between panels 48 and the uppermost portion of the upper surface of the panels 12 should be at least a half of an inch long. The panel 48 is confined between side wall protrusions 52 and 54. Positioned above and spaced from panel 48 by at least 3⁄8 inch is a similar panel 50.

## FIGURE 1.35: TIGHT-FITTING CIRCULAR CHANNEL FOR CONDUIT

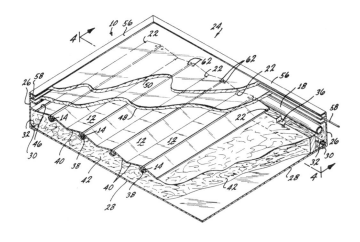

*a.*

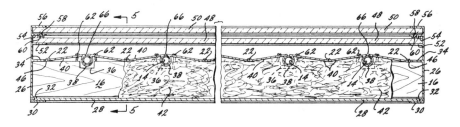

*b.*

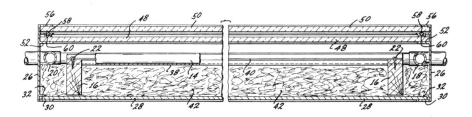

*c.*

(a)  Partial perspective of solar heater
(b)  Partial longitudinal cross-sectional view
(c)  Partial end view

Source:   U.S. Patent 4,011,856

The panel 50 is confined between side wall protrusions 54 and 56. In some applications, panel 48 may be omitted. Panel 50 also forms the top of container 26 and, therefore, to contain the heated air between the enclosed panels 12 and panel 50 a seal 58 is provided between side wall protrusion 54 and the lower portion of panel 50. The seal 58 is preferably formed from resilient material having a circular cross-sectional configuration. The seal 58 nests in a slot 60 provided in protrusion 54. The panel 50 deforms the resilient seal 58 between the slot 60 and its lower surface when the panel is installed, thereby forming a pressure seal therebetween. A seal 60 of any configuration suitable to form a pressure seal as described may be used to practice the process.

In the preferred embodiment the panel is formed from aluminum. The upper or solar energy exposed surface of the panel is coated with a radiant energy absorbent coating having a high efficiency. The preferred coating is black in color and is either electrostatically coated, electroplated or anodized on the panel surface. The undersurfaces of the panels, those away from radiant energy exposure, are generaly untreated except for a preservative which may be needed to prevent deterioration over an extended time span.

Positioned along the longitudinal center line of the panel 12 is a fluid carrying conduit 14. The conduit is positioned and held firmly within the open circular channel 38 of the panel 12. The channel diameter is slightly less than the conduit diameter to ensure a good mechanical connection between the channel walls and the outer surface of the conduit to ensure maximum heat transfer therebetween. The panels are mounted in edge contacting relationship, as hereinbefore described, to ensure sufficient pressure at the contacting surfaces of the panels. An additional edge pressure applying means 62 is shown as a screw with an enlarged head surface passing partially through aperture 64 (restricted by the enlarged head) and into a support 16. As the edge pressure applying means is forced downward into the support, the panel is likewise forced downward, thereby applying additional force at the edge of the panel. A plurality of means 62 on each side of the panel center may be required depending on the amount of additional force desired.

As can be seen by the various figures, the channel 38 forms an incomplete circular cross-sectional configuration at opening 66. This opening allows the panel to be sprung downward, thereby expanding the channel 38 to receive the enlarged diameter conduit 14 therein. When the expanding force is removed, the natural spring or elasticity of the panel material returns the channel to its normal diameter thereby causing the channel to grip the conduit. The opening also provides the required independent movement of the portion of the panel effected by the edge pressure applying means.

The panels are secured together and edge pressure applied, as hereinbefore described, at an ambient temperature (any convenient temperature below the panel operating temperature) so that when the panels are exposed to radiant energy and their temperatures rise, the edge pressure as well as the conduit holding pressure will rise to ensure maximum heat transfer between the panels, the conduit and the fluid within the conduit.

The cross-sectional panel configuration, as shown by the various figures, is downward sloping from the center opening 66 to the outer edges at an angle of between 5° and 15°. An optimum angle is approximately 8°. This sloping feature provides a more direct surface area exposure to perpendicular radiant energy as the sun moves during the day. The angled surface of the panel collects radiant energy in the same manner that the facets of a gem reflect light energy striking from different angles. In addition, the angled surfaces effectively provide more surface area to the panel for a given width.

## Inverted V-Shaped Grooves

An inclined heat absorptive and conductive panel including downwardly opening inverted V-shaped grooves formed therein extending downwardly from the upper end portion of the panel toward the lower end portion of the panel is provided by *C.D. Folds and D.A. Gilbert; U.S. Patent 3,995,804; December 7, 1976.* In addition, a structure is provided for introducing a heat absorptive liquid into the upper end portions of the grooves and a second structure is provided for receiving and collecting liquid from the lower ends of the grooves.

The cross-sectional shape and size of the grooves is such to allow at least substantially all of the liquid introduced into the upper ends thereof to be retained therein by the cohesive and surface tension properties of the liquid during its movement downwardly through the grooves by gravity toward the lower end of the panel. The panel comprises an inclined partition secured across the interior of an upwardly opening housing and a substantially fluid tight cover secured across the top of the housing above the panel. Further, the structure by which liquid flowing downwardly to the lower end of the panel is collected includes an additional structure whereby a partial vacuum is maintained within the housing between the transparent cover and the heat absorptive panel.

Referring to Figure 1.36a, there is shown one section of a roof structure covered by means of conventional shingles 18 and a plurality of solar heat collector panels. Each of the collector assemblies 20 includes a shallow upwardly opening and inclined housing referred to by reference numeral 22 including a thick insulative bottom 24 and upstanding insulative peripheral side walls 26. At least the interior of the housing may include a waterproof coating or layer 28 and an inclined heat absorptive panel 30 is secured across the interior of the housing 22 a spaced distance above the bottom 24, the panel including peripheral edge portions 32 overlying and sealed relative to the upper marginal edges of the side walls 26.

Further, a peripheral spacing frame 34 is sealingly secured over the peripheral edge portions of the panel and supports a transparent sheet 36 therefrom for closing the upper portion of the housing 22, a peripheral retaining frame 38 being secured over the frame 34 with spaced opposing surfaces of the frames 34 and 38 clampingly engaging the peripheral edges of the sheet 36, which edges may include peripheral seal means 40.

The interior of each assembly 20 is thereby divided into a lower compartment 42 and an upper compartment 44 disposed below and above, respectively, the panel 30. The compartments are sealed relative to each other and the exterior of the housing.

The panel defines a plurality of downwardly opening grooves 46 extending from the upper end thereof to the lower end thereof. The grooves are defined by V-shaped ridges formed in the panel, although the grooves could be cut into the lower surface portions of a thicker panel. In addition, the grooves may be of different cross-sectional shape than their inverted V-shaped cross-sectional shape. Still further, the grooves generally parallel each other and are longitudinally straight, extending in directions paralleling the longitudinal center line of the panel **30**. However, the grooves need not necessarily be either parallel or longitudinally straight; although straight longitudinal grooves are the least expensive to manufacture.

### FIGURE 1.36: INVERTED V-SHAPED GROOVES

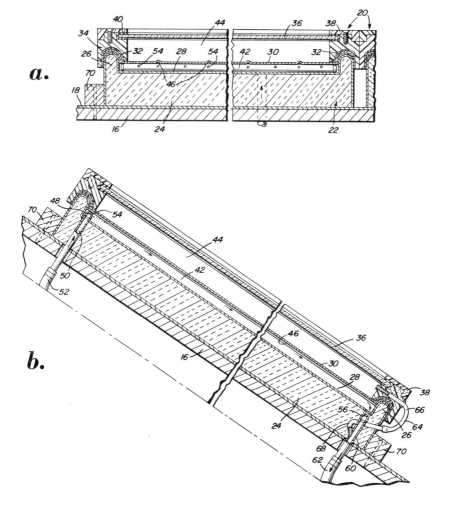

(a) Vertical cross section of collector
(b) Vertical cross section taken on a line perpendicular to Figure 1.36a

Source: U.S. Patent 3,995,804

A header pipe **48** is disposed transversely in the upper portion of the lower chamber or compartment **42** and receives liquid under pressure through a delivery pipe **50** extending upwardly through the bottom **24** (see Figure 1.36b) from a liquid supply line **52**. The header pipe includes a plurality of longitudinally spaced generally horizontally outwardly opening outlets **54** aligned with the upper ends of corresponding grooves **46** and the outlets thereby function to discharge liquid under pressure into the upper ends of the grooves.

A collection pipe **56** is embedded in the lower portion of the bottom wall **24** and drain outlets **58** communicate the interior of the lower portion of the chamber **42** with the interior of the collection pipe. A drain pipe **60** extends downwardly from a central portion of the collection pipe through the roof and to the inlet end of a return line **62**. Still further, a vacuum line **64** includes an inlet end portion **66** opening into the lower portion of the interior of the compartment **44** and an outlet end portion **68** which opens in a downward direction into the drain pipe and is thereby subject to reduced pressure by venturi action of liquids flowing downwardly through the drain pipe. Accordingly, the vacuum line and the venturi action of the liquid flowing downwardly through the drain pipe on the outlet end **68** of the vacuum line function to maintain a partial vacuum within the compartment or chamber **44**.

A seal molding **70** extends around the grouped solar heat collector panel assemblies **20** on a roof section and is secured to the roof. The sheet **36** is of transparent material and therefore allows a large percentage of the available radiant energy from sunlight incident on the assemblies to pass downwardly through the sheet onto the upper surface of the panel **30**, which upper surface may be provided with a dark color heat absorptive coating if desired.

A heat absorptive liquid is pumped from a reservoir (not shown) therefor upwardly through the liquid supply line **52** and into the header pipe **48** for spray discharging into the upper ends of the grooves **46** after which the liquid flows downwardly through the grooves and is retained therein by the cohesive and surface tension properties of the fluid until the fluid reaches the lower ends of the grooves whereupon it strikes the inner surface of the lower side wall **26** of the housing **22** and flows downwardly along the inner surface of the lower side wall and into the collection pipe **56** for subsequent discharge downwardly through the drain pipe **60** creating a partial vacuum in the vacuum line **64** to partially evacuate the chamber **44** immediately beneath the sheet.

The inverted V-shaped cross-sectional configuration of the grooves is preferable in that the liquid flowing downwardly through the grooves enjoys contact with the undersurface portions of the panel over a reasonably large area thereof. Of course, the liquid flowing downwardly through the grooves is warmed by the panel which is heated by the radiant energy of the sunlight incident thereon. Further, the liquid flowing downwardly through the line **62** is returned to the aforementioned reservoir and suitable heat exchange mechanisms may be utilized to withdraw heat from the liquid within the reservoir for any desired purpose.

### Conduit Coiled About Black Body

The solar sensor-heater of *L.H. Sallen; U.S. Patent 3,985,117; October 12, 1976* comprises a fluid conduit coiled about a black body enclosed in an insulated container. One side of the container is transparent to allow solar radiation to impinge upon the fluid conduit and black body. A pump is located in the fluid conduit output. A temperature sensing device is located upon the fluid conduit and senses the temperature of the fluid in the conduit and thereby turns the pump on or off as required.

A solar sensor-heater means **10**, as shown in Figure 1.37, is self-contained within container means **12**, a box-like device comprising base means **30**, side means **33** and top means **36**. The base means and side means form the outer support and comprise an insulating material such as wood or like applicable insulating material. Top means **36** is connected to the container and is disposed in at least partially sealed relation to the remainder of the container. Accordingly, the top means serves to prevent air flow within the container means. In the preferred embodiment, top means **36** is formed from transparent glass, plastic or similar applicable material. The transparent top means is disposed for substantially maximum exposure to ambient solar radiation.

Through at least one side means pass a plurality of fluid connector means and at least one electrical connector means. As shown in Figure 1.37a, the fluid connector means comprises fluid input means **22** and fluid output means **24** wherein fluid flow is indicated by directional arrows **23** and **25** respectively. Electrical connector **26** is connected to pump **18** and also extends through the side means.

Base means generally indicated as **30** comprises a first insulation means **31** for isolation of the interior of the container from the outside environment. Overlayed upon the base is second insulating means **32**. This serves to further insulate the interior of the container from the exterior. First and second means may comprise wood, plastic or like at least semirigid insulating material. Superimposed upon the second insulation means is reflector means **34**. Typically, the reflector comprises a reflective foil; however, any reflective material would be suitable.

The fluid to be subjected to solar radiation is put into solar sensor-heater **10** through input means **22**. The fluid then flows through fluid conduit **16** comprising a series of coils **17** arranged in predetermined, preferably continuous fluid communicating relation to one another. These coils are formed from hollow tubing of any applicable configuration and are disposed such that solar radiation impinges upon maximum surface area of the fluid conduit. Fluid then passes from the coils to pump and then to the output conduit.

The maximum solar radiation is obtained by having **fluid conduit 16** coiled about black body means **14**. Black body means in the preferred embodiment comprises a sheet of aluminum; however, any applicable material which is capable of absorbing solar radiation and acting as a heat sink so as to conduct collected heat to fluid conduit means **16** may be used. Beneath the black body is reflective foil **34**. The surfaces of the fluid conduit and the black body which are exposed to solar radiation are coated with absorptive material by solar radiation absorptive means **38**, which comprises black paint.

An important structural feature of the apparatus includes bracket body means **14** defined, at least in part, by an undulating configuration. Fluid conduit **16** is thereby disposed in direct engagement with oppositely disposed surfaces of the black body sheet **14**. More specifically, adjacently positioned and spaced apart conduit portions are each disposed in direct engagement with opposite surfaces of black body sheet **14** as best shown in Figure 1.37c. In the embodiment shown therein the conduit portions are disposed in heat conductive engagement in troughs disposed on the opposite surfaces of the black body sheet.

FIGURE 1.37:  CONDUIT COILED ABOUT BLACK BODY

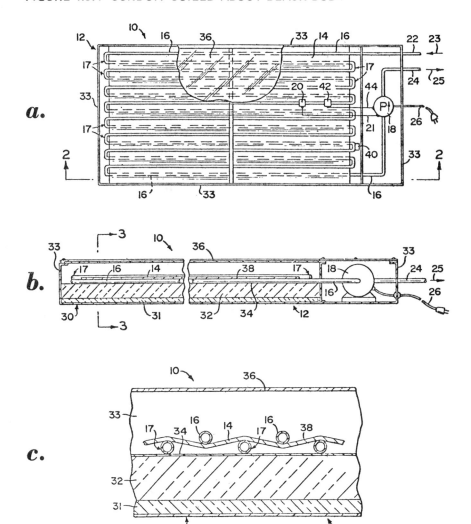

(a)  Top plan, partly cut away, of sensor-heater
(b)  Sectional view along line 2—2 of Figure 1.37a
(c)  Detailed sectional side view along line 3—3 of Figure 1.37b

Source:  U.S. Patent 3,985,117

The fluid to be subjected to solar radiation is circulated through the system by the pump connected in fluid communication to the output fluid conduit 24. A temperature sensing-signaling means 20 is electrically connected to the pump and comprises a temperature sensitive switch located on the fluid conduit. Specifically, the temperature sensing-signaling means is in electrical communication with the pump by electrical conductor 21. The temperature sensing-signaling means has at least two modes, an off mode and an on mode.

A boil protection means comprises an in-line fluid sensor set at a specific predetermined temperature to automatically activate a fluid release to the atmosphere upon sensing a predetermined temperature. Upon sensing that temperature of the fluid in the fluid conduit is below the preset level, boil protection means 40 closes the fluid release. In the preferred embodiment, the boil protection means comprises a spring loaded pressure sensitive valve located in the fluid conduit and operable upon sensing a predetermined high temperature of the fluid in the fluid conduit.

Freeze protection is accomplished by a second temperature sensing-signaling means 42 in electrical communication with pump means 18 by electrical conductor means 44. The temperature sensing-signaling means has two modes. When the temperature of the fluid conduit is above preset level, close to the freezing point of the fluid in the fluid conduit, the pump is deenergized. When the temperature falls below the predetermined level, the temperature sensing-signaling means causes the pump to activate, causing fluid to flow through the fluid conduit. This will protect the system against freezing during a night operation or whenever the sun is not shining in a subfreezing environment by a reverse operation of the system.

In operation, the system typically performs as follows. There is cool fluid within the fluid conduit means, thus setting temperature sensing means in its second state. The pump means is thus deenergized and the fluid is retained within the fluid conduit means. Solar radiation impinges upon fluid conduit means and black body means. The fluid conduit means and black body means absorb the impinging radiation and a temperature increase results. When the temperature of the fluid conduit means and the fluid contained therein reaches a predetermined level, temperature sensing means changes from off mode to on mode.

In the on mode state, temperature sensing means energizes pump means and fluid is forced to flow through conduit means. Fluid continues to flow through fluid conduit means so long as temperature sensing means remains in state 1, indicating that the fluid is being heated to a predetermined temperature. When the fluid is no longer heated to a predetermined temperature, temperature sensing means changes state from state 1 to state 2 and thereby deenergizes pump means. Fluid no longer flows through fluid conduit means and remains in the solar sensor-heater until such time as temperature sensing means indicates that a predetermined temperature of the fluid has been reached.

It can be seen that the solar sensor-heater is a self-contained unit which accepts fluid, allows the fluid to be heated by solar radiation to a predetermined temperature and then permits the fluid to pass onward for use.

## Liquid Supply Channel of Specific Hydraulic Radius

A method of heating a liquid and a solar heating panel therefor is described by *E.J. Gramer and M.O. Johnson; U.S. Patent 3,965,887; June 29, 1976.* The method comprises forming one or more obstruction free, longitudinally extending liquid passageways one side of each passageway being formed from a metallic material whereon the outer surface of the metallic material contains a solar radiation heat absorbing coating and each passageway has a width to depth ratio varying between approximately 6.5 and 15 and a mean hydraulic radius varying between approximately 0.018 and 0.027, exposing the solar radiation heat absorbing coating to solar radiation energy, and heating a liquid by passing the liquid through the passageway and simultaneously maintaining a substantially constant cross-sectional area flow path through the passageway.

Referring to Figures 1.38a, 1.38b, 1.38c and 1.38d, a solar heating panel **14** is shown comprising a base member **16**, a solar heat absorbing member **18** and an inverted cup-shaped member **20**.

The base member is preferably formed as a composite member. The base member is formed to provide a liquid impervious upper surface **24**. The base member may be formed by vacuum forming an outer skin from a plastic material, such as an acrylic, for the base member. It is believed that the outer skin may also be formed from a polycarbonate. The outer skin will be liquid impervious. The outer skin, as formed, will then be filled with an insulating material (such as a urea-formaldehyde); however, the composite base member will exhibit good insulative properties, thereby minimizing loss of heat therethrough.

A plurality of laterally spaced apart fluid supply recesses **26** (see Figures 1.38a and 1.38c) are formed in the liquid impervious upper surface and extend longitudinally of the base member. An inlet manifold **28** and an outlet manifold **30** are also formed in the liquid impervious upper surface **24** of the base member **16**. Each manifold extends transversely across one of the respective ends of the base member and, also, is disposed in fluid communication with each of the fluid supply recesses **26**. The base member also includes an inlet port **32** disposed in fluid communication with the inlet manifold and an outlet port **34** disposed in fluid communication with the outlet manifold.

The base member preferably includes a fluid return recess formed in the liquid impervious upper surface **24** of the base member along one side thereof, the right hand side as viewed in Figure 1.38c. The fluid return recess **36** is adapted to be placed in fluid communication with an outlet port **34** such as through the use of a hollow tubular member **38**. A plurality of spaced apart strips **40** are formed on the liquid impervious surface **24** of the base member **16**. The planar strips **40** are disposed intermediate each of the recesses **26** and **36** and adjacent to the outer side of the outwardly disposed recesses **26** and **36**.

The solar heat absorbing member **18** is formed from metal having good heat conducting characteristics such as aluminum. It has been found that the upper surface of the member should be maintained generally planar in order to obtain an efficient operation of the panel **14**. Thus, the member is rigidly formed to resist bowing thereof as a result of thermal expansion or contraction of the upper surface **24** relative to the thermal expansion or contraction of the member. The upper surface of the member contains a black, solar radiation absorbing coating **42** thereon. Preferably, the coating comprises a special layer of spectrally absorbent black paint. The solar heat absorbing member is securely bonded to the liquid impervious surface **24** of the base member **16** by an elastic adhesive means **22**. As bonded, the solar heat absorbing member cooperates with the recesses **26** and **36** formed in the liquid impervious upper surface **24** to form a plurality of liquid supply channels **44** and a liquid return channel **46** (see Figure 1.38b). This construction isolates each of the channels **44** and **46** one from the other.

FIGURE 1.38:  LIQUID SUPPLY CHANNEL OF SPECIFIC HYDRAULIC
RADIUS

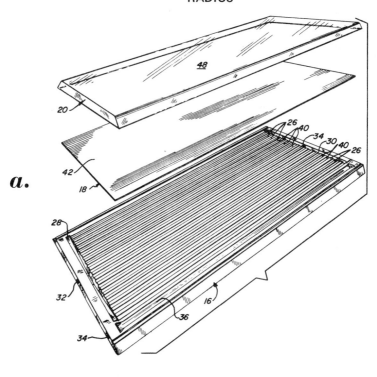

*a.*

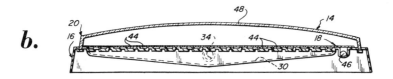

*b.*

(continued)

FIGURE 1.38: (continued)

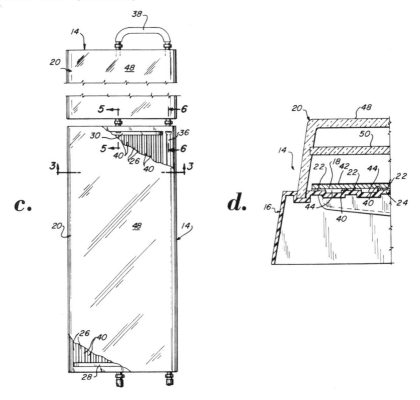

**c.**    **d.**

(a) Exploded view of solar heating panel
(b) Cross-sectional view taken along line 3—3 of Figure 1.38c
(c) Plan view, partially broken away, of two interconnected panels
(d) Enlarged, fragmentary, cross-sectional view taken transversely of the panel

Source: U.S. Patent 3,965,887

The inverted cup-shaped member **20** is formed from a transparent material such as glass or plastic. The material selected must be resistant to weathering, ultraviolet radiation, breakage, cracking and pitting which might otherwise result from hail or wind storms. The upper surface **48** is of a slight dome configuration, i.e., it is the segment of a generally spherically-shaped surface having a chord to radius ratio of not more than about 0.19. It has been found that the upper surface **48** of member **20** has, when viewed in cross section, a generally convex surface having a radius of curvature of approximately 3.65 meters (135 inches).

Such a configuration provides good strength characteristics for member **20** to resist forces due to thermal expansion and contraction and, also, to enable automatic drainage of moisture from the upper surface thereof. The upper surface **48** is disposed in spaced apart relation to the coating **42** of the member **18**. It has been found that good results are obtained from a panel **14** of this process where the upper surface **48** of member **20** is maintained approximately 4.4 cm (1¾ inches) above the coating **42** formed on member **18**.

In order to obtain solar radiation impingement across the entire surface of the coating **42** of member **18** for the longest period of time possible, the upper surface of the member must be maintained generally planar. More specifically, if the upper surface of the member bows in either direction, there will be reduction in the amount of time that solar radiation waves may impinge thereon. It has been found that the upper surface of the member **18** may be maintained generally planar by using an elastic adhesive means having flat bonding characteristics over the environmental temperature range to be encountered during use of the panel **14**. The use of silicone adhesive such as G.E. silicone RTV-630 has been found to be suitable for this application.

An important feature of this process is to utilize liquid supply channels which enable the transfer of heat energy from the member **18** to the individual molecules of liquid in order to raise the temperature of the liquid to a desired level while same is flowing through the channels. It has been unexpectedly found that same may be accomplished through the use of fluid supply channels or passageways which are generally rectangular in cross section and have a width to depth ratio varying between approximately 6 and 15 and a mean hydraulic radius varying between about 0.018 and 0.027. The mean hydraulic radius is defined as the cross-sectional area of the fluid supply channel or passageway divided by the wetted perimeter thereof.

Preferably, the width to depth ratio of each liquid supply channel or passageway should vary between approximately 9 and 13.5 and excellent results have been obtained where the width to depth ratio equals approximately 10. Preferably, the mean hydraulic radius of each liquid supply channel should vary between approximately 0.018 and 0.023 and excellent results have been obtained where the mean hydraulic radius is equal to approximately 0.023.

The fluid return recess **36** is preferably formed in the liquid impervious upper surface **24**. Formation of the fluid return recess **36** in the liquid impervious upper surface has been found to be additionally beneficial in improving the overall efficiency of the solar heating panel since the liquid does not lose any heat in flowing therethrough; rather, a slight increase in heat of the liquid normally occurs.

Illustrative dimensions of a solar heating panel constructed in accordance with this process are as follows:

> Width of panel—22 inches (56 cm)
> Length of panel—4 feet (122 cm)
> Number of liquid supply channels—19
> Width of each liquid supply channel—0.5 inch (1.3 cm)
> Depth of each liquid supply channel—0.05 inch (0.127 cm)
> Width to depth ratio of each liquid supply channel—10
> Mean hydraulic radius of each liquid supply channel—0.023
> Flow through 19 liquid supply channels—1 gallon per minute
>   (3.8 liters per minute)

Reynolds number—1708
Solar heat absorbing member—aluminum alloy 47 inches x 22⅝
  inches x 0.032 inch (119.4 cm x 57.5 cm x 0.081 cm)

## Tubing Fastened to Panel with U-Brads

*W.B. Edmondson; U.S. Patent 3,952,725; April 27, 1976* describes a solar water
heater and method of constructing same, the heater being of the type in which
the sun penetrates one or more panes of light-transmitting material and impinges
on a blackened layer of soft-tempered conductive foil on which are disposed conductive water-conveying tubes. Loosely packed glass wool between the pane
and the foil inhibits convection currents and resilient, dense glass wool on the
lower side of the foil, backed by a rigid panel, supports the foil.

Conventional fasteners such as U-brads are used at spaced intervals on the tubing to fasten the tubing to the panel drawing the tubing against the foil and
creating an elongated depression or trough in the foil beneath the tubing. Conductive cement or paint is applied in the trough prior to or after the fasteners
are secured to maximize heat transfer from the foil to the tubing.

Figure 1.39a illustrates the general construction of the heater which is relatively
simple. Rigidity is provided primarily by a backing panel 12 which may be plywood, metal or other suitably rigid material including the planking of an unfin-
ished roof. Overlying the panel is a layer of insulation material 14 which is at
least slightly deformable and preferably resilient, fiberglass wool being very suitable.

A sheet of soft tempered aluminum foil or other deformable heat-conductive
material 16 is disposed flush with the upper surface of the insulation 14 and
overlying this sheet is an arrangement of tubing, generally indicated at 18. The
tubing can be constructed of aluminum, copper or any other heat conductive
material and in all configurations portions of the tubing are mutually parallel
with the spacing between the parallel lengths being between 3 and 6 inches for
optimum performance. It is contemplated that the foil thickness will be between
0.002 and 0.005 inch, and the tube spacing selected will be proportional to the
foil thickness since increased foil conductivity permits greater separation of the
tube portions.

The attachment of the tubing, foil, insulation and panel is very simply and
quickly done by hand. A plurality of spaced fasteners 20 engage the tubing
and are secured through the foil and insulation layer into the backing panel.
Any suitable fasteners can be used, but the U-brads of Figure 1.39a are preferred.

The installation of the fasteners draws the tubing down against the foil, and the
resilient insulation layer 14 molds troughs 22 into the foil beneath the tubing
which increases the thermal contact between the foil and tubing. To further
increase conductivity, a conductive sealant is applied in the troughs which occupies the airspace around the tubing. Two types of sealant have been found
effective, the first being conductive adhesive or cement, one example being a
graphite-filled cement, Thermon. The cement is thick-textured and must be applied either prior to mounting of the tubing, or the tubing and foil must be separated lightly by depressing the foil by hand beneath the tubing. The cement
layers are illustrated at 24.

FIGURE 1.39:  TUBING FASTENED TO PANEL WITH U-BRADS

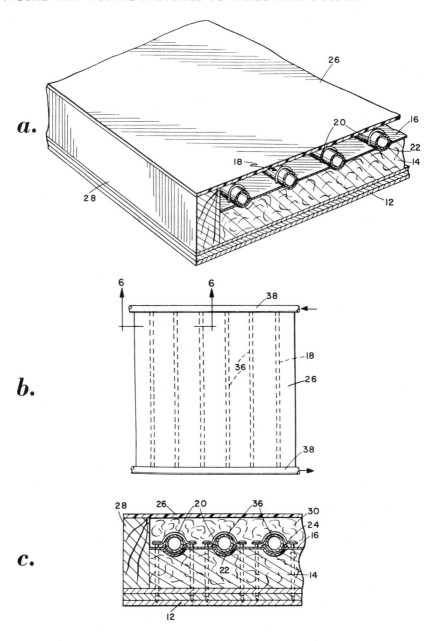

(a)  Perspective view, in section, of portion of panel
(b)  Top plan view
(c)  Enlarged sectional view taken on line 6—6 of Figure 1.39b

Source:  U.S. Patent 3,952,725

The other type of sealant is black paint with dispersed particulate graphite, which has a much thinner consistency than Thermon and can be applied over the entire surface of the foil and tubing after the tubing is installed. The paint will seep into the troughs around the tubing to provide an effective thermal bond. It is preferred to use the graphite paint even if the cement sealant is also used inasmuch as it accomplishes the desired blackening of the upper surface of the foil and tubing and additionally increases conductivity. Either or both of the sealants provide an increased thermal conductivity between the tubing and foil which is comparable in effectiveness to welding or soldering but is simpler and cheaper to use.

Disposed above and parallel to the foil sheet is a pane of light-transmitting material 26. This pane is preferably a two or four mil panel of Tedlar. The Tedlar may be reinforced with wire mesh or supported on a transparent fiberglass panel, and in the latter case possibly being corrugated for additional strength and to allow for expansion when heated without buckling or warping.

In the modular version of the heater, each unit has a peripheral border 28 of wood, high density glass wool or the like which provides a mounting for the pane 26 and seals the unit from outside air currents. The border may simply be adhered to the pane and the panel with a silicone adhesive, and the necessary holes are provided for the inlet and outlet of the tubing.

In order to minimize convection currents in the heater, a very open fibered or loose-knit layer 30 of glass wool may be provided between the foil and the light-transmitting pane. A suitable material for this purpose is a fiberglass air filter medium produced by Owens-Corning, a 1-inch layer of which will transmit 85% of the incident light. Especially when the panels are used in a nonhorizontal position conducive to the circulation of connection currents the baffling effect of the wool more than compensates for the slight shadowing it produces on the foil. If additional support is required for the Tedlar pane, the loose fiberglass can be sprayed with a stiffening adhesive to which the Tedlar adheres for reinforcement.

**Wound Absorber Using Black Liquid**

A solar radiant energy collector described by *J.E. Minardi; U.S. Patent 3,939,819; February 24, 1976; assigned to The University of Dayton* comprises a source of liquid having a medium dispersed therein with a high absorptance to solar energy, a transparent tube of an extended length wound in a configuration to provide a flat-like planar surface for maximum exposure to solar radiant energy, a reflector surface positioned on the opposite side of the planar surface to that exposed to the solar radiant energy; a liquid inlet and outlet joined with the transparent tube; and liquid pressure means to cause the liquid to flow from the inlet through the tube and to the outlet.

With reference to Figures 1.40a, 1.40b and 1.40c there is illustrated the basic structure of the process. An elongated tubing 14 of transparent material is wound in a manner for greatest solar exposure, but covering a minimum overall flat sheet area. The tubing is wound in a circular path, a curved path or a rectangular path or it may be wound in a back and forth path. It is appreciated that with each configuration there is a liquid input means 10 and liquid output means 12, such as couplings.

## FIGURE 1.40: WOUND ABSORBER USING BLACK LIQUID

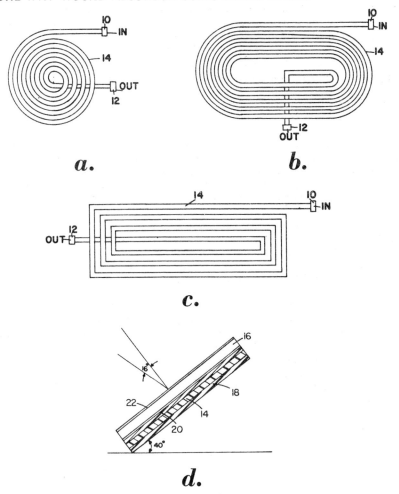

(a)(b)(c)  Tubing configurations
(d)  Collector

Source:  U.S. Patent 3,939,819

The tubing **14** is plastic since there are plastic tubings commercially available that can be physically wound. The essential criterion is that the tubing be clean—that is, a minimum amount of radiant energy absorption by the tubing per se.

Equally significant to the transparent tubing is that the liquid passing therethrough be black. The liquid utilized is the energy collector; accordingly, black is intended to include colloidal suspensions, selective or nonselective black materials such as carbon black, a mixture of colloids, selective or nonselective pure liquid compounds of one or a mixture of components, or liquids with dyes or solutes.

The need for a metal absorbing surface along with its coating material is thus eliminated and the solar radiation is directly absorbed in the liquid heat transfer medium. In this way the heat losses are reduced since the liquid heat transfer medium is the hottest material in the collector.

In that the radiant energy collector is the liquid passing through the tubing, it can be appreciated that the liquid at the outlet 12 has the maximum exposure time. In this way there is a gradual elevation of temperature as fluid moves from the input 10 through the tubing with the maximum temperature at the outlet 12. This is in contrast to the metal collectors which operate with a more nearly uniform high temperature over their entire surface. The lower surface temperatures reduce the radiant heat losses from the black liquid collector. In addition, edge losses from the collectors would be lower as the entire outside edges of the configurations in Figures 1.40a and 1.40b would be at the lower temperatures while at least one edge of collector in Figure 1.40c would be at the lower temperature.

With reference to Figure 1.40d there is illustrated a constructed embodiment having an overall liquid collector configuration similar to the schematic of Figure 1.40a. This embodiment comprised the clear plastic tubing of approximately 25 turns.

In this embodiment the tubing had an overall planar arrangement. In this way the tubing was wound but yet retained maximum exposure to solar radiant energy. The tubing 14 was enclosed in a box-like housing 16. The housing in turn provided heat insulation to prevent losses but yet permitted radiation to pass to the tubing 14. The box-like housing had as its base a layer of foam insulation 18, the tubing positioned directly thereon. Placed immediately above the tubing is a sheet of clear Plexiglas 20, thereafter an air space and another sheet of clear Plexiglas 22.

In a first test of this embodiment the black liquid comprised mixing 91 grams of Acheson's Aquadag paste (a dispersion of high purity colloidal graphite in water) with 1 liter distilled water. The fineness, purity and excellent suspension properties of the graphite particles enabled the diluted product to be employed in an extensive range of applications for which large particle size dispersions and graphite powders are unsuitable.

The overall structure was oriented $40°$ above the horizontal facing magnetic South. The highest liquid temperature achieved in the collector (no flow) during the first test was $185°F$ at an ambient temperature of $78°F$. The estimated direct solar radiation intensity was at solar noon calculated to be 283 Btu/hr/ft$^2$.

A second test conducted included modifications on the housing structure to provide more efficient insulation and heat retention to reduce heat losses. The highest liquid temperature achieved in the collector (no flow) was $210°F$ (the boiling point of this black liquid) at an ambient temperature of $36°F$.

## THIN FILM SYSTEMS

### Collector Contacted by Liquid Film

The collector of *Y.-N. Yu; U.S. Patent 3,943,911; March 16, 1976* comprises a
solar heat exchanger having a base and an extended surface thereon for facing
frontwardly toward the sun; means communicating with that surface to conduct
liquid to flow adjacent that surface, as by gravity flow; and a sheet overlying
that surface and spaced therefrom to cooperate with the surface for filming the
flowing liquid, the sheet adapted to receive solar radiation for promoting heat
transfer to the flowing liquid.

In Figures 1.41a and 1.41b the base **10** of the collector **11** typically consists of
molded plastic material, e.g., polyurethane or ABS, which is lightweight and relatively inexpensive.  The base, of rectangular outline, has opposite sides **12** and
**13**, top **14**, bottom **15** and back and front surfaces **16** and **17**.  If desired, a
lightweight metallic frame **18** may be provided to extend about the base.  Further, the base may itself consist of lightweight metallic material, particularly at
surface **17**.

FIGURE 1.41:  COLLECTOR CONTACTED BY LIQUID FILM

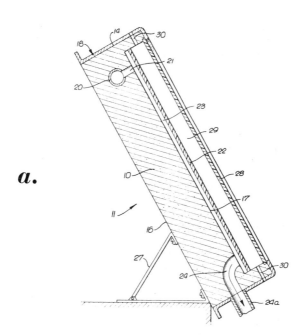

*a.*

(continued)

FIGURE 1.41: (continued)

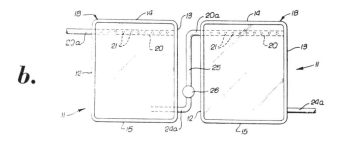

*b.*

(a)    Side elevation
(b)    Frontal view of pair of collectors in series

Source:   U.S. Patent 3,943,911

The means to conduct fluid to flow adjacent surface **17**, which is recessed into the base, may comprise a duct **20** extending horizontally laterally in the base beneath the level of surface **17**, and small openings **21** communicating between duct **20** and the upper extent of surface **17**.  Duct **20** may consist of plastic pipe molded into the base, such pipe projecting at **20a** in Figure 1.41b.

The sheet **22** in Figure 1.41a consists of thin plastic material, e.g., Mylar, which is transparent, or at least translucent, to transmit sunlight to impinge on surface **17**. The latter is dark to absorb solar radiation and may be covered with black paint for example.  As a result, the absorbed radiation is converted to heat which is transferred by conduction to the water or liquid filming at **23** over and draining downwardly along the surface in the small gap between surface **17** and sheet **22**. The sheet may be peripherally retained to the base in any suitable manner.

The surface **17** is typically tilted downwardly at an angle sufficient to promote downward drainage of the filming liquid **23** for reception and outward drainage as via a duct **24** in the base.  Figure 1.41b shows a modified duct **24a** extending laterally from the lower interior of the base.  That duct may be connected with the inlet **20a** of an adjacent and like collector **11** so that the liquid may be heated further.  If desired, a pump may be utilized in the connecting pipe stretch **25**, as indicated at **26**.  Figure 1.41a shows a support **27** extending from the rear side of the base to the ground level to retain the base in angled position with surface **17** directed toward impinging sunlight.

A further feature shown in Figure 1.41a comprises a translucent or transparent panel **28** outwardly spaced from sheet **22** and extending generally parallel thereto. The panel, e.g., consisting of plastic or glass, protects and confines space **29** containing air trapped between the sheet and panel, producing a so-called greenhouse effect.  The latter is characterized by entrapment of heat in space **29** enhancing the heat collection and transfer efficiency of the device.  Vents **30** in the base may release excess heat in space **29** so as to avoid melting of the plastic materials of which the collector unit is made.

If desired, the sheet **22** may itself be darkened so as to absorb solar radiation and transmit heat to the liquid filming and draining at **23**. It should be observed that sheet **22** is flexible and tends to drape against surface **17** in the absence of liquid flow as described. Alternatively, the sheet **22** may be darkened and consist of metallic material closely spaced to surface **17**, e.g., aluminum painted a dark color on both sides.

### Liquid Flow Based on Bernoulli's Theorem

*W.B. Harris, Jr., W.B. Harris, Sr. and R.R. Davison; U.S. Patent 3,620,206; November 16, 1971; assigned to U.S. Secretary of the Interior* describe a system in which radiant energy is used to heat a liquid by passing the liquid between two level, flat, heat exchange surfaces, the top surface resting freely on the lower surface and being exposed to the radiant energy. Liquid flows between the surfaces and is maintained in a thin, continuous and substantially uniform film by operation of Bernoulli's Theorem.

Referring to Figure 1.42a, the heat exchange device **1** comprises a relatively rigid and flat basal member **2** disposed in a substantially horizontal attitude. Resting on the basal member and conforming generally to the size and shape of that member is cover plate **3**. Liquid from supply or storage means **4** passes through conduit **5** to pump **6**. From the pump, the liquid is passed, via conduit **7**, to a central area between basal member **2** and cover plate **3**. Liquid then flows outwardly toward the periphery of the basal member and cover plate in a thin channel **8** formed between the two. Liquid is recovered in collecting means **9** and is returned to storage means **4** by means of conduit **10**.

By operation of Bernoulli's Theorem, liquid flowing through channel **8** is maintained as a compressed, thin and evenly distributed film. As required by that theorem, if liquid flow tended to channel in one direction, the increased rate of flow would reduce the pressure in the channelling area. Reduction in pressure would in turn cause the cover plate to press more tightly on the basal member in that area thus diverting excess flow to areas of lower flow rate. While Figure 1.42a shows liquid being introduced through a central portion of the basal member, this is not necessary to proper functioning of the device. It is also possible to introduce liquid at an edge, but this is a less effective and less preferred arrangement.

### FIGURE 1.42: LIQUID FLOW BASED ON BERNOULLI'S THEOREM

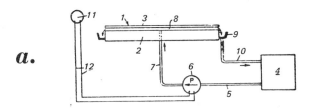

*a.*

(continued)

FIGURE 1.42: (continued)

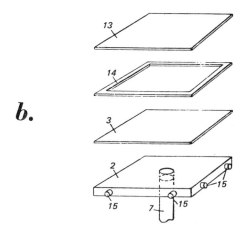

*b.*

(a) Diagrammatic view of heat extracting system
(b) Oblique, exploded view of single heat exchange module

Source:  U.S. Patent 3,620,206

In operation, cover plate **3** is exposed to an external heat flux such as solar radiation.  Liquid, such as water, is passed through the heat exchange device as previously described.  The heated liquid may be used for any conventional and appropriate purpose, may be in turn heat-exchanged with another liquid or gas, or may be used as storage means for heat energy.

When the source of external heat flux is variable, such as is solar radiation, radiation-sensitive control device **11** may be connected by means of control wires **12** to control the operation of pump **6**.  Controlling liquid flow through the heat exchange device responsive to external heat flux changes permits almost instantaneous response to nonheat gain conditions.  This rapid response time coupled with the very small quantity of liquid exposed to heat exchange conditions results in large efficiency gains.

Figure 1.42b shows an oblique, exploded view of one preferred embodiment. In this embodiment, basal member **2** is constructed of a material, such as foam glass, having insulating properties and having a specific gravity less than that of the liquid being circulated.  Cover plate **3** comprises a relatively flat and transparent material resting directly on the basal member and conforming in size and shape to that member.

Plate **3** may be constructed of glass, plastic sheet or plastic film.  Generally, a rigid material such as glass is preferred.  A second transparent member **13** forms in cooperation with spacer **14** an insulating, dead air space.  Member **13** may comprise a glass plate or may comprise plastic film or similar materials.  Liquid is delivered to a central point on the upper surface of basal member 2. Moving liquid forms a thin, relatively uniform film between member 2 and plate 3 and overflows at the edge portions of these two members. The upper surface of member 2 preferably is treated with a dark, heat-absorbing coating as is well-known in the art. Figure 1.42b represents a single module; a multimodular unit can also be assembled according to the process.

## MISCELLANEOUS

### Panel with Lightweight Frame

According to the process of *H.E. Stout and B. Stout; U.S. Patent 3,918,430; November 11, 1975* a lightweight, low-cost, solar heating system is provided for use with homes and other buildings. Solar heating panels are mounted on a roof or other support and connected to the building's heating system. Water or other liquid medium is pumped to the elevated upper end of each unit and is allowed to drain down through each panel by gravity feed back into a storage tank where the heated water is circulated, on demand, through the building.

Each heating panel is comprised of a rigid foam plastic frame having a back wall over which is disposed a reflective stratum. A sheet of plastic material having a black surface is bonded to the reflective stratum along spaced parallel lines to define a plurality of parallel channels extending lengthwise of the panel. Manifolds are provided at opposite ends of the panel to feed water into and drain water from the channels. Spaced layers of flexible, transparent plastic film are mounted to the frame across the front of the panel to pass radiant heat from the front to heat water in the channels and trap the heat absorbed by the panel.

Referring to Figures 1.43a, 1.43b and 1.43c, the reference character 10 generally indicates a solar heating panel made according to the invention and generally organized about a rectangular frame 12 of a lightweight, thermally insulating, inexpensive material. Preferably the frame is molded from Styrofoam or other rigid, foam plastic material which is light in weight, inexpensive yet structurally strong and having excellent thermal insulation characteristics. The frame is of a rectangular configuration formed with integral, relatively short surrounding side walls 16.

Typically, the panels are made up of rather long sections of about 10' to 20' and in width of about 3'. Wall 14 should be relatively thick to provide good thermal insulation for the unit. In this regard, Styrofoam is particularly effective as a thermal insulator in addition to its advantageous structural characteristics. The wall may be ½" in thickness to provide both strength and proper insulating protection for the panel.

Side wall 16 is about 1½" to 2" both in height and width to reinforce the assembled panels as well as to provide a clearance of possibly ¾" between the inner face of wall 14 and the top of wall 16. Side walls 16 extend the full length of the panel. End walls 18 and 20 are formed integral with the frame across the full width of the panel and are of the same height as the side walls. The end walls are hollow to form a manifold chamber 22 for communication with an inlet conduit 24 for the wall 18 and an outlet conduit 26 for wall 20. Walls 16, 18 and 20 are formed with a groove or recessed portion 28 extending about the upper outer edges of the walls to receive in nesting engagement stacked spacers **30A**, **30B** and **30C**, mounted one on top of the other over walls **16**, **18** and **20** to provide a predetermined spacing between multiple layers of transparent film **32A**, **32B** and **32C**. The function of the multiple layers of transparent film **32** is to transmit radiant energy from the sun into the solar heating panel **10** while insulating the panel against heat losses through conduction and convection.

**FIGURE 1.43: PANEL WITH LIGHTWEIGHT FRAME**

*a.*

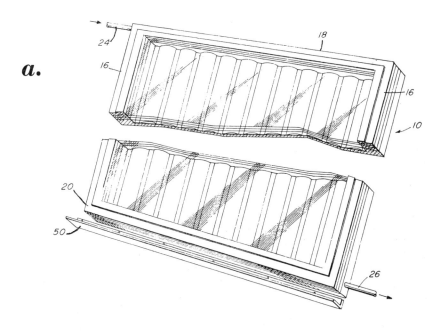

*b.*

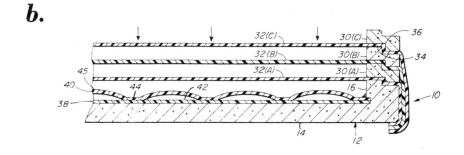

(continued)

FIGURE 1.43: (continued)

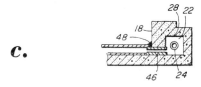

c.

(a) Perspective view of panel
(b) Fragmentary sectional view
(c) View similar to Figure 1.43b showing further details

Source:  U.S. Patent 3,918,430

In the preferred form of the system, film layers **32** are spaced apart from one another by a distance of approximately ½" and, ideally, are two or three in number.  The spacers **30** are of matching size and configuration having a length and width corresponding to that of the panel **10** and formed about its inner lower corner with a recess **34** adapted to nest with the recess **28** of walls **16, 18** and **20** as well as with a recess **36** formed about the upper outer edges of each of the spacers.

In fabricating the panels, the film layers are stretched over the frame walls to a relatively taut and smooth surface.  In practice, the innermost film layer **32A** is first placed in position and securely bonded to the frame **14**.  One mode of assembly that has been found to be particularly satisfactory is the use of heat shrinking techniques involving thermoplastic films by which the films are shrunk tightly onto the frame.  Once the first layer **32A** is in position, the spacer **30A** is mounted over the walls and the second transparent film **32B** is applied.  The same operation is repeated for the next spacer.  A final optional spacer **30C** may be applied to form a protective member about the assembled structure.

Various types of films may be employed and should be selected according to their light transmission characteristics, durability, weathering characteristics, bonding qualities and the like.  Various types of polyethylene, PVC, and other plastic films are suitable for this purpose.  The spacers are preferably of the same material as the frame.

Within the solar panel there is disposed a reflective stratum **38** applied to the upper face of the frame wall **14** and, for this purpose, aluminized plastic, aluminum foil or other high reflective material, including aluminized paint, may be employed.  The reflective stratum covers the entire surface of the frame wall and forms with a ply **40** a plurality of spaced, parallel, water channels **42** disposed lengthwise across the width of the solar panel.  The ply, in the preferred form of the system, is a moldable plastic material such as PVC or the like and is relatively light in weight, waterproof and preferably adapted for thermal-forming techniques.  The ply is bonded along seams **44** extending in parallel longitudinal relation to stratum **38**, as best shown in Figure 1.43b. Typically, bonding seams **44** are about ⅜" wide with channels **42** being about 4" in width. As shown in Figure 1.43b, ply **40** between the seams is raised somewhat from the face of the reflective stratum and typically an elevation of perhaps ⅛" provides adequate flow of water.

The function of the channels is to form water into a relatively thin stream to facilitate heat transfer. In this regard, the ply should be a black body and is either of an entirely black material or has its surface coated as at **45** with a dull black substance which will readily absorb the radiated heat from the sun. The combination of the black body absorption characteristics of the ply along with the reflective characteristics of the stratum causes rapid heating of water flowing through the channels. On a typical sunny day, temperatures of about 225° to 250°F are obtainable within a relatively short period of time.

Each of the water channels communicates with the manifold chambers **22** in the upper and lower end walls **18** and **20** as by tubes **46** (Figure 1.43c) extending between the chambers and into the ends of the water channel. A fillet **48** of sealing compound may be applied along the joints to prevent leakage.

In practice, each solar panel is mounted in a tilted position with the end wall **18** raised above the end wall **20** in the manner shown so that water fed into the upper manifold through the conduit **24** will flow by gravity down through the water channels into the manifold of the end wall **20** and drain out through the conduit **26**. Typically, the solar panels are mounted on a pitched roof and a number of panels may be installed depending upon the particular requirements of the building.

### Device to Control Convection Flow

An energy transmission device is described by *N. Laing; U.S. Patent 4,015,583; April 5, 1977* through which energy may pass comprising an optically active layer adapted to face the sun and a plurality of parallel extending U-shaped channels having vertically extending legs covering the side of the layer facing the sun wherein the channels are formed by a single sheet of a thin film-like radiation-permeable plastic material folded along fold lines to form the U-shaped channels.

The device has a weight means positioned exteriorly of the channels along the fold lines whereby when the channels are pressurized, the plastic material will move against the weight means to form an end of a leg of the U-shaped channel, and wherein the width of the U-shaped channels is less than the height thereof to reduce convection currents within the channels.

The device reduces convection flow over the optically active layer of energy transmission devices by providing a plurality of parallel extending U-shaped channels on the optically active layer in which the width of the channels is less than the height in order to reduce convection currents within the ducts over the layer. The optically active layers preferably have on their surface heat-absorbing or emitting tubes arranged in a grid formation. The tubes are made of material which has desirable optical characteristics. A first requirement for the material is resistance to ultraviolet radiation such that the tubes will not be destroyed by sunlight. A second requirement for the material of the tubes when the tubes are used as sun collectors is that the tubes should possess significant resistance to temperature. In the case where the devices are used for cooling purposes, i.e., to radiate heat into the ambient air, the main requirement for the tube material is that the spectral profile of the material be such that long-wave radiation can penetrate unimpeded. The material must be as highly optically permeable in the infrared region as possible.

In devices utilized to absorb the sun's energy, a high degree of reflection in infrared regions should be provided on the side of the optically active layer facing away from the sun in order that loss of radiation in the infrared region should be rereflected towards the roof of the building on which the devices may be mounted. Examples of materials which can be made into thin films to form thin wall tubes and which further have the required radiation permeability are polyethylenes, polypropylenes and silicone rubbers.

Figure 1.44a illustrates a device having an outward facing wall 4 which for the purpose of preventing cooling by ambient air is, according to the process, covered by optical and radiation-permeable sheet F of approximately 0.5 mm thickness which forms a plurality of channels or ducts 103. The film preferably is made of a polyethylene, polypropylene or a silicone rubber material. The sheet is deformed to the profile illustrated and joined to the optically active layer 102 along the strips 101 by heat sealing. The air enclosed in the ducts acts as an insulator so that no adverse effect is produced by convection of ambient air across the surface of the optically active layer.

As shown, legs of portions of adjacent ducts abut each other and extend perpendicularly to layer 102 to which they are joined. In this form of the device, the legs are joined to the layer at an acute angle with the strip portion 101, in turn being heat-sealed to the layer. The width of the ducts is less than the height so as to reduce any convection currents within the ducts themselves. Preferably, the device is so arranged that the ducts 103 when placed in use will extend in a substantially east-west direction to further enhance the direction of solar rays contacting the device and further expand its heat absorption efficiency.

## FIGURE 1.44: DEVICE TO CONTROL CONVECTION FLOW

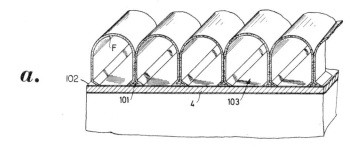

*a.*

(continued)

FIGURE 1.44: (continued)

**b.**

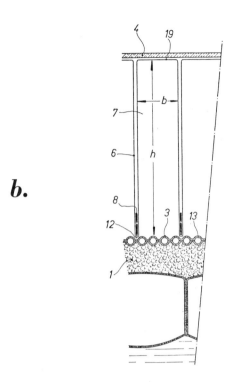

(a) Perspective sectional view of a first embodiment
(b) Sectional view of a second embodiment

Source: U.S. Patent 4,015,583

Referring to Figure 1.44b, a further embodiment is illustrated in which the optically active layer **3** acts as a heat absorption layer where the layer rests on a further layer of foam material supported by hollow floating bodies **1**. The layer has a super black surface which forms a plurality of ducts **13** through which a liquid heat carrier may flow to dissipate the heat absorbed by the layer.

Channels **7** are formed on top of the heat absorption layer by a thin film which is folded in the region **12** such that the walls **6** of the channels are formed by two wall portions each. In order to make the film walls heavier and to hang in the position shown, a sheet metal strip **8** is positioned in the folded edge. A low air pressure is maintained within the channels so that the film which forms the channels is pressed in the region **19** against a cover plate **4** which is transparent to solar rays. As shown, the walls **6** do not contact the optically active layer. The film forming the channels may comprise a polyvinyl fluoride material which preferably is about 0.01 mm thick. The film in this form of the device is much thinner than that shown in the embodiment of Figure 1.44a since the transparent sheet 4 provides a degree of protection for the film against weather elements and pollution. In this form of the device as well as in all forms, the width b of the channel is less than the height h which reduces any tendency for convection flow of air within the channel itself with the general rule that the smaller b is with respect to h, the less the opportunity of any convection flow occurring.

### Lensed Flat Plate Collector

*J.N. Minnick; U.S. Patent 3,981,295; September 21, 1976; assigned to The Raymond Lee Organization, Inc.* describes an essentially flat plate collector containing a plurality of lenses in the housing at the top thereof to magnify and concentrate the rays of the sun on the copper sheets to heat the water between such sheets.

The solar heating system of the device comprises at least one solar heating unit. The unit comprises a thermal insulated housing 1 with a plurality of sides, of which two sides 2 and 3 are shown in Figure 1.45a. It has a bottom 4 and a transparent top 5. A pair of copper sheets 6 and 7 are provided on the bottom of the housing. A plurality of spacers 8, 9, 10, 11, and so on between copper sheets 6 and 7 maintain the sheets in spaced substantially parallel relation.

A water input 12 supplies cold water to the space between the copper sheets. A water output 13 withdraws heated water from the space between the copper sheets. A lens system is provided in the housing at the top thereof for magnifying and concentrating the rays of the sun on the copper sheets, and more specifically, on the copper sheet 6, to heat the water between the sheets. The lens system comprises a plurality of lenses 14, 15, 16, 17, 18, 19, and so on, in close adjacent matrix configuration in rows and columns. Each lens may be of generally circular or cylindrical configuration or may be of generally elongated configuration.

The copper sheets are spaced less than ½" from each other, and preferably $\frac{1}{16}$" from each other, since the closer the copper sheets, the more effective and the more rapid the heating action.

### FIGURE 1.45:  LENSED FLAT PLATE COLLECTOR

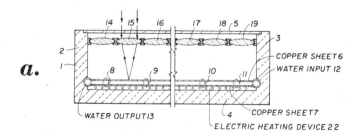

(continued)

**FIGURE 1.45:** (continued)

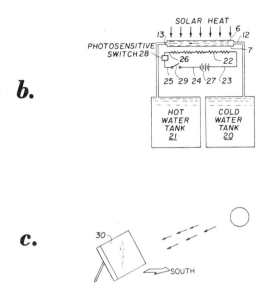

**b.**

**c.**

(a) View, partly in section, of solar heating unit
(b) Block and circuit diagram of solar heating unit
(c) Perspective view of solar heating system having one solar heating unit

Source: U.S. Patent 3,981, 295

As shown in Figure 1.45b, the cold water may come from a cold water tank **20** and the hot water may be stored in a hot water tank **21**. Furthermore, an electric heating device **22** is provided in the housing, beneath the copper sheet **7**, for heating the water between the copper sheets. An electrical circuit **23, 24, 25, 26** electrically connects the electric heating device, a source of electrical energy **27**, which may comprise any suitable source of electrical energy, e.g., a commercial power source or any suitable type of battery or batteries, and a photosensitive switch **28** and an on-off switch **29** in circuit.

The circuit connections are such that the water between the copper sheets is heated by the electric heating device under the control of the photosensitive switch when the sunlight is beneath a predetermined brightness level. Thus, when the sunlight is bright enough to heat the water, the photosensitive switch keeps the circuit of the electric heating device open. However, when the sunlight becomes too weak to heat the water, the photosensitive switch closes the circuit of the electric heating device and the heating device heats the water.

In one embodiment, shown in Figure 1.45c, a single heating unit **30** is inclined at an angle of approximately 45° with the horizontal.

## Flexible Panel of Silicone Rubber or Resin Sheets

Many systems have been proposed for collecting and converting energy from the sun as an alternative to the use of fossil fuels for energy generation. With rising costs of fossil fuels the collection of solar energy provides an attractive alternative. However, a major drawback so far of large-scale solar energy use has been the initial cost of installation and relative inefficiencies of collection.

Glass elements are difficult to fabricate and are subject to breakage due to vandalism, accident during installation, breakage by hail storms, and cracking due to heat differentials caused by shadows. Furthermore, they are heavy and require substantial labor in construction. Although flexible elements have been tried in the past, wind damage and degradation due to exposure to the sun have been problems. Although various configurations using plastic materials have been proposed, none to date has been commercially significant.

*R.W. Hagarty; U.S. Patent 4,008,708; February 22, 1977; assigned to Dow Corning Corporation* has prepared a solar energy collector panel in which flexible sheets, desirably of silicone rubber or resin material, are spaced from one another by a plurality of parallel-spaced extruded members which desirably are also silicone rubber. The extruded spacers provide therebetween channels for insulation and channels for the passage of fluid heat transfer medium such as water or air to carry energy from the collector to a point of utilization.

The entire device is easily fabricated by calendering the silicone rubber or silicone resin sheets of transparent material for light transmitting portions and light absorbing material for the absorbent portion of the collector and adhering the sheets to the extruded spacers with silicone sealant to provide an integral device. The collector element along with its insulative window can be simply rolled up and laid out by installers at the point where it is to be used. Installation personnel can safely walk on the panels during installation with little danger of breakage.

Silicone materials by their nature are extremely resistant to the effects of weather and do not degrade as many other polymeric materials do. Thus, installation can take place with a minimum of labor and care and little maintenance is required after installation. The panel may be laid directly on the roof of a building or even over uneven ground, preferably with a layer of insulation laid under the panels.

Figure 1.46 shows a perspective view of a solar energy collector laid on an insulative body 1 which may be, e.g., a layer of foam insulation on the roof of a building. The collector proper is simply laid on top of the insulation or in the case of a well-insulated building may be laid directly on the roof panels without further insulation beneath.

The collector proper comprises a sheet of solar energy absorbing flexible material 2 at the bottom thereof which is preferably made of a pigmented silicone rubber and over which an energy absorbing fluid is passed through a plurality of channels 3 and 4 defined by a plurality of spaced D-shaped tubular spacer elements 6 which are adhered to the absorber 2 by means of a silicone sealant. The spacer elements are desirably also made of pigmented silicone rubber but may be made of transparent silicone rubber with a relatively small loss in efficiency. In both the sunlight absorbing sheet 2 and the spacer elements 6, the pigment should be chosen for maximum solar energy absorption and may be, e.g., a combination of ferric oxide and carbon black. Adhered to the top surface of the spacer members is a light transmitting sheet 7 of relatively clear silicone rubber. Alternatively, a silicone resin may be used. Clear silicone rubber and resin materials comprising organopolysiloxanes reinforced with finely divided silica are commercially available. If desired, the sheet may be reinforced with a mesh of glass fibers for added strength. Such sheets can be made by simply calendering the silicone rubber on the glass fiber mesh.

FIGURE 1.46: FLEXIBLE PANEL OF SILICONE RUBBER OR RESIN SHEETS

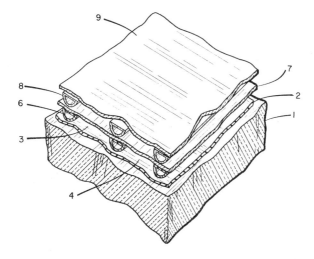

Source: U.S. Patent 4,008,708

Desirably, added insulation is provided on top of the solar energy collector per se to prevent heat loss to the atmosphere surrounding the collector. For this reason, it is commonplace to provide an air space above the collector which is closed by a second light transmitting panel spaced from the first. In accordance with the embodiment shown, a second plurality of extruded flexible spacer members 8 which may be identical to the members 6 but should be of light transmitting material for heat efficiency are adhered in spaced parallel relationship over the outside surface of the light transmitting panel 7.

Adhered to the outside surfaces of the spacer elements 8 is a second light transmitting panel or solar window element 9 which may be identical to the light transmitting panel 7. Alternatively, the panel 9 can be reinforced with a glass fiber mesh as described in connection with the panel 7, while the panel 7 is nonreinforced because it is not exposed to the elements. In the embodiment wherein the solar window panel 9 is made of reinforced material, it is desirable that the sheet 7 be made of nonreinforced silicone rubber for ease in rolling the completed article, making it easier to handle. The pair of light transmitting panels 7 and 9 separated by the spacers 8 thus form a solar window for the energy absorption portion of the collector comprising the channels 3 and 4 on the energy absorbing panel 2.

Instead of making the panel 7 covering the channels of light transmitting material, this panel can be pigmented to make it light absorbing. In such case the heat absorbed by the panel is carried to the liquid or gas in the channels by conduction from the panel and the fluid absorbs no energy directly from solar energy impinging on it. In such case it is desirable to add an additional solar window sheet above the configuration to provide further thermal insulation.

## Module with Interlocking Inlet and Outlet Ports

Solar collector units are well-known and consist of an enclosure for the entrapment of air to be heated; a dark plate mounted within the box; and a top covering of at least one layer of glass. The space between the glass top and the black plate becomes heated due to the entrapment of the solar energy. The problem with such units is that each system must be custom-built to fit the particular need.

Thus, if it is desired to construct a solar heating system on a roof of a house, a person skilled in construction, usually a carpenter, would be called upon to construct the framework on the roof. This construction would be typically made from wood with a glass covering. This is an expensive and time-consuming method of construction and does not lend itself to being built by the typical homeowner. In fact, because of the weight of such systems they typically cannot be used on an existing house without altering structure.

The solar collectors which come as individual lightweight units are also not practical for home use since each unit is typically connected to the next unit by a series of pipes, each pipe being run exterior to the unit. In addition to the construction problems with such an arrangement, there is the problem that exterior piping allows for an excessive heat loss which at the same time cuts down on the available surface area available for collecting the solar energy. Also, exterior piping suffers from an inability to carry the volume of air necessary for efficient use of solar energy. An example of such a modular unit where external piping is used is U.S. Patent 3,399,664.

*M.R. Quick; U.S. Patent 3,996,918; December 14, 1976* has described a modular solar collector unit which is arranged for symmetrical connection to other similar collectors to form a solar energy collection system. The individual units are arranged to be interlocked without special tools and without special know-how on the part of the person constructing the system. The units are adapted so that the heated air passes entirely internal to each solar collector unit through mating ports from one unit directly to the next unit.

A solar collector unit is constructed as a square box made from a lightweight insulating material, such as foamed polyurethane or Styrofoam, with a glass top. The top of the box is open and carries at least one pane of glass. Near the bottom of the box there is located a black metal plate. The area between the black plate and the glass top defines a cavity through which the air to be heated flows. Solar energy is trapped between the glass top and the metal plate. An inlet port is formed in one side wall of the unit and an outlet port is formed in an opposite side wall. Air or any other medium to be heated passes into the unit through the inlet port and moves through the cavity between the metal plate and the top glass surface thereby becoming heated from the available solar energy. The heated air then moves through the outlet port and directly into the inlet port of the next adjacent abutting unit.

The inlet and outlet ports of the units are arranged for interlocking mating relationship with each other such that air seals between adjacent units are easily achievable. On the side walls which do not contain inlet and outlet ports, there are formed mating interlocks so that laterally placed next adjacent units can be interlocked in much the same manner as are adjacent boards in tongue and groove woodwork construction.

As shown in Figure 1.47a, solar collector unit **10** is arranged in the form of a square within which is carried a glass top surface **31** and a metallic plate **33** which plate is mounted near the bottom of the square. In one side wall **15** of the unit, an input port **20** is formed having lip **11**. In the opposite side wall **17** there is formed an output port **21** having an opening just large enough to accept the lip in mating relationship. Air which is forced into the unit through port **20** passes between the glass surface and the metal plate thereby becoming heated from the available solar energy. The heated air is then forced out through port **21** and into a next adjacent unit. As will be shown, a number of such units can be interconnected to form a matrix of units thereby covering the available surface area.

Each unit is also constructed having one side wall **18** with a groove therein and another side wall **16** with a lip **13** adapted to fit into groove **14**. Thus, when the units are placed in abutting fashion the unit on the right has its lip **13** in mating relationship with unit **10**, groove **14**, while unit **10**'s lip **13** is in mating relationship with groove **13** of the unit next adjacent on the left. Accordingly, all of the units next adjacent unit **10** are mated with unit **10** in an interlocked fashion to form an easily constructible and rigid structure.

For added support, an adhesive could be used on the mating parts to prevent any possibility of air leakage or movement. The entire structure can be easily attached to a roof or other surface by a small amount of adhesive under each unit. Since the units are lightweight they can be mounted on top of the existing roofing material thereby protecting against water leakage into the building.

In Figure 1.47b unit **10** is shown reversed with the input port **20** now on the right and the output port **21** on the left. Of course, it will be noted that the unit works with air flow in either direction and the designation of one port as an input port and one port as an output port is only for convenience of discussion herein.

In Figure 1.47c there is shown a cross-section view taken along 3–3 of Figure 1.47b. Unit **10** is shown having sides **18** and **16**. Side **18** has formed therein groove **14** while side **16** has formed thereon lip **13**. The unit has bottom **30** above which is mounted black metal plate **33**. Above the plate is a glass sheet **32** carried in grooves formed on the interior of unit **10**. Above glass sheet **32** is a top glass sheet **31**. The purpose of the double glass sheets is to increase the effectiveness of the solar collector by enhancing the entrapment of solar energy. This results since glass is opaque to heat waves, thereby cavity **34** formed between glass sheet **32** and plate **33** becomes heated from the sun's rays.

## FIGURE 1.47: MODULE WITH INTERLOCKING INLET AND OUTLET PORTS

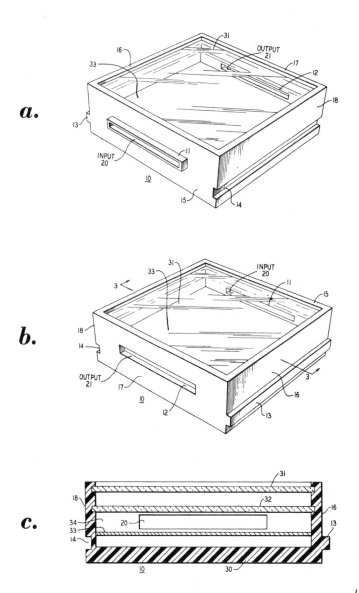

(continued)

FIGURE 1.47: (continued)

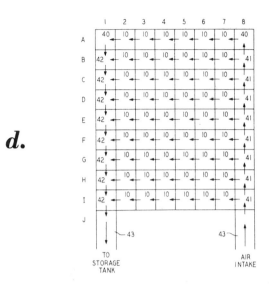

d.

(a) Right side view of collector
(b) Left side view of collector
(c) Sectional view taken along **3–3** of Figure 1.47b
(d) Schematic of a modular system

Source:   U.S. Patent 3,996,918

The heated air in unit **10** gives off long rays of energy which do not pass through the glass.  The lower layer of glass sheet **32** provides a barrier to the radiation outward of heat and also acts as a thermal insulator by creating a dead space between glass sheets **31** and **32**.  However, it should be noted that only a single top sheet of glass or other athermanous matter need be provided.

Air to be heated is forced by a fan (not shown) into input port **11** directly into cavity **34**.  This air is heated by the energy trapped in the cavity and then continues out of the cavity via output port **12** and then directly into the energy cavity of a next adjacent unit.  In this manner the air is heated as it passes through the individual units of the system.  Since the units abut each other the warmed air is not allowed to cool between units.

In Figure 1.47d there is shown an entire system; a number of individual units **10** are interconnected together to form a matrix of columns.  For purposes of discussion, the individual units of the system will be referred to by the intersection point on the grid formed by the rows labeled **A** to **J** and the columns labeled **1** to **8**.  Air intake **43** which is located at grid position **J8** can be a number of individual units **10** if it is mounted where solar energy is available.  Air intake **43** can be constructed in the same manner as unit **10** with input and output ports except that a polystyrene top can be used instead of glass. However, since air intake **43** must pass a large volume of air the input and output ports are ideally made much larger than the regular size input and output ports of unit **10**. For use at corners appropriate shapes can be made available, all having internal mating ports for the conducting of air. Distribution units **41** located at grid positions **B8** and **I8** are each constructed as a solar collector exactly as is unit **10** except that two output ports **21** are provided, one being larger than the other.

One output port (the larger of the two) of unit **41** mates with the large input port of the next adjacent unit **41** and the other (regular size) output port mates with the next adjacent input port of unit **10**. For example, looking at unit **41** at position **H8** it will be seen that its large input port mates with the large output port of unit **41** at position **I8**. The larger one of its output ports mates with the large input port of unit **41** at position **G8** while the regular size other one of its output ports mates with the input port of unit **10** at position **H7**.

Unit **40** at corner **A8** is constructed having a large input port and a regular size output port on an adjacent side to mate with the units at positions **B8** and **A7**, respectively. Unit **42** at position **B1** is constructed having a large and regular size input port and a single large output port. Thus, by combining a number of different types of units, each constructed with internal passages and mating ports, an entire system can be constructed easily and without special tools or ability. By using half sizes and curved sizes any number of system configurations can be achieved to cover the available surface area.

### Glass Composite Building Panel

An all-glass composite building panel suitable for use as an integral structural member in roofs, ceilings, walls and floors is described by *C. Deminet and R.B. Gillette; U.S. Patent 3,981,294; September 21, 1976; assigned to The Boeing Company.* The panel is constructed of three layers of glass separated by integral raised walls fused to the adjacent glass layers to define three possible combinations of two enclosed spaces; two layers of contiguous individual vacuum cells; one layer of contiguous individual vacuum cells and one layer comprising a serpentine passageway for liquid flow therethrough, the serpentine passage containing a heat absorptive material; or two layers comprising individual serpentine passageways for liquid flow.

Referring to Figure 1.48a, the preferred embodiment of the device is an all-glass composite structure as shown. The structure consists of an insulation layer **10** bounded by a top glass plate **12** and a middle glass plate **14** and liquid path layer **16** bounded by a bottom glass plate **18** and the middle glass plate **14**. As shown in Figures 1.48b and 1.48c, the internal structure of the insulation layer is defined by external glass insulator walls **20** and internal glass insulator walls **22** which are fused to the top glass plate, the middle glass plate and each other at all points of contact to form a series of contiguous cells **24**. As part of the forming process, the cells are substantially evacuated to form a partial vacuum which provides the insulating characteristics of the insulation layer.

The internal structure of the liquid path layer is defined by external glass liquid walls **26** and internal glass liquid walls **28** which are fused to the bottom glass plate, the middle glass plate and each other at all points of contact to form a serpentine path for liquid flow. A liquid inlet pipe **32** and a liquid outlet pipe **34** are provided in external glass liquid walls **26** at opposite ends of the serpentine path.

FIGURE 1.48: GLASS COMPOSITE BUILDING PANEL

*a.*

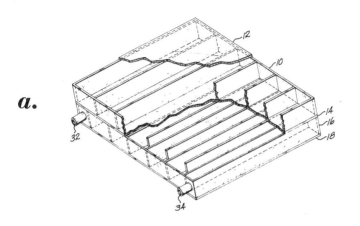

*b.*

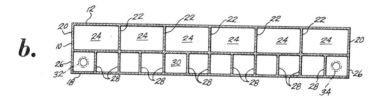

*c.*

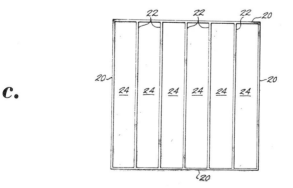

(continued)

FIGURE 1.48: (continued)

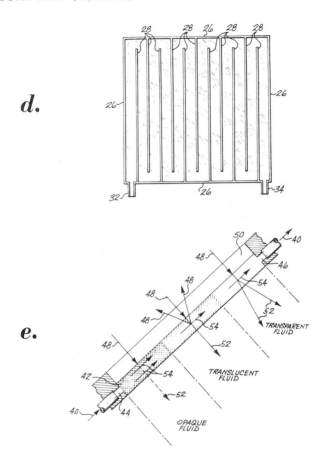

d.

e.

(a) Collector panel
(b) Cross section through panel
(c) Top view of the vacuum cell layer
(d) Top view of the liquid path layer
(e) Representation of the three basic modes of operation

Source: U.S. Patent 3,981,294

When used in its primary function as a solar energy collector panel, the process is contemplated as operating in three basic fluid modes as shown in Figure 1.48e. Many variations and degrees of operation are possible since the energy is absorbed directly by the fluid; however, each can be identified with one of the three basic modes to be described. As depicted in Figure 1.48e, a liquid **40** enters the liquid path layer **42** at liquid inlet pipe **44**, passes through the liquid path layer and exits via the liquid outlet pipe **46**. Rays of solar energy **48** pass through the insulation layer **50** to the liquid where they are converted to light

52 and heat **54**. If the liquid **40** is substantially transparent as depicted by the upper portion of Figure 1.48e the light **52** transmitted to the interior of the building will be maximum and some heat will be generated. This configuration would optionally be for a mild winter condition where light is needed to offset the gloom. If the liquid is substantially translucent, possibly containing reflective characteristics, as shown in the middle portion of the figure, the solar energy **48** will be partially reflected and only partially converted to light and heat. This mode of operation is the most adaptable.

Finally, if the liquid is substantially opaque as shown in the bottom portion of the figure, the solar energy will be virtually totally converted to heat with little or no light transmitted to the interior of the building. This configuration would be particularly useful to gather heat for operation of air conditioning equipment in areas of extreme sunlight and temperature.

It is important to note that the panel and use of various colors of liquid need not be coupled with addition of heat to or subtraction of heat from the circulated liquid. The panel can be used in essence as an integral shade. For shade from the sun or privacy, an opaque, metallic or colored liquid could be pumped through the panel. To admit light, a transparent liquid would be substituted. Further discussion in the patent details the use of this panel in building walls and floor and ceiling panels.

While the configuration described heretofore is the primary use configuration contemplated for the apparatus, the two other configurations previously mentioned have significant value when used alone or in combination with the primary configuration.

The first secondary configuration to be considered is that of two layers of vacuum cells. Both layers would be contiguous vacuum cells as depicted in Figure 1.48c. Such a panel would be strong and a good insulator. A typical use would be as in the insulation/light conductive panel.

The second secondary configuration is that of two layers of liquid serpentine path as depicted in Figure 1.48d. This configuration could be used in conjunction with the primary configuration to provide a heat exchanger.

### Adjacent or Telescopic Columnar Arrangement

The process of *E.M. Barber, Jr.; U.S. Patent 3,980,071; September 14, 1976; assigned to Sunworks, Inc.* provides a module which comprises a housing member, a collector plate member having a selective surface adapted to absorb solar radiation, and a plurality of liquid heat exchange tubes in intimate heat relationship contact with the collector plate. The housing members in one form also include support portions adapted to be supported on spaced-apart joists of the structure. The modules are further so constructed that they may be arranged in adjacent or telescopic columnar relationship and the conductors of one module connected to the other.

Each of the modules as shown in section in Figure 1.49c includes a housing member **13** having a bottom pan portion **14**, upstanding side wall members **15**, extending into a flange **16** and an upright end portion **17**. The housing may be so formed that an upstanding small rib **18** is defined as wall **15** and flange **16**.

As shown, flanges **16** support the housing **13** between adjacent joists **11** and rest on a piece of flexible or compressible insulating material. A piece of flexible insulation **19** is laid over a joist with the ends extending downwardly to provide insulation between the joists and the housing **14**. Disposed within the housing along the bottom thereof is insulating material **20** such as a section of rigid fiber glass. Disposed above the insulation is a solar collector plate **21** which has a zinc sulfide-nickel sulfide electroplated coating which will be referred to as a selective surface.

Each collector includes a tubular heat exchanger **22** (Figure 1.49b). Disposed in intimate heat contact relation with plate **21** are a plurality of heat exchange tubes **22a, 22b, 22c, 22d** and **22e** which extend in substantially parallel spaced-apart relationship between headers **23** and **24**. As shown, the plate is formed with troughs or wells which receive the heat exchange tubes and headers and it will be understood that the tubes may be either downwardly or upwardly disposed with respect to the collector plate. If desired, additional insulating material may be affixed to the underside of the housing as by means of studs **25** and large lock washers **25a**. Alternatively, the housing may be deepened in the vertical dimension to accept a greater dimension of insulating material.

### FIGURE 1.49: ADJACENT OR TELESCOPIC COLUMNAR ARRANGEMENT

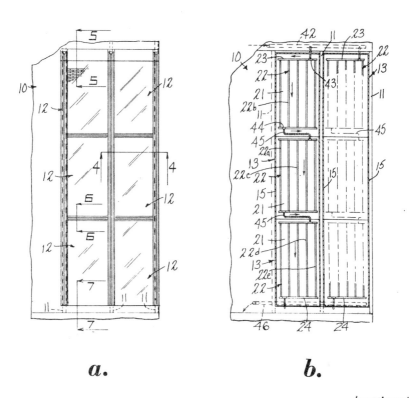

a.

b.

(continued)

FIGURE 1.49: (continued)

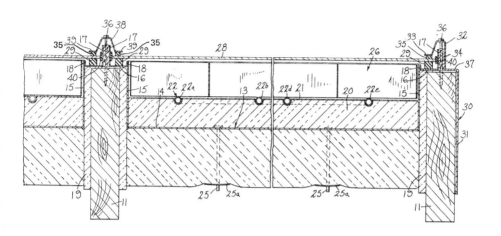

*c.*

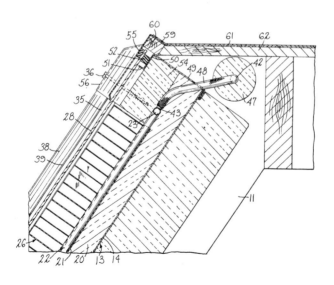

*d.*

(continued)

**FIGURE 1.49:** (continued)

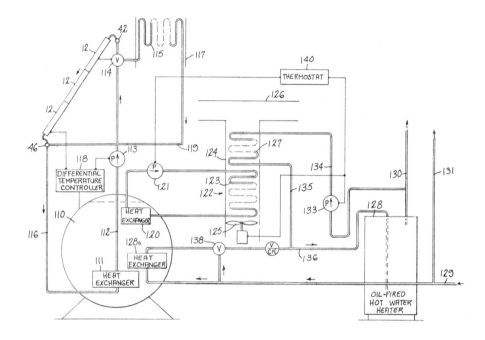

*e.*

(a)  Assembly of 6 modules
(b)  View of Figure 1.49a with the protective panels removed
(c)  Sectional view in the plane of line **4—4** of Figure 1.49a
(d)  Sectional view in the plane of line **5—5** of Figure 1.49a
(e)  Schematic diagram of system utilizing the apparatus

Source:  U.S. Patent 3,980,071

Included within housing **14** and supported from the upper rib portions **18** is an assembly **26** which is adapted to retard convection currents over the collector plates.  The assembly **26** is a honeycomb arrangement and is made of reflective material such as aluminum foil or thin sheet material.  Moreover, the edges of plate **21** stop short on contact with side wall members **15**.

The plate is preferably of copper or other heat-conductive metal and preferably has thereon a selective surface which is designed to permit the absorption of solar radiation by the copper plate and decrease thermal radiation from the plate. The assembly serves the function of inhibiting convective currents of air within the housing above the collector plate.  The assembly is also spaced a small distance, perhaps ⅛" to ¼", above the surface of **21** so that it will not conduct heat from plate **21** and act as a radiator. A transparent cover member **28** is supported above the plate and in short-spaced relation from assembly **26**. The member has its side edges supported on the joists **11** through the flanges **16** and rests on gaskets or seal **29**. A border or frame of aluminum extrusion (not shown) may be provided on each cover member for ease of handling and installation. On one side of the joists there is no additional module. On this side (the right side as viewed in Figure 1.49c) a sealing and flashing member **30** is utilized to seal the collector from the elements.

Member **30** may be made of various lengths. It has a flat side portion **31** tightly fitted against the joist **11**. The side portion extends into an upright cap portion **32** and a lower flange **33**. Disposed between the cap portion and upright portion **17** of side wall members is a length of gasketing material **34**. A further sealing member **35** is disposed between flange **33** of member **30** and cover member **28**. Member **30** receives a plurality of lag bolts **36** which extend through cap portion **32** and gasketing material **34** into joist **11**. As the bolts are set, the seals. **29** and **35** are compressed to effect a completely watertight assembly.

A conventional piece of sheathing material such as plywood (not shown) may be extended from the top of the joist and shoulder **37** of member **30** to provide the foundation for conventional roof covering if the roof has extended beyond. Conventional flashing may be utilized at this joint.

Where modules are mounted on opposite sides of a joist, the construction is as shown on the lefthand portion of Figure 1.49c. A sealing cap member **38** having flanges **39** is provided to span across the seals **35** of the adjacent modules. Additional seals **40** may be provided between each end of the cover member and the side wall members. In some instances, it may be preferable to border the edges of the cover members in a border for ease of handling. An extruded aluminum mullion may be used and seated directly on flanges **16** behind ribs **18** or seated on the gaskets **29**. This construction is preferred where the units are mounted above the joists or on separate structures.

An assembly of six modules in two columns between three successive joists is exemplified in Figure 1.49a. Figure 1.49b shows the same modules with the cover and seals removed. The heat exchange tubes **22a** to **22e** of each module extend substantially parallel between end headers **23** and **24**. The heat exchangers are preferably of copper for greatest heat exchange efficiency.

As shown, the end headers of the uppermost modules are connected to a manifold **42** and the lower headers are connected to the upper header of the next lower module. The headers are provided with T-connectors or stubs **43** and **44** between which is led a flexible or bendable tubing connector **45** to provide connection between adjacent heat exchangers. The lower header **24** of the last heat exchanger in a column is connected to a return manifold **46**.

Referring to Figure 1.49d, the manifold **42** is preferably encased in a sleeve of insulating material **47**. A lead-in **48** is connected to upper header **23**. Housing member **13** includes removable end walls **49**. However, the end walls will not be removed from the upper and lower modules of a column. The end wall has an inwardly directed flange **50** and an upstanding finger or lip **51**. Resting on the flange is an elongated seal **52** which extends across cover member **28**. The lip **51** extends between the rib-like members **18** and provides a dam for any moisture which might enter the upper module of a column. If such moisture did enter it would be caught by the lip and would then run down on the outside of the ribs.

Insulation **54** is disposed between the joists above the upper module of a column. The upper module has connected thereto an upper sealing and flashing member **55** which has a trough **56** defined therein to overlay the cap member **37**. Member **55** as shown has a rear extending flange **59** adapted to extend over a transverse structural member **60**. Thereafter, conventional roofing material **61** may be placed over sheathing **62** on the roof of the structure. The member is flashed out to provide a seal on the side of the structure.

To minimize handling, it is preferred that each module be provided with its own cover member **28**. For sealing purposes an elongated sealing member, preferably of neoprene, extends across the horizontal upper and lower edges of adjacent covers and has pockets to receive such edges therein. Key-like flexible inserts are then inserted into members so that the ends are sealingly engaged.

Figure 1.49e exemplifies a system embodying the process. A large water storage tank **110** holds a large reservoir of water for heat exchange purposes. The solar heating piping system includes a heat exchanger **111** in the tank. A line **112** from the heat exchanger leads through a pump **113** to a temperature-responsive directional valve **114**. The valve will direct the heat exchange medium to either a heat dissipating coil **115** or to manifold **42**. After passing through the collectors, the heat exchange medium enters manifold **46** and returns to the heat exchanger through line **116**. Valve **114** is responsive to the temperature of the fluid. If the fluid temperature exceeds a predetermined value, e.g., 220°F, the valve directs the heat exchange medium through the heat rejection or dissipating coil.

Coil **115** is preferably finned, not shown, and disposed in a belvedere **117** or at a vent. The heat in the coil may be used to provide a stack effect for building exhaust. A differential temperature controller **118** senses the temperature of the collector plates and the water temperature in the tank. Whenever the collector plate temperature exceeds the water temperature by a predetermined amount, e.g., 5°F, the controller turns on the pump.

A second heat exchanger **120** is disposed within the tank and furnishes hot water or other heat exchange medium to a heating system. Water heated in the heat exchanger is conveyed by means of a pump or circulator **121** to a heating system which may comprise one or more fan-coil heating units **122**. The units include one or more heat exchange coils **123** disposed in a housing **124**. A motor-driven fan **125** may move air over the coils, as shown, or be positioned for drawing air over the coils. As the fan blows or draws air over the coil, the heated air is conveyed via duct work **126** to various areas to be heated.

Housing **124** contains a further air heating coil **127**, connected to a standby and domestic hot water heater **128**. The heater may receive heated water from heat exchanger **128a** in the tank and supplies domestic hot water through line **130**. Domestic cold water is supplied over line **131**. Water is supplied to heat exchanger **128a** through supply line **129** from a well or other water source. Heated water is returned to the tank through a tempering valve **138** and line **136** which may mix cold water from line **129** to maintain the water in heater **128** at a predetermined temperature, e.g., 140°F. Whenever the temperature of the water in the tank falls below the predetermined temperature, the heater commences to operate to heat the water. The heater will also supply hot water through pump **133** over line **134** to coil **127** for standby operation upon demand. A return line **135** from the coil leads to tank return line **136**.

In operation during a usual heating period, the differential temperature controller **118** will sense that the collector temperature is higher than that of the water in tank **110**. This will cause pump **113** to operate and the heat exchange medium will be conveyed through valve **114** and through the collectors. The heat exchange medium absorbs heat from the collectors and returns to heat exchanger **111** in the tank to heat the water therein. If for any reason the temperature of the collectors or the fluid exceeds a predetermined value as previously specified, the pump is turned off. The valve will connect the collector coils to a dissipating coil **115**.

The fluid will then circulate from the coil through conduit **119** back through the collectors. This direction of fluid is due to the hotter, less dense fluid in the collectors rising and the cooler, more dense fluid falling after passing through the coil. This will maintain the water in the tank in a predetermined temperature range suitable for heating. Alternatively, the pump may be operated to direct fluid from the heat exchanger through the coil. In such an arrangement, the conduit would return to the heat exchanger.

When heating is called for, pump **121** will draw water from heat exchanger **120** through heating coil **123** and air blown over the coil by fan **125** may be used for heating purposes. It will be understood that in some instances it may be preferable to use hot water baseboard heating or radiant floor heating rather than the fan-coil unit disclosed. A thermostat **140** is provided to control operation of the pumps when heat is called for. When the thermostat calls for heat for a given space, only pump **121** and fan **125** will initially operate. If the space temperature continues to fall, then pump **133** will also operate. Fan **125** will continue to operate in response to the thermostat calling for heat.

The system as disclosed is generally designed to provide a given percentage of the total heating requirements for a structure from solar energy. The domestic hot water heater is selected to be of a size to supply the design heat loss of a structure plus a given percent thereof for domestic water heating.

### Module with Divided Chamber

The solar heating module of *G.H. Hamilton, R.M. Turner and J.L. Ward, Jr.; U.S. Patent 3,939,818; February 24, 1976; assigned to Solar Energy Company* comprises a sealable chamber having cross-flow radiator means therein dividing the chamber into a fluid inlet compartment and a fluid outlet compartment and, preferably, at least one perforated sleeve in the inlet compartment. The process also comprises an assembly of the modules into a unitary heater having a common intake manifold.

Referring to Figures 1.50a, 1.50b, 1.50c and 1.50d, there is shown solar energy heating assembly **10** comprising a plurality of individual modules **11**. While the modules have been shown in perspective view as being in an essentially vertical position, in use the assembly will be made to face toward the south and tilted at an approximate 60° angle from the horizontal. The modules 11 comprise sealable fluid-tight chambers of generally rectangular shape formed by a top wall 12, bottom wall 13, side walls 14, rear wall 15 and front wall 16. All of the walls, except the front wall, are preferably made of a non-heat-conductive material, such as wood or plastic, although metals can also be used.

The front wall is formed of a transparent material such as glass or plastic film 17, preferably a plastic film such as polycarbonate (Lexan). It is preferred to use two spaced-apart layers of plastic film as shown in Figure 1.50d, the spacing aiding in preventing heat loss through the front wall. The interior of the chamber, with the exception of the front wall, is preferably lined with insulating material 18 such as an expanded plastic foam (Styrofoam) or any other material commonly used for this purpose.

### FIGURE 1.50: MODULE WITH DIVIDED CHAMBER

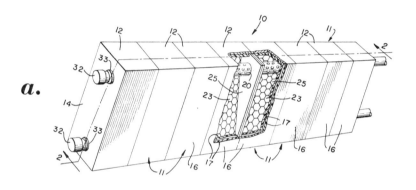

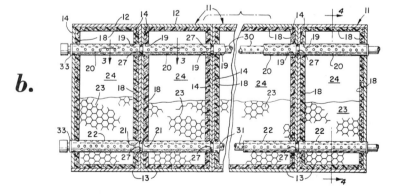

(continued)

**FIGURE 1.50:** (continued)

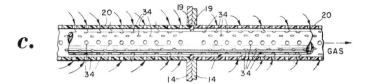

*c.*

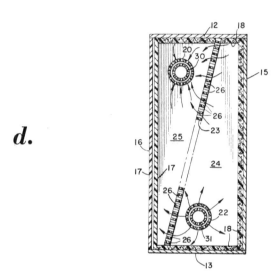

*d.*

(a) Perspective view, partially broken away, of an assembly of modules
(b) Sectional view taken along line 2–2 of Figure 1.50a
(c) Sectional view taken along line 3–3 of Figure 1.50b
(d) Sectional view taken along line 4–4 of Figure 1.50b

Source:  U.S. Patent 3,939,818

The exposed outer surface of insulating material **18** is covered with a heat absorbing material such as a black film or black paint of the type conventionally
used.  Upper aligned openings **19** are provided in side walls **14** and upper perforated sleeve **20** extends across the interior of the module from one opening to
the other.  Sleeve **20** can be attached to the chamber by having the diameter of
openings **19** and the sleeve matched so that it is force-fitted into the openings
and securely held in place as shown in Figure 1.50c.  Though not shown, the
seals can be fashioned so that the flanges thereof extend for a substantial distance into the chamber.  The flanges can then be perforated to aid in control of

fluid flow as discussed below and sleeve 20 dispensed with. In like manner, lower aligned side openings 21 are provided in side walls 14 with lower perforated sleeve 22 or seals with extended flanges affixed therein and spanning the module 11. Although not depicted, there can be two or more upper and lower sleeves, or seals with extended flanges, utilized together with the necessary complementary additional upper and lower aligned openings.

Radiator means 23 are provided in the module and are attached to the insulation 18 by nailing thereto or embedment therein. The radiator means, preferably extending diagonally from the top wall 12 to bottom wall 13, divide the interior of the module into fluid inlet compartment 24 and fluid outlet compartment 25 with perforated sleeve 22 in the inlet compartment and perforated sleeve 20 in the outlet compartment.

The radiator means is preferably a cross-flow radiator of the honeycomb type having cells 26 therein permitting a ready passage of fluids therethrough in a cross-flow path. Such honeycomb is commercially available as Hexcel. The radiator means is coated with a heat-absorbing material of the same type used on insulating material 18. Honeycomb cells 26 act as heat traps and further give a greater amount of surface area to increase the heating efficiency of the module by collecting as much of the radiation as possible. In addition, as opposed to conventional flat plate collectors, honeycomb radiator 23 because of the depth of cells 26 can collect heat across a wide angle of sun exposure.

The individual modules are assembled simply by placing one against the other in abutting relation and sealing the entire assembly by utilizing suitable sealing means such as bushings 27 at side wall openings 19 and 21. The bushings are of a size so as to also function to interconnect the perforated sleeves 20 and 22 in each of the modules to form, when the modules are assembled, an aligned series of perforated sleeves 20 and sleeves 22 all being in fluid flow communication.

Perforated manifolds 30 and 31 made of metal or plastic, are then inserted through the perforated sleeves so as to extend through the entire module assembly with the outermost ends of each manifold suitably sealed by attaching cap 32 thereto. Not shown is the fan or other means used to drive the fluid, such as water or air, into the bottom manifold 31 out through the perforations in the manifold 31 and sleeve 22 and into the chambers where the fluid is heated by the rays of the sun. The heated fluid, due to the force of the fan and by being heated, will flow into the inlet compartment, through the radiator and into the outlet compartment where the fluid will enter into the perforations of sleeves 19 and manifold 30 to be returned to the structure being heated.

Suitable means such as gaskets 33 are utilized to seal the manifolds where they extend beyond the limits of the module assembly. An important feature of the process is that the manifolds are perforated only along certain spaced intervals of their length. This is best illustrated in Figure 1.50c wherein the manifold 30 is not perforated for a portion of its length where the two modules are abutted.

Perforations 34 can be varied in size so as to control the flow of fluid into the modules. Perforations in sleeve 22 can also be varied in size and location to assist in controlling the flow of fluid in conjunction with perforations in manifold 31. In addition, there is no need to insulate the manifolds since they are enclosed in the modules.

Solar Heat Absorbing Tubing

An improved form of solar heat absorbing tubing described by *D.H. Spielberg; U.S. Patent 3,968,786; July 13, 1976; assigned to Universal Oil Products Company* comprises a plastic material which contains small subdivided black body absorber particles which are fully distributed throughout the thickness of the tubing. A preferred form of tubing will utilize electrical conductive carbon, or carbonized particles, in an amount to provide conductivity to the resulting tubing such that there may be electroplating or electrostatic spray coating for the tubing to further enhance its absorptive and reradiation properties.

The ultraviolet light between the atmospheric absorption cutoff of 0.29 $\mu$ and the lower edge of the visible spectrum, 0.4 $\mu$, is called the solar ultraviolet. A suitable plastic binder will be transparent to this solar ultraviolet radiation, allowing the black body material in the binder to absorb the radiant energy. In addition, the plastic binder will preferably transmit the remainder of the solar radiation spectrum, i.e., from about 0.3 to 1.2 $\mu$.

Various types of plastic materials may be used; for example, the optical properties of acrylic ester resins and their ease of forming and stability to heat and light make them suitable candidates. Poly(methyl methacrylate) transmits extensively in the solar ultraviolet range and has almost perfect transmission in the visible range. Other polymers, such as polystyrene, aliphatic polyesters, cellulose esters, and polyamides, contain groups that also show considerable transmittance in the solar ultraviolet.

Almost all of the thermoplastic and thermosetting plastic materials are sensitive to sunlight and tend to deteriorate and crack unless there have been added materials to provide stabilization and antioxidation properties to the binder material. In general, various types of antioxidation additives may be used and should have no effect with respect to interfering with the composition for a solar heat collecting tubing. Actually, the darkening of plastic materials through the aging process will in no way be harmful to the collector tubing inasmuch as the resulting improved tubing will be black from the black body material being combined with the plastic binder material in order to enhance the heat absorbing properties.

It is also a particular feature of the process to provide a solar heat collecting tubing which is formed from the complex of a plastic binder material and pyropolymeric conductive organic-refractory oxide particles such that there is a resulting tubing which can possess a controlled electrical conductivity. This type of material is described in U.S. Patent 3,651,386.

The material is formed by the deposition of the pyropolymer on the surface of a base material at a relatively high temperature in the range of from 400° to 750°C. Organic substances such as aliphatic hydrocarbons, cycloaliphatic hydrocarbons, aromatic hydrocarbons, aliphatic halogen derivatives, aliphatic oxygen derivatives, carbohydrates, etc., may be pyrolyzed over the surface of a subdivided refractory oxide material. The refractory oxide may be alumina in various forms, such as gamma-alumina and silica-alumina; however, various other refractory oxides may be used. Preferably, the carbonaceous pyropolymer, the graphite or other carbonaceous material which is to be combined with the plastic binder will be utilized as a finely divided powder where the particulates are generally of about 10 $\mu$ in size or less. These particle sizes can be obtained by milling the filler material in a volatile solvent medium by means of a roll mill, colloidal mill or ball mill and thereafter flashing off or evaporating the solvent to obtain the dried powder. It is also to be noted that the carbonaceous filler material need not be in the finely divided powder form, inasmuch as ultrafine diameter strands or fibers which have the carbonaceous coating may well be utilized. For example, small diameter fibers or filaments may be of a refractory inorganic oxide and may be made in accordance with teachings of U.S. Patent 3,614,809, issued October 26, 1971.

This type of refractory fiber may be chopped into short lengths and subjected to the treatment of U.S. Patent 3,651,386 to in turn provide a desired carbonaceous pyropolymer with electrical conductivity properties. It may be of advantage to add a very thin electroplated or electrostatically coated layer of a metal such as copper, nickel, chromium, cobalt, silver, etc., which helps reduce the reradiation of the higher wavelength radiations, while at the same time permitting the lower wavelength solar energy to pass through into the black body material.

Where the tubing is sufficiently electrically conductive then such tubing may serve as its own electrode in an electroplating type of operation such that there is the direct deposition of a desired metal component onto the surface of the tubing. Also, an electrically conductive tubing will permit an electrostatic type of coating operation, where there is a suitable charging of the tubing such that there can be an adhering coating of particles from the spraying of powdered metals onto the surface of the tubing and then the subsequent binding therewith in a suitable elevated temperature heating operation.

Such types of selectively absorbing coatings may be unnecessary with the use of certain of the selective types of plastic materials, such as the aforementioned poly(methyl methacrylate) binder material which has selective transmission properties but can be of particular advantage in connection with all of the various binders that do not provide the integrated greenhouse effect.

Referring to Figure 1.51, there is indicated a tubing 1 which is formed from a complex of a thermoplastic material, or thermosetting plastic material, as a binder having a high percentage of carbonaceous black body material 2 which is distributed throughout the full thickness of the tubing. In addition, there is indicated an ultrathin coating layer 3 over the outer surface of the tubing. The black body material may comprise carbon or a carbonaceous pyropolymer formed on a refractory oxide base material in order to provide a high degree of black body effect and the preclusion of the reradiation of a higher wavelength spectrum received from the solar energy.

In general, the greater the quantity of black body material and the darker the coloration of the resulting tubing, the better is the efficiency provided from the use of the resulting ray absorbing tubing. Also, in order to obtain the desirable aspects of having an electrically conductive tubing which can bleed off electrostatic charges, there will generally be required a high content of conductive black body material in the resulting tubing.

It should be noted that the powdered filler material, or the carbonized refractory oxide filament pieces, will have a desirable reinforcing effect on the resulting plastic tubing to provide a higher melting point for the tubing and increase structural rigidity. As still another aspect, the utilization of the black body carbonaceous material will assist in ultraviolet stabilization properties for the plastic binding material. Additional free radical inhibiting additives might also be included provided they did not alter the transmission properties of the plastic binder in the solar ultraviolet region.

## FIGURE 1.51: SOLAR HEAT ABSORBING TUBING

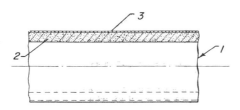

Source: U.S. Patent 3,968,786

The exterior coating **3**, to provide a selectively absorbing type of surface may, to some degree, be considered optional, depending upon the type of plastic binder material being utilized to form the tubing. In other words, as heretofore noted, where the plastic binder does not provide a desirable greenhouse effect to preclude reradiation of the higher wavelength radiation, then it is desirable to add a very thin film of a suitable metal component which will provide a selectively absorbing effect and preclude or inhibit reradiation. Such coatings may be provided in accordance with generally conventional methods of electroplating or electrostatic coating procedures which are well-known in the coating and plating arts.

The present type of tubing may be utilized for positioning in front of flat plate reflecting means or within focusing collectors. Flat plate collectors are preferable in many instances in that they can diffuse solar radiation and perform to some extent on cloudy and overcast days. They may also be utilized in a fixed position and do not need to be moved to follow the sunlight.

### Mounting Member for Collectors

A solar collection system is described by *H.S. Katz and P.R. Rittelmann; U.S. Patent 3,937,208; February 10, 1976; assigned to Sunearth Construction Company, Inc.* wherein first and second solar collectors of the fluid circulating type are supported by opposite sides of a mounting member having a recess for receiving a substructure. A header on one collector is coupled to a header on an adjacent collector by way of a flexible conduit extending through openings in the mounting member. The system is designed so that minimum assembly is required at the job site. The system **10** as shown in Figure 1.52a is inclined at an acute angle with respect to the horizontal, such as 45°. The system includes the substructure **12** and **14** of a roof such as rafters, I-beams, etc. Between adjacent

substructures there is provided one or more of the solar collectors **16, 18, 20**.
A mounting member **22** is provided for the substructure **12** and a mounting
member **24** is provided for the substructure **14**. The mounting members **22** and
**24** cooperate with each other to support the solar collector **16** disposed therebetween. Thus, each mounting member partially supports a solar collector on
opposite sides thereof. A mounting member is provided for each substructure.
The distance between adjacent substructures may be varied as desired. It is preferred to space the substructures so that they are about 32" on center.

## FIGURE 1.52:  MOUNTING MEMBER FOR COLLECTORS

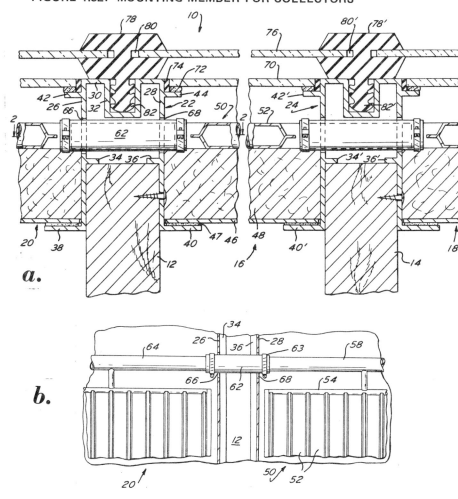

(a) Sectional view through a roof embodying the system
(b) Sectional view taken along line **2–2** in Figure 1.52a

Source:  U.S. Patent 3,937,208

The mounting members 22 and 24 are identical. Only mounting member 22 will be described in detail with corresponding primed numerals being provided on the mounting member 24. Mounting member 22 is preferably extruded from a lightweight noncorrosive metal such as aluminum. Mounting member 22 has parallel longitudinally extending side walls 26, 28 and a top wall 30 extending therebetween. The top wall is provided with a recessed channel 32 extending along the length thereof.

The mounting member 22 has intermediate walls 34 and 36 extending towards each other from the side walls 26, 28 respectively at approximately the midpoint of the height of the side walls. The walls 26, 28, 34, 36 cooperate to define a recess on one side of the mounting member 22 for receiving substructure 12. At the free ends of the side walls 26 and 28, there are provided outwardly extending flanges 38, 40 respectively. Also, outwardly extending flanges 42, 44 are provided on side walls 26 and 28, respectively, adjacent to the top wall. The flanges 42, 44 are shorter than the flanges 38, 40 as shown in Figure 1.52a.

Each of the solar collectors 16, 18, 20 is identical. Hence, only solar collector 16 will be described in detail. The solar collector includes a layer of insulation 48 provided on its lower surface with a sheet 46 which is a vapor barrier. The sheet is sealed to the flanges 40, 40' by any suitable material such as putty 47. The layer of insulation may be any suitable material but preferably is lightweight rigid insulation such as Fiberglas having a thickness of about 2".

A tube sheet 50 of the fluid-circulating type overlies and is supported by the layer of insulation. The tube sheet has a plurality of longitudinally extending parallel flow passages 52 and is made from a lightweight noncorrosive material such as aluminum. The width and spacing of the flow passages may be varied as desired. It is preferred to use flow passages which are 2½" on center. The upper or outward surface of the tube sheet is preferably coated with a black heat-absorbing paint or equivalent. In order that the tube sheet may be supported by the layer of insulation, the latter is preferably rigid and precut.

The tube sheet may be a fluid-circulating expanded metal honeycomb-type panel prefabricated to have an inlet header 54 at one end and an outlet header at the other end. The inlet header communicates with an inlet manifold 58, while the outlet header communicates with an outlet manifold. One header on the tube sheet communicates with a header on the tube sheet associated with solar collector 20 by way of a flexible conduit 62. The flexible conduit 62 is provided with quick-release hose clamps 63 on each end. One end of the conduit is connected to the manifold 58 while the other end of the conduit is connected to the manifold 64.

The mounting member 22 is prefabricated so as to accommodate the flexible conduit. See Figures 1.52a and 1.52b wherein the side walls 26, 28 are provided with openings 66, 68 respectively at an elevation above the elevation of the flanges 34, 36 and below the channel 32. The conduit may interconnect one inlet header with another or one inlet header with an outlet header on the adjacent tube sheet.

An inner layer of transparent material 70 is supported by the flanges 44, 42'. A seal 72 is provided between the flanges and the inner layer while a seal 74 is provided between side wall 28 and the side edge of layer 70. The layer is preferably a sheet of ⅛ inch thick double-strength glass having an integrated trans-missivity of about 87% or more. The seals **72, 74** provide a pressure seal be-tween the layer **70** and the mounting member **22**. A similar seal is provided in conjunction with the mounting member **24**. The upper surface of layer **70** is substantially flush with the upper surface of top wall **30**.

An outer layer of transparent material **76** is provided above and spaced from the layer **70**. Layer **76** is preferably a layer of ³⁄₁₆ inch thick rolled water-white crystal glass with an integrated transmissivity of at least 90.5%. Opposite side edges of layer **76** are supported by gasket mounting strips **78, 78'** of resilient material such as neoprene rubber.

The gasket mounting strip **78** is provided with slots on opposite sides thereof for receiving the side edge portion of the layer **76** to provide a watertight seal. Strip **78'** is provided with a similar slot **80'**. The strips are provided with a longitudinally extending spline or tongue **82, 82'**. The tongues are force-fit into their respective channels on the top wall of their respective mounting members. It will be noted that member **78** has a flat bottom surface which engages the upper surface of the top wall on opposite sides of the channel **32**.

### Adjustable Convection Plate

The solar heating system of *D.W. Butterfield; U.S. Patent 3,799,145; March 26, 1974* includes solar chambers each comprising a housing having a lens suitably mounted on the uppermost terminal side of the housing and a convection plate disposed parallel between the lens and the back wall of the housing operable to divide the heating chamber into a convection plenum and a heating chamber cavity which is operable to circulate fluid, reservoir means, and pumping means.

# FOCUSING COLLECTORS

## PARABOLIC

### Reflector with Plurality of Flow Tubes

A solar energy heat exchanger described by *L.B. Haberman; U.S. Patent 4,015,584; April 5, 1977* includes a housing formed by parabolic shaped walls and a transparent front plate connecting the walls. A longitudinal focal tube is positioned about the focal line of the parabolic housing. The transparent front plate is faced toward the sun, permitting the rays to pass therethrough, some of which pass onto the front part of the focal tube.

The inner surface of the parabolic walls reflects the rest of the sun rays which pass into the housing, and sends the reflected rays to the back part of the focal tube. A plurality of flow tubes can be positioned adjacent the inner surface of the parabolic walls to receive the sun rays as well. The flow tubes can have reflective coatings around them to aid in reflecting the sun rays on to the focal tube. Top and bottom covers on the parabolic housing have holes therein which are located above and below both the focal tube and the flow tubes, permitting a pipe assembly to connect to the tubes for providing the entry and exit of a fluid into the tubes. The solar energy heat exchanger can be placed inside a dwelling, with the transparent front plate serving as the actual windowpane of a window aperture.

Referring to Figures 2.1b, 2.1c and 2.1d there is shown the solar heat exchanger 10 of the present process including a wall structure 12 shaped in the form of a parabola. The ends 14 of the parabolic shaped walls are open and are interconnected by means of a transparent front plate 16. A top cover 18 and a bottom cover 20 complete the enclosure of the heat exchanger. Positioned within the heat exchanger is a focal tube 22 extending longitudinally throughout the height of the heat exchanger. The focal tube is positioned about the focal line 24. Such focal line is formed by the locus of focal points for the parabolic curved wall 12. The focal tube walls can be made of glass such as Pyrex glass.

The transparent front plate **16** would be positioned to face the sun and thereby receive the rays of the sun which can pass through the front plate and into the housing.  The inner surface **26** of the walls **12** is made at least partially reflective such that rays passing through the front plate onto the parabolic walls **12** will be reflected from the walls in a direction towards the focal line.  The focal tube will receive direct sun rays **28** passing through the transparent front plate and onto the focal tube wall.  Additional rays **30** passing into the housing will be reflected off the inner surface of the housing walls and onto the focal tube. Approximately one-half of the focal tube, and specifically the front semicylindrical portion thereof, will receive the direct sun rays; while the rear half, and specifically the back semicylindrical surface thereof, will receive the reflected sun rays.

### FIGURE 2.1:  REFLECTOR WITH PLURALITY OF FLOW TUBES

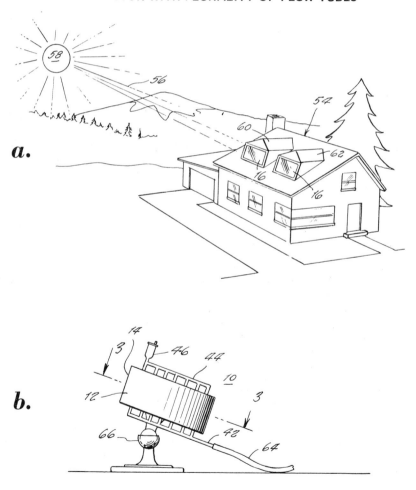

(continued)

FIGURE 2.1: (continued)

**c.**

**d.**

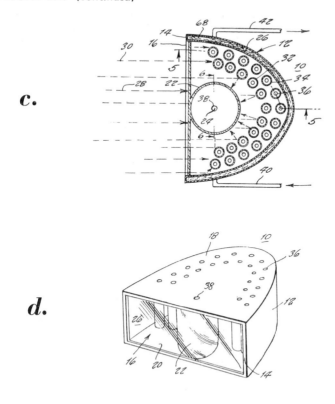

(a) Perspective view of collector installed in
   a house
(b) Side elevation view
(c) Cross sectional view taken along line **3—3**
   of Figure 2.1b
(d) Perspective view of collector

Source: U.S. Patent 4,015,584

In order to increase the efficiency, it is possible to make the front half of the
focal tube transparent to direct sun rays and the rear half of the focal tube
absorptive to reflected rays. Such absorption can be achieved by painting the
rear half of the cylindrical tube black. Additionally, other absorptive material
can be coated onto the rear surface of the focal tube.

In addition to the focal tube, additional tubes can be included within the parabolic housing. A first plurality of such flow tubes **32** is positioned adjacent
to the inner surface of the parabolic walls at spaced interwalls along a first parabolic line parallel to the parabolic housing walls. The flow tubes can be made
of glass, or of a reflective material such as aluminum. When made of reflective

material, these tubes serve to aid in the reflection of sun rays passing through the front plate and into the parabolic housing. A second plurality of flow tubes **34** can also be included. Flow tubes **34** are located in spaced apart relationship along a second parabolic line parallel to the parabolic housing wall and positioned between the parabolic housing wall and the first parabolic line containing the first plurality of flow tubes **32**. Tubes **34** can also be made either of glass or of a reflective material such as aluminum, whereby they will also serve to reflect the sun rays passing through the transparent front plate.

Focal tube **22** can be positioned in a spaced relationship from the transparent front plate. Alternately, if both the front plate and the focal tube are made of glass, it is possible to form the focal tube as an integral part of the front plate and make them both a single molded one-piece construction. This will even further increase the efficiency of the unit. The top and bottom plates include holes **36** in registration with each of the flow tubes and hole **38** in registration with the focal tube. The bottom holes would typically be identical to the holes in the top cover. The holes can be made smaller than the actual size of the tube to permit the fluid to remain within the tube a greater period of time and be heated to a higher temperature.

A pipe assembly is included to bring the fluid into the system, pass it through the various tubes and then bring it out of the heat exchanger. The fluid will enter along line **40** and exit along line **42**. The fluid will flow into the outermost set of tubes **34** and then pass through the pipe assembly **44** going from one tube to the next adjacent tube. A float valve **46** is shown included within the system to assure the proper pressure within the system and to bleed off excess air that may accumulate with the pipe assembly. Such float valves are well known in the heating industry.

After the fluid has passed through the outer flow tubes **34**, the fluid can then pass into the inner flow tubes **32**. Since the inner tubes **32** are closer to the front plate **16**, they will receive a higher temperature from the sun rays. Utilizing the two rows of flow tubes, the outermost row will permit the return of the line fluid from the heating pipe. The fluid on its return has had its heat dissipated within the pipes of the dwelling heating system. This return fluid will then first pass through the outer tubes and be gradually heated. Then, the fluid will pass into the inner flow tubes to be additionally heated.

The system can then include pipes whereby all of the fluid from the inner flow tubes will pass into the focal tube to receive the greatest amount of heat. This gradual heating from the outer flow tubes to the inner flow tubes and then to the focal tube prevents heat shock to the materials and improves the efficiency of the system. From the focal tube the fluids can then pass out along line **42** to the heating system within the dwelling to pass through radiators and other equipment used for heating.

Alternately, it is possible to have a double flow fluid system. Specifically, the inner focal tube can be utilized for the heating of the dwelling. The focal tube fluid will of course attain the highest heat in the heat exchanger. The flow tubes including both the inner and outer groupings can be used to provide the hot water for the dwelling. Such hot water need not be heated to the same high temperature which is used for heating of radiators and accordingly the lower temperature from the flow tubes will be satisfactory for such a hot water system.

## Parabolic Concentrator

*E.R. Hurkett; U.S. Patent 4,011,858; March 15, 1977* provides an apparatus for collecting solar energy, the apparatus including a parabola shaped reflector around a pipe enclosed in a glass tube, the pipe being located at the focal point of the parabola shaped reflector, so that sunlight rays are reflected thereagainst, so to concentrate their heat thereagainst, the pipe extending outwardly of opposite ends of the reflector, so that water passing through the pipe is thus heated for practical uses. The parabolic reflector is rotatable, so to follow the path of the sun, in order to obtain maximum efficiency therefrom.

Referring to Figures 2.2a, 2.2b and 2.2c the reference numeral **10** represents a solar concentrator, according to the process, wherein there is a reflector **11** of elongated character, and which is of parabola cross-sectional shape, the reflector being open upon its upper side, the inside surface of the reflector being coated with a reflective material **12**.

The opposite ends of the reflector **11** include opposite end walls **13**, each one of which is integral with an outwardly extending sleeve **14**, fitted around a metal pipe **15** that extends through the solar concentrator, and through both sleeves which are axially aligned. As clearly shown in Figure 2.2b, it is to be noted that the pipe runs along the axis of the focal point of the parabola shaped reflector, so that light rays **16**, from the sun shining against the reflective surface **12**, of the reflector, are directed toward the pipe **15**. A glass tube **17** is fitted around the outer side of the pipe.

## FIGURE 2.2: PARABOLIC CONCENTRATOR

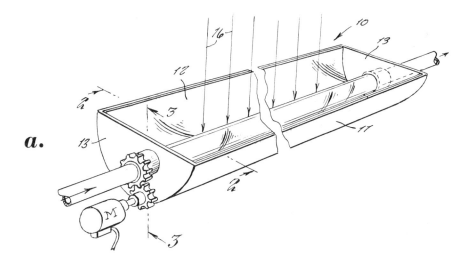

*a.*

(continued)

FIGURE 2.2: (continued)

**b.**

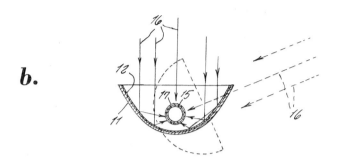

**c.**

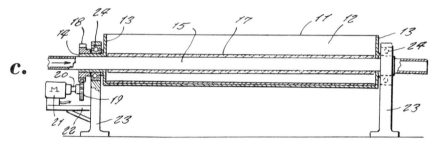

(a) Perspective view
(b) Transverse cross-sectional view taken on line
    **2–2** on Figure 2.2a
(c) Cross-sectional view taken on line **3–3** of
    Figure 2.2a

Source:  U.S. Patent 4,011,858

A gear **18** is fixedly secured to one of the sleeves **14**, the gear **18** being engaged
via teeth with a gear **19** mounted upon a shaft **20** of an electric motor **21**.
The motor is mounted upon a shelf **22**, integral with a stanchion **23**, which,
at its upper end, supports a bearing **24**, within which the sleeve **14** is supported,
in order to rotate relatively friction-free.  The opposite end of the solar concentrator likewise includes the above described stanchion **23**, supporting the bearing **24**, for supporting the sleeve of the end wall **13**.

In operative use, the reflector can thus be automatically turned, in order to
face the sun position, if the motor is activated by a switch controlled by the
sun position.  Thus, water traveling through the pipe **15** can be heated within
the pipe portion that extends within the solar concentrator, so that the water
can be utilized for heating purposes.

### Device for Increasing Thermal Efficiency of Cylindrical Collector

In the process of *B.T. Chao and A. Rabl; U.S. Patent 4,007,729; Feb. 15, 1977; assigned to the United States Energy Research and Development Administration* a device is provided for improving the thermal efficiency of a cylindrical radiant energy collector. A channel is placed next to and in close proximity to the nonreflective side of an energy reflective wall of a cylindrical collector. A coolant is piped through the channel and removes a portion of the nonreflective energy incident on the wall which is absorbed by the wall. The energy transferred to the coolant may then be utilized.

Referring to Figure 2.3a, there is shown the transverse cross section of means for improving the thermal efficiency of cylindrical radiant energy collectors. The cylindrical collector is a trough-like device whose structure is formed by extending the cross sections shown along an axis perpendicular to the plane of the cross section to form a trough-like structure. The function of the collector is to concentrate radiant energy impinging within a given acceptance angle upon entrance aperture **10** of each collector **11** onto the surface of an energy absorber **12**. Here there is shown a plurality of collectors positioned side by side. The device may also be utilized with a single collector. The energy absorber **12** may be, for example, a pipe containing fluid.

### FIGURE 2.3: DEVICE FOR INCREASING THERMAL EFFICIENCY OF CYLINDRICAL COLLECTOR

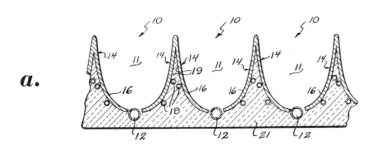

*a.*

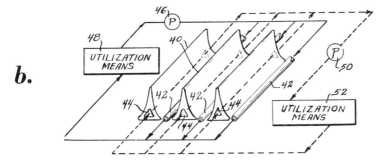

*b.*

(continued)

FIGURE 2.3:  (continued)

C.

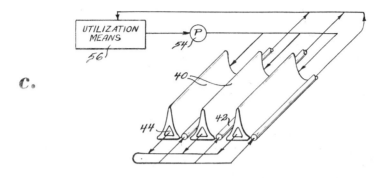

(a)  Transverse cross section of the device
(b)(c)  Arrays of trough-shaped collectors utilizing
the process

Source:  U.S. Patent 4,007,729


As shown in Figure 2.3a, the side walls **14** include one side **16** of each wall
**14** upon which the radiant energy is incident which is of a reflective material
such as aluminum or silver.  Since all reflective surfaces, no matter how care-
fully made, are not perfect mirrors, a portion of the energy incident on side
**16** of each wall **14** is absorbed into the wall.  If the side wall is simply formed
of thin metal plate bent to the desired contour as shown in Figure 2.3a, the
heat is absorbed by the metal of wall **14**.

The removal of heat absorbed by the metal wall and not reflected is facilitated
by attaching smaller tubes **18** to the side **19** of wall **14**, the nonreflective side
**19** being opposite reflective side **16**.  The attachment of the tubes should be
with good thermal contact and material forming the walls of the tubes should
also be a good heat conductor.  Copper or brass tubes soldered to surface **19**
are satisfactory.  A heat transfer fluid is made to flow through tubes **18** and
removes heat transferred to tubes **18** from walls **14**.  Air or water or any other
well-known coolant is satisfactory.  As the tubes **18** on surface **19** will radiate
some of the absorbed heat, a generous amount of insulating material **21**, for
example, a urethane foam, may be disposed in the region between walls **14** defined by opposing surfaces **19**.

Utilization of the heat obtained from the energy absorbed by the mirrors can
be by numerous means including that shown in Figure 2.3b.  There is shown
an array of trough-shaped collectors **40**.  Each collector has a transverse cross
section which is extended along an axis perpendicular to the cross section to
form a trough-like cylindrical collector.  At the exit aperture of each collector
is a primary energy absorber **42**.  The absorber is shown as one of the type
which has a fluid flowing through it to carry away the concentrated heat.  Each
array of collectors **42** is provided with secondary heat removal tubes **44** for

removing heat absorbed by the side walls of collector **40** as previously described. The heated fluids from the primary and secondary heat removal means can be utilized separately or in a cooperative manner. In Figure 2.3b the utilization is separate. Thus, primary absorbers **42** are coupled together and fluid is pumped through them by pump **46** and heat from the primary fluid is utilized by utilization means **48**. The secondary heat removal tubes **44** are coupled together and fluid is pumped through them by pump **50** and heat from the secondary fluid is utilized by utilization means **52**. This separate arrangement might be advantageous where the incoming primary fluid has a relatively high temperature such as where utilization means **48** is an absorption air-conditioning system. The utilization means **52** might advantageously use the secondary fluid for a different purpose, such as hot water preparation.

In Figure 2.3c tubes **44** and the primary absorbers **42** are serially coupled so that the secondary tubes **44** serve as preheaters. Fluid is pumped first to the secondary tubes **44** and then to the primary absorbers **42** by pump **54** and heat from the common fluid is utilized by utilization means **56**. This configuration might be advantageously used where utilization means **56** provides for domestic space heating.

### Horizontal Elongated Reflectors

A collector is described by *W.C. Matlock and P.K. Somlo; U.S. Patent 4,000,734; January 4, 1977* which comprises a plurality of elongated reflectors mounted for movement each around a heating tube arranged in the linear focus of the reflectors and linked to a tracking mechanism which causes the reflector to be trained toward the location of the sun so that it receives a maximum amount of solar energy. The plurality of solar energy parabolic-like reflective type collectors mounted in a rack to move in unison with a common stationary fluid heat transfer tube passing through the focal point of each of the collectors is adaptable to such applications as home heating, heating water for swimming pools, and general home use.

Referring to Figure 2.4 a heat exchange or solar energy collector **10** comprises one or more pairs of reflectors or reflecting troughs **11A** and **11B** which may be parallelly arranged in a frame **12** for pivotal movement in unison each about a part of a fluid flow line **13**. The fluid flow line may comprise in part a blackened solar ray absorbing copper tube of about $1/2$ to $1\,1/2$ inches in diameter comprising, inter alia, portions one of which is arranged along the longitudinal axis of the associated curve trough. The portions of the fluid flow line pass through the ends of the associated reflecting trough and are interconnected, as shown, and comprise an inlet **14** and an outlet **15** which may be controlled by one or more valves **16**.

Each reflecting trough is pivotally mounted on the frame at points **17** and they are moved in unison by a rod **18** which is threadedly engaged at one end with a thread bore **19** in flange **20** forming a part of frame **12**. This rod is also supported at its other end in a bearing flange **21** and driven by an electic motor **22** the rotation speed of its armature being reduced by a step-down gear mechanism **23** which, in turn, is connected to rod **18** for rotation thereof at a greatly reduced speed such as a few revolutions per minute.

FIGURE 2.4:  HORIZONTAL ELONGATED REFLECTORS

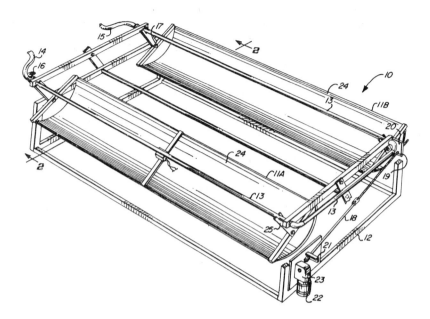

Source:  U.S. Patent 4,000,734

It should be noted that the reflecting troughs present a highly reflective surface 24 to the sun having a proper curvature in vertical cross section to bring the sun rays to a focus along a line parallel with the longitudinal axis of the surface of the reflecting trough and coincident with the center of the portion of the flow line 13 passing through it.  For this reason, the reflecting troughs are mounted on stirrups 25 pivotally mounted on the frame on the ends of the portion of the fluid flow line passing therethrough for rotation around the associated fluid flow line portions.

A bank of reflecting troughs may be mounted on a frame to form the collector. The orientation of the reflecting troughs should preferably lie in a parallel series forming a planar configuration, whose plane is at right angles to the plane of the meridian and preferably, though not necessarily, parallel to the earth's axis. The longer axes of the reflecting troughs are approximately horizontal, and at right angles to the plane of the meridian.

The reflecting troughs are rotatable about the axes of the portions of the fluid flow line 13 in the troughs and the several troughs are connected by a link whereby all such reflecting troughs of a series may be rotated simultaneously through an angle of 60° or more or less.  The screw shown or equivalent means, is adapted for this purpose.  This linkage is so adjusted that the reflecting troughs 11 are oriented similarly with respect to the sun at all times, whatever be the angle of setting by the linkage.  A light sensor is provided to sense the position of the sun and energize the motor **22**, if not properly oriented, to align the reflecting troughs toward the sun. By these means all the reflector elements may be properly oriented continually so that the axes of their parabolic cross-sectional curves shall all lie in planes including the center of the sun. Under these circumstances the rays of the sun will continually focus upon the heater tubes independently of the altitude of the sun above the horizon. In such a manner the orientation is accomplished by such simple mechanisms thus far described, requiring only slight and intermittent attention by the sensor without the use of elaborate clockwork or costly mechanisms such as are ordinarily used to focus sun rays in astronomical instruments or solar engines.

The heater elements or reflecting troughs are associated in series covering an inclined planar area of 6 by 10 feet more or less, all operated by a single linkage, as above described. Other similar series may be situated adjacent thereto. Thus, large areas, suitable to the collection of immense quantities of solar energy, may be utilized in one power plant. In operation, this system may be used for either heating or cooling. When it is desired to collect solar radiation and to transfer the heat thereby accumulated, the heat-transfer fluid within the fluid flow tubes will rise to a predetermined temperature of, for example, 180°F. When it is desired to dissipate heat to the natural climate condition, fluid such as water is circulated through the fluid flow tubes to be cooled by radiation to the colder atmosphere. The reflector is inexpensively formed from aluminum over a reusable form. Its inside surface may be chrome plated by an inexpensive process to provide an ideal reflective surface.

### Reflecting Surface Shaped as Paraboloid Revolution

*J.M. Trihey; U.S. Patent 3,996,917; Dec. 14, 1976; assigned to Malz Nominees Pty. Ltd., Australia* describes solar heating apparatus for heating a heat transfer medium comprising a support structure, a light absorbing surface arranged to transmit heat to a heat transfer medium, focussing means mounted on the support structure for focussing solar energy upon the light absorbing surface, and tracking means for tracking movement of the sun and moving the focussing means relative to the support structure to maintain the solar energy focussed upon the light absorbing surface.

The device illustrated in Figure 2.5a comprises light focussing means **2** for focussing solar energy upon a solar energy absorbing target **4** located at the focal region of the focussing means. The focussing means may comprise a convex lens, Fresnel lens, or parabolic reflecting surface, in which case the focal region will comprise a relatively sharp point. The focussing may however comprise a cylindrical lens or reflecting surface, in which case, the focal region will comprise a line. The illustrated arrangement shows the focussing means in the form of a reflecting surface **6** which has the shape of a paraboloid revolution.

The reflecting surface may conveniently be pressed from a square sheet of aluminium or other highly reflective metal. It may be coated with corrosion resistant materials so that its reflective properties are maintained. Small drainage holes may be punctured through the surface **6** to permit rain water to drain therethrough. Alternatively, it may have a flat sheet of glass extending across its front and hermetically sealed to the peripheral edges of the surface, and have the space between the glass and the surface filled with an inert gas to avoid surface deterioration of the surface **6**. Alternatively, the glass may be curved to closely conform to the shape of the reflecting surface **6**, or if desired directly mirrored.

Light which impinges upon the reflecting surface **6** and is parallel to its optical axis will be reflected through the focus of the surface **6**. For effective operation, it is important to ensure that the optical axis **5** of the surface **6** is pointed directly at the sun and for this reason it is necessary to move the surface **6** so that this relationship is maintained. In accordance with the process, the focus of the surface **6** is located at a fixed point in space therefore making it possible for the target to be stationary.

**FIGURE 2.5:  REFLECTING SURFACE SHAPED AS PARABOLOID
REVOLUTION**

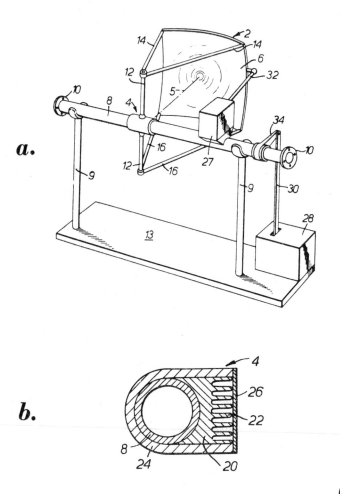

(continued)

**FIGURE 2.5:** (continued)

*c.*

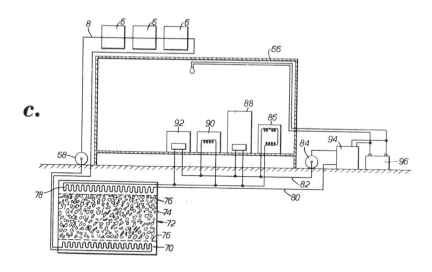

(a) Perspective view of basic form of the apparatus
(b) Cross-sectional view through heat absorbent target
(c) Domestic application of the apparatus

Source: U.S. Patent 3,996,917

In the arrangement illustrated in Figure 2.5a, the target **4** is not truly stationary since it is arranged to rotate about a horizontal axis as the sun is tracked, enabling simple support and movement of the focussing means **2**, as will be described below.

The target **4** is mounted upon or forms part of the surface of a conduit **8** for a heat transfer fluid, the conduit **8** being mounted horizontally in a pair of yokes **9** which permit the conduit **8** to rotate about its longitudinal axis. The yokes are connected to a base structure **13** which can be mounted upon a roof or other fixture at the side of the apparatus. Two opposed support rods **12** project radially from the conduit **8** (in an ideal apparatus, an imaginary line joining the adjacent ends of the rods **12** would pass through the focus of the surface **6**).

Pivotally connected to the outer ends of the rods **12** are upper and lower pairs of adjustable support arms **14** and **16**. The ends of the arms **14** and **16** remote from the rods **12** support respective corners of the surface **6**. Thus, the surface **6** is supported by the conduit whereby rotation of the conduit **8** about its axis will cause a corresponding rotation of the surface **6** about the same axis. The surface **6**, however, can rotate relative to the conduit **8** by virtue of the pivotal connection of the arms **14** and **16** of the rods **12**. It is desirable to include in the arms **14** weak-points which will fail under strong wind conditions to thereby effectively restrict damage to the arms **14** and surface **6** and prevent more serious damage to the remainder of the apparatus. The conduit 8 is provided at its ends with flanges 10 to enable coupling to similar conduits 8 or to an end coupling which must permit rotation of the conduits 8 and still maintain sealing contact therewith.

In operation, a heat transfer liquid, such as oil, is pumped through the conduit 8 so that it is heated on passing the target 4 which has intense solar energy focussed upon it. Figure 2.5b shows one form of target which comprises a thermally conductive body 20 in intimate contact with the conduit 8. The body 20 has a finned heat absorbent surface 22 onto which the sun's rays are focussed by the surface 6. The body 20 and the conduit 8 are mounted in an open faced housing 24, the open face of which is spanned by a transparent protective sheet 26.

The space between the absorbent surface 22 and the sheet 26 is filled with an inert transparent gas, or evacuated to prevent oxidation of the surface 22, and to reduce heat losses therefrom by conduction and convection. The axis is perpendicular to both the axis of the conduit 8 and the optical axis 5 of the surface 6. With this construction, the surface 6 can be rotated about an axis which is coincident with the axis of the cylindrical target surface 22, whereby, if the focus of the surface 6 is initially on the cylindrical target surface, during subsequent rotations of the surface 6, the focus will always remain on the cylindrical surface.

The focussing means 2 must be moved so that the optical axis 5 is always directed at the sun so that a very high temperature is established and maintained at the heat absorbent surface 22. For this purpose tracking means is provided and will be described in more detail below. The apparatus includes a base structure 13 which is mounted such that the conduit 8 is horizontal and extends in a north-south direction so that rotation about the axis of the conduit can be used for elevation tracking of the sun. For complete tracking of the sun in elevation, 180° of movement of conduit 8 about its axis is sufficient for the optical axis 5 of the surface 6 to track the sun from its rise until its setting. However, it is preferred to permit 360° of rotation of the surface 6 so that it can be caused to enter an inverted position, with the optical axis 5 directed downwards, to prevent dew formation upon the surface 6.

With regard to tracking in azimuth, the extent of rotation required of the surface 6 about the rods 12 depends upon the latitude of the place where the apparatus is to be set up. In general, the greater the distance from the equator, the greater the range of rotation required for azimuth tracking. The tracking means includes an elevation mechanism 28 mounted upon the base structure 13 and provided with an arm 30 pivotally connected to a flange 34 mounted upon the conduit 8. Movement of the arm 30 controls the elevation angle of the optical axis 5 of the surface 6. The tracking means includes an azimuth tracking mechanism 27 mounted upon the conduit 8 and having an arm 32 pivotally connected to the surface 6.

Movement of the arm 32 causes the surface 6 to rotate about the axis of the rods 12 and thus controls the azimuth angle of the optical axis of the surface 6. The tracking mechanisms must therefore be capable of moving the arms 30 and 32 in such a way that the optical axis of the surface 6 correctly follows the elevation and azimuth angles of the sun.

In one form the tracking means may include motor driven cams arranged to cause the arms **30** and **32** to follow paths appropriate for causing the surface **6** to follow the sun during a day. These cams would need periodic adjustment by a futher cam to account for the seasonal changes in the sun's path. To this end a crystal clock could be provided and arranged to make daily adjustments to the cam to ensure correct following of the sun throughout the year.

Figure 2.5c illustrates a domestic application of the solar heating apparatus of the process. A building **66** has three interconnected surfaces **6** mounted on its roof with their transfer fluid conduits **8** connected in series. A pump **68**, pumps the fluid through the conduits **8** and through a heat exchanger **70** located at the bottom of a heat store **72**. The heat store comprises a thermally insulated subterranean tank **74** having grids **76** the space between which is filled with a heat storing medium such as crushed rock. The tank **74** is then filled with oil such as reclaimed sump oil to make it void free and enhance heat transfer with the heat exchanger **70**.

A second heat exchanger **78**, located in the tank **74** above the upper grid **76** is provided to enable heat to be withdrawn from the store **72**. The exchanger **78** is connected in a circuit which includes a supply duct **80**, return duct **82**, and circulating pump **84**. The supply duct is arranged to supply heat to such devices as a stove **86**, absorption refrigerator **88**, heater **90** or absorption cooler **92**. It also supplies heat to a motor generator set **94** which is arranged to charge a battery **96**. Electric power from the battery **96** is used for lighting purposes, electronic equipment, such as radios, and for driving the pumps **68** and **84** and the solar tracking devices for the reflecting surfaces **6**.

## Vertical Elongated Collector

An elongated solar heat collector described by *L.T. Wilson, Jr.; U.S. Patent 3,954,097; May 4, 1976; assigned to Wilson Solar Kinetics* is formed by means of a heat exchanger having two thin-walled tubes arranged coaxially of one another, a cylindrical, transparent heat shield positioned coaxially around the tubes and an elongated parabolic reflector mounted to locate the focal axis of the reflector on the axis of the tubes and shield. The outer tube of the heat exchanger has helical corrugations extending along a greater portion of its length and the valleys of the corrugations are made to contact the outer surface of the inner tube so that a helical passageway is defined between the inner and outer tubes.

The straight elongated passageway of the inner tube and the helical passageway between the coaxial tubes communicate with one another at one end of the elongated collector so that two fluid flow paths defined by the passageways are serially connected and permit a fluid heat exchange medium such as water to flow in and out of the exchanger. With such construction, solar energy directed from the reflector through the transparent shield heats the water or other medium by conduction when the medium flows in one direction through the inner tube as well as when the water flows in the opposite direction in the helical passageway within the outer tube.

Figure 2.6a illustrates the elongated solar heat collector projecting vertically from a roof for exposure to solar radiation. The roof is part of the structure heated by a system to which the collector **10** is attached.

## FIGURE 2.6: VERTICAL ELONGATED COLLECTOR

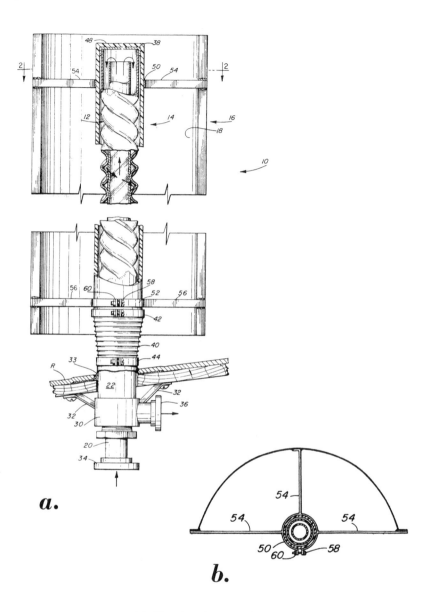

*a.*

*b.*

(a) Elevation view, partially in section
(b) Top plan view

Source: U.S. Patent 3,954,097

While the collector is shown mounted vertically from a roof, it may also be mounted vertically from the side of the structure if such mounting should happen to provide the greatest exposure to solar radiation and protection from other elements such as wind and dust which reduce the heat transfer character-istics of the collector.

The collector is comprised principally of an elongated heat exchanger 12, an optically transparent heat shield 14 mounted coaxially over the exchanger and an elongated reflector 16 having a parabolic reflecting surface 18 which focuses incident solar energy onto a focal line located colinearly of the axis of the heat exchanger and shield. The reflecting surface directs solar energy through the transparent heat shield to the heat exchanger and a fluid heat exchange medium such as water is circulated through the exchanger from the heating system within the structure to assimilate the collected energy.

The heat exchanger is comprised of a thin-walled inner tube 20 and a thin-walled outer tube 22 mounted coaxially of the inner tube. Both tubes are made from copper or aluminum for high thermal conductivity. The outer tube has a series of helical corrugations along a substantial portion of the tube wall exposed above the roof. The corrugations define a series of helically extending ridges and valleys on the inner and outer surfaces of the tube 22, and the valleys on the inner surface contact helical sealing areas on the outer surface of the inner tube 20 to define at least one helically extending passageway about the tube 20 for the heat exchanging medium. More than one helical passageway is defined if the corrugations are formed by more than one continuous helix.

The valleys of the corrugations on the inner surface of the tube 22 may be mechanically pressed into contact with the outer surface of the inner tube 20 to establish the helical sealing areas between adjacent convolutions of the corru-gations, or other suitable sealing means may be provided. The mechanical con-tact seal between the two tubes can be generated while the corrugations are produced on the outer tube by twisting and axially compressing the outer tube 22 over inner tube as explained in greater detail in U.S. Patent 3,730,229. The shallow corrugations produced on the inner tube generate a slight swirling motion of the heat exchange medium for improved heat transfer as the heat exchange medium is pumped axially along the elongated passageway defined by the inner tube.

At the bottom end of the heat collector below the roof, the heat exchanger 12 is supported by a bracket 30 and three struts 32 connected with the inner side of the roof. Suitable flashing 33 would also be used between the heat exchanger and the shingles in order to provide a weather seal. The lower end of the heat exchanger is also provided with couplings 34 and 36 for connection with other plumbing of the associated heating system. The coupling 34 is connected to the inner tube 20 and preferably serves as the inlet for a heat ex-change medium. Correspondingly, the coupling 36 is connected to the outer tube 22 and serves as the outlet.

At the upper end of the heat exchanger 12 the outer tube 22 extends beyond the adjacent, open end of the inner tube 20 and is closed by means of a cap 38. Effectively, the cap 38 serves as an end wall which interconnects the elon-gated passageway through the inner tube 20 and the helical passageways defined between the corrugations of the outer tube **22** and the outside surface of the inner tube **20**. From this construction it will be understood that there are two coaxially arranged flow paths defined by the elongated passageway and the helical passageways. A fluid heat exchange medium enters the inner tube **20** below the roof at the coupling **34** and passes upwardly through the elongated passageway of the tube **20** while receiving heat energy by direct conduction through the tube walls at the helical sealing areas of the tubes **20** and **22**. The fluid then returns to the coupling **36** through the helical passageways and receives heat energy by conduction through the corrugations of the outer tube walls. An annular spacer is soldered in place between the lower ends of the inner and outer tubes **20** and **22** to insure that the fluid medium is diverted out through the coupling **36**.

The heat shield **14** is provided to prevent trapped solar energy within the annular region between the outer tube **22** of the heat exchanger **12** and the inner surface of the shield from escaping by convection. The shield is cylindrical in shape and fits loosely over the corrugations of the outer tube **22**. The upper end of the shield is closed by an end wall **48** so that the shield may simply rest on the cap **38** of the heat exchanger. The lower end of the shield is fastened to the outer tube **22** by means of a tubular boot **40** and a pair of removable clamps **42** and **44**. The upper end of the boot surrounds the lower end of the cylindrical shield and is held tightly against the shield by the clamp **42** while the lower end surrounds a smooth cylindrical portion of the tube **22** below the corrugations and above the roof, and is held tightly against the tube by the clamp **44**. The boot **40** thus seals the annular space between the shield **14** and the heat exchanger **12**.

An optically transparent material such as a clear acrylic plastic is utilized to fabricate the heat shield. Solar radiation may then pass through the shield to the heat exchanger but cannot readily leave the exchanger. Wind, rain and other environmental influences are prevented from carrying heat away from the surface of the heat exchanger and operational efficiency is thus improved.

The elongated reflector **16** is mounted on the heat shield **14** by means of two mounting brackets **50** and **52** having annular portions circumscribing the shield and a plurality of generally radially extending arms **54** and **56**. The bracket **50** and the radially extending arms **54** shown in Figure 2.6b extend between the shield and reflector adjacent the upper end of the elongated heat exchanger **12** while the bracket **52** and arms **56** extend in similar fashion between the shield and reflector adjacent the lower end of the exchanger. Each bracket is constructed as a clamp and has a clamping screw **58** and nut **60** shown more clearly in Figure 2.6b for securing or releasing the brackets on the shield and permitting the reflector **16** to be turned angularly about the heat exchanger **12** to any desired position.

The reflecting surface **18** of the reflector **16** is an elongated and generally parabolic surface. The radially extending arms **54** and **56** have lengths selected to locate the focal axis of the reflecting surface colinearly with the central axis of the heat exchanger **12**. Thus the reflector can be rotated about the heat exchanger to a position which optimizes the amount of solar energy focused on the corrugated surface of the heat exchanger during any given portion of the daylight hours. To further improve the absorption characteristics of the heat exchanger, it is contemplated that the outer surface of the tube 22 may be painted black to reduce its emissivity and thereby allow the exchanger to more nearly exhibit black body characteristics in the infrared spectrum.

While the collector 10 has been described in a form suitable for absorbing solar radiation, it may be partially disassembled for use as a radiator of heat to cool a medium circulated through the heat exchanger 12. By loosening the clamp 44, the reflector 16, the shield 14 and the boot 40 can be slipped upwardly over the corrugations of the heat exchanger 12 and be entirely removed. If a heat exchange medium is then circulated through the tubes 20 and 22 when the ambient temperature surrounding the heat exchanger is less than that of the medium, heat will be transferred away from the medium. Thus the heat exchanger can be used to cool the medium at night when the outside temperature drops below, for example 65°F, and if sufficient quantities of the cooled medium are held in storage, the structure below the roof may be cooled during the following day when elevated temperatures exist outside of the structure.

## Dish-Shaped Collector

A solar device of dish-shaped configuration is provided by *L.A. Pauly; U.S. Patent 3,993,528; November 23, 1976* for the reflection of solar rays toward a heat exchanger through which passes a heated medium. The reflective surface of the device comprises a miltitude of mirror elements incorporated into a fiberglass reinforced plastic structure with each of the mirror elements located so as to reflect rays toward a common focus.

A wire grid spaces each of the mirror elements during furnace construction. Each of the mirror elements is temporarily supported on a loosely woven fiberglass cloth permitting each element to individually adapt to the curvature of a convex mold. Subsequent application of fiberglass and resin to the thickness desired results in a rigid dish-shaped structure within which may be incorporated support components.

With reference to Figure 2.7 the reference numeral 1 indicates generally a solar furnace of dish shape having concave-convex sides indicated at 2 and 3. Concave surface 2 comprises a multitude of mirror elements 4 each disposed having a reflective angle to redirect solar rays toward a focus whereat a heat exchanger 5, served by conduit 5A-5B, is located. The mirror elements 4 constituting the concave surface of the furnace are in closely spaced disposition with each of the elements having its sides spaced or offset from the adjacent side of adjoining mirror elements. The mirror elements 4, are of straight sided, planar configuration.

The dish-shaped device so constructed is well able to withstand exposure to the elements. The type, size and shape of the heat exchanger used will be dependent upon the particular use to which the furnace is applied. In one embodiment the furnace utilizes mirror elements three quarters of an inch square and a mold having a diameter of 48 inches. The energy imparted to heat exchanger 5 for heating of the medium passing therethrough is adequate to heat water for household uses which may include a space heating system.

FIGURE 2.7:  DISH-SHAPED COLLECTOR

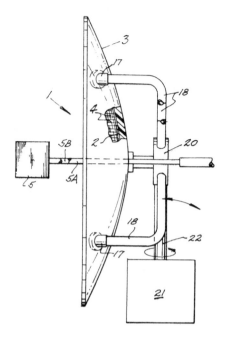

Source:  U.S. Patent 3,993,528

**Lightweight Collector**

*F.W. Oakes, Jr.; U.S. Patent 3,985,119; October 12, 1976* describes a solar
energy collector system providing a mechanically oriented parabolic trough
direct radiation collector having along the focal line a portion of a first fluid
conduit system and outside the focal line a portion of a second fluid conduit
system, sectionally in arcuate array about the first fluid conduit system.  A greenhouse energy-collection effect to conserve heat at the fluid conduit systems
is provided by means of a second collector system including a glass-front
enclosure over the parabolic trough collector, and preheating of fluid entering
the solar heat collection system is provided by means of an insulated compartment behind the parabolic trough through which return tubing of the first
and second fluid collector systems pass; a valve provides for separate or for
serial connection of the two systems; and an aluminum foil covering over a parabolic form provides for renewal of the reflective surface.

Figure 2.8a illustrates the collector **10** in operation in an exposed location **L**
such as a rooftop.  A horizontally extended reflector **12** having a parabolic
cross section **14** is provided for optical efficiency in radiation collecting and
focussing.  This may advantageously be of molded fiberglass with a reflective
surface of cemented-on aluminum foil **12a**.

# FIGURE 2.8: LIGHTWEIGHT COLLECTOR

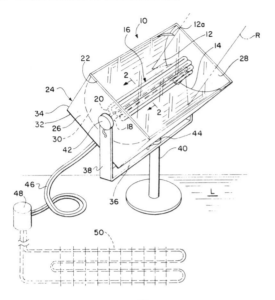

*a.*

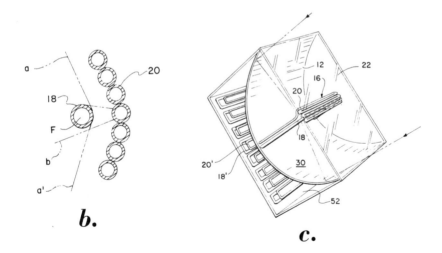

*b.*

*c.*

(a) Isometric view
(b) Sectional detail adapted from 2–2 of Figure 2.8a
(c) Isometric view of a detail of Figure 2.8a

Source: U.S. Patent 3,985,119

The reflector collects radiation **R** from the sun and focuses the radiation collected onto a tubular conduit array **16** comprising a first tube system **18** having a tube extending parallel with the reflector in the focal line and a second, folded, tube system **20** extending parallel with the first but outside the focus of the reflector, and generally forming a hemispherical group of tubes in section. Fluid in the conduit array is heated directly by the radiation and also by greenhouse effect heating of the air surrounding it, contained by transparent front panel **22** which preferably is of lightweight plastic material having the general transmissive characteristics of window glass. Alternatively, the front panel may be of ordinary window glass or double pane insulating glass.

The front panel is held in place and the air around the tubular array is confined hermetically by a box-like frame **24** which preferably is molded of fiberglass, with insulation within, but which may be of lightweight metal having an insulative covering on the inner face, or which may be of weather-resistant insulative fiberboard, or other suitable material. The ends **26**, of the frame have reflective sheet **28** such as aluminum foil applied to the inner faces in heater chamber **30** defined by the ends, the reflector and the front panel. The frame has a back **32**, top **34** and bottom **36**, and has pivot supports in altitude **38** and azimuth **40** to permit continuous orientation toward the sun, as for example, by selsyn (self-synchronized) motors **42**, **44** and controlled by a selsyn programmer, not shown, or by any other usual heliostat mechanism.

Fluid in the tubular array, which may be water, ethylene glycol, Freon, or other conventional liquid or gas used for the purpose of heat transfer, passes, after heating, through conventional means such as insulated flexible tubing **46**, urged by any conventional means for pumping **48**, and then through a conventional heat exchanger coil **50** in the space to be heated, and back into the tubular array in the heater exchanger for reheating.

In Figure 2.8b, a section of the first tube system **18** portion and the second tube system **20** portion is at the focal line **F** of the reflector. The peripheral rays **a** and **a'** of the full beam on-axis heat tube system **18** and any portions of the beam such as **b** which pass by or reflect from the tube system **18** heat the tube system **20** surrounding, outside the focus, that portion of the tube system **18** lying along the focal line. This makes the system efficient when illuminated off-axis, when overfilled by scattering of sunlight, and when the reflector contour is less accurate than would otherwise be required.

Figure 2.8c, a detail view of the frame with the rear end removed to show associated parts, indicates the relation of the transparent front panel **22**, the tubular array **16**, with the proximate portions of the tube systems **18** and **20**, the reflector **12**, the heater chamber **30**, and rearward of the reflector the preheat compartment **52**.

In the preheat compartment the tubes of the first and second tube systems leading from the pump are folded into respective proximate heat exchanger coil sections **18'** and **20'**, insulated from the outside and warmed by heat transfer from the heater chamber. Fluid warmed here is then passed into the focal area, heated further, circulated out by the pumping means for heat exchange in whatever space is to be warmed, and returned for reheating.

## Semicylindrical Reflector with Combination Bearing and Seal

The process of *N.P. Salvail; U.S. Patent 3,847,136; November 12, 1974* relates to the fabrication and operation of a solar water-heating system utilizing semicylindrical reflecting surfaces. The semicylindrical reflecting surfaces are formed from foamed or expanded plastics with a combination bearing and seal at each end, through which the longitudinal, heat collecting tubes pass. A center, fixed support bearing that maintains the sealed enclosure is provided for longer heat collecting tubes. A linear actuating linkage is provided for rotation to follow the sun's motion daily and seasonally. The measurement of differential temperatures within the enclosure of the reflecting surface controls operation of the circulation pump that circulates the heated liquid to a heat exchanger.

With reference to Figure 2.9, the system functions as most solar water-heating systems which utilize forced circulation of the heat-transfer fluid. During operation of the system, the reflecting surfaces 5 are pointed by means of a rotating threaded shaft 6 which, by means of a linear actuating linkage 24, tilts the surfaces such that the sun's rays are brought to focus on the fluid transport tubes 7.

The heat-transfer fluid is circulated through the tubes 7 where heat is absorbed; then the fluid is circulated through insulated lines 8 to another heat exchanger coil 9 in a hot-water storage tank 10. A check valve 11 is incorporated to eliminate heat loss during periods without sunlight due to the natural convection currents that occur when the hot-water storage tank is located below the level of the heat collector.

### FIGURE 2.9: SEMICYLINDRICAL REFLECTOR WITH COMBINATION BEARING AND SEAL

*a.*

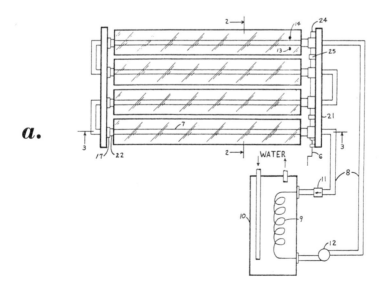

(continued)

FIGURE 2.9: (continued)

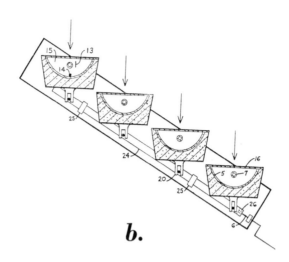

**b.**

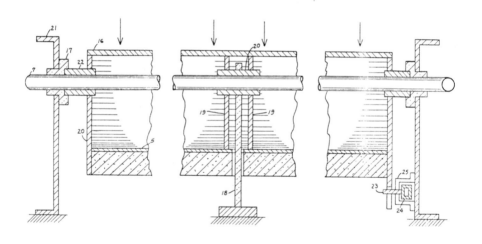

**c.**

(a) View of the system incorporating the
    semicylindrical reflectors
(b) Collection assembly
(c) Longitudinal cross section of semicylindrical
    tube

Source:  U.S. Patent 3,847,136

Operation of the circulation pump **12** is controlled with a differential temperature measurement **13** and **14** in one of the semicylindrical tubes. Thermistor sensors are proposed for this purpose, with one located at the focal point **13** and one sensing the shaded temperature **14** in the closed tube chamber **15**. The sensor at the focal point **13** is required to be 15° above the shaded temperature point **14** before the circulation pump is activated. The use of differential temperature in the semicylindrical tube assures that the heat-transfer fluid is only circulated when there is sensible heat to be collected and thereby conserving energy required to run the circulation pump.

Since the principle factor influencing the widespread acceptance of a solar water-heating system is cost, a different approach has been taken to achieve this goal. Construction of the semicylindrical reflecting tubes is based on the use of a foamed or expanded structural plastic with suitable strength and environmental exposure properties. Units have been fabricated from rigid polyurethane foam with satisfactory results. Other plastic compounds such as polystyrene, acrylonitrile-butadiene-styrene, or polyvinyl chloride may provide advantages.

These semicylindrical tubes may be either foamed, molded, or extruded. The reflecting surface **5** in the inner surface of the tube may be one of several materials. A highly reflective aluminum foil or aluminized material such as polyester has been utilized with good results. The transparent surface material **16** used is acrylic plastic sheeting, but significant cost savings can be realized by going to a thin film such as Teflon or Tedlar with a thickness of 0.010 inch for the fabrication concept illustrated.

The fluid-transfer tubes **7** chosen were cylindrical due to the ease of fabrication and availability. This also permits the use of an unusual combination bearing and seal as shown in Figure 2.9a and Figure 2.9c. Both parts of the bearing and seal **17** and **22** are fabricated of a plastic material such as nylon, with a silicon-grease lubricant between the sliding surfaces. The outer piece of the assembly **17** is fixed in the end support structure **21**; the inner piece **22** is fastened to the end closure **20** of the semicylindrical tube, rotating about the fluid-transfer tube **7** and transferring structural loads to the outer bearing piece **17**. The fluid-transfer tube **7** is fixed and does not rotate within the outer bearing **17**. The bearing-and-seal assembly acts as a barrier to outside rain and dust, providing a sealed, low-friction bearing for ease of pointing.

The pointing-and-actuator mechanism is shown in Figures 2.9a, 2.9b, and 2.9c. Figures 2.9b and 2.9c show the end closures **20** of the semicylindrical tube with actuator slots for movement. By means of these actuator slots and fixed pins **23** on the actuator linkage **24**, a linear motion within the actuator-linkage guide bearings **25** causes rotation of the semicylindrical tubes about the bearing surface of the fluid transfer tube. By means of a stationary, rotating, threaded rod **6** and threaded bearing **26** in the end of the actuator linkage **24**, the semicylindrical tubes can be pointed toward the sun as it moves daily and seasonally.

The screw thread **6** in a low friction, threaded bearing assembly **26**, such as a fluoroplastic, has provided a simple but rugged mechanism to point the reflecting surfaces. A small reversible motor with a gear reduction unit has been utilized in the process to turn the threaded rod. The consolidation of the pointing

and actuator mechanisms in the same end as the heat-transfer-fluid inlet and
outlet has the advantage of simplifying the installation of this solar water-heating system. Since rigid, semicylindrical reflecting tubes of the proper length
(less than 10 feet) require no central supports, they can be freely supported
with a bearing-and-seal assembly **17** and **22** at each end as shown in Figures 2.9a
and 2.9c.

### Curved Reflecting Roof

*I.R. Barr; U.S. Patents 4,004,574; January 25, 1977; and 3,994,435; Nov. 30,
1976; both assigned to AAI Corporation* describes a solar energy concentrating
and collecting arrangement and method in which a curved oblong concave re-
flector/concentrator forms the roof of a house, school or other building, particularly a heat utilization building. A collector is movably supported in spaced
relation above and along the length of the oblong roof/reflector concentrator,
for pivotal movement, by a solar reflection energy sensing and seeking drive
control arrangement, to a zone of maximum confluence of solar energy rays
reflected from the roof/reflector concentrator as a result of variations of sun
path during the various parts of the year and also to further accommodate each
day's movement of the sun.

Movement of the collector is by pivotal movement about an axis parallel with
the center of curvature or curvatures of the roof/reflector concentrator and
disposed adjacent the roof/reflector concentrator. The roof/reflector has a
plurality of radii, for enabling accommodation of wide variations of the sun
angles during the various seasons of the year and during each day of a given
season, while still affording a desired concentration of solar energy on the collector. The concentrated solar energy collected by the collector is transferred to
a fluid, such as water, passed along the length of collector, by a pump forming
a part of a heat utilization system, which may include heating and/or cooling
of the building and/or additional buildings or other structures. The roof/reflector
concentrator is oriented with its center of curvature axes running East-West and
with its surface tilted toward the equator, the degree of tilt being dependent
upon the latitude of the reflector.

Referring now in detail to Figure 2.10a through Figure 2.10e, a heat utilization
building structure, such as a house, school, factory, etc., generally indicated at
**11**, has a curved roof/reflector concentrator surface **21**, and may also have a
further roof surface or surfaces of any desired configuration as indicated at **31**.
The extent of reflector concentrator surface **21** is generally dependent upon the
amount of solar energy needed for a given desired use. For maximum energy
collection from a given roof size, the entire roof may be formed as a reflector
concentrator **21**. Windows **15** may be provided in walls **13f**, **13e**, and **13b**, as
desired.

Roof/reflector concentrator **21** may be formed of any suitable solar reflective
material, such as metal, glass, plastic, and such materials may be of load-bearing
type and provide some, a major portion, or all of the roof surface construction
strength or may be of nonload-bearing type as, for instance, a thin reflective
coating on a load-bearing substrate. The desired curvature of roof/reflector concentrator **21** may be formed as a smooth curve or as straight or curved line
segments. For instance, a curved metal roof surface may be formed in one

continuous sweep, or in several panels, or various normally straight panels of metal, glass, plastic, etc., may be utilized in suitably joined relation to form the desired over-all curved shaped roof/reflector concentrator surface **21**. The roof **21** may also be only partially reflective in parts thereof or in whole, if so desired, in order to provide for natural lighting of the interior of the building by light passage through the roof/reflector concentrator **21**. Similarly, the section **31** of the roof may also transmit light to the building interior if so desired. The roof/reflector concentrator **21** faces and is inclined toward the South, with its opposite ends oriented directly East-West.

The stationary reflector-concentrator **21** reflects and concentrates solar energy into a zone of maximum confluence which varies as a function of the angle of the sun with respect to the horizontal, as measured in a North-South vertical plane passing through the reflector concentrator **21**. A solar energy collector **51** is movably mounted, as by pivot arms **45**, for back-and-forth movement in a North-South direction above the reflector concentrator **21**. The collector pivot support arms **45** are pivoted along a horizontal East-West line which may extend beneath, above or at the surface of reflector concentrator **21**, with generally only small differences in effectiveness of the reflector concentrator **21**/collector **51** assembly.

FIGURE 2.10: CURVED REFLECTING ROOF

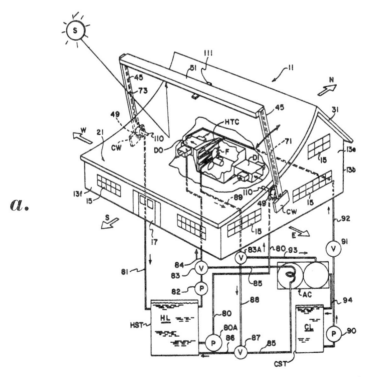

a.

(continued)

FIGURE 2.10: (continued)

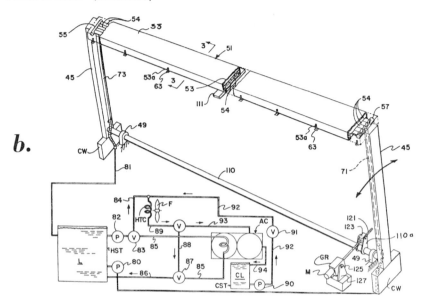

**b.**

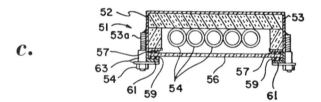

**c.**

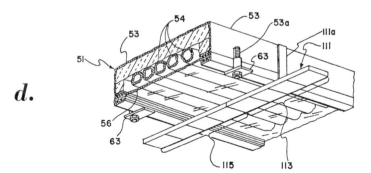

**d.**

(continued)

FIGURE 2.10: (continued)

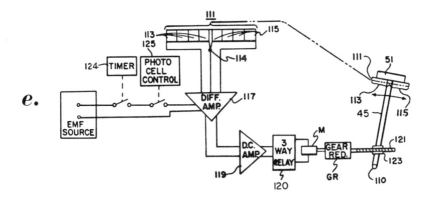

e.

(a)  Schematic view of building embodying system
(b)  Schematic view of pivoted collector and overall
     heat exchange system
(c)  Section view taken on line 3–3 of Figure 2.10b
(d)  Fragmentary view of collector showing the
     differential energy-sensing photocell arrangement
(e)  Schematic diagram of maximum energy-seeking
     null-type drive control arrangement

Source:  U.S. Patent 4,004,574

Arm and collector assembly **45, 51** may be desirably suitably counterweighted,
as by counterweights **CW**, and are desirably interconnected at the pivot zone by
a torque tube or shaft **110** for desired added rigidity. Collector **51** may be
suitably formed with a plurality of laterally side-by-side fluid flow heat transfer
tubes **54**, through which a suitable fluid, such as water, gas, etc., may be flowed
for collection of the reflected solar energy from reflector concentrator **21**.
Headers or manifolds **55, 57** may be employed at either end for interconnecting
the parallel flow tubes **54** with common feed and return conduits **71, 73**
mounted on the two end support arms **45**.

As shown in Figure 2.10c, the collector **51** is formed with its black body energy
absorption tubes **54** facing toward the pivot axis of the arm and collector assembly **45, 51**, and thereby facing the solar reflection thereto from reflector
concentrator **21** at a given proper angle of this assembly with respect to a given
sun elevation angle.

Collector **51** preferably is insulated at its outer surface facing away from reflector concentrator **21** and the pivot axis of the collector **51**, as by insulation
**52**, with a rigid opaque U-shaped cover plate **53**. A solar energy transparent
cover glass plate or plates **56** may be secured beneath the energy absorption
tubes **54**, and the entire assembly may be secured together as by threaded studs
secured as by welding to the cover plate **53** at spaced longitudinal intervals along

its length, with securing nuts and securing brackets, holding the glass plate **56** and headers **55, 57** in place, the glass plate being preferably sandwiched between two layers of elastic shock-resistant material **59**, such as soft rubber.

Fluid feed and return lines **71, 73** may be suitably connected to a desired heat utilization system, such as a heat storage and building interior heating arrangement, and/or a cooling system, such as one based on absorption cooling principles. Alternatively, various machinery may be caused to perform work by energy derived from the solar heat transferred to the fluid in collector **51**, or other desired and suitable heat-energy-derived work may be performed. With this process, fluid temperatures, such as for water as the fluid, may be raised to as high as 300°F or more, dependent on fluid flow rate, relative sizes of collector and reflector, etc. Practical heating and absorption cooling may be accomplished well within and below this temperature extent for the fluid **L** flowed through the collector **51**.

As an illustrative example, a liquid fluid such as water may be pumped by a pump **80** through lines **71, 54** and **81** to a hot liquid storage tank **HST**, in which the hot liquid is stored for subsequent heating or cooling use as desired. For heating of the interior of building **11**, or other desired area, a conventional hot water heating system may be employed, as with a pump **82**, two- or three-way valve **83**, conduit **84**, heat transfer coil **HTC**, fan **F**, further two- or three-way valve **83A**, conduit **88**, two- or three-way valve **87** and return line **86**. The fan **F** may pump air over the coils **HTC**, where it is heated and thereupon flows through ducts **DO** throughout the building **11**, with return in the conventional fashion through ducts **DI**.

For cooling, an absorption cooler **AC** may be provided, with hot liquid **HL** pumped through the unit by pump **P**, through valve **83**, conduit **85**, valve **87** and return conduit **86**. Cooled water or other cooling fluid **CL** is pumped through cooler **AC** by pump **90**, through cool storage tank **CST**, and out through valve **91**, conduit **92**, thence through coils **HTC**, and return through conduit **93** to cooler **AC**, conduit **94** and cool storage tank **CST**, with the valves set for flow in the cooled liquid conduits and for closure of the conduits **84** and **88**.

The pivot arms **45** may be pivoted about their axis by suitable reversible drive means. In the illustrative embodiment a motor **M** rotates a threaded drive screw shaft **121** through a gear reduction unit **GR**, the motor **M** and gear reduction unit **GR** and shaft **121** being pivotally mounted as a unit as at **125** on a suitable pivot support **127**. A nut follower **123** threadedly engages drive screw shaft **121** and is pivotally secured on a torque arm **110a**, in turn secured on torque tube **110**. The motor **M** is suitably driven to position the arm and collector assembly **45, 51** during the various days of the year and the various insolation hours of each day as may be desired.

Suitable reflected energy-responsive control means are employed for controlling the drive motor **M**. To this end, a differential solar energy-sensing means **111** in the form of a pair of sets of photocells **113, 115** or other photo- or heat-responsive elements, all of which may be generally termed as solar energy-sensing elements, is mounted on the collector **51** for movement therewith.

For simplicity of description, such sets of solar energy-sensing elements may be generally referred to simply as photocell sets or photocell set arrays. Photocell sets 113 and 115 are disposed transversely of the length of collector 51 and preferably at right angles thereto, as illustrated, with the effective midpoint or cross-over point therebetween lying on the effective longitudinal center line of the collector 51.

The outputs of photocell sets 113 and 115 are balanced against one another, as by employing a common output junction 114 for the two photocell sets, the outputs of which feed in balanced relation into a differential amplifier 117, having a DC output proportional to the difference in input signals from photocells 113 and 115.

The DC output from differential amplifier 117 may be suitably amplified, as may be necessary or desired, as by a DC amplifier 119, which in turn may control a three-way relay 121, having forward, reverse, and neutral or balanced stop positions for controlling electrical power to a DC or other suitable drive motor M. Drive motor M in turn drives the arm 45/collector 51 assembly forward and rearward about its pivot axis 110, through the medium of a gear reduction unit GR, drive screw 121, and drive nut follower 123 secured or otherwise suitably connected to arm 45.

As shown in Figures 2.10a and 2.10b, motor M may be suitably pivotally mounted, and drive nut follower 123 may be suitably pivotally connected to arm 45, to accommodate angular changes in the linkage connections during movement of arm 45.

Photocell sets 113, 115, formed of photocells or other solar energy-sensing elements, may be of the active or passive type, and in the instance of some relatively large signal output types of solar energy-sensing elements it may be feasible to feed the outputs of the solar energy-sensing elements in balanced relation directly to a three-way relay 120, or other switching arrangement for motor M.

In lieu of photocells 113, 115, other suitable solar energy-sensing means may be employed, if desired. For instance, heat-energy-responsive resistance-changing wires may be employed, again arranged in a balanced output relation, as by employing two sets of one or more such wires on the collector 51 and disposed transversely of the reflector-facing surface of the collector 51 and having their electrical outputs feeding a suitable differential amplifier 117 or other differential output-sensing means, the differential between the outputs of, or resulting signals across, the two sets of heat-energy-responsive resistance-changing wires being employed either directly or in amplified form to control the forward, reverse, or stop condition of a motor M and associated drive train arrangement as in the embodiment of Figure 2.10e.

Alternative to reversing motor M, a similarly solar-energy-balance/unbalance-controlled reversing gear train and clutch arrangement may be employed, and a neutral gear position may be employed in lieu of stopping the motor M, although the latter condition would normally be undesirable in view of unnecessary energy expenditure in continuously driving motor M.

## COMBINATIONS OF CURVED SURFACES

### Reflector of Concavo-Convex Hyperbolic Shape

*D.J. Lightfoot; U.S. Patent 4,003,366; January 18, 1977* describes a collector comprised of a panel or bank of heat collector modules each of which has a fluid carrying tube of an elongated triangular shape in transverse cross section formed with longitudinally extended inwardly projected heat radiating fins. A tube is mounted within a concavo-convex reflector of a hyperbolic form such that the side walls of the tube are subjected to reflected rays of solar radiation over an effective range of solar exposure of about 150°. The reflected rays are concentrated in a longitudinally extended focal zone on each side wall of the tube and these zones of concentrated solar radiation move transversely of a side wall in response to the angle of the solar rays falling upon the reflector.

The relative arrangement and construction of the reflector and fluid carrying tube in the heat collector module provides for an extremely efficient collection of solar radiation which efficiently takes place over a wide angle of solar exposure without requiring the use of tracking devices to maintain a predetermined relation between the sun and the reflector. The fluid-carrying tube is continuously subjected to reflected solar rays, the radiated heat from which is concentrated in focal zones extended longitudinally on each side wall of the tube. By virtue of the inwardly projected heat radiating fins in the tube, the radiant heat collected by the tube is efficiently transferred to the heat conducting fluid in the tube for delivery into a room heating system or the like.

With reference to Figures 2.11a and 2.11b, each heat collector module **18** includes a housing **24** of an elongated box shape having side walls **26**, end walls **27** and a bottom wall **28** of a metal or fiberglass construction; and a transparent top cover or wall **29**. The top wall is of a double pane construction that includes an upper pane **31** made of Tedlar, a polyvinyl fluoride plastic film having a thickness of about 4 mils, arranged in parallel spaced relation with a fiberglass transparent lower pane **32** about 0.040 inch in thickness known as Sun-Lite (Kalwall Corporation). Tedlar is known for its ability to withstand the elements and has the characteristic of selectively transmitting only the short-wave frequencies of light and of being opaque to long-wave infrared. The top wall **29** thus functions to prevent reradiation of solar rays into the atmosphere.

Mounted within and extended longitudinally of the housing is a reflector **33** of a concavo-convex shape in transverse cross section, the concave surface **34** of which faces upwardly toward the top wall. The reflector may be constructed of either reflectorized sheet aluminum or stainless steel and has a curvature which follows generally the shape of a section of a hyperbolic spiral. The lower pane **32** lies in the plane of a chord that extends between the extremities of the arc formed by the reflector. Thus, as shown in Figure 2.11b, the maximum lateral dimension or depth **D** of the reflector occurs in a plane normal to the chord and is located inwardly from the arc extremity **36**, a distance equal to about one-third the length of the chord, as indicated by **L**.

The shape of the arc is maintained by its support on transverse form retaining members **37** mounted within and spaced longitudinally of the housing. A suitable thermal insulation **38** is filled in between the form retaining members to thermally insulate the convex or bottom surface of the reflector against the conduction or radiation of heat toward the side and bottom walls of the housing.

FIGURE 2.11:  REFLECTOR OF CONCAVO-CONVEX HYPERBOLIC SHAPE

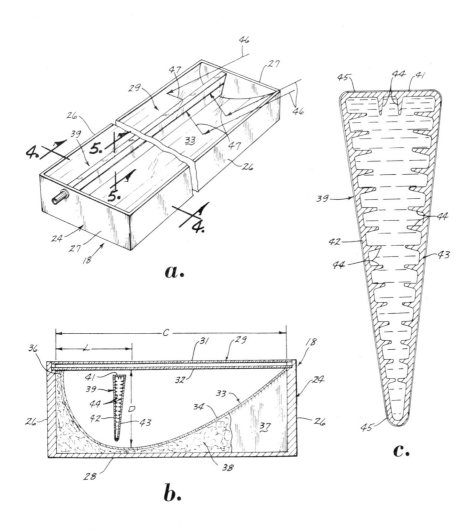

(a)    Perspective view of collector
(b)    Sectional view of collector along line 4-4
(c)    Enlarged cross section of fluid carrying tube

Source:  U.S. Patent 4,003,366

In one embodiment of the apparatus, the housing is 7 inches high, 20 inches wide and about 8 feet long; the reflector has a developed rectangular shape of about 2 feet by 8 feet and a chord length **C** (Figure 2.11b) between the arc extremities of the reflector of about 19 inches; and the panes **31** and **32** of the top wall **29** are rectangular in shape and spaced about ½ inch apart. In this embodiment, the maximum depth or lateral dimension is about 6¼ inches at a distance from the arc extremity of about 6 inches. At a distance of about 3 inches from the extremity the lateral depth of the reflector arc is about 5¼ inches and at distances of about 10 and 14 inches from the arc extremity the lateral arc depths are about 5½ inches and 3⅝ inches respectively.

Mounted within and extended longitudinally of the reflector is a fluid carrying or heat collector tube **39** of an elongated triangular shape in transverse cross section (Figures 2.11b and 2.11c) having a base or top wall **41** and side walls **42** and **43** of substantially equal length. In the above mentioned embodiment of the process the base wall is about 2 inches wide and the side walls are about 6 inches wide. The collector tube has the base wall **41** spaced from the housing top wall **29** with the side wall **42** adjacent to and substantially parallel with the plane at the maximum lateral depth of the reflector arc.

The collector tube is made of aluminum and formed by extrusion with spaced heat radiating fins **44** extended longitudinally of the tube and projected inwardly from the inner surfaces of the tube walls **41**, **42** and **43**. The outer surface of the tube is painted or coated with a black colored heat absorbing material, indicated at **45**, such as Nextel. The Nextel material has a capacity of absorbing about 98% of the heat directed or reflected thereon. Where desired a selective coating for the heat collector tube may be used. Details for various mounting arrangements for the collector modules are included in the patent.

### Sea Shell Shape

*A. Rabl; U.S. Patent 3,991,740; November 16, 1976; assigned to the U.S. Energy Research and Development Administration* provides a device for the collection and concentration of solar radiant energy including a longitudinally extending structure having a wall for directing radiant energy. The wall is parabolic with its focus along a line parallel to an extreme ray of the sun at one solstice and with its axis along a line parallel to an extreme ray of the sun at the other solstice. An energy absorber is positioned to receive the solar energy collected.

Referring to Figures 2.12a and 2.12b, there is shown a transverse cross section of two embodiments of the cylindrical solar energy concentration and collection device. As the device is a cylindrical collector, the physical structure of the collector is formed by extending the cross sections shown along an axis perpendicular to the plane of the cross section to form a trough-like structure, as will be described with reference to Figure 2.12c. The function of the collection device is to concentrate energy from the sun onto the surface of an energy absorber **10**. The energy absorber may be, for example, a pipe containing fluid or any other type of energy receiver responsive to radiant energy.

The process provides a collector having a concentrating side wall for reflecting energy incident thereon onto the energy absorber. In particular, the concentration factor of the collector, which is defined as the width of the entrance aperture divided by the width of the exit aperture, is to be seasonably variable, with either peak concentration in summer or winter, as desired.

# FIGURE 2.12: SEA SHELL SHAPE

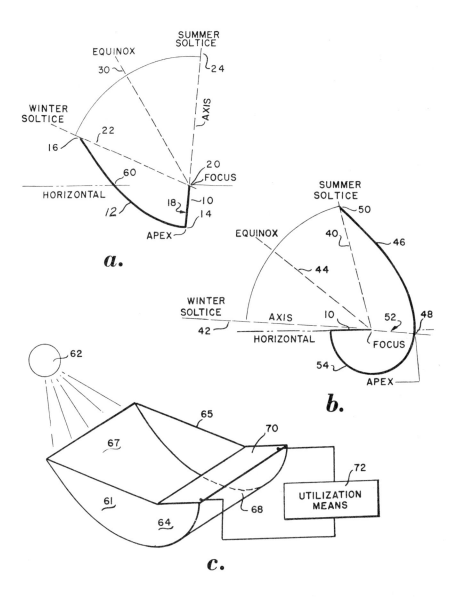

(a)   Cross section of collector of maximal summer output
(b)   Cross section of collector of maximal winter output
(c)   Longitudinally extended structure of collector

Source:   U.S. Patent 3,991,740

Referring to Figure 2.12a, there is shown a collector with peak concentration in summer. The collector includes a concentrating wall **12** which extends between points **14** and **16**. The concentrating wall directs energy incident thereon within particular angles, depending upon the time of year, out exit aperture **18**. Wall **12** is parabolic in contour with its axis **24** parallel to an extreme ray of the sun at summer solstice. The wall extends between point **14** which is at the apex of the parabola and point **16** which is at the juncture of wall **12** and a line **22** parallel to an extreme ray of the sun at the winter solstice. The angular difference between lines **22** and **24** is about 72±36° on either side of the line **30** parallel to a ray of the sun at equinox. This angular difference is generally constant regardless of location. However, the angle between the equinox position, line **30**, and the horizontal, parallel to the earth's surface, varies depending upon latitude.

An extreme ray of the sun is one which is at the largest angle with respect to a ray of the sun at equinox that a ray of the sun will make. This will occur twice on each solstice, in the morning and in the evening, when the same extreme angle with respect to the equinox line will be made by the extreme ray from the sun. The references to solstices and equinox are based on solar time, i.e., the actual equinox for a particular location.

The parabolic shape of reflecting wall **12**, as herein described, will have a variable concentration with respect to energy exiting exit aperture **18**. The concentration factor is a measure of the ratio between the width of the entrance aperture and the width of the exit aperture. The exit aperture out which energy is directed by wall **12** is between point **14**, the apex of the parabola, and focus **20** of the parabola, which lies along the apex axis. The actual distance between points **20** and **16** is a matter of choice since all parabolas are concentric as all circles are concentric, differing only in size.

Absorber **10** is positioned to extend from focus **20** to point **14**. The entrance aperture is the opening of the collector within which rays of the sun are concentrated by the collector. In the figure, as the sun moves from summer solstice to winter solstice, the entrance aperture decreases, being zero at winter solstice. As the sun moves from winter solstice to summer solstice the entrance aperture increases. The increase or decrease varies with the cosine of the angle of an axis through the entrance aperture and the position of the sun. Thus the concentration factor varies from zero in winter to 3.4 in summer without inclusion of the cosine factor which will depend on the latitude. Such a variable concentration would be ideal to drive absorption air conditioners with a minimum of equipment. Note that during any particular time of year the area of absorber **10** to which energy is directed by the collection device varies. At the extreme conditions, at solstices, the energy is concentrated on either end of the absorber, while around equinox the energy is more equitably distributed.

Referring to Figure 2.12b, there is shown a collector having a variable concentration with peak concentration in winter. The summer solstice line **40**, winter solstice line **42** and equinox line **44** are as described in Figure 2.12a for lines **24**, **22** and **30**, respectively. However, in Figure 2.12b the parabolic concentrating wall **46**, which concentrates energy incident on the entrance aperture out the exit aperture, has its axis along the winter solstice line **42**. The parabolic wall **46** extends from its apex point **48**, along line **42**, and extends to line **40** at point **50**. In this instance, the maximum output at exit aperture **52** between the focus on apex **42** and apex point **48** occurs at winter when the concentration factor is about 3.4 and minimum output is at summer when the concentration factor is about 0 without inclusion of the cosine factor. The energy concentrated by the collectors is directed onto energy absorber **10**. In Figure 2.12a the absorber is shown positioned at and along exit aperture **18**. In Figure 2.12b the absorber is positioned with the surface of the absorber facing downward to minimize radiation loss which might otherwise occur if positioned at exit aperture **52**. This is accomplished by providing an additional wall **54** for directing, without concentration or dispersion, the energy exiting the exit aperture onto the absorber. Wall **54** is circular, having its center point at point **52** and being of radius equal to the width of the exit aperture **52**. The circular wall and the downward facing absorber may also be used in the embodiment shown in Figure 2.12a.

An example of the practical application of the process is shown in Figure 2.12c. Here one embodiment of collector **61** is shown concentrating energy from the sun **62**. The collector has a transverse cross section which is extended along an axis perpendicular to the cross section to form a trough-like cylindrical collector. Flat reflective end walls **64** and **65** fully enclose the collector. Concentrating wall **67**, whose contour is generated as described with reference to Figures 2.12a and 2.12b, and the side walls have a reflective material thereon which reflects substantially all of the solar energy incident from the sun, for example, aluminum or silver. The reflected energy is directed by additional circular wall **68** onto downward facing absorber **70**. Connections are provided to the absorber to allow utilization of the energy absorbed by utilization means **72**.

### Scoop Shape

A focused solar heating system is provided by G. Falbel; U.S. Patent 3,923,039; December 2, 1975 having a focusing reflector which is generally scoop shaped. A solar collector plate is mounted on the front of the focusing reflector to directly accept direct solar radiation and diffuse radiation which strikes the front surface of the plate. The remainder of the entrance aperture of the focusing reflector accepts both on- and off-axis solar direct and diffuse radiation which is reflected by the focusing reflector and applied to the rear surface of the solar collector plate.

The focusing reflector has a concave reflective surface made up of first and second merging curves which are optimized so that the front and rear surfaces of the solar collector plate accept the larger solid angle of both direct and diffuse rays from the sun and provides an optical gain which increases the efficiency of the system.

The solar collection system may be incorporated in a vertical wall of a building and made partially transmissive, or may be incorporated in a separate structure for supplementing the heating or cooling of a building or providing hot water therefor.

Referring to Figure 2.13a, the focusing solar energy collection system of this process includes a solar collector plate **10** having a front, short-wave length transparent surface **12** and a similar rear transparent surface **14** with a grid of pipes **16** between. The pipes carry a liquid medium which is circulated through the pipes and is heated or cooled by the radiation applied to the collector plate. The liquid is circulated by conventional circulating pumps (not shown) and used by conventional means to heat the building or supply hot water, or to cool it by radiation to the cold night sky.

FIGURE 2.13: SCOOP SHAPE

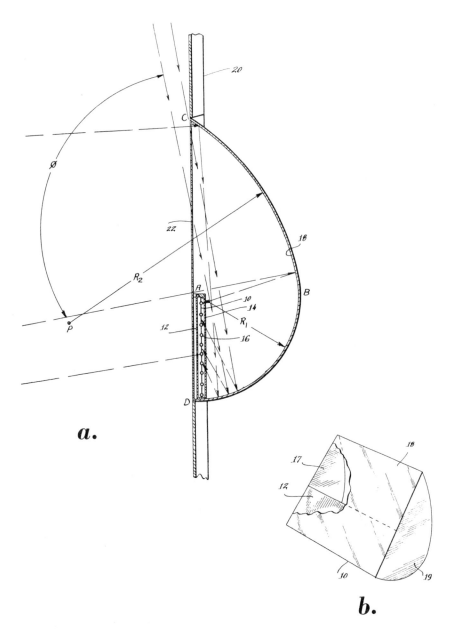

a.

b.

(a)  Side elevation of collector
(b)  Isometric view of collector

Source:  U.S. Patent 3,923,039

The liquid medium which is circulated in the pipes may be of any suitable type, such as water, oil or air. If required, the liquid medium may include suitable antifreeze additives to resist freezing if this is a problem. Furthermore, additives may be added for blackening the absorbing fluid to enhance the absorption of solar energy applied thereto.

Referring to Figure 2.13b, the solar energy system embodied in the process includes a concave reflective surface 18 bounded by reflecting side walls 17 and 19. The concave reflective surface may be of any suitable material, such as polished aluminum, a suitable plastic having a reflective casting thereon, or any other type of suitable mirrored surface which collects and reflects the solar energy applied thereto to the back surface 14 of the solar collector plate 10. In a vertical orientation as shown, the solar collector plate is located and covers the lower portion of the focusing reflector 18 and is positioned substantially in the plane of the entrance aperture of the focusing reflector. The focusing reflector along with its side walls and the solar collector plate mounted thereon have a general scoop shape configuration.

Referring again to Figure 2.13a, the concave reflective surface 18 which is also referred to as the focusing reflector has an entrance aperture CD, covered in part by the solar collector plate 10 from points A to D, which forms the direct entrance aperture where solar energy, both direct and diffuse, is applied directly to the front surface 12 of the solar collector. The remaining portion of the entrance aperture CD comprises the reflective entrance aperture AC. The focusing reflector or concave reflective surface is made up of two curvatures BC and BD which are joined at point B, with point B located by passing a plane perpendicular to the entrance aperture CD at point A and intersecting surface 18 at B. In its simplest configuration, the reflective surface has a substantially cylindrical curvature from B to D, having a radius $R_1$ projecting from point A, which is equal to the collector plate height AD, with AB being equal to AD and perpendicular thereto.

Curvature BC is so constructed that all rays entering aperture AC making an angle $\phi$ are either reflected by curve BC or passed directly through the aperture AB and are thus applied to the back surface 14 of the solar collector plate 10. Curve BC is optimized so that the vertical ray angle $\phi$ is maximized concurrently with the dimension AC, thereby maximizing the elevation angle entrance product of rays passing through AC which also pass through AB. Once having passed through AB the rays may or may not be reflected by the curve BD, but they all finally reach the rear surface 14 of the collector plate and accordingly are absorbed thereby.

The simplest construction of curve BC is obtained by centering a radius $R_2$ of approximately 3 x $R_1$ at a point P in the zone in front of and below the normal to direct entrance aperture AD at point A. This arrangement results in a dimension AC being 2 times AD and a value of $\phi$ equal to approximately 95° to 100°. Since the flat ends 17 and 19 of the focusing reflector 18 are parallel and reflective, a solid angle ray bundle having dimensions of 100° in elevation by 180° in azimuth passes through the reflective entrance aperture AC, ultimately reaching the rear surface 14 of the collector plate. This solid angle represents 100% of the solid angle of diffuse sky radiation that could have been collected by a normal flat collector plate whose front surface makes an angle of 100° with the horizontal. However, since the reflecting entrance aperture AC is 2 times the direct entrance aperture **AD**, this diffuse energy, as well as the direct solar energy, is increased in intensity per unit collector area by a factor of approximately 2. Furthermore, since the front surface **12** of the collector plate **10** also absorbs direct and diffuse solar irradiance, the overall gross energy gain per unit area of the collector plate, assuming 100% reflection and window transmission, is approximately 3 to 1, as compared to a single flat collector having a vertical dimension of **CD**. This results in desirably higher collector plate temperatures.

It should be emphasized that a single radius $R_2$ centered at point **P** represents only the simplest implementation of the apparatus. Further optimization using parabolic, hyperbolic or similar curved functions for the reflective surface **BC** is possible, thereby further increasing the value of reflecting entrance aperture **AC** times $\phi$ solid angle combination. As is shown in Figure 2.13a, the solar collecting system is incorporated in the vertical side wall **20** of a building. In this configuration, the entrance aperture **CD** is vertical and the ratio of the reflecting entrance aperture **AC** to the direct entrance aperture **AD**, i.e., AC/AD, can be made larger than 2:1 at the expense of an allowably smaller value of solid angle $\phi$, thereby increasing the energy intensity gain as compared to a single-sided vertical flat plate collector even further.

Conversely, if it is desirable to increase the elevation angle $\phi$, and/or azimuth angle, if the cylindrical axis of the focusing reflector **18** is rotated, the ratio of the reflective entrance aperture **AC** to the direct entrance aperture **AD** can be made smaller, resulting in a commensurate increase in the solid angle $\phi$.

In the configuration shown in Figure 2.13a, where the solar energy system of the process is embodied in a vertical side wall of a building, the reflecting surface **BC** can be made partially transparent. In this way, occupants of the building can look out, and sunlight can come in through the window formed by the reflecting aperture **AC**, thus allowing the solar collector to form part of a usable sidewall which significantly increases the area providing solar energy collection without reducing substantially the window area of the building. This also provides desirable solar shading or reflective glass, thereby reducing solar heat loads for the building air conditioning in the summer.

In this configuration the amount of solar energy collected by the solar collector plate is reduced only a relatively small amount, because it is characteristic of partially transparent aluminized coatings that they transmit well, e.g., 10 to 20% in the 0.4 to 0.5 micrometer blue-green visible region of the spectrum, while the reflectivity of such a coating rapidly increases at longer wavelengths, i.e., 0.6 to 2.0 micrometers, where most of the solar heat energy is located in the spectrum.

The entire entrance aperture **CD** is preferably covered with a transparent material, such as a glass plate or transparent plastic **22**, which would protect both the collector plate and the reflecting surface from the elements. Otherwise a buildup of moisture in the form of rain, snow or other precipitation, or a buildup of dust, soot or other environmental deposits would seriously hamper the proper functioning of the solar collection system.

### Fixed Reflector with Spiral and Parabolic Sections

*R.H. Smith; U.S. Patent 3,974,824; August 17, 1976; assigned to Solergy, Inc.* describes a solar heating device utilizing a cylindrical reflector with a spirally extending section and a parabolically extending section for concentrating solar energy on an axially disposed absorber carrying a fluid to be heated. Substantially all of the energy impinging upon the reflector is reflected inwardly and ultimately strikes the absorber. The curvature of the reflector is such that the device can be mounted in a fixed position and deliver a large amount of concentrated solar energy to the absorber throughout the year.

As illustrated in Figures 2.14a and 2.14b, the heating device includes a housing 16 having a top wall 17, a bottom wall 18, a front wall 19, a rear wall 21 and end walls 22, 23. The walls are fabricated of a rigid material such as sheet metal, wood or plastic, and they are fastened together by suitable means to form a unitary structure. The housing also includes a window 24 which is mounted in an opening formed between top wall, front wall and end walls. The window is fabricated of a material which is transparent to solar energy, such as glass or a transparent plastic. It permits radiant solar energy to enter the housing and prevents the loss of heat energy through the opening by convection.

An absorber 26 is mounted within the housing and is supported by the end walls. The absorber includes a longitudinally extending pipe 27 which defines an axially extending flow passageway 28 for a fluid to be heated. The ends of the pipe extend through suitable openings in the end walls and provide means for making connections to the passageway externally of the housing. In the embodiment shown, the absorber also includes a plurality of tines 29 which extend radially from pipe 27. The tines support and are enclosed by a cylindrical shroud 30 of heat conductive material on which solar energy is absorbed. Both the pipe and the tines are fabricated of a thermally conductive material, and the tines provide a plurality of high conductivity paths from the surrounding shroud to the interior pipe.

A second cylindrical shroud 31 is disposed generally coaxially about absorber 26 and encloses the same. This shroud is fabricated of a thermally insulative material which is transparent to solar energy, and it serves to prevent heat loss from the absorber to the housing walls by convection.

A cylindrical reflector 36 is mounted within the housing generally parallel to the absorber and facing generally toward the window for directing solar energy passing through the window toward the absorber. The reflector extends away from the absorber along a spiral path 37 from a point 38 proximate to the outer periphery of the absorber to a point 39 which is spaced from the absorber. In the preferred embodiment, point 38 lies on a circle 41 which coincides with the periphery of absorber shroud 30 and is centered about the axis of passageway 28. Point 39 lies on a line 42 tangent to circle 41 at a point 43 spaced from point 38 by an angle A.

The reflector provides a greater concentration of solar energy on the absorber as angle A is made larger, but the field from which the reflector will accommodate radiation decreases as this angle increases. It has been found that angles on the order of 330° to 360° can be used if desired. Path 37 can be any desired spiral having a radius of curvature which increases with distance from the absorber. In the preferred embodiment for the generally circular absorber shown, the spiral is an Archimedes spiral, or involute, in which the radius of curvature increases. Such spiral can, for example, be generated by wrapping a piece of string about a circular template of a size corresponding to circle 41 and unwinding the string beginning at point 38, describing the desired spiral.

FIGURE 2.14:  REFLECTOR WITH SPIRAL AND PARABOLIC SECTIONS

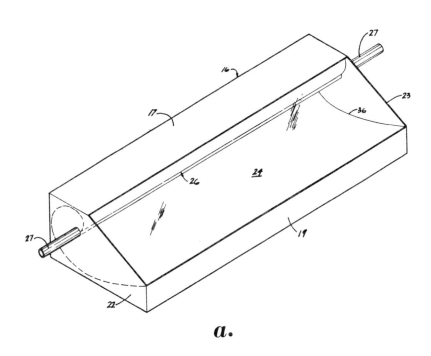

*a.*

*b.*

(continued)

FIGURE 2.14: (continued)

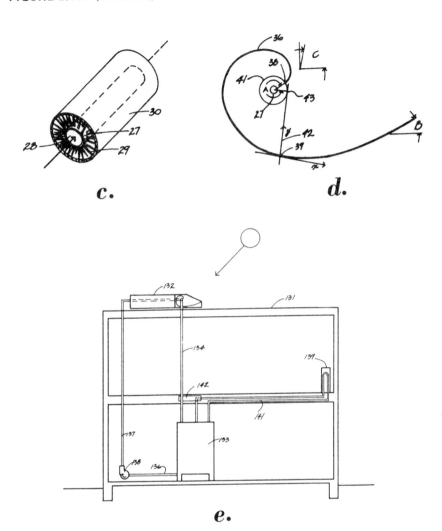

c.

d.

e.

(a) Isometric view
(b) Enlarged cross-sectional view
(c) Enlarged isometric view of the absorber
    of Figure 2.14a
(d) Schematic illustration of the reflector
    of Figure 2.14a
(e) Schematic illustration of a heating device
    according to the process

Source: U.S. Patent 3,974,824

Reflector **36** extends beyond point **39** along a generally parabolic path to a point **44** which is spaced farther from the absorber than is point **39**. In the preferred embodiment, the parabolic path is defined by the relationship $y = (\frac{1}{4}F)x^2$, where x and y are Cartesian coordinates in a system having its origin at point **39**, with the y-axis extending along line **42**, and F is the distance along the y-axis between point **39** and the outer periphery of the absorber. In the embodiment illustrated, circle **41** coincides with the outer periphery of the absorber, and the y-axis intersects the absorber at point **43**.

As illustrated, the curves of the spiral and parabolic portions of the reflector are matched so that the curvature does not change abruptly at junction point **39**. In the preferred embodiment, the location of point **44** is such that line **46** tangent to the reflector at that point is inclined at an angle B relative to bottom wall **18** corresponding to the zenith angle of the sun at its winter solstice. Similarly the y-axis is preferably inclined relative to wall **18** at the angle C corresponding to the zenith angle of the sun at its solstice. The acceptance angle of the reflector, which defines the field of view covered, is equal to the difference between angles C and B, and in the preferred embodiment, the acceptance angle is slightly greater than 46°, corresponding to the range of zenith solar elevation angles between the summer and winter solstices.

Reflector **36** is fabricated of a suitable material such as sheet metal or extruded plastic, and its inner surface is made reflective to solar energy by polishing or coating with a suitable material such as aluminum or silver or by adhering a layer of mirrorized plastic sheet. The reflector is mounted on end walls **22, 23** of the housing and supported by suitable means such as mounting brackets, not shown. As indicated above, fluid to be heated is passed through passageway **28**. Suitable fluids include water, Therminol, oil, air and refrigerant gases such as Freon and ammonia.

As illustrated in Figure 2.14e, the heating device of the process can be utilized in connection with other heating or cooling apparatus in a building. In this figure, the building is designated generally by reference numeral **131**, and the heating device, designated **132** is mounted in a fixed position on the roof of the building. The liquid circulating through the absorber is delivered to a thermal storage unit **133**, such as a condenser, located within the building. For this purpose, suitable piping **134** is connected between the pipe at one end of the absorber and the inlet of the condenser.

The outlet of the condenser is connected to the other end of the absorber pipe by suitable piping **136, 137**, and the fluid is circulated by a pump **138**. Within the building, heat energy is transferred from the condenser to equipment which utilizes heat, such as heater **139**, by additional piping **141**. Suitable measuring and control equipment shown generally at **142** is provided for regulating the flow rate of the working fluid through the absorber and the rate at which energy is delivered from the condenser.

## TUBULAR

### Double-Walled Glass Collector

Solar radiation is made up of two primary components. There is a component designated as $S_B$ which is incident upon the surface of the earth from the position of the sun at any given time. The component $S_B$ is a collimated beam of light. An additional component of the total solar energy available is a diffuse-radiation component designated as $S_D$. This component is not collimated and the rays are not parallel, but rather this component is available at a surface from many directions.

In the case of a flat plate collector, the major energy absorption takes place at the time when the beam $S_B$ is overhead or at solar noon. At this time, there is no loss of available energy to a flat surface as a result of the beam $S_B$ being inclined due to diurnal effects. Throughout the day, the beam $S_B$ moves in response to the relative motion of the sun. Particularly during the winter in areas away from the equator, the sun's position is lower in the sky, thus making the angle at which the beam $S_B$ strikes a horizontal flat surface lower, thereby causing loss in energy available to a horizontal flat surface as a result of the angular incident of the beam $S_B$. This problem may be solved to some extent by inclining a flat collector array to compensate for the sun's elevation.

Despite this deficiency, for a given area covered with a solar energy-absorbing array, the flat plate allows the maximum availability of energy for absorption as versus an array of tubular collectors. However, arrays of tubular collectors offer significant advantages in that such an array is capable of operating at a higher output temperature than is the flat plate type collector and in that the weight and expense of a tubular array may be somewhat less than a flat plate collector.

In Figure 2.15, *G.R. Mather, Jr.; U.S. Patent 4,002,160; January 11, 1977; assigned to Owens-Illinois, Inc.* illustrates one type of tubular collector array.

## FIGURE 2.15: PERSPECTIVE VIEW OF TUBULAR COLLECTOR

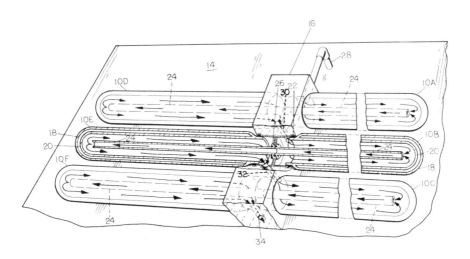

Source: U.S. Patent 4,002,160

The tubular collector array shows six tubular collectors **10A** through **10F**. The tubular collectors are mounted on each side of a manifold **16**. The manifold is positioned transversely to the pitch of a roof, which includes the diffusely-reflecting surface **14**, on which the collector array would be mounted. Thus, the tubes **10D**, **10E** and **10F** would be "down" relative to the tubes **10A**, **10B** and **10C**. This relationship is important, if the working fluid is a liquid, to prevent air locks and to allow the use of gravity flow whenever possible to keep pumping pressures low.

All of the tubular collectors are identical in construction and the collectors **10B** and **10E** have been shown completely in cross section in order to explain the structure of the collectors. An outer transparent glass tube **18** has one closed end which extends beyond the manifold and an open end which is adjacent to the manifold. The tube is completely transparent around its entire circumference to allow maximum collection of solar radiation. This differs from such tubes in the prior art which were generally at least partially mirrored or coated in some manner.

An inner tube **20** is sealed to the outer tube **18** near the open end of the outer tube. The inner tube may be glass, but also could be a metal tube. The inner tube may be blackened or provided with an overall selectively absorbing coating to absorb the solar energy. The space between the tubes is evacuated or reduced to subatmospheric pressure to reduce conduction and convection losses from the collector. The open end of the inner tube is in sealing engagement with an opening in the manifold in a gasket **22**. Note that while the inner tube is shown as sealed in the manifold, in practice either the outer tube or the inner tube could be sealed in the manifold. In most general terms, the tubes form a double-walled tubular member with a closed end remote from the manifold and an open end in sealing engagement with the manifold.

A cross-connecting tube **24** extends from a position adjacent the closed end of the inner tube of the collector **10B** to a position adjacent the closed end of the inner tube of the collector **10E**. The collectors are in communication only through the cross-connecting tube **24**, and the cross-connecting tube is mounted in a gasket **26** within the manifold to ensure that the only path available for fluid travel is along or through the cross-connecting tube. The cross-connecting tube may be either a glass or a metal tube material.

The working fluid to be heated by solar energy enters the manifold through an inlet line **28**. The fluid is first directed along the length of the tubular collector **10A** around the outside of the cross-connecting tube which connects the tubular collectors **10A** and **10B**. The fluid flows down the length of the cross-connecting tube and into the tubular collector **10D**. During this passage and during the time it is in the collector **10A** the fluid has been heated by extracting energy from the absorber surface.

As the fluid reaches the open end of the tubular collector **10D** and enters the manifold, a cross-connecting passage **30** formed in the manifold directs the fluid into the open end of the tubular collector **10B**. The fluid then flows along the length of the tube **10B** and along the cross-connecting tube **24** which connects the tubes **10B** and **10E** and enters the cross-connecting tube at the closed end of the tubular collector **10B**. Fluid flows down the length of the tube and into the tubular collector **10E**. The fluid then passes back along the length of the tubular collector and once again enters the manifold.

A second cross-connecting passage **32** directs the fluid into the open end of the tubular collector **10C**. The path of the fluid is identical for that previously described with respect to the collectors **10A, 10B, 10D** and **10E** with respect to the collectors **10C** and **10F**. That is, the fluid goes down the length to the collector **10C**, enters the cross-connecting tube, exits into the collector **10F** and then flows back into the manifold. The fluid coming from the tubular collector **10F** may be utilized at this point for its energy content by removing it from the manifold through a passage **34**. If desired, however, the working fluid may be passed through still further tubular collectors and additional solar energy collected before the fluid is utilized. A system which uses parallel flow as opposed to the series flow shown could also be successfully utilized.

## Glass Collector with Helical Baffle

The collector of *Y.K. Pei; U.S. Patent 3,952,724; April 27, 1976; assigned to Owens-Illinois, Inc.* is made from common glass tubing lengths of different diameters and comprises a first outer clear glass cylindrical tube having approximately a semicylinder surface portion mirror coated for reflection and a collector tube inside the first tube having an energy absorbing coating on its exterior surface. The tubes resemble oversized test tubes in that one end is closed.

The collector is held in place inside the outer tube by a spacer-support element snapped on the closed end of the collector. The open end of the outer tube is sealed to the wall of the collector, and the space is evacuated. An open ended fluid handling tube of glass is inserted into the collector tube and has a spiral or baffle along its length to guide working fluid issuing into the collector near its closed end along the wall thereof and absorb collected heat.

Several of the energy collectors are detachably connected into a manifold for circulation of working fluid (air or water or the like) into the handling tube and receive working fluid flowing from the collector tube. The manifold provides for collector tubes to depend on opposite sides as a module covering predetermined area of rooftop or like exposure. The working fluid carrying the energy is utilized in a heating or cooling system.

Shown on Figure 2.16a is a typical in-use setting for the apparatus. The module is shown in detail on Figure 2.16c. It comprises a central longitudinal manifold section **13** that extends down the roof section (Figure 2.16a). Depending outwardly from either side of the manifold are plural collector units **14**. The collectors are of a plug-in type of connection into the side ports **15** spaced along the opposite vertical side walls **16** and **17** of the manifold. Internally of the manifold are longitudinal passageways **18** and **19** running along the ports on either side of the manifold. Sandwiched between the passageways **18** and **19** is a central passageway **20** defined by the longitudinal interior vertical walls **21** and **22**. Along these walls there are spaced apart ports **23**. The ports **15** and **23** are matched as sets on the same central axis, i.e., the ports are coaxial.

The manifold connects into a fluid handling system illustrated by the duct **24** having an upper conduit passage **25** and a lower conduit passage **26**. The duct **24** extends between the heating or cooling system (labelled Fluid Heat Exchanger on Figure 2.16c) and the solar converter module **12**. The passage **25** carries the relatively cool fluid medium, such as water, air or the like, and introduces it through the matching aperture connection **39** in the vertical wall **24a** of duct **24** and aperture **27** in the vertical end wall **28** of the manifold.

FIGURE 2.16: GLASS COLLECTOR WITH HELICAL BAFFLE

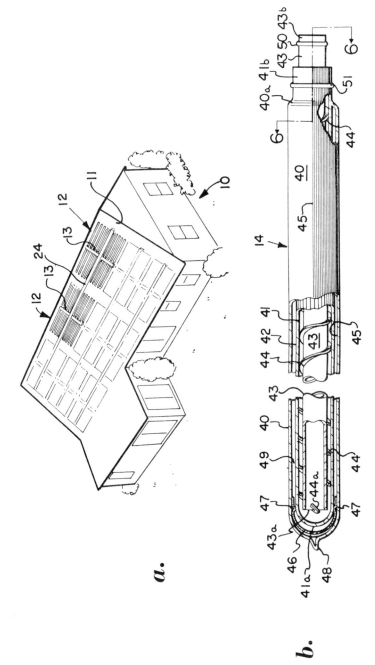

(continued)

FIGURE 2.16: (continued)

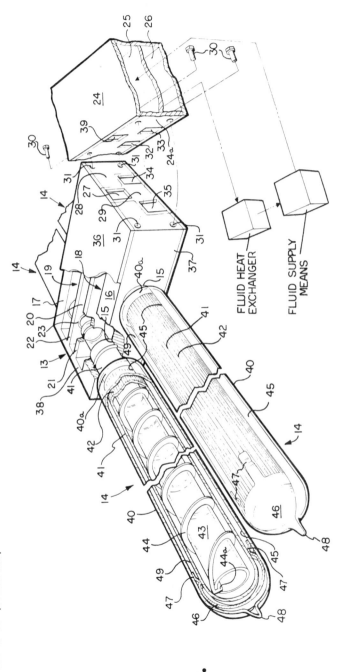

c.

(a) Perspective view showing collectors on a roof
(b) Side view, partly broken away and in section, of collector
(c) Exploded perspective view, partly broken away and in section, wherein collector units depend on either side of the manifold

FLUID HEAT EXCHANGER

FLUID SUPPLY MEANS

Source: U.S. Patent 3,952,724

The aperture 27 connects into the central passageway 20 of the manifold. The duct 24 and manifold are connected and sealed together by the gasketed facing 29 held by cap screws 30 threaded into end wall 28 at 31. The gasket may be any suitable compressible gasket material that will withstand moderately elevated temperature service. Matching lower apertures 32 and 33 in wall 24a and 34 and 35 in wall 28 connect the respective passages 18 and 19 with the duct passage 26 for carrying the heated fluid medium coming from the collectors. The manifold is enclosed by top and bottom walls 36 and 37, respectively, and at its outer end by vertical wall 38.

Collectors 14 are all constructed alike, and each comprises an outer glass tube 40 that is of convenient length (4 to 7 feet) and of standard diameter similar to a fluorescent light tube (2 inches o.d.). Approximately a semicylindrical one-half of the interior surface of the tube on the lower region of Figures 2.16b and 2.16c is coated with a reflecting material 45, such as by silvering that surface area in the manner well known in the art of producing glass mirrors. This lower mirrored surface will reflect radiant energy onto the absorber tube 41 of the collector.

The interior tube 41 is made of glass and is of somewhat lesser diameter and of slightly greater length. This tube has its exterior surface precoated with an energy absorbing coating 42 having a very high absorptivity and very low emissivity. Examples of such coating materials are black chrome, nickel, lampblack, carbon or copper compounded for suitable application, such as by painting the compound on the exterior surface of the tube and to the axial extent shown on Figure 2.16c.

Inside tube 41 there is a fluid delivery glass tube 43 for conveying relatively cool fluid medium into the collector interiorly of the tube 41 and adjacent the closed end wall 41a. The inner end 43a of the delivery tube is open. Along the length of the delivery tube is a spiral or helical baffle member 44 that is hooked at the end edge 43a at the slotted portion 44a and spirally wrapped on edge along the length of the outer wall of tube 43. The helical baffle may be constructed of a metallic material or plastic material, the latter being selected from plastic materials that will withstand temperatures in the 250° to 300°F range. One example of such a plastic is Teflon.

The baffle helix 44 provides two primary functions: (1) It serves to maintain the delivery tube outer wall surface 43 spaced from the inner wall surface of coated absorber tube 41 and provide a flow passage for fluid introduced by delivery tube 43. (2) It distributes the fluid and provides a washing contact of the fluid over the entire inner wall surface of absorber tube 41 to enhance efficiency of heat exchange from the absorber to the fluid medium.

In assembly, the absorbing tube already coated on the exterior with the energy absorbing compound is further provided with the snap-on end support cap 46 which provides inner end support means for tube 41 in tube 40. The cap comprises a semispherical shell and multiple (either 3 or 4) legs 47. The cap is made of metal or plastic having some resiliency to maintain its force fit on the inner end of the tube. The tube 41 is then inserted into the outer tube 40 and is fastened by fusing its open end onto the tube at the juncture 40a. Thereafter, a vacuum is pulled through the opposite end of tube 40 and sealed off at the tip 48 in the manner known to those skilled in the art, the resultant sealed space 49 between the outer tube **40** and the absorber tube **41** being highly evacuated, viz on the order of $10^{-4}$ torr of vacuum. Next, the delivery tube and baffle helix **44** thereon are inserted interiorly of the absorber tube.

Each of the collector units is detachably assembled into the manifold as follows. The free end **43b** of the delivery tube **43** is approximately the same o.d. as the diameter of the ports **23** in the interior walls **20** and **21** of the manifold. A rubber O-ring **50** is provided on free end **43b** of the delivery tube to seal the latter in port **23**. Similarly, free end **41b** of the absorber tube is approximately the same o.d. as the port **15** in either of vertical side walls **16** or **17**. A rubber O-ring **51** is provided on free end **41b** of the absorber tube to seal it in port **15**. The ports are each provided with recessed grooves to receive the gasket O-rings therein.

Utilizing the assembly shown in Figure 2.16c, and described earlier herein, a fluid medium (for example, air) is pumped in duct **25** into central passage **20** of the manifold. The free ends **43b** of the several collectors **14** communicate with passage **20** and are sealed therein so that the air flows lengthwise of the delivery tube **43** and exits at the inner end **43a**. Solar rays penetrate the upper glass of tube **40** and energy therefrom is absorbed by the coating of the absorber tube.

Solar energy that passes tube **41** tangentially or beyond is reflected by the mirror coating on the inner surface of the lower half of tube **40** and is absorbed by coating on tube **41**. The air circulated on the interior of tube **41** traverses the passage defined by helical baffle **44** and heat exchange therewith increases the temperature of the air as it travels toward the free end **41b** of the tube. When heated air reaches the free end of the tube connected thereat into either passageway **18** or **19**, as the case may be, the heated fluid media flows by gravity or power, depending upon the system, into the lower duct **26** and is utilized to either heat or cool the dwelling.

### Collector Using Air System

*K.L. Moan; U.S. Patent 4,016,860; April 12, 1977; assigned to Owens-Illinois, Inc.* provides an air system for the collection and utilization of solar energy. Tubular solar collectors are made with a transparent glass tube having a cylindrical outer wall, spaced and sealed at one end to a cylindrical absorber tube that has a solar energy absorbing surface. The sealed space between the glass tube and absorber tube is evacuated.

Several of the collectors are connected into a manifold split into separate chambers by a dividing wall. A divider strip is fastened as a continuation of the dividing wall of the manifold by a novel detachable fastener means. The divider strip fits snugly inside the absorber tube of each collector dividing it in half and spanning nearly the entire length thereof. Pressurized air is supplied into the one high pressure chamber of the manifold and is connected into the half section of the absorber of each collector at the open end connection, guided by the dividing strip the length of the absorber tube into the other half of the absorber tube and back into the other compartment of the manifold, which is at lower pressure. The reverse flow of air the length of the absorber tube exchanges solar heat absorbed on the solar energy absorbing surface. Heated air in the lower pressure chamber is conveyed to a heat exchange storage element and/or load device operable for heating or cooling purposes.

# FIGURE 2.17: COLLECTOR USING AIR SYSTEM

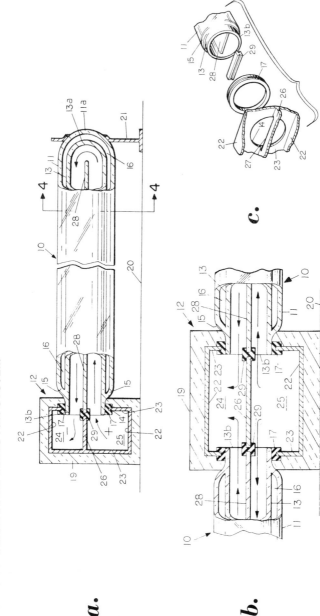

(a) Sectional end elevational view taken through the manifold
(b) End sectional view of another embodiment in which tubular collectors depend from the opposite sides of a single manifold
(c) Parts and assembly for detachably connecting tube-dividing strip to manifold

Source: U.S. Patent 4,016,860

As illustrated on Figure 2.17a, tubular solar collectors **10** are made with a transparent glass outer tube **11** having a closed end **11a** remote from the manifold **12** and an open end adjacent to the manifold. Inside the tube there is a tubular absorber member **13** comprised of a glass tube having a closed end **13a** remote from the manifold and an open end **13b** connected with an aperture **14** in the manifold. The outer surface **13c** of the absorber member is a solar energy absorbing surface extending between the ends. Preferably, the absorbing surface comprises an overall wavelength selective coating having high absorptance and low emittance; for example, one having 0.8 or greater absorptance and 0.1 or lower infrared emittance.

The selective coating is made by way of one example by the vacuum deposition of a thin layer (1000 A) of aluminum on the glass absorber tube's outer surface. Chromium is then electrically vaporized and deposited over the aluminum substrate as black chrome to a thickness of about 1500 A. Alternatively, the surface may be blackened as an energy absorbing coating with an over-coating of an infrared energy trapping material such as magnesium oxide, magnesium fluoride, etc.

The absorber member is sealed along the wall to the outer tube by a glass-to-glass seal at the open end of the outer tube, such as by fusion at **15** of the glass of the outer tube onto the wall of the inner glass absorber tube. The tubes **11** and **13** are, of course, of differing sizes (diameter) such that a space **16** is provided therebetween. The space, after the end wall sealing, is evacuated to a hard vacuum, on the order of $10^{-4}$ torr. The vacuum is pumped off at the tip end of the outer tube and a tubulation thereat sealed off (not shown), which is a known expedient for evacuation of space **16**. The vacuum in space **16** will reduce, in fact substantially eliminate, conduction and convection losses from the collector. The open end of the absorber tube, at **13b**, is in sealing engagement with an opening **14** in the manifold in a gasket **17**, which in the version shown comprises a grommet style of gasket molded from a silicon rubber compound.

The manifold structure **12** may take different construction forms. A first form is shown in Figure 2.17b, wherein an elongated duct is comprised of metal top and bottom walls **22** and opposite side walls **23**. The apertures or openings **14** for receiving the tubular collectors are provided in an aligned, spaced arrangement along both the side walls. The duct of the manifold is divided into two longitudinal over-and-under chambers **24** and **25** by a central wall **26**. As may best be seen on Figure 2.17c, this central wall is stepped or recessed at **27** opposite the aperture **14** in the walls to accommodate the tubular collectors. Otherwise, the central wall extends from one side wall to the other and seals off chamber **24** from chamber **25**.

The manifold assembly includes the central dividing strip or web **28**. The width of the strip is preferably slightly oversize of the internal diameter of the absorber tube **13** such that a friction tight fit of strip **28** inside the tube is provided. The strip may be made of relatively flexible material such that when it is inserted inside the tube, it takes a slight bow. The strip is slightly shorter in length than the axial length of the tube and when assembled, as shown on Figure 2.17a, there is a space between the inner end of the strip and the closed end wall of the absorber tube at **13a**. With the strip in place, the tubular collector **10** is inserted into the manifold aperture and the end of the strip at the open end **13b** of the absorber tube is connected to the central dividing wall **26** of the manifold by a rubber grommet bar **29**. The grommet is molded of silicon rubber, for example, having oppositely facing notches to receive the plate of wall **26** and the strip **28** therein and seal off the chambers **24** and **25** at the connection point.

The manifold may be constructed as a single side collecting unit in which the tubular collectors **10** depend from one side wall **23** only of the manifold duct. This form is shown on Figure 2.17a. A double side collecting unit comprised of the manifold duct of another type is shown on Figure 2.17b, in which the tubular collectors depend from apertures in the opposide side walls of the manifold. A third structure is also possible in which, in effect, two of the units of Figure 2.17a are placed back-to-back. The assembly of the collectors and dividing strip therein is similar in either case.

The dividing strip in the collectors may be made of metal, corrugated paperboard, plastic or wood. The preferred material is metal, such as thin gauge aluminum or copper sheet. The choice of material for the dividing strip will, of course, depend upon the temperature conditions in the collector during operation.

The manifold ducts **22**, **23** are insulated by encasing them, except for the apertures **14** for assembly of the collectors **10**, with a jacket **19** of a moldable cellular, polymeric insulation material. The exterior surface of the insulation jacket should be protected by a sealant such as an outer layer of a paint, plastic or polymer. A preferable insulation jacket construction is a moldable foamed polyurethane material of a bulk density of about 8 pounds per cubic foot, or less.

### Collector Using Liquid Medium

There are in operation, at least on a limited scale, two basic types of solar energy collecting systems: A flat-plate collector comprised of a plate of glass and an energy absorbing surface spaced therebeneath, i.e., away from the sun; at the back of the absorbing surface the heat exchange media in either gas or liquid form form is circulated to exchange the heat of the sun to the exchange media. The other type is the double-walled glass tubular collector in which a glass outer tube is sealed to a spaced inner tube and the space evacuated; the inner tube has an energy absorbing coating over its exposed surface and the heat exchange media is circulated on the inside of the inner tube to absorb solar heat collected by the inner tube.

Several of the tubular collectors are connected into a manifold system which furnishes the media to the tubes and transfers the heated media for storage or use of the sun's energy that is absorbed in the apparatus. One of the drawbacks of the tubular collector, as compared with the flate-plate collector, is the difficulty with which many tubes of a collector assembly may be connected to a manifold and function as a unit.

The process of *Y.K. Pei; U.S. Patent 4,018,215; April 19, 1977; assigned to Owens-Illinois, Inc.* provides a manifold for tubular collectors for operation with a liquid heat exchange media which is designed to simplify the connection of several tubes to the manifold and reduce the cost of the manifold. More particularly, the process provides for a channel for the liquid flow in series between the several tubular collectors. The manifold provided is inexpensive to manufacture and provides for ease of assembly of the tubes in connecting them to the manifold for operation, or for replacing them. Also, the performance of the solar collector assembly is enhanced. This is attributable to the fact that the series flow of the liquid heat exchange media provides the same volume of liquid to each collector tube in the series assembly.

Figures 2.18a, 2.18b and 2.18c illustrate a preferred embodiment of the process and the operation of a solar collector in accordance therewith. A plurality of tubular collectors of a solar energy collection system are arranged in an array or module fashion. The tubular collectors, shown as part of this module, are indicated at **10A** through **10D**. The balance of the collectors in a module are the same as those shown.

The tubular collectors are mounted on each side of a manifold **11**. All of the tubular collectors are identical in construction. Collectors **10B** and **10D**, opposite each other on the sides of the manifold, have been shown partially broken away and in cross section in order to explain the structure of the collectors and their connection into the manifold and their operation in conjunction therewith.

An outer transparent tube **12** has one closed end which extends beyond the manifold and an open end which is connected into the manifold. An inner tube **13** is sealed to the outer tube near the open end of the outer tube. The inner tube may also be glass, but could be metal, and is blackened or coated with a material which provides an overall selectively absorbing coating layer to absorb the solar energy directly. The space **14** between the tubes is evacuated or reduced to subatmospheric pressure to reduce conduction losses of energy (heat) from the collector.

The manifold receptacle for the collector tubes is comprised of an annular wall which is divided by the integral center wall **20** into two compartments **22, 23**. The compartments are connected through the center aperture punched in the wall by means hereinafter described. The open end of the outer tube is held in an aperture **15** provided by the manifold and in sealing engagement in a gasket or O-ring **16** comprised of rubber or plastic of known composition. An annular cross-connecting tube **17** extends from a position adjacent the closed end of the inner tube **13** of the collector **10B** to a position adjacent the closed end of the inner tube of the collector **10D**. The collectors **10B, 10D** are in communication only through the cross-connecting tube, and the cross-connecting tube is mounted in a seal gasket **18** secured within the center aperture of wall **20** dividing compartments **22, 23** to ensure that the only path available for fluid travel from one compartment to the other is along and through the cross-connecting tube.

The solar energy that is incident upon the coated inner tube **13** will result in a temperature increase of the tube. The working fluid, e.g., water, to be heated is pumped from a source in the system (not shown) and enters the manifold through an inlet line **19**. The fluid is first directed along the length of the tubular collector **10A** around the exterior of the cross-connecting tube and in heat exchange contact with the inner surface of the inner tube **13** of the collector. The fluid flows along the length of the tube to near its far end and there enters the cross-connecting tube. From there, the fluid flows the length of tube **17** and exists at its opposite end inside of tubular collector **10C** near its closed end.

The fluid, laden with some solar energy, enters the space inside the inner tube **13** of collector **10C** and flows back toward the manifold. In the return pass, solar heat absorbed by the coated tube is exchanged (added) to the working fluid, adding more solar energy and increasing temperature of the liquid.

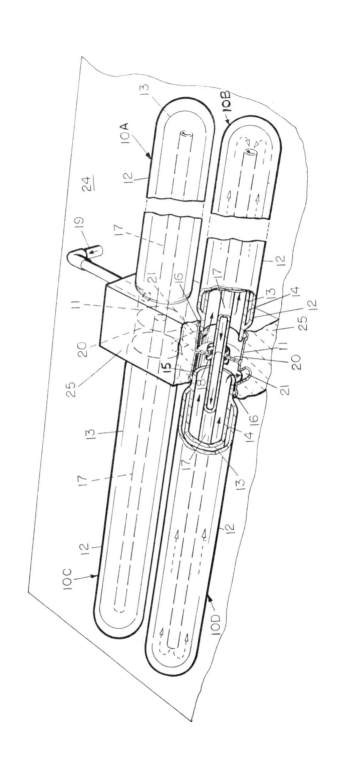

FIGURE 2.18: COLLECTOR USING LIQUID MEDIUM

*a.*

(continued)

FIGURE 2.18: (continued)

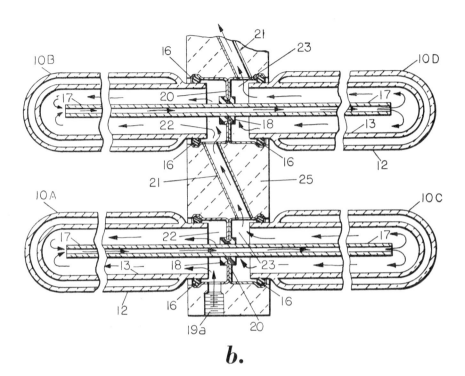

**b.**

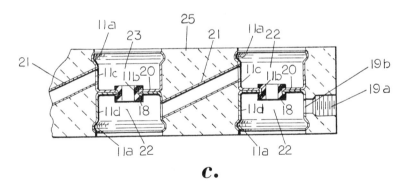

**c.**

(a) Perspective view, partly broken away and in section,
of portion of collector assembly
(b) Sectional plan view of Figure 2.18a
(c) Partial sectional plan view of portion of manifold
shown in Figure 2.18b

Source: U.S. Patent 4,018,215

The heated fluid then empties into manifold **11** at the inner open end of tube **13** of the collector **10C**. Since the manifold has an interior web wall **20**, the fluid must enter the exit passage **21** connecting the first cell or receptacle unit of the manifold for collectors **10A** and **10C**, respectively, with the next cell or receptacle of manifold **11** into which tubular collectors **10B** and **10D**, respectively, are connected.

The fluid now travels along the wall of inner tube **13** of the collector **10B** and enters the end of the cross-connecting tube **17** for this collector. Fluid flows the length of tube **17** which extends between the interior of collectors **10B** and **10D**, and ultimately empties into the inner tube **13** of collector **10D**. The fluid then passes back along the length of the tubular collector **10D** collecting solar energy from the heated (coated) inner tube **13** and, as before, enters the left-hand compartment **23** of this manifold cell. This compartment has an exit passage **21** leading to the next inlet side **22** of the succeeding manifold cell.

The flow pattern is repeated through each oppositely mounted pair of collectors on manifold **11** until all collectors are traversed. In the last downstream cell or receptacle of the manifold (not shown), the exit passage **21** connects to an exhaust pipe of the system which transports the heated fluid to a place of use, such as a heat exchanger or water supply, engine, etc. (not shown).

The selected array of tubes on a manifold section comprise a module, illustrated on Figure 2.18a. This module may be connected in series or in parallel with another module or modules, as the need arises. Quite often the module comprises 8 or 12 pairs of collector tubes, but the number is variable to suit a particular installation.

In the manufacture of the manifold **11**, the module number of manifold cells or receptacles is encased with an insulation **25**, such as a cellular polymer composition. An example of this insulation is a foamed polyurethane having a density of about 8 pounds per cubic foot, or less, or a foamed polyethylene. Fiberglass insulation may also be utilized, or asbestos, depending upon the operating temperature requirements; however, the preferred insulation is a moldable cellular polymer material, such as the polyurethane or polyethylene, because of its ease of handling in manufacture, molding and the like.

The exterior of the insulation may be sealed, as desired, by a waterproof, weatherproof coating, or by enclosure in a surface structure, such as sheet metal. The only need for this surface protection is to preserve the insulation in use against weathering, cracking, breakage or deterioration.

Referring to Figures 2.18b and 2.18c, the manifold is shown in greater detail. This form of manifold is made by assembly of metal stampings. Metal sheet (e.g., steel) of suitable gauge may be used and stamped in various dies to provide the end grooves **11a** in which the gasket or O-ring **16** is seated. The center web wall **20** is shown of double thickness as a result of folding the metal inwardly and pressing it together in the die. The center seal gasket **18** for the cross-connecting tube **17** is held in a punched, centered aperture **11b**. The upper or inlet compartment **22** of the manifold cell or receptacle is cylindrical and the port opening for pipe **21** is formed in the metal side wall **11c**. Cross-over pipe **21** from exit compartment **23** to the next cell or receptacle inlet compartment **22** is welded onto the side walls **11c** and **11d**, respectively, at the respective punched-out openings.

The cells or receptacles of the manifold stampings for a module are laid out in series, as shown, in however many such cells are needed for a solar collector module (say 8 or 12), and the last exit compartment has a pipe connection at the cross-pipe **21** threaded thereon for coupling the module into a system; i.e., the outlet connection will be constructed substantially like the inlet connection **19**, **19a, 19b**, but at the opposite longitudinal end of the manifold. This outlet pipe may be connected to the inlet fitting of a next module of the system or to the fluid supply and storage system, as may be desired. A discussion of similar tubular collectors, which are not connected in series, is given by *K.L. Moan and Y.K. Pei; U.S. Patent 3,960,136; June 1, 1976; assigned to Owens-Illinois, Inc.*

## MISCELLANEOUS CONFIGURATIONS

### Roof Lens Collector

An array of linear lenses described by *L.L. Northrup, Jr. and M.J. O'Neill; U.S. Patent 3,991,741; November 16, 1976* is used as a combination roof-sky-light-solar collector. The lenses are oriented at a given latitude to face the most remote of the earth's poles inclined by the local latitude angle. Moving absorbers are used to receive the sunlight at the focal spot of each lens. The absorbers move back and forth during the day as the sun's position changes, causing the focal spots to move.

Figure 2.19a is an illustration of a portion of a panel. Panel **20** comprises a plurality of lenses which are integral one with another to form a weathertight body. For example, lenses **21** and **22** are joined together or are common at the boundary **21a**. Lenses **22** and **23** join at boundary **22a**. The longitudinal axes of the lenses **21** to **23** are horizontal and extend in east-west direction. The entire panel **20** is tilted at an angle preferably corresponding with the local latitude at which the building housing the collector is located.

By way of example, the individual lenses, such as lens **21**, may have a major axis of the order of 6 inches in length and a minor axis of about ½ inch. Panels formed of such lenses may be of the order of 5 feet wide and 10 feet long. There is no necessary limitation on the lens size or the panel width or length other than the physical parametric considerations generally applicable to use of structures employing glass panels.

An array **30** of solar energy absorbers is provided. Array **30** comprises longitudinal tubes such as the tubes **31, 32, 33**. Tube **31** is mounted in a suitable support system (not shown) as to be moveable under the control of an actuator **40** so that absorbers **31, 32, 33** will always be positioned at the point at which the sun's rays incident upon the lenses **21, 22, 23**, respectively, are focused. This concentration of the sun's rays thus provides for an efficient collection of solar energy by tubes **31, 32, 33** as concentrated by lenses **21, 22, 23**.

The angle of the tilt may be varied, however, for any given latitude and the control of the actuator **40** adjusted to accommodate the differences thus involved. The actuator is coupled to the array by way of an inter-connecting linkage **40a** which ties the members of the array together to form a unitary structure. A similar linkage (not shown) may be provided on the other end of the array. Suitable supports **40b** such as a track channel over which the array travels may be

# FIGURE 2.19: ROOF LENS COLLECTOR

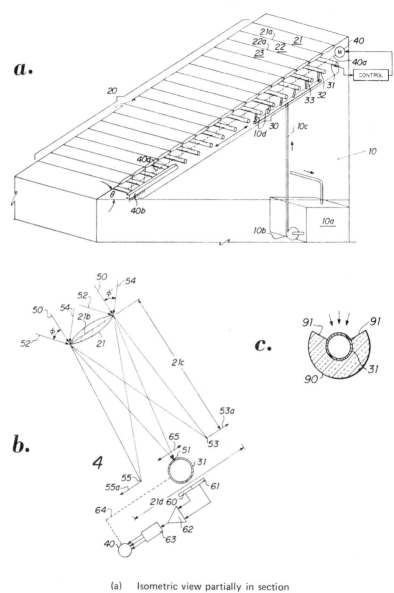

(a)  Isometric view partially in section
(b)  Variations in the position of the focus
     of light rays impinging on the lens
(c)  Sectional view of a collector tube

Source:  U.S. Patent 3,991,741

made part of the building structure. The actuator is controlled to move the array to compensate for variations in the sun's elevation angle relative to the lens array. Elements of array **30** are hollow tubes, such as tube **31**. A heat transfer liquid flows through the tube for exchange of energy between the array and a utilization system. As shown, a heat utilization reservoir **10a** is connected to receive flow of liquid from the array. Pump **10b** forces fluid through line **10c** and manifold **10d** to supply all the tubes of the array. The reservoir may be a water heater, for example.

A control system is provided for the actuator **40** to control the north-south position of the array. The control system may be of the form diagrammatically illustrated in Figure 2.19b. A pair of light sensors **60** and **61** are mounted beneath the tube **31**. The sensor outputs are then applied to a differential amplifier **62** whose output is applied by way of a power amplifier **63** to operate the actuator, which is a differential actuator having a mechanical output coupled by way of linkage **64** to the element **31** so that the element, along with the other elements in the array, may be moved in accordance with arrow **65**. The output from sensors **60** and **61** will at all times be nulled, indicating that the sun's rays are refracted to a line positioned centrally on the upper surface of the element. The control system functions to maintain the elements of the array so as to receive the sun's rays as focused by the lens elements.

While the collector tubes **31** are shown as metal pipe, they preferably will be at least partially insulated as indicated in Figure 2.19c. The pipe is illustrated with an insulating partial cylinder **90** extending the length of the tube. The tube has the upper surface thereof exposed, with the remainder covered by the insulator **90**. The walls **91** preferably will be reflective so that any incident light would be reflected onto the exposed surface of the pipe.

### Lens of Alternate High and Low Refractive Surfaces Combined with Focusing Lens

*S.A. Meyer and S.R. Gray; U.S. Patent 3,970,070; July 20, 1976* describe a solar heating system comprising a lens collector arrangement, an insulation area, and a storage section positioned in an enclosing structure, and an associated utilization means.

The collector lens is an array of light guide lenses having alternate high and low refractive surfaces. The array is contoured in a capping relationship over a focusing lens to provide an extremely high concentration of solar energy irrespective of the angle of the sun. The light guide lenses increase by several orders of magnitude the amount of solar energy striking the surface of the focusing lens. The focusing lens is a plurality of flat surface type of lenses stacked one over the other in spaced relationship and operable to concentrate the solar energy to a central region.

Surrounding the perimeter of the plurality of focusing lenses is an array, in a "wall" configuration, of light guide lenses similar in construction to the aforesaid capping light guide lenses. The angle of the reflective surfaces of the capping lenses and the wall lenses is such to receive and direct to the focusing lenses the maximum amount of radiation at all times of the day and season. The insulation area is positioned between the collector lens and the storage section to provide a convective barrier for the storage area without inhibiting the passage of solar radiation. The storage section is of a high absorption material with an auxiliary conventional heat source.

With reference to Figure 2.20a, the solar heater comprises a housing or enclosure **10**, solar energy concentrator **20**, an insulation area **30**, a heat storage section **40** and a utilization means **50**. In principle of operation, the concentration lens arrangement **20** is capable of directing a maximum amount of solar radiation to a focusing lens. The solar radiation is directed to the focusing lens from all angles irrespective of the position of the sun overhead or on the horizon.

The focused solar radiation passes through a heat insulation barrier **30** to a thermal storage section **40**. The insulation barrier is such that it does not inhibit the solar radiation but does inhibit the passing of thermal radiation (convective barrier). Once solar radiation is converted to thermal radiation the heat is retained in the storage section until otherwise depleted by the utilization means. In actual operation the storage area is the heat source. With a given capacity and the extremely efficient solar radiation concentrator lens **20**, the storage section does generate and retain an extremely large amount of thermal energy. In the event the storage section should exceed a certain predetermined thermal gradient such as can occur for extended periods of sunny days, a heat sink **41** to the storage section is provided to dissipate the excess energy. Additionally, a shutter arrangement, temperature controlled in a conventional manner, would be provided with the collector lens **20**.

## FIGURE 2.20: LENS OF ALTERNATE HIGH AND LOW REFRACTIVE SURFACES COMBINED WITH FOCUSING LENS

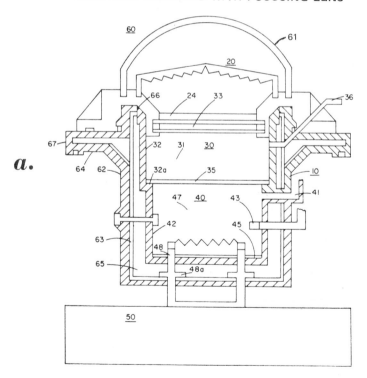

*a.*

(continued)

FIGURE 2.20: (continued)

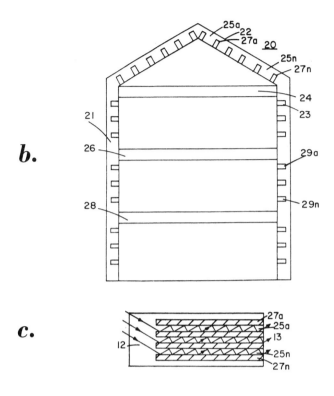

(a) Cross-sectional schematic view of collector
(b) Preferred lens arrangement shown generally as
    collector lens **20** of Figure 2.20a
(c) Planar view of lens

Source: U.S. Patent 3,970,070

Basically each light guide lens in the array comprises alternate areas of high refractive (transparent) material **25a** through **25n** and low refractive (reflective)
material **27a** through **27n**, as shown in cross section in Figure 2.20b and in a
planar view in Figure 2.20c. The dimensions of the low refractive material are
highly exaggerated and in actuality are extremely thin, striplike with a very high
polished surface. A thicker surface would be a light block. In principle the
light **12** (solar radiation) incident on the array travels in a straight path through
the transparent material until it strikes a reflective surface of the walls of the
low refractive material. The light is then reflected back and forth by the reflective surfaces of the light guide and transmitted therefrom.

In the preferred embodiment shown in Figure 2.20b, the collector lens **20**, in
itself a unitary structure, comprises an array of light guides in an upper or top
capping lens **22**, wall lens **21** and a plurality of focusing lenses **24**, **26** and **28**.

To increase the amount of incident solar radiation striking the focusing lens 24 additional focusing lenses 26 and 28 are utilized in a stacked and spaced relationship to the focusing lens. The focusing lens 26 will receive the transmitted radiation from lens 24 and similarly lens 28 will receive the transmitted radiation from lens 26. Surrounding the lenses 24, 26 and 28 and the spacing between is the light guide wall lens array 21. This lens, too, like the capping lens 22, is made up of high and low refractive (transparent and reflective) material. Accordingly, in addition to the solar radiation striking the capping lens, solar radiation also strikes the reflective surfaces 29a through 29n of the wall light guide lenses 21 to direct the solar radiation to the surface of the focusing lenses 26 and 28. In the preferred embodiment, the wall lens 21 is cylindrical and the top lens 22 is circular with an angle peaking at the center, i.e., conical.

Referring again to Figure 2.20a, the solar radiation focused by the focusing lens 24 is directed through the insulation area 30. The insulation area is in sealed engagement with the insulator 33 comprising a pair of plates with an insulating material between, the thermal storage 40, and the insulated side walls 32. The purpose and function of the insulation cavity is to act as a heat convection barrier to the thermal storage area when the solar radiation has diminished; that is, to seal off the thermal storage area from any heat loss but yet not inhibit the passage of the solar radiation received from the collector lens arrangement 20 if an auxiliary heat source is being utilized.

Particularly, the insulating area is a liquid container. The container comprises outside wall 32, bottom panel 35 positioned in a sealed engagement with shoulder 32a, and at its top the focusing lens 24. The liquid comprises a solution 31 of water and salt, in the preferred embodiment a 15% NaCl solution. In operation of the insulation cavity, as the solar radiant energy is converted to thermal energy (heat), the thermal radiation passes up through the bottom panel and to the liquid solution. As the heat increases the solubility of the salt increases, causing the solution to form into heat resistant layers, horizontal stratification. The greater the heat, the greater the increase in solubility and hence the greater the number of layers. With the salt layers of the preferred embodiment and the heat loss from thermal storage and in the presence of temperature gradiant above and below in closed container, the liquid solution becomes an internal nearly isothermal layer.

Positioned in the lower region of the thermal storage section is the heat collector and extraction assembly 47. The collector assembly per se is conventional and may take other known forms. Connected to both sides of the collector plates is the conductive thermal transfer assembly, in this instance a heat pipe 48. In turn the heat pipe is connected to heat utilization means 50, which may also be conventionally operable.

The solar heater of the process is intended as the primary heat source and may be utilized for the home or commercially. The size of the unit (which relative to other solar units is very small) would be increased depending on the increased area to be heated. However, with the extremely efficient collector lens, in reality it is only the storage area that need be increased. Alternatively, and more expediently, several storage areas distributed throughout a given area may be connected in tandem to provide a uniform heat distribution.

The construction of the enclosure **10** comprises a cover of clear glass or plastic dome **61** operable primarily as a protective cover. This cover is fixedly positioned and sealed to outside casing **62**. The enclosure comprises as a primary support a metal jacket **63** and an outer wall of insulating material **64** with an outdoor finish. The walls **32** and **42** above noted relative to the insulation area **30** and storage section **40** are an inner wall liner of high temperature material. Insulating material fills the void **65** between the metallic casing **63** and the inner liner **32** and **42**. The outside and inner liners, and the metallic casing are joined in a supporting relationship as shown at junction **66**. However, prior to outside wall **64** joining with the supporting metallic casing, the inner liner **32** and the insulating material **65**, the outer wall is formed into a supporting collar **67**. This permits the entire unit to be supported structurally adjacent to the enclosure to be heated.

### Flat Lens Panel

The solar heat collector of *B.C. Rogers; U.S. Patent 3,929,121; December 30, 1975* positions a flat lens panel in spaced relation to a collector panel having a plurality of interconnected heat collector elements through which a fluid medium to be heated is circulated. Individual lenses in the panel focus on the individual heat collector elements and dark colored heat collecting partitions therein. Flat Fresnel lenses formed in accordance with Fresnel's reflection formula in inexpensive, transparent, synthetic resin material are preferred.

As seen in Figure 2.21a, the solar heat collector comprises a frame **10** having a lens supporting portion **11** and a heat collector element supporting portion **12** spaced by a plurality of frame members **13**. In plan views as seen in Figures 2.21b and 2.21c, the frame is substantially square. It is hinged at one of its ends by hinges **14** to a rotatable base **15** which is rotated on its vertical axis. The opposite side of the frame is secured by a secondary hinge **16** to a bracket **17**, which carries an electric motor **18** and a gear reduction unit driven thereby and engaged on a threaded shaft **19** which in turn is hinged at its lower end by a third hinge **20** also secured to the rotatable base. Broken lines in the figure indicate the positioning of the solar heat collector in an alternate position to that shown in solid lines, and it will occur to those skilled in the art that the solar heat collector thus supported can follow the sun.

By referring to Figure 2.21b of the drawings, a plan view of the lens supporting portion of the frame may be seen to position a plurality of flat sections **21** of transparent plastic material in which Fresnel lens configurations **22** have been formed, such as by molding the same integrally with the plastic material.

By referring to Figure 2.21c, a plan view of the heat collector elements supporting portion **12** of the frame may be seen supporting a plurality of heat collector elements **23** interconnected in series with suitable fluid carrying tubing **24** so that fluid medium to be heated enters as shown by the arrows of the drawing at **25** and flows successively through the plurality of heat collecting elements and leaves at point **26**. Each of the heat collecting elements is preferably a thin, flat, two-part glass bulb having oppositely disposed and tangentially arranged inlet and outlet portions **27, 28** with a transverse dark colored partition **29** positioned in spaced relation with respect to the front and back portions of the heat collecting element.

FIGURE 2.21:  FLAT LENS PANEL

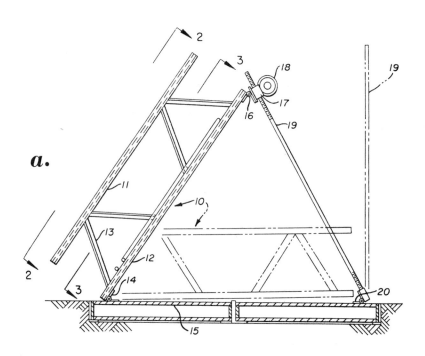

**a.**

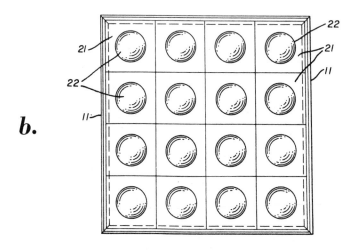

**b.**

(continued)

FIGURE 2.21:  (continued)

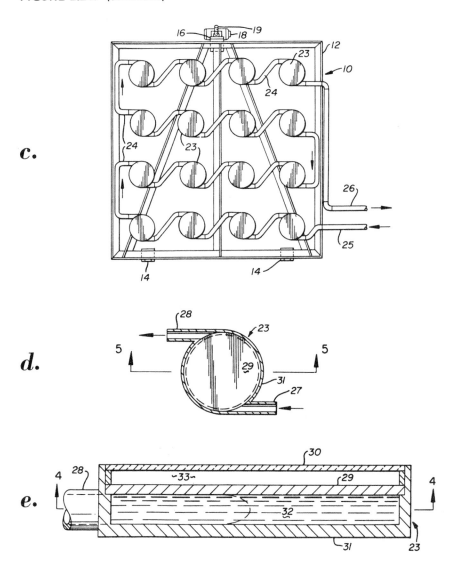

c.

d.

e.

    (a)   Side view of collector
    (b)   Plan view on line **2–2** of Figure 2.21a
    (c)   Plan view on line **3–3** of Figure 2.21a
    (d)   Enlarged transverse section of heat collector element
    (e)   Enlarged section on line **5–5** of Figure 2.21d

Source:  U.S. Patent 3,929,121

The dark colored heat collecting partition forms two chambers in each of the heat collecting elements. The larger of these chambers is indicated by **32** and communicates with the tangentially positioned inlet and outlet, the arrangement being such that fluid entering the heat collecting element is confined to the larger chamber where it wipes the one surface of the dark colored heat collecting partition. The partition is sealed with respect to the back portion **31** of the heat collecting element and the front portion **30** of the heat collecting element is spaced with respect to the partition and sealed to the annular flange forming the peripheral edge of the back portion, so that a dead-air space or a partial vacuum chamber **33** results to insure against loss of heat directed against the partition by the lenses **22** as previously described.

When the plurality of lenses **22** are spaced desirably with respect to the heat collector elements, the focal points of the lenses are on the partitions **29** so that the same are heated rapidly to a very high temperature by the magnified sunlight. It may be desirable to provide insulation on the back side of each of the heat collecting elements to insure against heat loss and that the communicating means **24** interconnecting the elements may also be suitably insulated.

### Low Profile Concentrating Collector

*H. Anderson, Jr.; U.S. Patent 3,861,379; January 21, 1975* describes a solar ray collector having the ability to track the diurnal path of the sun, concentrate its rays upon a single field while maintaining a low structural profile for easy incorporation into present dwelling architecture. Solar concentration is accomplished by focusing a plurality of parallel reflectors, rotatable about parallel longitudinal axes, upon a single field parallel to the reflectors. A photoelectric device attached to the mechanism tracks the sun, accounts for its diurnal variation and, through use of an electromagnetic device, causes the reflectors to rotate about their axes to maintain the focus of the sun on the single field.

Referring to Figure 2.22, reflecting surfaces **10, 12**, etc. to **n** are pivotably mounted for rotation about their longitudinal axes on a framework **14**. The framework is shown flat, but may comprise a parabolic cross section. While only six such reflecting surfaces are illustrated, it is to be understood that the drawing is merely illustrative and that many more surfaces may be utilized to achieve the desired collector area. The reflecting surfaces may comprise a mirror, metallic or nonmetallic, transparent or nontransparent, to provide a front or back surfaced reflector, or any other type of light reflecting coating. The reflectors are shown as rectangularly shaped, although any other suitable configuration, such as parabolic or circular cross section to achieve solar concentration may be used.

The framework is fixably mounted on structure **16**, such as a dwelling roof, and is tilted to insure that the plane of the framework is perpendicular to the declination plane of the sun. Perpendicularity would not be necessary to track the sun **20**, but it would be an optimum setting for the collector **24**, which may comprise a boiler tube, at a specific time of the year because of the perpendicularity of the sun's incident rays upon the reflectors. At other times of the year, the efficiency of the collector would be slightly reduced. In areas distant from the equator, retilting the framework twice a year would improve the overall efficiency of the collector. In operation, each of the reflecting surfaces are prefocused during assembly to the framework onto a boiler tube **24**, wherein incident solar rays **18** from the sun are reflected from the reflector surfaces as reflected rays **22** to

FIGURE 2.22: LOW PROFILE CONCENTRATING COLLECTOR

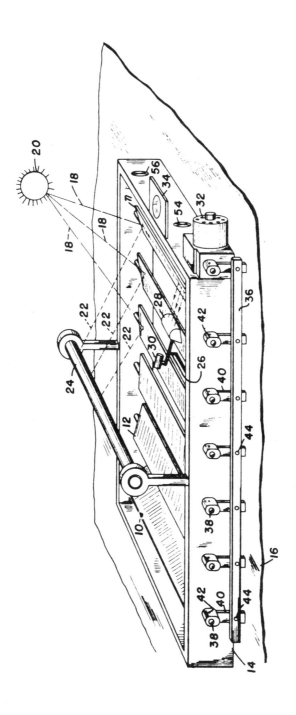

Source: U.S. Patent 3,861,379

be intercepted by the boiler tube (collector). The boiler tube **24** is shown as a single tube and as long as the reflecting surfaces, but it can also have a non-circular cross section, or may comprise an arrangement of more than one tube, and further may be made of a metallic or nonmetallic material. Insulation on the nonirradiated area, or a secondary reflector to trap rays reflected from the boiler tube, can also be included. A medium, such as liquid or vapor, flowing through the boiler tube is heated by reflected rays **22** and can be utilized for heating purposes or other practical uses.

A sun detector **26** is shown attached to the framework comprising cylindrical lens **28** and a photoelectric device **30** situated in the focal line of the lens. The focal line of detector **26**, since it uses a cylindrical lens, lies in the reflective plane comprising the center lines of the boiler tube and an arbitrary reflector **n**, both of which are parallel to each other, is adjusted such that when reflector **n** is properly focused on the boiler tube, the photoelectric device in the detector is illuminated by the reflected rays from the sun. Movement of the sun during the day results in the movement of the reflected rays, whereby the photoelectric device becomes unilluminated, or shaded. When shaded, it causes an electro-magnetic device **32**, to which it is electrically connected, to uniformly rotate, through a system of gears and levers to be described hereinafter, all the reflec-tive surfaces (**10, 12**, etc.) in such a direction that the photoelectric device is once again illuminated.

When this occurs, the rotation of the reflectors is stopped by electrically stop-ping the electromagnetic device, and the sun's rays reflected from reflector **n** are once again properly focused on the boiler tube. Since all the reflecting sur-faces are prefocused on the boiler tube during assembly, when reflector **n** is fo-cused on the boiler tube, all reflective surfaces are properly focused. In this manner, the sun is tracked in it diurnal path while maintaining proper focus of its rays.

Reflectors **10, 12**, etc. are coupled to one another and the electromagnetic device **32** through the alignment bar **36**. Pivot shaft **38** is firmly attached to reflector **10** and is coupled to collar and lever assembly **40** by a set screw **42** or similar functioning attachment or clamping arrangement. The assembly is also pinned to alignment bar **36** by element **44** to allow free rotation. Similarly, reflectors **12** to **n** are coupled to the alignment bar, and thereby to each other, in an identi-cal manner. The distance between shafts **38** and elements **44** pinning assemblies **40** to the alignment bar **36** are equal, such that when the bar is caused to move by electromagnetic device **32** to which it is connected, all the reflectors rotate through the same angle, for reasons to be described hereinafter. The levers and bars can be replaced by gears, chains or sprockets to achieve the same effect.

The advent of a partly cloudy day could disrupt the tracking of the sun. To eliminate this potentiality, a second photoelectric device **34**, mounted to the framework is employed. If it were shaded, due to a cloudy day, it would inter-rupt a rotation signal from the photoelectric device **30** to electromagnetic device **32** and prevent rotation of the reflectors. When the photoelectric device **34** is re-illuminated by the incident rays from the sun, photoelectrical device **30** would be allowed to complete its aforementioned task.

The preceding discussion applies to a situation when the sun's position leads that of the position of the sun detector **26**, and occurs when the normal tracking of the sun is interrupted by clouds. In the morning, at the beginning of the track-ing day, a reverse situation occurs in which the position of the sun could lag that of the position of the sun detector. To eliminate premature and erroneous tracking of the sun, the physical geometry of photoelectric device **34** is such that it cannot be illuminated by the morning sun before it is possible, by the limit of the angle of rotation of reflecting surface **n**, for the sun to illuminate the photo-electric device **30** of the sun detector. A timer or a limit switch **54**, which may be mounted to the framework and activated at the end of the day, causes the motor **32** to return the reflectors to the morning position.

## Pyramidal Reflector

A system is provided by *G. Falbel; U.S. Patent 3,841,302; October 15, 1974; assigned to Wormser Scientific Corporation* in which a solar collector is positioned inside what would be the attic under a conventional roof of a building. The in-side surfaces of the roof rafters and top surfaces of the ceiling joists are utilized to mount reflective surfaces thereon to reflect and focus incoming rays from the sun onto a small collector mounted on the ceiling joists of the structure.

These reflective surfaces mounted in the attic form a pyramidal reflector which focuses the sun's rays onto the collector. A movable hinged reflective panel, which forms the base of the pyramidal reflector when closed, is opened and closed by a geared electric motor. This movable reflective panel is opened when the sun is out, and may be closed when it is cloudy or at nighttime. It also may be positioned at an optimum angle, depending upon the elevation angle of the sun.

Referring to Figures 2.23a and 2.23b, one form of conventional building struc-ture is shown and generally referred to with the reference numeral **10**, having side walls **12**, a ceiling **14** and a slanting roof **16**. The structure is provided with a hinged movable panel **18** which is positioned between the roof and the ceiling or base member of the structure. The process utilizes the space between the roof and the ceiling, which is what is normally considered attic space. The attic space is enclosed by reflective surfaces **22, 24, 26, 27** and **28**, made of suitable noncorroding reflective material, such as protected polished aluminum foil, alu-minized plastic or any other suitable mirror surface or reflective material, form-ing within the attic space a truncated pyramidal reflector **25**, which is best seen in Figure 2.23c.

A black solar collector **30** may be positioned on the ceiling joists **14**, near the surface **26** (which may be vertical or some other optimum angle) of the trun-cated pyramidal reflector. The solar collector is covered by a fixed or removable glass window **32**, appropriately coated or uncoated, which functions to pass so-lar radiation to the collector while providing some insulation for any conductive loss of heat from the solar plate back into the attic, and the coating (if used) re-flects the long-wavelength emitted energy from the collector back onto the collector.

The truncated reflective pyramid which is formed in the attic space may be opened and closed by the movable hinged panel **18** having an inside reflective surface **19**. The panel may be controlled by a motor **20** driving a cable **21** or other suitable means which is attached to one end of the panel, which in turn is hinged to the structure at **17**. The movable panel functions to open the reflector to the sun's rays for directing solar energy onto the collector. By controlling the angle of the movable reflective panel by the motor, the panel can be set at any angle to maximize the sun's rays which reach the collector at any season and any latitude. For example, in the winter the sun's rays come in at a lower angle and the panel would be open a larger angle; whereas the summer rays (used to heat domestic hot water) are higher with the panel open less. Similarly, at latitudes nearer the equator, the angle of the sun's rays are steeper and the panel should be opened to a smaller angle. The function of the pyramidal reflector is to focus the sun's rays on the collector. For radiative cooling in summer days the glass cover on the collector is removed and the movable panel is set to the largest angle to prevent the sun's rays from reaching the collector.

The solar collector will normally contain a medium such as water which is heated by the sun's rays which are absorbed by the collector. This medium can then be pumped to a heat sink for storing the heat provided by the sun's rays until it is ultimately utilized for heating the structure.

## FIGURE 2.23: PYRAMIDAL REFLECTOR

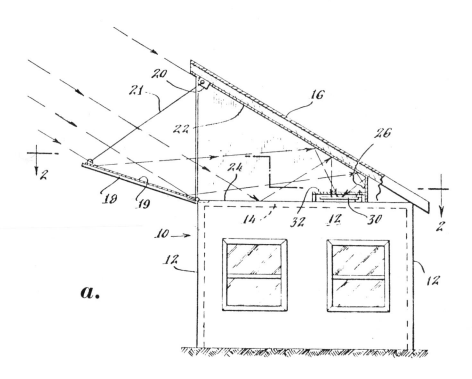

(continued)

FIGURE 2.23: (continued)

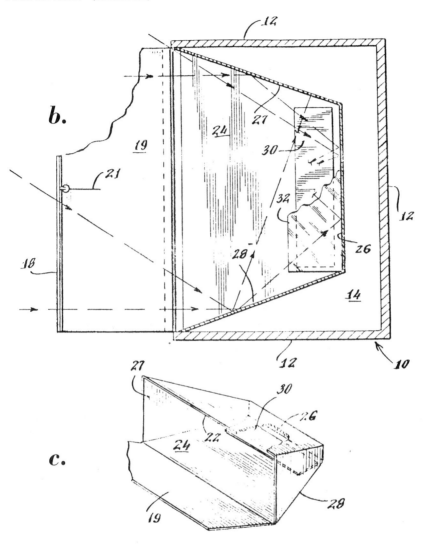

(a) Side elevation view, partly in section, of a building incorporating reflector
(b) Sectional view taken along lines 2–2 of Figure 2.23a
(c) Isometric view, partly broken, of pyramidal reflector

Source: U.S. Patent 3,841,302

# UPRIGHT COLLECTORS

## WINDOW-MOUNTED SYSTEMS

### Venetian Blind for Solar Heating

*D.J. Angilletta; U.S. Patent 4,002,159; January 11, 1977* describes a venetian blind with a heat-absorptive surface on one side of the slats which distributes solar heat into the ambient air of a room. For space heating, the vertically-oriented, highly heat-absorptive surface of the blind has its temperature increased as solar radiation generally in the form of direct sunlight passes through the glass of the window sash and impinges on the energy-absorbing surface.

Ambient air from the room moving by natural convective action enters the air space between the window sash and venetian blind through openings in the bottom rail and between slats of the blind, passes over the heated surface in heat exchange relationship thereto, is warmed, leaves the air space through openings in the head rail of the blind and re-enters the enclosure at an elevated temperature. The other side of each slat of the blind has a reflective surface which when turned to receive the solar radiation, as in the summer, reduces heat entry into the room.

As seen in Figures 3.1a and 3.1b, the venetian blind **10** is secured within the recess of the frame of a window **12** comprised of the sash **38**, glass pane **26**, the generally horizontal sill **36** at the bottom, vertical window jambs **40** at opposite sides and a horizontal lintel **42** at the top. The head rail **20** seats against the side jambs **40** and rests against the lower horizontal face **44** of the lintel **42** and is fixedly attached thereto by end brackets **46** attached by suitable means (e.g., nails, screws) to the jambs **40**. In the fully extended condition the bottom rail **30** of the blind **10** rests upon the window sill **36**. The assemblage of horizontal slats **14** lying generally in a plane parallel to the transparent glass pane **26** of the window **12** have an air space **48** between the pane **26** and the slats **14**. The improvements in the venetian blind of this patent result in one embodiment for a modified design of the head rail and bottom rail, each of which has a plurality of holes passing through its exposed surfaces. The head

FIGURE 3.1:  VENETIAN BLIND FOR SOLAR HEATING

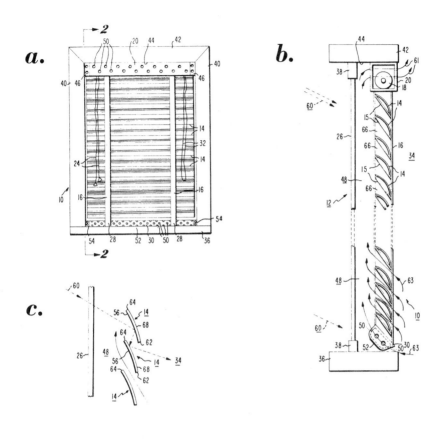

(a)  Front elevational view
(b)  Side view
(c)  Enlarged partial side view

Source:  U.S. Patent 4,002,159

rail **20** is an elongated, rigid, e.g., sheet metal, generally U-shaped channel open at the top and ends and having a plurality of vent holes **50** in each face.  For the free passage of air the bottom rail **30**, which is hollow, has holes in every surface including the bottom surface **52** which is curved away from the flat surface of the sill **36** or in a tilted position when the slats are tilted.  Caps **54** at both ends provide ornamental closures for the bottom rail **30**.  Vent holes in the caps and end brackets enhance air circulation.

The slats are finished on the concave face **56** with a highly heat absorbent coating, e.g., black paint, to efficiently absorb solar radiation **60** entering through the glass window pane **26** and impinging directly (or by reflection) on the concave surface.  Slat temperature increases as energy is absorbed.  Generally solar radiation is best absorbed and room heating is effective when the blind slats are oriented to the approximately vertical "closed" position (Figure 3.1c) with concave faces facing the window glass and with the lower edge **62** of each slat overlapping and concealed by the upper edge **64** of the next lower slat as seen through the window pane.

As the temperature of the slats increases because of the absorption of solar radiation, air in contact or in close proximity with the slat faces is heated and rises by natural convection. Air on the room side **34** of the slats moves freely in a natural circulating manner from the heated slats to the interior of the room. Air in the air space **48** between the window glass and the closed slats is heated by contact and proximity to the concave absorptive faces **56**, rises and leaves the air space through the plurality of vent holes **50** in the head rail **20**. (Air outflow is generally represented by arrows **61** in Figure 3.1b.)

To replace the outflowing heated air, cooler air from the room enters the air space, passing through a plurality of holes in the surfaces of the bottom rail **30** and through the narrow passages **66** which exist between adjacent slats even in the closed position. (Air inflow is generally represented by arrows **63** in Figure 3.1b.) Air enters each passage **66** between the lower edge **62** of the hot concave face **56** and the convex room-facing face **68** of the slat below and rises by natural convection in effective heat transfer relationship with the hot absorptive face **56**. Thus, both slat faces **56, 68**, i.e., facing the room interior and facing the window glass, are active in transferring solar radiation into the room ambient environment when the radiation absorbent surfaces face the window and when a complete circuit for convective air flow between window pane and slats is provided.

The air space **48** is of sufficient width to allow substantially unimpeded natural circulating flow between the room and the air space; approximately four inches between the slats and the window glass provides effective performance. The number, shapes and spacing of vent holes in the head and bottom rail is not critical, performance improving generally as flow area increases. In the head rail and bottom rail, a series of staggered holes approximately 0.625 inch in diameter spaced approximately 0.75 inch apart in parallel rows approximately one inch apart provide effective performance.

### Window Heat Trap

The process of *J.W. Restle, A.J. Algaier and G.R. Krueger; U.S. Patent 3,990,635; November 9, 1976* provides an apparatus that might be classified as a heat trap mounted in or across the window opening. This heat trap consists of overlying spaced apart inner and outer sheets of transparent material that are substantially coextensive in size and shape with the window opening and extend across the opening. The outer sheet is transparent, but the inner sheet is only partially transparent since one side is treated to reflect heat energy, i.e., infrared rays, while the other side has means to absorb the infrared rays of solar energy.

For heat conservation during the heating season, the reflective side faces inwardly and the other side faces outwardly. Reversal of this relationship, by which the inner sheet becomes the outer sheet and its reflective surface faces outward, adapts the apparatus to use in hot weather when entry of solar energy through the windows is undesirable.

During the heating season when the infrared ray absorbing surface faces out-wardly, the heat energy trapped thereby heats the space between the inner and outer sheets, and when the temperature therein reaches a predetermined level, thermostatically controlled valves open and communicate the space between the sheets at its top and bottom with the room interior. The above mentioned re-versal of the sheets reduces the transmission of solar energy into the room. The apparatus thus has year-round utility.

Referring to Figures 3.2a through 3.2d, the numeral **3** identifies a typical double-hung window mounted in the conventional way in a window opening **4** of an existing outside wall **5** of a room. In accordance with this patent, a unitary conversion unit **6**, upon being mounted on the wall **5**, not only eliminates or at least greatly minimizes heat loss through the window, but in addition uses solar energy to heat the room during the heating season.

The conversion unit comprises a rectangular frame **7** of a size and shape to en-compass the window opening and enable its attachment to the wall **5** on the inside surface. The frame has upright side rails **8** and top and bottom cross bars **9** and **10**, respectively. The top cross bar is considerably larger in cross section than the side rails and bottom cross bar, and, as seen in Figure 3.2b, it comprises a back wall **11** that is flush with the back surface of the side rails,

### FIGURE 3.2: WINDOW HEAT TRAP

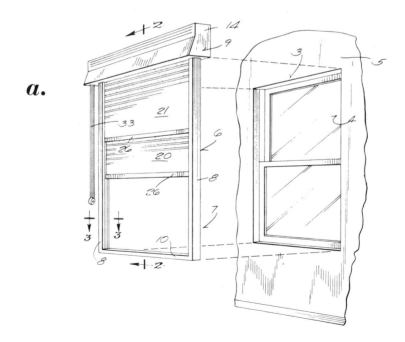

a.

(continued)

FIGURE 3.2: (continued)

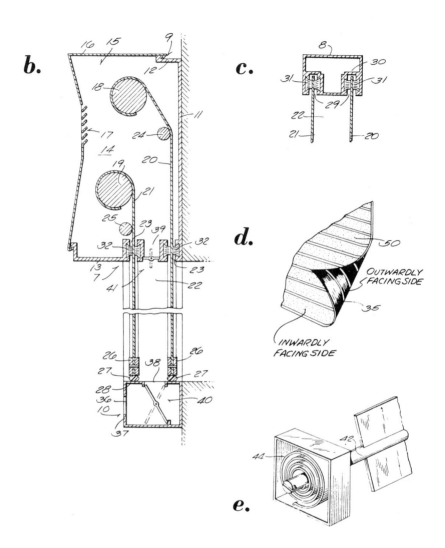

(a)   Perspective view illustrating typical window and one embodiment of
       apparatus
(b)   Vertical section through Figure 3.2a on the plane of line **2—2**
(c)   Horizontal section through Figure 3.2a on the plane of line **3—3**
(d)   Both sides of the inner sheet
(e)   Perspective view of an end portion of one of the circulation controlling
       valves

Source:   U.S. Patent 3,990,635

top and bottom walls **12** and **13**, respectively, and end walls **14**. Together, these walls define a box-like housing **15** that is completed by a stamped sheet metal valance **16** having louvers **17** through which the housing is communicated with the room interior. Mounted in the housing **15**, one above the other, are two rollers **18** and **19**. The ends of these rollers are journalled in bearings (not shown) that are fixed to the end walls **14**, so the rollers extend across the full width of the frame **7**.

Attached to the rollers **18** and **19** are outer and inner sheets **20** and **21**, respectively, which, upon being pulled down in the manner of an ordinary window shade, form an air space **22** between them. Both sheets are made of transparent flexible material, preferably a plastic capable of withstanding sunlight.

The bottom wall **13** of the housing **15** has spaced parallel slots **23** through which the shade-like sheets pass, and to assure alignment of the sheets with these slots as the sheets are drawn from the rollers, guides **24** and **25** are provided. Obviously these guides span the distance between the end walls **14**, and, if desired, could be freely rotatable. The bottom edges of the inner and outer sheets are clamped between stiff metal bars **26**, to the bottom of which sealing strips **27** are secured to seat upon the top wall **28** of the tubular cross bar **10** when the sheets are drawn all the way down.

As shown in Figure 3.2c, the side edges of the sheets **20** and **21** are slidably received in channels **29** formed in the inner walls **30** of the tubular side rails **8**; and since it is important to seal off undesired access to the space between the sheets **20**, **21** the mouths of the channels **29** are provided with seals **31** that snugly, yet slidably, grip the marginal side edge portion of the sheets. Similar seals **32** are located in the slots **23** through which the sheets enter and leave the housing **15**.

The rollers **18** and **19** may be equipped with conventional retraction springs, so that the sheets **20**, **21** can be drawn down from the rollers and rewound thereon like ordinary window shades, or the rollers can be freely rotatably mounted at both ends and rotated in both directions by chords **33**.

Since the primary objective of this patent is to utilize solar energy whenever possible and thereby conserve energy by reducing the load on the home heating plant, the outwardly facing side of the inner sheet **21** is provided with means to absorb the infrared rays of sunlight entering the window, and thereby heat the space between the sheets. There are obviously different ways in which that heat energy can be abstracted, one of which consists in coating selected areas of the outwardly facing side of the inner sheet with a dull dark or opaque coating composition that can be applied to the material of which the sheet is made. As shown in Figure 3.2d, the thus coated selected areas can be arranged side-by-by-side stripes **35**.

Merely heating the space between the sheets is not enough. That heat must be delivered to the room. For that purpose the space between the sheets is controllably communicable at its top and bottom with the interior of the room so that the room air can circulate through the space. To that end the hollow bottom cross bar **10** has an inlet opening **36** in its inside wall **37** through which air from the room can enter the cross bar, and an outlet opening **38** in its top wall **28** that leads to the space between the sheets; and the bottom wall **13**

of the top cross bar has an elongated opening **39** through which air can pass
from the space between the sheets into the housing **15** and from it through the
louvers **17** into the room. Obviously, the openings **36, 38** and **39** could be provided by rows of individual holes.

Unless the temperature in the space between the sheets is higher than room temperature, the valves **40** and **41** that control communication between the room
and, respectively, the bottom and top of the space between the sheets are closed.
While these valves can take any desirable form, for purposes of illustration they
are shown as dampers mounted in the housing **15** and the hollow bottom cross
bar **10** for rotation about fixed axes between open and closed positions. The
valves **40** and **41** could be manually adjusted to their open positions whenever
a thermometer having its sensor, positioned to be influenced by temperature
changes in the space between the sheets, indicates that the temperature of the
space is above room temperature. However, a more practical way of controlling
the valves is by thermostatically actuated or governed automatic drive means.

In Figure 3.2e, the shaft **42** of the valve (damper) has the inner end of a curled
bimetal actuator **44** fixed thereto, the outer end of which is anchored. In
practice, the valve actuators would be located in the housing **15** and the hollow
bottom cross bar **10** where they would be responsive to temperature changes in
the space between the sheets. Communication between the room interior and
the space between the sheets exists only when the temperature in the space exceeds a predetermined magnitude. At all other times, the valves are closed so
that an insulating dead air space extends across the window to minimize heat
loss. If desired, locking means may be provided to secure the valves closed.

While the provision of heat trapping opaque surface areas on the outwardly
facing side of the inner sheet **21** alone effects a considerable saving in energy,
even greater benefits are achieved by providing the inwardly facing side of the
inner sheet with infrared ray reflecting areas **50**. These areas reflect room heat
away from the window and thereby significantly reduce heat loss at times when
the temperature in the space between the sheets is below that at which the circulation controlling valves are open.

To adapt the unit for nonheating season use, the sheets **20** and **21** are inter-
changed so that the transparent sheet **20** is innermost. For this purpose, the
rollers **18** and **19** must be readily removable from their bearings. In addition,
for nonheating season use, the sheet **21** is reversed so that its reflective areas
face outward to minimize the passage of infrared rays into the space between
the sheets. With such interchange of the sheets and the reflective side of the
sheet **21**, much of the heat energy of sunlight striking the window is kept from
entering the room, and with the circulation controlling valves closed, the resulting dead air space between the sheets serves as a heat barrier across the window opening to further limit the passage of solar energy into the room.

**Box to Be Mounted to Window Sash**

According to *D.J. Angilletta; U.S. Patent 3,960,135; June 1, 1976,* distribution
of solar heat into the ambient air of an enclosed space and a reduction of thermal energy loss from the ambient air and from the enclosed space is provided
by means of a box attached to the inner side of a conventional window sash.
A vertically-oriented, highly heat absorptive surface within the box has its

temperature increased as solar radiation generally in the form of direct sunlight passes through the glass of the window sash, enters the front of the attached box and impinges on the energy absorbing surface. Ambient air from the enclosed space moving by natural convective action enters the box through side and bottom openings in the box, passes over the heated surface in heat exchange relationship thereto, is warmed, leaves the box at or near the top and reenters the enclosed space at an elevated temperature.

With reference to Figure 3.3, the solar heating unit 15 is applied to a conventional window by attachment to the lower window sash casing 10 which generally is made of wood or metal, e.g., aluminum. Only windows having an orientation to receive solar radiation either directly or by reflection are suitably fitted with the solar heating units.

The solar heating unit attached to the window sash has a box-like configuration and is comprised of four relatively narrow rectangular side panels 12 approximately 2 inches wide, a front cover 14 consisting of a pane of untinted transparent glass, and two equal-sized back panels 16 which when closed cover the back of the box assembly.

Edges of the glass front cover 14 are covered by a flexible gasket 18, e.g., rubber, neoprene or foam, which protects and seals under pressure both the inner glass surface 20 and the outer glass surface 22 along the entire periphery of glass 14. Glass cover 14 is dimensioned to match window sash 10 so that when attached to sash 10 front glass cover 14 with flexible gasket 18 in place forms a complete seal against inner frame surface 11 of the sash.

The seal produces a dead air space 24 which acts as an insulator between the conventional glass window pane 26 and the front cover glass pane 14. A generally flat metal frame 28, on which rests the gasket 18, has holes 30 in its surface through which pass screws or bolts 32. The screws or bolts 32 also pass through holes 19 in flexible gasket 18 and attach to window sash casing 10. By tightening action upon the fasteners 32 gasket 18 is compressed and air seals are created at surfaces 11, 20, 22.

In a preferred embodiment of this process, box side panels 12 are wood with a plurality of slots cut therethrough to allow free passage of air. The four side panels comprise a frame approximately 2 inches deep (or deeper if the window frame allows) attached by fasteners 36, i.e., threaded bolts, passing therethrough and engaging threaded holes 38 in metal gasket frame 28. The inside surfaces 13 of slotted side panels 12 are preferably highly heat absorbing, e.g., a dull black finish.

In other configurations of this process, the box sides may be fabricated of materials other than wood, such as plastics, as long as the material is of low conductivity; alternatively, the box sides are constructed with insulation to separate the exterior from hot interior surfaces. Rigid back panels 16 are attached to side panels 12 by vertically oriented hinges 40 which permit the back cover of the heater unit to swing out into the room to permit access for cleaning of interior surfaces and to allow viewing through the window. A simple latch device 42 holds back door panels 16 in a closed position when the heater operates.

FIGURE 3.3: TOP SECTIONAL VIEW OF WINDOW UNIT

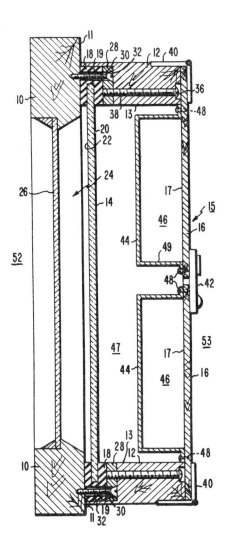

Source: U.S. Patent 3,960,135

A plurality of slots at the top and bottom of back panels **16** allows free circulation of air into and out of the box. The internal surface **17** of back panels **16** is highly heat absorbing, e.g., a dull black finish, but the panel itself is made of low thermal conductivity material or is insulated so that the exterior of the box is not too hot to touch.

Solar radiation entering the box-like assembly through glass panes **14** and **26**, impinges on two heating surfaces **44** which lie generally in a plane parallel to the glass panes **14** and **26** and back panels **16**. Air passages **46** and **47** separate the heating surfaces **44** from facing glass **14** and back panel surfaces **17**. The heating surfaces **44** are made of thin substantially flat sheet metal having a highly heat absorptive finish, e.g., dull black paint, applied thereon. This surface when exposed to solar radiation absorbs a large percentage of the solar energy and becomes elevated in temperature. The heat absorbed by the heated surface is subsequently transmitted to the ambient air as described below. In other embodiments of this process, corrugated, fluted, finned and other surfaces in many differing arrangements may be employed by methods well known to those versed in this technology to increase the effective heat transfer area of the heating surfaces. The energy absorbing surfaces are attached with screws **48** to back panels **16** by means of mounting flanges **49** formed from vertical folds in the heating surface metal.

In operation with the box assembly attached to the window sash, the sun's rays pass through the double glass panes and impinge on the thermally absorptive surfaces **44** within the solar box, resulting in a substantial elevation in surface temperature. Air in the internal box passages **46** and **47** on both sides of the heated surfaces becomes warmer because of contact or proximity with the heated surfaces and rises passing out of the box assembly through the plurality of slots provided in the top, side, and back panels.

Cooler air from the enclosed space **53** which is to be heated, e.g., living quarters of a house, enters the box assembly through the slots in the bottom, side and back panels by natural convection and is in turn heated and rises. Reliance is made upon the chimney effect produced by the heated vertical air passages **46** and **47** within the box assembly and no means of forced convection is required to induce the desired air flow and heat transfer.

When the sun fails to shine on the heat absorbing surfaces **44**, or at any other time, the hinged back doors **16** with the heating surfaces **44** attached may be swung to the open position permitting light to directly enter the enclosure **53** and permitting unobstructed viewing through the window.

### Window System for Circulation of Ambient or Heated Air

*L.A. Boström; U.S. Patent 3,955,555; May 11, 1975; assigned to Clima Wall Ltd, Switzerland* describes a building where the window openings in the facade and/or ceiling are provided with two spaced apart window panes at least one of which has the property of absorbing sun-heat radiation and between which air is allowed to pass, the building being provided with an air and heat circulation system comprising a combination of two different air duct systems.

One system comprises at least one closed channel system for circulating air absorbing the heat from the window, which system includes spaces between the window panes and, in the walls, floor and/or ceiling, channels communicating with the spaces. In this system the air is brought to circulate at a speed depending on the desired room temperature. The other system includes a special channel system connected to the rooms for supplying intake air to the rooms. In this system the air is brought to circulate at a speed determined by the desired room ventilation.

The building of Figure 3.4a, a three-storied building, has in the window openings in the facade two spaced apart single or double glazed window panes **1** and
**2**. At least one of the window panes has the property of absorbing heat radiation from the sun.

The spaces between the window panes form part of a channel system **4** provided
in the walls, floor and/or ceiling, for circulating air, which is represented by continuous arrows in the drawing. This air is thus allowed to pass between the window panes to absorb heat therefrom. The rooms **3** in the building are connected
to a special channel system **5** for supply of fresh air, represented by broken arrows, to the rooms. Both systems include fans **12** adapted to impart to the air
the speed suitable for the purpose.

### FIGURE 3.4: WINDOW SYSTEM FOR CIRCULATION OF AMBIENT OR HEATED AIR

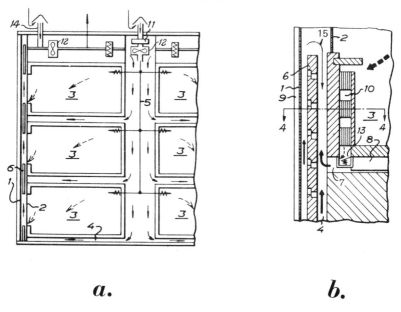

### a.                                                    b.

(a) Longitudinal sectional view of building
(b) Detail according to Figure 3.4a

Source:  U.S. Patent 3,955,555

As appears from the embodiment shown in the drawing, the rooms are connected
to the channel system via nonreturn valves **13** or like means in such a way that
the waste air passes to the channel system without any risk of the air in this
system **4** passing into the rooms. The simplest way of obtaining this effect is to
keep the pressure in the channel system lower than in the rooms.

One or both of the window panes has the property of absorbing radiation over
a wavelength range of 700 to 2,000 nm. By adding a transparent color correc-
tion layer absorbing radiation over the wavelength range 300 to 500 nm, there

is obtained a color restoration of residual visual light admitted into the rooms, which substantially will comprise the wavelengths 500 to 700 nm in the spectrum.

At the side of the window openings the building is provided with particular sun-heat absorbing elements **6** which are included in the channel system so that the air in the system passes the elements. According to the drawing the elements are positioned at such a distance inwardly of prolongations of the window panes **1** that the air in the channel system passes on both sides of the elements.

The favorable equalizing effect produced by a heavy wall structure with high heat-storing capacity is, in this building, suitably transmitted to the concrete floors. This is effected by allowing at least certain portions of the air from the spaces between the window panes to pass through apertures **7** in the concrete floors. In order to give the concrete floors a high heat-storing capacity the surfaces of the apertures are provided with closely spaced flanges **8**. Alternatively, the channel system may be arranged so as to pass other parts of the building having high heat-storing capacity.

It is important, especially in summer time, to supply to the channel system as cold air as possible from outside in order to carry away heat. For this purpose the channel system is provided with an intake **14** communicating with the outside air and positioned on the shady side of the building. If desired, the channel system may be provided with several intakes which are in the shade during different parts of the day, and when supply of cold outside air is desired that intake is used which is in the shade for the time being. Alternatively, when the air at some distance from the building has a lower temperature than the air adjacent the building, the air intake may be in the form of a chimney.

In addition, to the window panes described above, the facade contains elements **9** ventilated by the outside air and permeable to aqueous steam to give the air circulating in channel system **4** the desired humidity. The elements will thus form walls of the channel system. The channel system also contains water-cooled permeable elements to give the circulating air a lower temperature. These elements may consist of the elements **9**.

As is apparent from Figure 3.4b, the connection **10** of the rooms with the channel system is situated adjacent the outer wall of the building and includes or is formed as a sound-absorbing means. The channel system includes the passages formed of the apertures **7** in the concrete floor and opening at the front edge of the floor, the rooms being connected with the passages inwardly of the openings of the latter so as to reduce noise caused by the resistance to sound in countercurrent air indicated in Figure 3.4b by the arrow **15**.

### Apertured Collector Plates

A solar wall system is described by *J.L. Schoenfelder; U.S. Patent 3,863,621; February 4, 1975; assigned to Iowa State University Research Foundation Inc.* where the wall has a collector plate for gathering solar energy and converting it into heat energy. The collector plate is an apertured collector plate having substantially no materials loss when compared to a solid plate of like material, weight and dimensions, but has increased surface area.

One embodiment of the process relates to a transparent solar wall system capable of transmitting light to the internal parts of a building structure. The transparent wall system utilizes the louvered collector plate. Another embodiment of the process relates to a very efficient opaque solar wall system which employs gang-nail collector plates.

An apertured collector plate, as that term is used herein, does not mean a collector plate which merely has holes punched therein. A collector plate having holes punched therein will naturally have a materials loss when compared to a solid plate of like material, weight and dimensions. Thus, the surface area of the overall collector plate will be decreased. In accordance with this process it has been found that apertured collector plates which have substantially no materials loss when compared to a solid plate of like material, weight and dimension, provide increased surface area, and in addition, will transmit light therethrough.

The increased surface area results in a greater increased efficiency for collection of solar energy and conversion of that energy into heat energy. Thus, while the collector plate does have apertures therein, the material displaced in forming the apertures is not completely removed from the collector plate. One example of such collector plates, formed without a materials loss, is a louvered collector plate wherein the metal is punched or otherwise pressed in a dye to provide louvers as shown in Figure 3.5a.

Thus there are apertures present but the material displaced in forming the apertures is not removed from the collector plate. Obviously then, the overall surface area for collection of solar energy is increased. Another type of aperture collector is illustrated in Figure 3.5b, the gang-nail collector plate. The process will be described in a connection with the cross-sectional views of Figures 3.5c and 3.5d.

While the collector plates shown in the drawings represent a preferred modular unit solar wall system, it should be appreciated that the solar wall system can equally as well, if desired, be built as an entire wall section. Where this is done the views of Figures 3.5c and 3.5d generally will represent a sectional view of the various layers, in laminar relationship, comprising the wall structure. Conventional wall frame means can be utilized to hold the various solar wall system layers into their hereinafter described relationship and thus this conventional frame structure will not be described here in detail.

In both Figures 3.5c and 3.5d, the left hand side thereof, represents the exteriorly exposed portion of the wall, with the right hand side thereof representing the interiorly disposed portion of the wall. With specific reference to Figure 3.5c, there is shown a transparent or see-through solar wall system. This system comprises an exteriorly exposed transparent member 18, a void space 20, and spaced apart from but behind the exteriorly exposed transparent member 18 is an interiorly disposed transparent member 22.

There can be more than two transparent members and if desired, the number can be from two up to four; however, for purposes of cost efficiency two transparent members are preferred. The transparent members can be conventional plate glass, or made of transparent Plexiglas material.

# FIGURE 3.5: APERTURED COLLECTOR PLATES

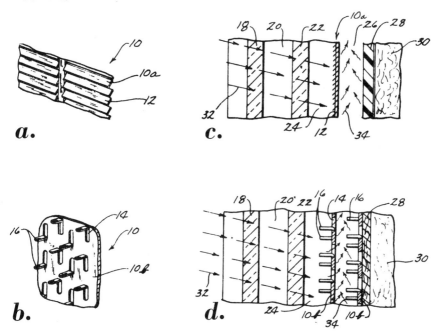

**a.**

**b.**

**c.**

**d.**

(a)     Fragmentary view of louvered collector plate
(b)     Fragmentary review of a gang-nail collector plate
(c)     Cross section of a transparent wall construction with louvered
          collector plate
(d)     Cross section of wall construction with gang-nail collector

Source:  U.S. Patent 3,863,621

Thermopane glass can be employed.  Behind the most interiorly disposed transparent member **22**, is an additional air space **24** and spaced apart from transparent member **22** and behind the member is a louvered collector plate **10a**.  Immediately behind louvered collector plate **10a** is an air space chamber **26** for collection and movement of warm air.

The rear wall of space chamber **26** can be defined by any conventional panel material **28** which in Figure 3.5c is transparent.  Behind panel **28** and in abutting relationship therewith is an insulation layer **30**.  Insulation layer **30** can comprise any well-known insulating material.  For example, it can be foam plastic insulation such as urethane foam; it can be a fiber insulation such as fiberglass butt; or it can be a loose fill insulation such as fiberglass pellets and the like.  The insulation layer is the most interiorly disposed portion of the solar wall system.  Behind insulation layer **30** can be any wall panel construction suitable for exposure within the internal wall of the building.  This could conceivably be wood paneling, any conventional dry wall construction, or the like.

The insulation layer is movably connected to the remainder of the solar wall system so that the insulation layer can be moved away therefrom to allow light to pass through the solar wall and to allow those within the building structure to see outside.

During in-use operation the solar wall system described in Figure 3.5c operates as follows. Sun rays represented by arrows 32 pass through transparent members 18 and 20 and hit the louvers 12 of louvered collector plate 10a. The collector plate is warmed by the sun rays 32 and the collector plate, which is typically painted flat black, converts the sun rays 32 into heat energy. Because of the increased surface area of collector plate over a simple metal sheet collector plate or over a corrugated collector plate, the absorption and conversion of solar energy into heat energy is increased.

The heat energy warms the air in air space chamber 26 and the warm air 34 can be swept away for heating the building structure. Heat loss of the collected heat energy is significantly decreased by the presence of panel 28 and insulation layer 30. Heat loss by conduction to the exterior of the wall construction system is prevented by design of collector plate 10a, and the spaced apart relationship of the transparent members 18 and 22. The means for sweeping away warm air and circulating it through the building structure are conventional, such as a fan system with a warm air storage unit.

The wall construction shown in Figure 3.5d is similar to that shown in Figure 3.5c but is specifically designed for a highly efficient opaque solar wall system. Those portions of the structure of like construction to those previously described will not be described here in detail. Like numerals have been utilized to represent like structure. In Figure 3.5d there is shown a first gang-nail collector plate 10b and spaced apart therefrom but behind first gang-nail collector plate 10b is a second gang-nail collector plate also represented by numeral 10b. The air space chamber then is defined by the back of first gang-nail collector plate 10b and the front of second gang-nail collector plate 10b.

Behind second gang-nail collector plate 10b is a panel 28 which can be wood or other opaque conventional materials since this wall system is an opaque one. Spaced directly behind panel 28 and in abutting relationship thereto is insulation layer 30. In the construction of Figure 3.5d, those rays which pass through the apertures of the first gang-nail collector plate will strike the second collector plate which is preferably in offset relationship with regard to the first collector plate. As a result an enhanced efficiency of solar energy collection is achieved. Moreover, the combined increased exposed surface areas of gang-nail collector plates make them extremely efficient in solar energy collection.

## Window Drape

*R.A. Mole; U.S. Patent 4,020,826; May 3, 1977* describes a system for selectively absorbing or reflecting radiant energy entering through a window of a structure, the system comprising a window drape having a decorative side and a back side, and a removable liner adjacent the backside of the window drape. At least one side of the liner or window drape backside is a radiant energy reflecting surface and another of the sides is a radiant energy absorbing surface. Thus, depending upon the season of the year, the system may be arranged to selectively provide the appropriate surface to optimize or minimize the radiant energy maintained within the structure.

The solar energy system is shown in Figure 3.6a and 3.6b and generally designated by the numeral **10**. In the preferred embodiment, drapery **12** and liner **13**, secured together by fastening means **14**, are supported by conventional hanger **15** adjacent window **16**.

## FIGURE 3.6: WINDOW DRAPE

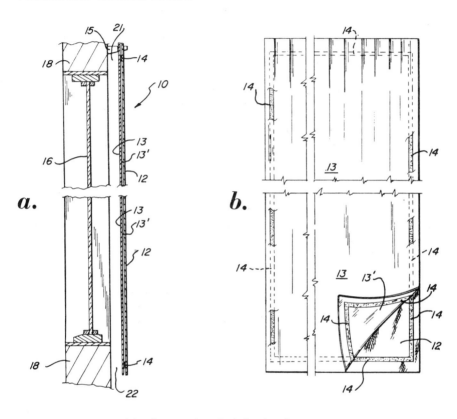

(a) Cross section of window hanging
(b) Rear view of window hanging

Source: U.S. Patent 4,020,826

At least one side of liner **13** is either a radiant energy reflecting surface or radiant energy absorbing surface. Either the other side of liner **13** or the backside of drapery **12** is the other of the radiant energy reflecting surface or radiant energy absorbing surface.

Preferably, as shown in Figure 3.6b, the exposed side of liner **13** is a radiant energy reflecting surface and the backside **13'** of liner **13** is the radiant energy absorbing surface. In this manner, both the liner and drapery **12** are always maintained adjacent window **16**. In warm weather, the energy reflecting surface of liner **13** is disposed towards the window and radiant energy passing through the window is reflected through the window. The double layer of the liner and the drapery serves to insulate against convection flow of heat absorbed by energy reflecting surface of the liner.

Conversely, on cold days, the radiant energy absorbing surface of either liner **13** or the drapery is exposed towards the window. Thus, the radiant energy is absorbed, the surface heated and the adjacent air between the drapery and window accordingly heated. In this manner, warmed air is flowed by convection between structure wall **18** and the drapery through upper opening **21**. Cooled air flows through lower opening **22**, defined between the wall and the drapery, to be heated by absorbed radiant energy.

For purposes of discussion of the solar energy system, a radiant energy absorbing surface is one that absorbs at least 75% of solar radiant energy falling there. On the other hand, a radiant energy reflecting surface is defined as one which reflects at least 75% of the solar radiant energy falling there. Preferably, the surfaces absorb or reflect at least 90% of the radiant energy falling thereon but worthwhile results are obtainable with the lower performance. Generally, white material will reflect 90% of the energy falling thereon and a deep black will absorb 95% of the energy falling thereon.

*Example 1:* A black lined drapery was positioned adjacent a window. On a 44°F sunny day with an ambient interior room temperature adjacent the room ceiling of 78°F, a substantial movement of air through the space at the top of the drape could be perceived. This air was measured at 104°F.

*Example 2:* A white lined drapery was positioned adjacent a window. On a 44°F sunny day with an ambient interior room temperature adjacent the ceiling of 78°F, very little movement of air through the space at the top of the drape could be perceived. The temperature was measured at 88°F.

## WALL-MOUNTED SYSTEMS

### Apparatus with Plurality of Energy Receiving Elements

*D.W. Pedersen; U.S. Patent 4,014,313; March 29, 1977* describes an apparatus and method for collection of solar energy which is particularly adaptable for being formed as a part of or integrated into an upright or vertical surface of a building or structure. The apparatus involves a closed compartment, including an exterior transparent cover, within which are located energy receiving elements, each having an energy receiving surface oriented to efficiently receive solar energy. The apparatus may also include an interior transparent cover and reflective surfaces for further enhancing the characteristics of the collector, and the interior of the apparatus may be evacuated.

The method may include the steps of providing a plurality of radiant energy receiving elements, each having an energy receiving surface at the exterior vertical surface of the building, and orienting the energy receiving surface at an angle for efficiently receiving radiant energy.

Referring to Figures 3.7a and 3.7b, there is shown an apparatus for collecting solar energy at a generally upright or vertical exterior surface which comprises a solar energy collector **10**. The solar energy collector **10** includes at least one energy receiving element **12**, although preferably a plurality of these elements are provided. Each element is provided with an energy receiving surface **13** for receiving and absorbing radiant energy, which will be described more fully subsequently. Each energy receiving element is located within a compartment **20**, which may be formed by an exterior transparent cover member **14** and an interior cover member **16** retained preferably in a spaced apart and parallel relationship by a frame member **18**.

In some cases, the compartment is generally closed or may be sealed by an airtight seal between the cover members and the frame member. The frame member is one means by which the solar energy collector may be retained at a generally upright or vertical surface of, for example, a building **22**. When so retained, the exterior cover member **14** faces outward toward the external environment of the building while the interior cover **16** faces toward the inside of the building.

**FIGURE 3.7: APPARATUS WITH PLURALITY OF ENERGY RECEIVING ELEMENTS**

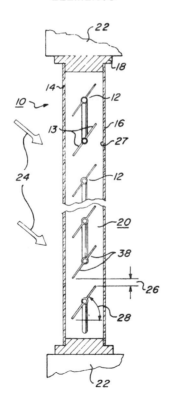

*a.*

(continued)

FIGURE 3.7: (continued)

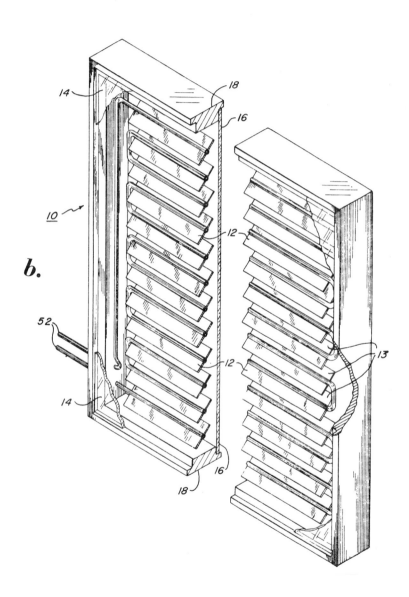

*b.*

(continued)

**FIGURE 3.7:** (continued)

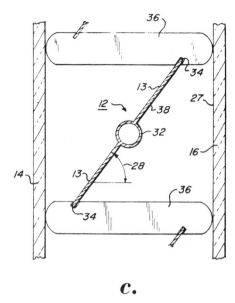

**_c._**

(a) Side view of a section of apparatus
(b) Perspective view
(c) Side view of element used in apparatus

Source: U.S. Patent 4,014,313

The exterior cover member is made of transparent material such as tempered glass or clear plastic. The transparent material allows the entry of radiant energy from the sun indicated schematically at **24**. The interior cover member may in some cases also be made of transparent material and thus provides that the solar energy collector may be advantageously used in a manner somewhat related to the use of a window in a building.

The energy receiving elements may be provided in a generally vertical column with a vertical space **26** between adjacent energy receiving elements. In the arrangement in which the interior cover member is transparent, the vertical space allows a sight path between the energy receiving elements through the solar energy collector from the interior of the building.

The dimension of the vertical space determines the degree of elevation of the sight path above the horizontal and variation of the space **26** along the column or throughout the collector may be desirable depending on the circumstances and requirements of a particular application. The energy receiving elements may also be arranged vertically with horizontal spaces between the elements. In this arrangement the sight path between the elements is not limited as to the degree of elevation relative the horizontal. In none of the embodiments is the sight path below the horizontal greatly impeded as is more apparent from the subsequent description. It may prove feasible to cause the elements to be movable to allow the elements to occupy various positions within the compartment **20**, such as for example, by tilting a whole array of movable elements. The outward facing surface of the interior cover member may be provided with a reflective surface **27**, which when member **16** is transparent, may be a transparent mirrored surface or a reflective plastic film.

The reflective surface need not prevent sight outward from the interior of the building, but prevents or impedes the transmittal of radiant energy **24** to the interior of the building. The reflective surface may cause radiant energy not initially impinging on the energy receiving elements **12** to be reflected back onto those elements. The reflective surface is also important in reducing reradiation or radiation of the energy absorbed by the elements through the transparent cover member into the interior of the building. This is a significant feature of the process since reradiation might otherwise amount to a considerable and undesirable influx of heat energy into the building. Other features of the process also aid in preventing reradiation as will be described subsequently.

When a plurality of energy receiving elements are provided within the compartment, it is usually advantageous that the energy receiving elements be oriented generally in parallel relation with one another. Oriented in a parallel relation, all of the elements can provide a greater collective absorption area or surface for receiving the radiant energy from the sun.

The energy absorbing surface **13** of each of the elements may usually comprise a flat surface as shown more clearly in Figure 3.7c, for example. Other geometric configurations may be advantageous also. The energy absorbing surface faces outwardly of the solar energy collector and generally provides a means by which the radiant energy is received and absorbed. The energy receiving surface may be of a color and texture particularly adapted for absorbing radiant energy. Generally the energy absorbing surface will be of a dull nature and dark, and its texture may be somewhat coarse, but such may also be determined empirically for particular applications.

The energy receiving element will typically be constructed of a good heat conductive material such as metal. The energy receiving element comprises a conduit or tube **32** to which are attached, for example by welding or soldering, two wings **34**. The wings are made of heat conductive material and readily absorb radiant energy that impinges upon them. The energy absorbed causes heat which is readily conducted to the tube by the heat conductive properties of the wings. The tube provides a means through which a fluid medium may be passed to transfer the energy absorbed by the energy receiving surface of the wings away from the elements and the collector.

Each of the energy receiving elements and the energy receiving surfaces is oriented at an angle **28** for efficiently receiving radiant energy. In the embodiment where a vertical space separates the elements, the angle is measured from the horizontal plane and may be best determined for a particular locale and application in which the solar energy collector is to be employed. In the embodiment with vertical energy receiving elements, the angle is measured from a north-south longitudinal line.

Generally speaking, the angle is that which normally would result in the greatest absorption of the radiant energy of the sun, depending on the particular latitude where the solar energy collector is employed, the direction or exposure that the collector faces, the particular climate, and the relative intensity of the sun during particular seasons of the year in a particular locale and other factors depending upon a particular application of the process. For example, an angle of 50° to 60° for horizontal energy receiving elements having a southern exposure and a latitude approximately midway in the United States may prove satisfactory.

It is noted that the angle of orientation for the energy receiving surface causes the energy receiving elements to be somewhat parallel to a downward sight path through the collector. Thus the downward line of sight is not greatly impeded.

Shown in Figure 3.7c, are support members **36** extending between the exterior cover member and the interior cover member. The support member may serve to brace the interior and exterior cover members to secure them against breakage, and may also support and orient the energy receiving elements at desired positions to provide the energy receiving surface at the angle for efficiently absorbing radiant energy. The support members **36** should also be of material resistant to the conduction of heat energy and should be of the smallest cross sectional area possible consonant with the requirements for strength to thereby reduce heat transfer between the cover members and to avoid obstructing the sight path between the elements. The rounded ends in contact with the cover members provide a small cross-sectional contact area to further reduce heat transfer. Other means to support the elements may be employed if the elements are movable.

The apparatus may also provide an inward facing surface **38** of the energy receiving elements **12** particularly adapted to reduce reradiation from the elements and to facilitate return of light toward the inside of the building. In Figure 3.7a, the surface is smooth and colored white or is silvered or mirrored to reflect reradiation back into the element **12**. The surface **38** also reflects light passing from inside of the building back to the inside.

As can be seen in Figure 3.7b, the fluid medium conduits of each of the energy receiving elements are connected. These fluid medium conduits thus connect the elements, for example, in series, as shown, so that the heat energy created by the absorption of radiant energy by the energy receiving elements may be transported from the solar energy collector **10** by fluid inlet and outlet means **52**. Although the energy receiving elements are shown connected in a series, it may be advantageous in some applications that these elements be connected in parallel.

The connections of the conduits must be flexible when the energy receiving elements are movable. The inlet and outlet means **52** may also be sealed in an airtight manner against frame **18** to secure the vacuum within the compartment **20** when employed.

From the foregoing description of the apparatus, a number of significant advantages are apparent. The process does not require that the solar energy collector be mounted on the roof of the building, and does not interfere with the building design or the space available for use in the interior of the building. Mounted at a generally upright or vertical surface, the solar collector is shielded from natural elements such as hail and snow.

A highly significant advantage is that it makes solar energy collection for large or high rise buildings feasible. The large vertical surface involved in such large or high rise buildings, for example, extending as much as 100 stories above the ground, provides a very large energy collecting area which is necessary if solar energy is to be used in a practically effective manner in such large buildings.

### Louvered Collector for Use Between Vertical Structure Members

*R.C. Bourne; U.S. Patent 3,971,359; July 27, 1976* describes a flat plate solar air heater for installation between light frame structural members, which comprises a pan of sheet stock such as sheet metal with one or more substantially transparent surface sheets to admit solar radiation into a sealed chamber between the pan and the transparent sheets.

A louvered structure placed behind the transparent surface sheets reflects high angle solar rays in summer yet admits low angle solar rays in winter into the black-surfaced absorbing chamber. The louvered structure also increases heat transfer to an air stream moving through the chamber, and directs most of the air flow against the absorber surface. The top and bottom of the pan may be chambered to permit various ductwork connections.

The partially cutaway isometric view of Figure 3.8a shows the basic elements of a preferred embodiment of the louvered flat plate collector. The basic structure of the collector is pan **1**, constructed from a flat sheet material such as sheet metal with long sides **3** which are typically bent at right angles to the essentially planar pan bottom **2**.

### FIGURE 3.8: LOUVERED COLLECTOR FOR USE BETWEEN VERTICAL STRUCTURE MEMBERS

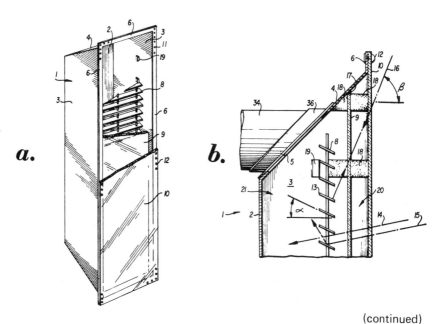

(continued)

FIGURE 3.8: (continued)

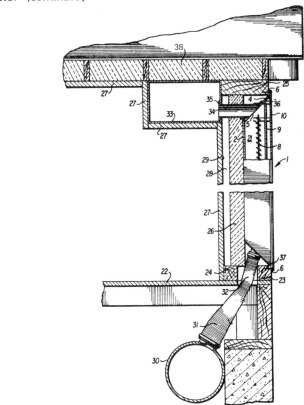

**c.**

(a) Partially schematic, partially cut-away
    isometric view of collector
(b) Partially schematic, vertical cross-sec-
    tional view of the top of collector
(c) Partially schematic, partially cut-away
    vertical cross-sectional view of col-
    lector installed within wood frame
    building structure

Source:  U.S. Patent 3,971,359

Short sides **4** (normally oriented as top and bottom) are here illustrated as bent
at about 45° from the plane of the pan bottom for reasons described in conjunction with Figures 3.8b and 3.8c.  The typical depth of the pan is somewhat exaggerated in order to more clearly illustrate the relationships of the various parts
of the system.  Intersections of sides **3** and **4** may be overlapped, and spot-welded,
screwed or otherwise connected together, then taped with a fabric duct tape to

make the system airtight. Narrow sides 4 are penetrated with holes 5 for inlet and outlet connections. All four sides may have outwardly bent flanges 6 for connection to structural members of a building. The pans as described may be constructed of sheets of steel, aluminum, or copper, but steel is preferred because of its greater strength and lower cost. 22 gauge steel is particularly appropriate for a preferred embodiment. The inner pan surfaces have a black coating (usually flat black paint) to absorb incident solar radiation. Dimensionally the pans are sized to fit between parallel structural members located in standard modular spacing patterns.

In a preferred embodiment, about, 1½" thick wood studs placed about 24" apart on center leave about 22½" wide spaces therebetween. Pans about 22¼" wide are recommended for this spacing to allow about ¼" for tolerance errors. About ¾" wide flanges 6 make overall collector width about 23¾". For wall applications, collector height typically corresponds to total wall height. For about 8 foot ceilings, pan height including flanges becomes about 94¾".

Louvered structure or sheet 8 included between the pan bottom 2 and substantially transparent surface sheets 9 and 10 provides the seasonally selective performance of the collector.

A preferred embodiment of the louvered collector uses damage-resistant clear acrylic sheet as the weather surface 10, and less expensive glass for the rear sheet 9. Aligned holes 11 in the pan flanges 6 and 12 in the acrylic sheet 10 are regularly spaced around the perimeter for screws or other fasteners to be driven into the structural members. Recommended fastener spacing is about 12" on center on the structural members.

The enlarged cross-sectional view of Figure 3.8b shows details of assembly at the top portion of the collector as well as the reflection geometry of the louver system. The louver sheet 8 is held in place with angle clips 19 spot-welded or otherwise attached to pan sides. Rubber tabs 18 made for example of dense neoprene, are adhered to pan sides 3 to space glass sheet 9 between louver sheet 8 and acrylic sheet 10, giving soft support to prevent glass breakage.

Latex or butyl caulk 17 may be applied continuously around the glass edge to create a tight seal between air flow cavity 21 and insulating chamber 20 which is between the two transparent sheets. For maximum insulating value, chamber 20 should be about ⅜" to about ½" thick. Overall pan depth or thickness is typically about 3½", leaving an air flow cavity 21 slightly less than about 3" thick. Within the airflow cavity, the center plane of the louver sheet is displaced toward the outside of the panel, and is preferably located about ¾" to about 1" behind glass sheet 9. In this location most of the air flow occurs in the absorbing portion of the chamber, between pan surface 2 and the louver sheet.

The louver surfaces are designed to reflect high angle rays 16 occurring in the summer or hot months, yet permit low angle rays 14 and 15 either to pass directly through the louver sheet as illustrated by ray 14 or be reflected from the upper surface of louver strip 13 onto the rear absorbing surface as illustrated by ray 15. The reflective upper surfaces of the louver strips 13 may comprise any highly light and heat reflective material such as polished bare metal such as steel or aluminum, an aluminum coating, a silvered mirror coating or any other suitable reflective surface.

The undersides of louver strips **13** may be either reflective or absorbing (i.e., either shiny or black). Reflective undersides cause more solar energy to be reflected onto the absorbing rear pan surface, and result in lower temperatures on the louvers. Absorbing undersides will result in higher louver temperatures, hence better heat transfer to the air flow through the chamber. For this reason, absorbing louver undersides are preferred.

Figure 3.8c shows a partially cut away, sectional view of the louvered collector installed in a wall of wood 2 x 6 construction. The structure consists of floor framing surfaced with plywood subfloor **22**. The vertical 2 x 6 studs are spaced about 24" on the center and rest on 2" x 2" sill plates **23** and **24** spaced about 2½" apart. A 2" x 6" top plate **25** is attached atop the studs and supports the floor or roof structure above. The fully assembled collector pan is fastened through flanges **6** to the wood structural members.

About 1½" thick rigid insulation **26** may be preadhered to the back of pan **1** to generate additional insulating airspace **28** between the rigid insulation **26** and interior surface panel **27** (usually gypsum wallboard) fastened to the inside of the wood framing members. A layer of reflective aluminum foil **29** may be used to further improve the insulating value of the wall.

Figure 3.8c demonstrates the advantages of the sloping pan ends **4**. Ductwork serving the collector may be channeled either vertically, as shown by flexible duct **31** inserted through duct opening **5**, or horizontally, as shown by sheet metal boot **34** inserted through top duct opening **5**, or at an intermediate angle if desired. Because it is desirable to locate ductwork within heated spaces, the configuration shown could be used in many applications of the process.

Cooler air flowing into the collectors enters from the bottom to take advantage of the upward air flow as the air is warmed by the sun. In many cases the air inlet ductwork is too large to be placed at the wall-floor joint within the room, as can be done at the ceiling where it does not interfere with furniture placement and occupant activities in the room. Thus, the supply duct must be placed below the floor. Round duct **30** supplies an array of panels each with its own flexible inlet duct **31**. To keep the air return duct **33** below insulated ceiling **38**, boot **34** is run substantially horizontally into the return duct which is surfaced with gypsum board **27**. Boot **34** may be equipped with flanges **35** and **36** for connecting with sheet metal screws to the return duct and the collector panel, respectively.

For other constructions, different air inlet and outlet systems may be used. For example, a typical two-story collector wall would have a vertical boot from the top of the first floor collector into the bottom of the second floor collector, so that the two could be connected in series, or the apparatus may easily be adapted for panel placement atop sloped roofs, with louver angles varied to provide the proper ratios or reflected energy as the seasons change.

### Porous Barrier Across Fluid Flow Path

A fluid such as air is heated by a heliothermal device of *J.G. Johnston; U.S. Patent 3,875,925; April 8, 1975* which provides a flow path for the fluid, and arranges across the fluid flow path a porous barrier which passes solar rays in one direction, but blocks heat from returning through the barrier in a direction opposite to that of the impinging solar rays. The barrier may be constructed in layers from a fibrous material, or as a fabric, metal, or synthetic resin mesh forming a screen.

Referring to Figure 3.9a and 3.9b, a solar heater **10** has a housing **12** forming a flow path for a fluid, such as air or other suitable gas, to be heated. Housing **12** includes a face **14** arranged for passing light rays impinging thereon, and especially shortwave solar radiation, and the like. It is to be understood that face **14** may be constructed in a conventional manner from suitable, known materials, such as glass, or a thermoplastic resin. If the latter, one important parameter to use in selection is that the material should be clear and readily transmit solar radiation.

Housing **12** further includes a back wall **16** spaced from and arranged substantially parallel to face **14** and provided with an inlet **18** and an outlet **20** spaced from inlet **18**. Both inlet **18** and outlet **20**, which may be constructed in a suitable, known manner as from the illustrated conduits, are arranged forming part of the flow path formed by housing **12**. As shown, a reflector **22** may be arranged beneath the housing and connected thereto for additionally increasing the efficiency of operation of heater **10** by increasing the amount of solar radiation reflected thereinto.

Also as shown, housing **12** is mounted in a conventional manner on a wall **24** of a building structure to be heated. This wall **24** must, of course, be provided with openings for receiving the conduits forming inlet **18** and outlet **20**. Housing **12** is completed using conventional construction techniques to include a top wall **26** and a bottom wall **28**. It is to the latter that reflector **22** is attached in a suitable manner.

A heat valve is arranged in the housing across the flow path thereof for accepting light received from face **14** and blocking the passage of heat back toward the face.

The heat valve advantageously, although not necessarily, is in the form of a substantially planar mat **30** which may be considered a filter medium in that it is constructed from a porous material, such as a fibrous synthetic resin, and formed from two layers **32** and **34**. Fiber glass such as conventionally used as insulation, air filters, and the like, may be employed for constructing mat **30**. Layer **32**, being the layer arranged directed toward face **14**, is selected to have a very low density, while layer **34**, arranged directed toward back wall **16**, has a density higher than the density of layer **32**. It may be stated in general terms that layer **32** is of minimum density, and layer **34** of medium density. Further, layers **32** and **34** should generally be colored black, or a dark color, while layer **34** may be of a lighter color, such as gray or white.

The mat **30** employed with heater **10** is arranged extending from a point **36** on the inner end of the conduit forming inlet **18** on a side thereof oriented toward outlet **20** across the flow path to a point **38** on face **14** opposite outlet **20**. As can be readily appreciated from Figure 3.9b, outlet **20** is arranged at a higher level than inlet **18** for creating a natural-circulation of the air or other medium being passed along the flow path defined by housing **12**.

FIGURE 3.9: POROUS BARRIER ACROSS FLUID FLOW PATH

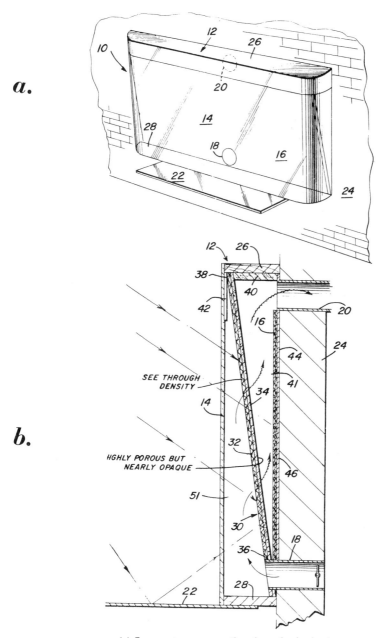

*a.*

*b.*

(a) Fragmentary, perspective view of solar heater
(b) Fragmentary, vertical, transverse sectional view

Source: U.S. Patent 3,875,925

A piece of insulation **40**, which also may be conventional fiber glass insulation or the like, is arranged along the inner surface of top wall **26** in order to co-operate with mat **30** and form a chamber **41** in which heat is collected. A double facing **42** constructed from a suitable, known material is desirably arranged along the upper edge of face **14** adjacent top wall **26** and extends from the latter to the depth of outlet **20**.

While back wall **16** may be constructed from an inexpensive material such as plywood which affords minimum insulation, conductance through back wall **16** can be tolerated since heat dissipated therethrough goes into the enclosure to be heated. A thin layer of an insulation **44**, which may be aluminum foil, and the like, covers back wall **16**, and a preferably black fabric **46**, such as a cheesecloth, covers insulation **46**. The latter covering absorbs heat, or more specifically solar radiation, passed through mat **30**, and completes the heat collecting chamber **41**.

### System with Minimum Mechanization

*E.J. O'Hanlon; U.S. Patent 3,964,678; June 22, 1976* describes an inexpensive solar air conditioning system simple to install and operating with a minimum of mechanism.

The various parts of Figure 3.10a and 3.10b are designated by the following numerals: shelter structure **1**, swinging door **2**, shelter structure wall **3**, shelter structure floor **3a**, shelter structure roof **3b**, transparent or translucent surface preferably corrugated **4**, air conditioner slanting floor **5**, down draft air elbows **6**, fastening devices **7**, cool air down pipe **8**, electric blower **9**, electric air blower **10**, warm air admission opening **11**, air exit opening **12**, pull cord for pulling down black shades **13**, black roller shade **14**, black shade roller tubular case **15**, underground footing for supporting wall structure **16**, polyurethane foam insulation **18**, sheet material enclosing foam **19**, support for holding platform **5** in position **20**, windows in shelter structure **21**, triangular end walls of air conditioner space **30**, triangular air conditioner space **31**, steps **33** up to door **2**, and ground (or soil) **34**.

The solar air conditioners of Figures 3.10a and 3.10b is erected by fastening roller case **15** to the outside of wall structure **3**. The black shade **14** is drawn down over windows **21** by pull cord **13**.

Air conditioner platform **5** composed preferably of three quarter inch plywood painted black on its upper surface is hingedly mounted at its uppermost end to shelter structure wall **3**. Triangular shaped insulated foam walls **30** are positioned as shown along each side of the platform and are likewise fastened to wall **3** by suitable angle irons not shown. A wide transparent or translucent surface (preferably corrugated) is hingedly mounted at its upper end to wall **3** on its exterior surface.

With wall **3**, platform **5** painted black on its upper surface and transparent or translucent surface **4** with the two triangular end foamed members **30** there is an enclosure or a triangular space capable of housing either warm air or cooled air, whichever it is desired that the air conditioner deliver to the interior of the shelter structure.

# FIGURE 3.10: SYSTEM WITH MINIMUM MECHANIZATION

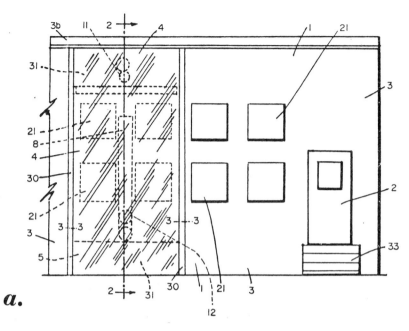

*a.*

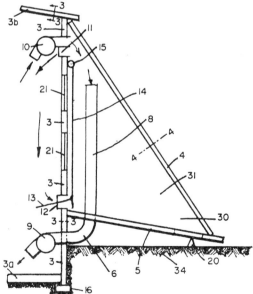

*b.*

(a) Shelter structure
(b) Sectional view along the section 2–2 in Figure 3.10a

Source: U.S. Patent 3,964,678

If the sun is shining it will readily be apparent that the internal triangular space will become warm and the air inside of it will begin to circulate. This warm air will enter shelter structure **1** through air port **11** and will turn downwardly toward air port **12** to reenter air conditioning space **31** where it will still further be heated by the solar heat before it again enters port **11** to go again into the shelter structure **1** through wall **3**. This warm air can be trapped along the way by a bin full of small cobblestones (or the like) if it is desired to hold the warm air condition in the shelter structure **1** over a 24 hour or longer time period.

On the other hand, if it is desired to cool the interior of the shelter structure, blower **10** can be started up, it will blow the cool air in the shelter structure through the triangular air conditioning space **31** after midnight (or until the sun comes up in the morning).

### Collector Formed by Dwelling Wall and Transparent Outer Wall

According to the process of *F. Trombe and J. Michel; U.S. Patent 3,832,992; September 3, 1974; assigned to Agence Nationale de Valorisation de la Recherche, France* a dwelling is equipped with an installation for natural convective air conditioning comprising at least one thermal enclosure bounded by a frontage element of the dwelling exposed to solar radiation and an outer wall transparent to solar radiation and opaque to the far infrared radiation. This outer wall is arranged close to the frontage element, the top and the bottom of this thermal enclosure being able to communicate with the dwelling. The thermal enclosure has at its upper portion first distributor means arranged to direct hot air into the dwelling or to the outer wall and the dwelling has a cold air inlet device provided with closure means.

**FIGURE 3.11: COLLECTOR FORMED BY DWELLING WALL AND TRANS-
PARENT OUTER WALL**

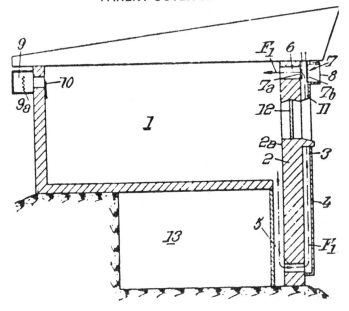

Source: U.S. Patent 3,832,992

# OTHER COLLECTORS

## ROOF DECK CONSTRUCTION

The process of *F.E. Carroll; U.S. Patent 4,006,731; February 8, 1977; assigned to Decks, Incorporated* relates to a building deck construction which is especially suited for synthetic polymeric sheet structural roof decks. The deck construction utilizes subpurlins formed from sheet metal and clips formed from sheet metal to provide a deck construction system which is extremely versatile.

The deck structures utilize formboard with insulating material to exterior and a structural synthetic polymeric sheet to the exterior of the formboard and insulation. The rigid formboard is laid on the sheet metal structural shape subpurlin and held in place by the sheet metal clips. The sheet metal clips further provide uplift resistance to the composite structure. The deck construction also provides for insulated decks of varying insulation capabilities and further provides for solar energy collecting roof construction.

The sheet metal structural shape utilized provides excellent structural characteristics while reducing weight and providing a structural shape that can be readily fabricated from sheet metal. It is highly desirable to fabricate structural shapes from sheet metal to minimize energy requirements in production and to conserve steel.

Prior subpurlins utilized in deck construction, have sometimes extended into the roof deck structure and thus the spacing of the subpurlins has been governed by the width of formboard or rigid board material laid between them. In this deck construction, the rigid board, such as formboard, is laid on top of the subpurlin and thus, the subpurlins may be utilized in closer spacing allowing thinner formboards, insulation and structural sheet decks to be placed on top of the closer spaced subpurlin structure. This deck construction allows the use of any width or length board to be placed upon the top surface of any desired spacing of subpurlins.

Referring to Figure 4.1, the sheet metal shape is shown as box section **20** having a lower horizontal base **21** resting upon purlin structure **30**, vertical sides **22** and

23 and upper horizontal flanges 24 and 25. Slot 26 between the terminal ends of flanges 24 and 25 is preferred to be continuous to permit the most flexible use of the sheet metal box section. However, it is understood that slot 26 may be discontinuous and flanges 24 and 25 joining to enclose the top of the box section where it is not necessary to utilize the sheet metal clips.

## FIGURE 4.1:  ROOF DECK CONSTRUCTION

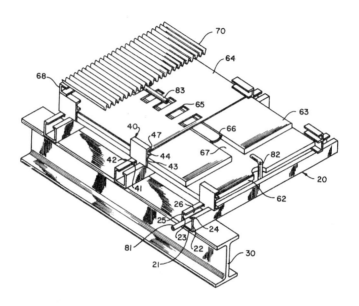

Source:  U.S. Patent 4,006,731

The sheet metal box sections may be fabricated by well-known roll forming techniques from sheet metal from about 20 gauge to about 14 gauge. It is preferred to use galvanized, commercial grade steel of 16 and 18 gauge.

The depth of the box section to be used as a subpurlin is preferably 2¼" to 2½". The width of the box section is preferably 1¾" to 2". The slot for receiving the sheet metal clip may be any width to suit the clip section. Slots about ⅝" are preferred.

The sheet metal clip is shown as 40 having opposing slots 42 between vertical portions 41 and 43 which engage flanges 24 and 25 of the sheet metal box section so that when the axis of the clip is 90° with the axis of the box section, the clip is anchored with the opposing flanges of the top of the box section engaging slots 42 with vertical portion 41 being within the box section. Vertical portion 43 of the sheet metal clip extends upward from the top of the box section a suitable height to provide horizontal portion 44, providing snug fitting of desired rigid board such as formboard 62, polymeric insulation 63 and, if desired, solar energy absorber 64, between horizontal portion 44 and the top flanges 24 and **25** of the sheet metal box section. Horizontal portion **44** extends a sufficient distance to provide such snug fitting. Vertical portion **43** may extend substantially vertically further upward for the desired distance to provide a support for structural shape **68** and polymeric sheet **70**. Sheet metal clip **40** may be provided with substantially horizontal portion **47** to which structural shape **68** is fastened providing uplift resistance and composite structure to the entire deck system. Structural sheet roof support shape **68** may be fastened to clip **40** by any suitable mechanical means, such as self-tapping screws. Likewise, polymeric sheet **70** may be fastened to structural shape **68** by any suitable mechanical means, preferably by plastic capped screws.

Clip **40** is readily inserted at any location into slot **26** by simply turning it so that the axis of the clip and the box section are parallel and inserting the clip for the distance so that slot **42** will engage flanges **24** and **25** and then turning the clip so that axis of the clip is approximately 90° to the axis of the subpurlin. The sheet metal clips may be fabricated by well-known stamping and bending techniques.

The vertical portion of the clip extending above the box section may be 1½ to 4½" to accommodate the thickness of various desired formboards and insulation. The vertical portion of the clip extending into the sheet metal box section may be any desired length so as to provide adequate stiffness of the clip when the flanges of the box section are engaged in the opposing slots of the clip. Horizontal portion **44** of the clip extends for a suitable distance to adequately hold the formboard insulation assembly in place, ½ to 1" being suitable.

Vertical portion **43** may extend upward beyond horizontal portion **44** for a suitable distance to provide support for structural shape **68** to which polymeric sheet **70** is fastened. At the upper end of vertical portion **43** may be horizontal portion **47** of suitable length to provide bearing surface for structural shape **68**, ½ to 1½" being suitable. Structural shape **68** may be of any suitable shape which provides flanges for attachment to the upper horizontal portion of clip **40** and for attachment of polymeric sheet **70**. Structural sheet metal shapes which are readily made by roll-forming, such as the channel shape shown in Figure 4.1, are especially useful for attachment to clips **40** and provide surface for fastening of polymeric sheet **70**.

The distance between polymeric sheet **70** and the top of the formboard-insulation assembly may be adjusted to fit particular needs of specific types of roofs. For example, structural shape **68** may be placed directly upon horizontal portion **44** of clip **40** and directly above the formboard-insulation assembly with the polymeric sheet roofing 70 fastened directly to structural shape **68**. In some cases, clip **40** would not have a vertical portion extending above horizontal portion **44**.

When it is desired to utilize the roof construction of this process for solar energy absorbing roof decks, it may be desired to space structural shape **68** from the upper surface of the formboard-insulation assembly as shown in Figure 4.1. Thus, it is seen that this process applies to both an insulated roof construction wherein a polymeric exterior sheet provides the weather and structural surface as well as roof construction wherein at least a portion of the roof surface provides for solar energy absorption. An embodiment of the roof deck for solar energy absorption is shown in Figure 4.1 wherein metallic absorber plate **64** providing a black body is placed directly above insulation **63**. Metallic plate **64** may be a solid absorbing surface having heat transfer pipes **83** in contact with its upper surface so that the solar energy passes through polymeric sheet **70**, is absorbed by the surface of sheet **64** acting as a black body, transferred by conduction to liquid flowing through pipe **83** which, in turn, is connected through riser pipe **82** to pipe **81** which is carried within the box section for distribution to the desired volume to be heated or to supply thermal energy for air conditioning cooling. It is seen that the box section as utilized in this process, in addition to providing the structural support for the roof, acts as carrier for transfer of the thermal energy from the solar absorber to the volume desired to be heated or cooled.

It is also readily apparent that pipes **81**, **82** and **83** may be totally eliminated and air from the room or volume to be heated may be circulated directly over absorber plate **64** and passed through box sections **20** and provided directly to the volume to be heated by having slots in the bottom of box section **20**. When such an air flow system is utilized, blowers (not shown) must be located at the entrance to or the exit from the roof deck structure. When a heat transfer liquid is utilized in pipes such as pipe **83**, it may be desirable to increase the solar energy collection efficiency by utilization of mirror surfaces as shown by parabolic mirror **66**. In this case, the direct sun rays are focused through slots **65** directly upon pipe **83**.

## COLLECTOR WITH ARCHED COVER

*H. Powell; U.S. Patent 3,987,783; October 26, 1976* describes a solar heating panel with a heat collector mounted on an insulating base and an arched cover over the collector mounted in clips at the edges of the base. One or two flexible covers are slidingly positioned in channels of the mounting clips, with a cover in sealing engagement with the insulating base and projecting downward below the top of the base. A plurality of the heating panels are mounted in an array on a roof or other structure and means for circulating water through the panels for withdrawing heat are provided.

Referring to Figures 4.2a and 4.2b, a plurality of solar heating panels **10** is mounted on a roof or other suitable support **11** in an array, preferably oriented at an angle as shown in Figure 4.2b for optimum exposure to the sun. The panels are interconnected by tubing **12** and a pump **13** provides for circulating a fluid, typically water, through the panels for heating the fluid.

A typical panel is in the order of 6" wide and 12' long. The panel includes a base **20** of a thermal insulating material, typically a plastic foam, with a heat collector **21** mounted on the top of the base as by bolts **22**. Various forms of heat collectors may be utilized and a preferred structure is shown in Figure 4.2c, consisting of a metal tube **24** with a metal plate **25** fitted tightly around the tube for good heat transfer from the plate to the tube. The plate typically is of aluminum and preferably has an etched upper surface with a black coating for maximum heat absorption.

A cover **27** is mounted on the base and preferably is a thin sheet of clear flexible plastic. Mounting clips **30** are provided at each edge of the base for receiving the cover. The clips preferably are bent from sheet aluminum and include a first portion **31** engaging the side of the base, a second portion **32** projecting outwardly and downwardly from the portion **31**, and a third portion **33** at right angles to the portion **31** projecting under the base.

## FIGURE 4.2: COLLECTOR WITH ARCHED COVER

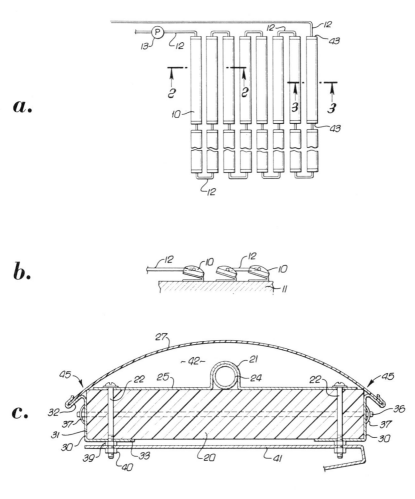

a.

b.

c.

(a)  View of an array of solar panels
(b)  Sectional view taken along line **2–2** of Figure 4.2a
(c)  Enlarged sectional view taken along line **3–3** of Figure 4.2a

Source:  U.S. Patent 3,987,783

A channel is provided in the clip portion **32** for receiving the cover.  The clips preferably extend the length of the panel and are held in place by spaced rods **36** extending through the base, and press-on clamps **37**.  In the embodiment illustrated, the bolts **22** have a first nut **39** for holding the heat collector and clips to the base, and a second nut **40** for holding a panel support strip **41**.  The support strip is not necessary but does provide for mounting the panels at an angle, as shown in Figure 4.2b.  The cover is easily installed by sliding one edge into one of the clips and then bending the cover to slide the opposite edge into the opposite clip. In the preferred embodiment illustrated, the clip is positioned so that there is a pressure engagement between the cover and the base at the corners **45** providing seals between the cover and base along the opposite edges of the air space **42**. The ends of the air space may be closed by caps **43** mounted at the ends of the base.

Also, the clips **30** are preferably positioned so that the entire clip is below the top surface of the base. This configuration serves to prevent moisture from entering the air space. The cover serves to protect the heat collector from the elements so that the heat absorbing surface does not deteriorate. The cover also serves to maintain an insulating barrier of air over the heat collector to reduce heat loss to the surrounding atmosphere. The configuration of Figure 4.2c provides a good compression seal at the corners **45** with the simple flat cover and clip.

## ROOF AS COLLECTOR AND FLUID STORAGE MEDIUM

*A.L. Pittinger; U.S. Patent 3,994,278; November 30, 1976* describes a heating and cooling system utilizing solar radiation as an energy source and a fluid body as a storage medium, the fluid body being distributed over the roof area of a dwelling or other structure with provision for controlling the absorption, storage and delivery of thermal energy to regulate the temperature in the enclosed areas of the structure.

Referring more particularly to the figure by characters of reference, Figures 4.3a, 4.3b and 4.3c disclose a simple dwelling or other structure **10** represented for purposes of illustration only as a rectangular configuration having four vertical walls **11** resting on a foundation or slab floor **12**. The system includes as its primary elements a flat horizontal metal ceiling **13**, shown herein as being corrugated, installed a short distance below the top of the walls **11** so as to form in cooperation with the upper extremities of the walls **11** a shallow impervious chamber **14**. Chamber **14** holds a quantity of liquid **15**. A shallow buoyant tray **16** extends substantially from wall-to-wall within chamber **14** and is covered by a transparent cover **17** supported over tray **16** at the top of the walls **11** and secured in place by a retainer cap **18**.

Cap **18** comprises a plurality of flat strips of wood or other suitable material which are laid over the edges of cover **17** about the perimeter of the top of the vertical side walls **19** of tray **16**, thereby serving as a retainer or stop which limits the maximum upward travel of the tray as it floats on the surface of liquid **15**. The portion **11'** of the walls **11** extending above the level of ceiling **13** is narrower than the main portion of the wall **11** so that a ledge **20** is formed on which the ceiling **13** is conveniently supported.

A transfer means such as pump **21** which may be located in a corner of chamber **14** or external to the chamber has its intake port **22** positioned at the bottom of chamber **14** and its exhaust port **23** directed into the top of the buoyant tray **16**. A baffle **24** in the form of a flat vertical plate installed diagonally across the corner of chamber **14** occupied by the pump **21** isolates the pump **21** from the main body of the chamber. An overflow pipe or pipes **25** installed in the bottom of tray **16** and extending vertically upward therefrom to a height just short of the top of walls **19** of the tray limits the height of the liquid level within the tray, the excess liquid flowing through pipe **25** into the chamber.

FIGURE 4.3:  ROOF AS COLLECTOR AND FLUID STORAGE MEDIUM

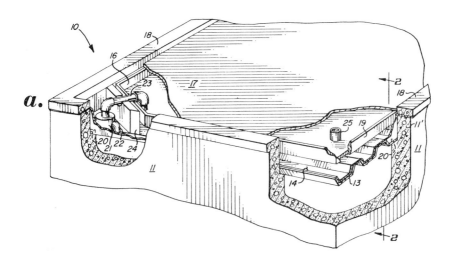

*a.*

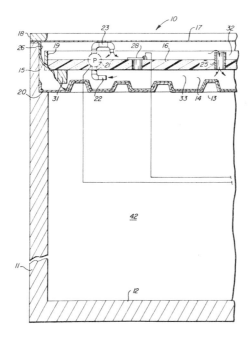

*b.*

(continued)

**FIGURE 4.3:** (continued)

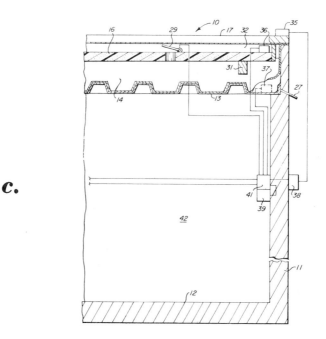

*c.*

    (a)    Isometric drawing of model structure incorporating heating and cooling system
    (b)    Cross-sectional view of the structure of Figure 4.3a taken on line **2–2**
    (c)    View similar to Figure 4.3b but illustrating the supporting tray in a
           different position

Source:  U.S. Patent 3,994,278

Chamber **14** is rendered substantially liquid-tight by means of an impervious liner **26** or other suitable coating which covers the inside vertical surfaces of the portion of walls **11** extending above ceiling **13**. Condensation appearing on the outer surface of the liner **26** is removed via a weep drain **27**.

The tray **16** is constructed of a cellular foamed plastic or other suitable material which readily floats on the surface of the liquid so that when any of a number of valves **28** or **29** is opened, any liquid contained in tray **16** will drain through valve **28** or **29** into the chamber below the tray as the tray rises in the liquid due to the buoyancy of its own mass. The valves **28, 29**, etc. may then be closed and the tray again filled with liquid by the action of pump **21**. As the tray is thus filled with liquid, it settles down into the liquid until it comes to rest at a new level equal to the volume of liquid displaced.

A pair of supports **31** in the form of rectangular projections running along two opposite edges of the underside of the tray transversely oriented relative to the corrugations of ceiling **13** prevent the under surface of the tray from settling completely to the surface of ceiling **13** so that in the lowest position of tray **16**, a passage for water remains between the tray and the ceiling. The tray is thus seen to divide chamber **14** into an upper liquid chamber **32** and a lower liquid chamber **33**, the volume of the lower chamber being diminished as liquid is pumped into the upper chamber. The relative dimensions of the lower chamber corresponding to the lowered and raised positions of the tray are shown, respectively, by left and right handed segmented illustrations of the tray in Figure 4.3b. Ceiling **13** utilizes the corrugated or other inflexible form as illustrated in Figures 4.3b and 4.3c to provide both strength and an increased surface area.

A number of sensors and control elements are also included in the system. Each of the controls is shown with light lines leading therefrom to the other elements of the system which they control or with which they interact. The sensors, including a sunlight sensor **35**, fluid temperature sensors **36** and **37**, outside air temperature sensor **38**, and inside thermostat **39** provide inputs to a control unit **41** which reacts by controlling the operation of the pump **21** and the valves **28** and **29** in a manner appropriate to effect the desired energy storage and delivery cycles as required to regulate the temperature of structure **10**.

When it is desired to store solar energy in the liquid medium, valves **28** and **29** are closed and tray **16** is filled with liquid by the action of pump **21**. The tray, its liquid charge and the transparent cover **17** comprise an elementary flat plate collector. Solar radiation passes readily through the cover and is absorbed as thermal energy by the liquid contents of the tray. Ideally, the cover is made of glass which has a transmittance of approximately 90% at the short wavelengths associated with solar radiation, but at the considerably longer wavelengths characteristic of thermal radiation from heated bodies its transmittance is very low. By virtue of these two properties the collected thermal energy is trapped inside the collector and is retained by the liquid storage medium held by the tray.

While these ideal characteristics of glass are only approximated by plastic films and sheets some such materials may be preferred because of their low cost and superior mechanical properties which make them less subject to damage by hail or falling objects. Combinations of glass and plastic may also be utilized to take advantage of the superior properties of both materials. In this instance the cover is presumed to consist of a single airtight sheet of weather resistant, ultraviolet light screening, plastic material of suitable thickness and physical properties. A positive air pressure is maintained within the enclosure to provide air space between the filled tray and the underside of the cover. This action also keeps the cover taut and prevents flapping due to wind effects.

The delivery cycle which involves the transfer of the collected solar energy to the interior of the air space **42** in the building below ceiling **13**, is accomplished by moving the heated liquid from the tray to the lower chamber. By virtue of the high thermal conductivity of the metal ceiling and because of its large surface area afforded by its corrugated form, the thermal energy passes readily from the liquid through the ceiling into the space, the transfer from ceiling to air being accomplished through radiation and convection.

During daylight hours in cold weather the liquid may be circulated continuously, being moved from the lower chamber to the upper chamber by pump **21** and returning to the lower chamber via pipe **25**. The liquid is heated during its passage through chamber **22** and its collected heat is released to space **42** as it passes through chamber **33**. In an alternate operating mode the tray is filled with liquid and the pumping action is terminated while the charge of liquid in tray **16** is heated. The valves **28** and **29** are then opened allowing the heated liquid to flow into the lower chamber **33** where it remains while heat is transferred to space **42**. In an automatically controlled system utilizing sensors **35** through **39** and control unit **41**, both modes of operation are utilized.

## HEAT RECOVERY FROM BLACK PARTICLES CONTAINED IN GAS STREAM

The process of *H.W. Poulsen; U.S. Patent 3,908,632; September 30, 1975; assigned to Universal Oil Products Company* provides a method for effecting the recovery of solar heat in a manner which comprises (a) passing a gaseous carrying stream with entrained black body particles to a heating zone for exposure to solar radiant energy; (b) passing the stream with resulting heated particles from the heating zone to a particle separation zone and effecting a separation to provide a particle stream and a primarily particle-free stream; (c) passing the particle stream from the latter zone to a heat exchange zone and recovering heat therefrom; (d) subsequently passing the resulting cooled particle stream to a mixing zone and therein combining it with the particle-free stream obtained from the separation zone; and (e) then recirculating the recombined particle-containing stream to the heating zone for reexposure to the solar energy.

It is not intended to limit the system to the use of any one gaseous carrying medium although air may well be used to advantage to effect the desired type of operation.

With respect to black body particles, various types of materials may well be utilized, for example, carbonaceous materials which may comprise carbon black, channel black, oil furnace black, lamp black and the like, or even crushed natural materials such as coal, coke, charcoal, etc.

There also may be utilized pyropolymeric conductive organic refractory oxide particles which are formed by the deposition of a pyropolymer on the surface of a base material at a relatively high temperature in the range of 400° to 750°C. For example, organic substances such as aliphatic hydrocarbons, cycloaliphatic hydrocarbons, aromatic hydrocarbons, aliphatic halogen derivatives, aliphatic oxygen derivatives, carbohydrates, etc., may be pyrolyzed over the surface of a subdivided refractory oxide material.

The refractory oxide may be alumina in various forms, such as gamma-alumina and silica-alumina; however, various other refractory oxides may be used. This type of material is described in U.S. Patent 3,651,386. Certain of the carbonized refractory oxide materials may be of advantage over other black body materials by reason of greater surface area for exposure to the solar radiations.

In the Figure 4.4, there is indicated diagrammatically the utilization of a plurality of tubular members **1** to provide a solar heating section where entrained black body particles may be exposed to solar energy and permit the absorption of infrared heat into the particles. The tubes **1** are also indicated as being encompassed by parabolic reflector members **2** such that there may be a concentration of radiant heat onto each of the tubes **1** and into the particulates being passed therethrough. There is further indicated the use of a fluid distributor header **3** receiving entrained black body particles from line **4** such that there may be a suitable distribution of the particles and the carrying stream into and through the plurality of conduits 1. For the collection of heated streams, there is indicated the utilization of a header means 5 along the other ends of the tubular members 1 and positioned to discharge a resulting elevated temperature particle stream by way of line 6 into a particle separator means 7 whereby the higher temperature particulates can be separated from the lower temperature gaseous carrying medium.

### FIGURE 4.4: HEAT RECOVERY FROM BLACK PARTICLES CONTAINED IN GAS STREAM

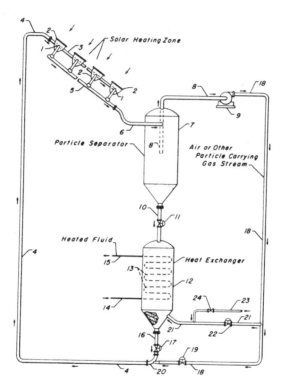

Source: U.S. Patent 3,908,632

As shown by the figure, the carrying medium will be withdrawn from the upper portion of the separator 7 by way of line 8 and blower means 9 while separated heated particles will fall to the lower end of the separator and be discharged by way of transfer conduit 10 and valve means 11 into the upper portion of the heat exchanger 12. Preferably, where the heated particles can flow by gravity, there will be the continuous downward movement of the particles through the height of the heat exchange means 12 to thus flow around and be in indirect heat exchange relationship with an internal coil 13 or other suitable fluid carrying passageway means. The latter is indicated diagrammatically as accommodating a fluid stream which enters the heat exchanger by way of inlet means 14 and is discharged as a heated fluid stream at **15**. The resulting substantially cooled black body particles are continuously discharged at the lower end of the heat exchanger by way of an outlet line **16** and valve means **17** to enter a mixing section **20** and the transfer conduit **4** for recycle back to the solar heating tubes **1**. In a preferred operation as shown by the figure, the particle-carrying air or other gas stream will be transferred from the blower means **9** through a conduit means **18** and a control valve means **19** to the mixing zone **20** below conduit **16** whereby there may be the resulting reentrainment of the particles with the carrying fluid and the transfer of the mixture by way of conduit **4** to the solar heating zone.

Normally there can be the mixing and the reentrainment of the particles from line **16** into line **4** through the use of a typical T or Y arrangement at **20**; however, where deemed suitable, special venturi-type mixing means or eductor means may well be utilized to effect the desired intermixing of the separated particles with the carrying fluid such that a well mixed, uniform entrainment of particles will result in the combined stream carrying to header means **3** and the solar heating tubes **1**.

There is also indicated in the figure that there may be the provision of a conduit **21** with valve means **22**, branching from line **18** that will provide for the introduction of the controlled amount of aeration fluid into the lower end of the heat exchange section **12**. In connection with dry particulates moving in a descending gravity flow, it may be of particular advantage to provide for some movement and turbulence of particles within the interior of the heat exchanger **12** such that there is enhanced contact between heated particles and the coil **13** (or whatever type of heat exchange surfaces may be utilized within heat exchanger means **12**).

Generally, it will be of advantage to use a portion of the particle-carrying gas for the aeration operation; however, where deemed preferable in any particular operation, there may be the use of the separate introduction of aerating fluid by way of line **23** and valve **24** into line **21** and the lower portion of heat exchanger **12**. For example, it may be desired to introduce another inert medium such as nitrogen, carbon dioxide, dry steam, etc., in lieu of a particular carrying fluid, for the desired turbulent movement within heat exchanger **12**.

## SYSTEM USING TWO LARGE SURFACE ELEMENTS

According to the process of *N. Laing; U.S. Patent 3,893,506; July 8, 1975*, in a device for the absorption of solar energy and/or for the emission of heat into free space, wherein a large surface element faces this free space and another surface element is exposed to an exchange of heat with a medium to be heated and/or to be cooled, so that one element acts as a heat absorbing sink and the other element as a heat emitting source, several pipes connected in parallel are provided between the two large surface elements, which pipes are filled with a fluid heat carrier present both in the gaseous and the liquid phases.

The large surface elements are preferably embodied in the form of sheets of high thermal conductivity and the pipes are preferably arranged at equal spacings parallel to each other and are firmly joined or integrated in the elements in good thermal contact therewith. In an advantageous embodiment, the pipes are so installed that the fluid heat carrier condensing at the heat source, i.e., the element which emits heat to the outside, flows back under gravity through the pipes towards the element which forms the heat sink and so constitutes the boundary of the room to be cooled. If, for example, in a cold climate, it is desired that the solar heat is always conducted from the free outer space towards an inside room without permitting the heat from the inside room to flow towards the outside, and considering the case when, for example, vertical wall elements are concerned, the pipes which enclose the heat carrier fluid (saturated vapor) are so installed between the two wall elements that the condensate liquid can flow by gravity towards the heat sink, i.e., towards the large surface element which faces the free outer space.

If, finally, e.g., in temperate climates, the heat flow sense is occasionally to be reversed and the converse effect is required, the process provides that the insides of the vapor pipes be lined in a manner known per se, with a coating which conveys the heat carrier condensate in the vapor pipe by capillary forces. In this instance, the coating acts as a conveying device.

Suitable heat carrier fluids are chlorofluorohydrocarbons, chain hydrocarbons, ketones, azeotropic mixtures of water and water-soluble hydrocarbons and other similar substances having the required thermal properties. Suitable substances for thermal storage capable of storing latent heat are disodium phosphate dodecahydrate, sodium sulfate decahydrate, lithium nitrate trihydrate, a mixture of 69 parts by weight of sodium sulfate decahydrate and 31 parts by weight of potassium chloride and a mixture of 77 parts by weight of sodium sulfate decahydrate and 25 parts by weight of ammonium chloride.

Figure 4.5a shows a panel for use preferably as a roof covering which acts as the large surface element of a device for solar absorption. Metal sheets forming panels are mounted with brackets **2** on a concrete baseplate **1**, so that the panels assume the positions shown in Figure 4.5c. An insulating layer **3** is placed between the concrete baseplate **1** and the panel. The panel itself is designed as a double wall and is built up of sheet metal, the outer facing surface **4** and inner facing surface **5** of which are smooth.

A large number of buttons **6** serve as spacers to maintain the distance between the sheets **4** and **5**. The sheets enclose between them along one margin a tubular section **7** which serves as a fluid channel. At the other parallel margin the sheets are bent over at **8a** as a U-section **1** and are seam welded along the seam **8**. The margin **8a** meshes with the tubular edge **7'** of the next plate. A lamina **9** of absorbent paper is arranged between the sheets **4** and **5**. The paper hangs between adjacent rows of buttons **6** and **6'** so that it touches both the upper wall **4** and the lower wall **5** between the rows of buttons. The metal sheet **4** is provided externally with a surface which, in the range of heat radiation of 9 $\mu$, has the highest possible thermal emissivity.

In the range of about 0.5 $\mu$, in applications where the main purpose is cooling, the emissivity should be as low as possible which can be achieved, for example, by applying a coating of titanium dioxide enamel, while in applications in which preferably heat is to be won the radiation is below 0.5 $\mu$, there will preferably be used carbon black matt paints. In principle, however, lamina synthetic resin is also suitable as a material for the surface, particularly when this is to be made vacuum tight by lamination with an aluminum foil. Finally, sheets for use can also be extruded; the buttons **6** may be formed while the extruded material has not yet solidified.

# FIGURE 4.5:  SYSTEM USING TWO LARGE SURFACE ELEMENTS

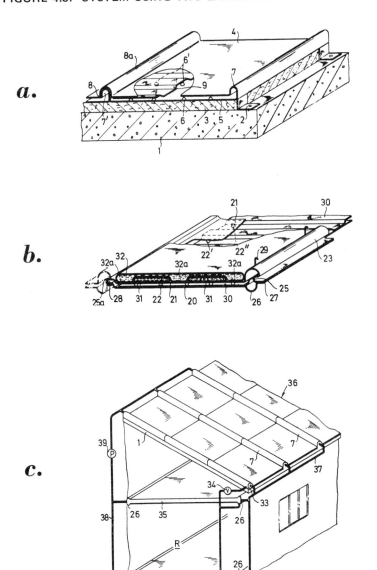

(a)  Panel suitable for a large surface roof element
(b)  Panel suitable for a large surface element exposed to an inside room
(c)  Arrangement of the large surface elements in a dwelling

Source:  U.S. Patent 3,893,506

Figure 4.5b illustrates a panel in a second embodiment of the process, when the panel which is in the form of a large surface element is to be mounted as a partition inside a building, as a ceiling or a wall element. The construction is, in principle, the same as that of a panel according to Figure 4.5a. By means of a folded sheet of metal or foil strip, a hollow body is formed resembling the form as described above. In this example, the sheet **20** presenting the inner surface is smooth, while the sheet **21** having the outer surface has the buttons **22**. The pipe section **23** has a profile with a groove-shaped indentation **25**. Fluid channels **26** are formed along the margins of sheet **20** in which the liquid heat carrier accumulates when the plate is arranged horizontally. The folded sheet is welded along a seam at **27**.

The folded edge **28** is formed as a projection which dovetails into the groove-shaped indentation **25a** of the adjacent panel. Hooks **29** serve for the suspension of the panel from the ceiling of a room. Between the rows of buttons **22'** and **22''**, which are seen in the cutaway section, a corrugated lamina **30** made of absorbent paper is provided, the corrugations of which touch both the upper sheet **21** and the lower sheet **22**. Pipes **31** and **32**, formed of thin conductive foil or sheet **22** are bonded to the upper sheet. The pipes **31**, closed at their ends, are filled to form a heat storage body having a thermal storage substance with a phase change temperature which must be above the dew point when the humidity of the air is normal.

Temperatures between 17° and 19°C have been found to be suitable as phase change temperatures for the cooling of rooms. The pipes **32** which touch the sheet **21** in three areas **32a** contain the latent heat storage substance, the crystallization or phase change temperature of which lies advantageously between 27° and 33°C.

Figure 4.5c includes a cross section through part of a building in which a device according to the process is installed including panels **35, 35'** which are arranged in two stories and are according to Figure 4.5b, as well as panels according to Figure 4.5a being arranged as a roof **36**. The pipe sections or channels **7** and pipe sections **23** of laterally adjacent panels are interconnected via pipes **37**. The channels **26** are connected with the inside of the roof panel **36** via a pipeline **38** in which a condensate pump **39** is arranged. A condensate collector **33** is connected with the inside of the panel **35** via a valve **34**. If heat withdrawal (i.e., cooling) is desired from the room R, the valve **34**, which may be thermostatically controlled, is opened.

The room heat heats the panels of the ceilings **35** and **35'** which deliver heat to the storage substance in the pipes **31**. The amount of storage substance is so chosen that only the heat quantity due to several days' heating is fully taken up latently by the entire storage substance within **31**. During the night, the sheet **36** of the roof which faces space, radiates energy so that this sheet cools down greatly. The inside of the panels and the pipes **37** and **38** are filled with the saturated vapor of a fluid, preferably an azeotropic mixture with methanol. Excessive condensate collects in the channels **26**.

Condensation takes place due to cooling between the sheets of the element **36**. The saturated vapor pressure reduction caused thereby leads to an evaporation in the hollow panels **35** and **35'** whereby the panels cool down. The stored heat of crystallization is thereby withdrawn from the storage substance in the pipes **31**. Condensate in the collectors **36** runs back through the valves **34** into the elements **35** and **35'** so that the thermodynamic cycle is closed. The system acts in this mode for emission of heat into free space as heat stored by the storage substance in **31** during the day is radiated into outer space while the heat of the incident radiation during the day is held back by the insulation **3**, (and possibly further insulation) from penetrating into the inner space. At the end of the summer, the valves **34** are shut. The condensate from the channels **26** of the panels **35** and **35'** is conveyed into the panels **36** by the pump **39**, or in an alternative arrangement by means including squeezable wicks (not illustrated) either of which acts as a conveying device.

This condensate is evaporated due to solar heat and flows through the pipes **37** and the pipe sections **23** into the panels **35** and **35'**. Condensation, with consequent heat release, takes place there. The storage substance in **32** is thus charged by the solar heat which also radiates through the inner surface uniformly via the surface sheets **20** into the room. The condensate so formed, is once again, conveyed upwards by means of the pump **39** (or by surface tension) so that the cycle is closed.

When the valve **34** is shut and the pump **39** is not switched on, the system remains ineffective. Heat in any substantial quantity neither enters the internal space nor is withdrawn from it.

## PIVOTABLE LOUVER PANEL CONTROLLED BY VAPOR PRESSURE

Apparatus for maximizing the transfer of solar energy to the interior of a structure and minimizing heat loss therefrom is described by *S.C. Baer; U.S. Patent 3,884,414; May 20, 1975; assigned to Zomeworks Corporation.* The apparatus includes at least one louver panel forming a portion of the exterior of the structure, the louver panel being pivotable about an axis passing through its center of gravity to open the panel. An interior reservoir is fixed to the interior surface of the panel so that the weight of the interior reservoir biases the panel in one direction to open it. An exterior reservoir is fixed to the exterior surface of the panel so that the weight of the exterior reservoir biases the panel in the opposite direction to close it. A tube provides fluid communication between the two reservoirs.

A partially vaporized volatile fluid, such as Freon, occupies the tube and the reservoirs. The relative proportions of liquid and vapor in the respective reservoirs are dependent upon the relative vapor pressure in the reservoirs, which is directly proportional to their temperatures. Thus, a higher temperature on the exterior of the structure or direct exposure to the sun raises the relative vapor pressure in the exterior reservoir to force liquid through the tube to the interior reservoir causing the panel to open and allow transfer of thermal energy to the interior of the structure. A higher relative temperature on the interior of the structure results in liquid being forced through the tube to the exterior reservoir to close the panel and minimize heat loss from the structure.

The general operation of this apparatus is illustrated by way of reference to Figure 4.6a. Apparatus **10** includes a frame **12** which is mounted to the ceiling **14** or other wall of the structure. The ideal location for apparatus **10** is on a south facing roof which is slanted 15° to 45° from the vertical. A plurality of louver panels **16, 17, 18** are mounted in frame **12** at their respective opposite ends. Each panel rotates about an axis passing through the center of gravity of the panel and each panel is thus balanced. In order to allow the louver panels to freely pivot with respect to the frame, ball bearings or other similar mountings are used to connect the panels to the frame.

## FIGURE 4.6: PIVOTABLE LOUVER PANEL CONTROLLED BY VAPOR PRESSURE

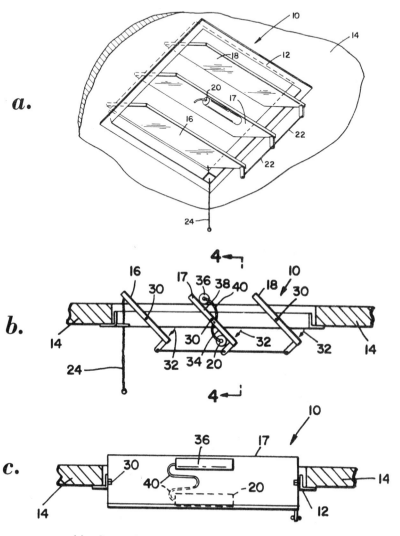

(a)   Perspective view of the apparatus forming part of a roof
(b)   Side elevation
(c)   Schematic view taken along line 4–4 of Figure 4.6c

Source:   U.S. Patent 3,884,414

One of the louver panels is provided with an interior canister 20 and an exterior canister (not visible) which controls both the opening and the closing of panel 17 as will be discussed below. In addition, the rods 22 are provided between louver panels 16, 17, 18 so that panels 16, 18 are slaved to panel 17 and the panels open and close in unison. If desired, louver panels 16, 17, 18 can be opened manually by pulling chain 24 and locking the panels in position.

Each louver panel is substantially impervious to the transmission of solar energy. Such panels are preferably constructed of aluminum skin having a foam core so that the panels are sturdy and provide thermal insulation but are relatively light-weight. When the panels are open as in Figure 4.6a, solar energy can freely be transmitted to the interior of the structure, and the sunlight lights the interior of the structure. When the apparatus is closed, it provides a thermal insulative wall panel which retains heat inside the structure.

The operation of the apparatus 10 is illustrated in more detail by way of reference to the schematic view of Figures 4.6b and 4.6c. The louver panels are pivotally attached to frame 12 along axis 30 passing through their respective centers of gravity. A skylight (not shown) is ordinarily used to cover the panels. The panels are rotatable in a first direction as illustrated by arrows 32 to open them. Rotation of the panels in the opposite direction closes them. Interior canister 20 is mounted on the interior face 34 of louver panel 17 at one side of the pivotal axis of the panel. A corresponding exterior canister 36 is mounted on the exterior face 38 of panel 17.

A tube 40 provides fluid communication between canisters 20 and 36. A volatile fluid such as Freon is provided in the canisters and occupies the tube as well. At ambient temperatures, the Freon will be partially vaporized and consists of both liquid and vapor.

When exterior canister 36 is exposed to direct sunlight or when the temperature on the exterior of structure 14 is greater than that of the interior, the internal temperature of the exterior canister will be greater than that of interior canister 20. As a result, the relative vapor pressure of canister 36 will increase, forcing liquid Freon through the tube until the vapor pressures are stabilized. As a result, the weight of canister 36 will decrease and that of canister 20 will increase, causing louver panel 17 and slaved louver panels 16 and 18 to open as illustrated by arrows 32. In this configuration, the solar energy is transmitted to the interior of the structure.

Conversely, when the internal temperature of exterior canister 36 is less than that of interior canister 20, the vapor pressure of the interior canister will be greater than that of the exterior canister causing liquid Freon to flow into the exterior canister and the window will close. Hence, the operation of apparatus 10 is automatic and is responsive to the ability of solar energy to heat the structure at any given point in time.

Freon is sufficiently volatile so that the apparatus responds to 1° variation in temperature. In order to prevent overheating of the structure on extremely warm days, chain 24 can be manipulated to close the louver panels and override the action of the canisters.

## WATER POND ON TOP OF ENCLOSURE

*H.R. Hay; U.S. Patent 3,563,305; February 16, 1971* describes a system in which enclosure temperatures are modulated by water heated by solar energy and cooled to ambient air. Control means include moving exterior insulation, enclosing or exposing the water, using forced air, and providing special means for heat storage and transfer. Water ponds horizontally disposed atop the enclosure, or in floor plenums and frequently in direct thermal exchange with underlying space, or water circulating in walls by thermosiphon action may be used separately or in combination with the control means.

# COATINGS

## SELECTIVE BLACK COATING

It has long been known that some materials are black in the visible spectrum but reflect or transmit to a considerable extent in the longer infrared regions. This has led to the application of black surfaces to obtain heat from solar radiation. Yet for flat-plate collectors without optical concentration devices, temperature is rather limited since heat losses from the receiver at higher temperatures, primarily from thermal radiation of the black surface, soon equal the incoming energy. Efforts have been made to find or synthesize selective black surfaces so that they differentiate in their absorption, reflection or transmission characteristics between wavelengths above about 2 $\mu$, i.e., in the thermal range and wavelengths below about 2 $\mu$, i.e., in the solar range.

According to *M. Telkes; U.S. Patent 4,011,190; March 8, 1977; assigned to Ses, Incorporated,* blacks of high effectiveness can be prepared by coating reflective metal particles with a layer of a selective black material. The coated particles can be mixed with a suitable vehicle to form a paint which can be applied easily as a thin film to any suitable surface.

In the process, the individual substrate or core is a highly reflective material having a low emissivity, i.e., less than about 0.1 and preferably less than about 0.05. Examples of such materials include aluminum, nickel, copper, and zinc, which are low in cost and which are usually available in the form of fine powder or flakes.

Other materials available in the form of flakes, or powder at a relatively moderate cost are: brass, or bronze, alloys of copper available in an extensive variety of composition, particle (or flake) size and shape. One of the most readily available materials is zinc powder or zinc dust, which is available in very small particle sizes at relatively low cost. The core particles desirably are small in diameter and range from about 0.5 $\mu$ up to about 10 $\mu$, and preferably up to about 5 $\mu$. The core particles are coated with a thin layer of a material having a high solar absorptivity and transmittance in the long infrared wavelengths. The coating material is generally a semiconductor. Exemplary materials are the

284

oxides or sulfides of metals such as copper, lead, molybdenum and the like. One or more materials can be used in the coating. The coating material should have an absorptivity ($\alpha$) of at least about 0.90 and preferably about 0.95 for energy in the solar wavelengths, reflectivity of less than about 0.1 and preferably less than about 0.05 for solar wavelengths, and transmit wavelengths longer than 2 $\mu$.

The coating can be effected by any suitable means. For example, a coating of copper oxide or copper sulfide can be prepared by depositing a thin film of copper on the core by electroless chemical deposition and then converting the copper to the oxide or sulfide. The coating can vary in thickness up to about 1 $\mu$. To provide sufficient coverage of the particle, it is preferred that the film be at least 2 molecules thick.

The coated particles can be used as a pigment in preparing a paint which can easily be applied to a desired surface as a thin film in accordance with known technology. For example, the coated particles can be mixed with a binder and volatile solvent to provide a paint which can be brushed or sprayed onto a substrate which can be metal, wood, masonry, or other desired material. The binder should, of course, be transparent for wavelengths longer than about 3 $\mu$. Such binders can be found in the group of silicones, which are commercially available.

*Example 1:* This example illustrates the preparation of coated particles. Zinc powder, which is inexpensive and readily available, is used primarily. The zinc powder is first cleaned to remove grease and any zinc oxide film present. A dilute solution of sodium carbonate or other detergent is effective to remove grease. A solution 2 to 5% HCl is effective to remove zinc oxide.

*CuO on Zn* — A solution was prepared by dissolving 10 to 20 g $CuSO_4 \cdot 5H_2O$ in 100 grams boiling distilled water and adding 0.05 N NaOH. Upon addition of the caustic, a precipitate forms at first and then rapidly dissolves. Sufficient caustic was added to provide 5 g solid NaOH for each 100 g $CuSO_4 \cdot 5H_2O$. Each solution was added to a suspension of 100 g of clean zinc powder of 5 $\mu$ particle size in hot distilled water. In a few seconds, the zinc powder became coated with an adherent black coating. The solution was decanted from the coated particles which were washed several times with deionized water and dried in air.

The concentration of each solution was varied to provide zinc powder coated with CuO in the following proportions, expressed as percent by weight copper: Sample A, 2.5% Cu; Sample B, 4.5% Cu; Sample C, 7% Cu; and Sample D, 12.5% Cu.

*CuS on Zn* — Separate solutions of copper tartrate, sodium hydroxide and tartaric acid are prepared in concentrations of 15, 35, and 20 g/l respectively and mixed at room temperature to form a coating solution. Cleaned zinc powder is mixed with distilled water and immediately mixed with the coating solution with rapid stirring. The coated powder is washed with distilled water to remove the salts, dried, and treated with a solution of sulfur in carbon disulfide. The sulfur solution should be very dilute so as to obtain a velvety black color rather than a yellowish color. The zinc particles coated with CuS are designated as Sample E.

*PbS + CuS on Zn* — For Sample F, zinc powder was immersion coated in a manner similar to that for Sample E. The coating ingredients were: sodium thiosulfate·$5H_2O$, 240 g/l; lead acetate·$3H_2O$; 25 g/l; potassium hydrogen tartrate, 30 grams per liter; and $CuSO_4 \cdot 5H_2O$, 20 g/l. The ingredients were dissolved separately in water and the solutions mixed. The coating was carried out by mixing 50 g zinc dust with 100 ml of solution at 50°C. A dilute solution of sulfur in carbon disulfide was used to convert the coating to the sulfide form.

*Example 2:* Solar absorption tests were conducted with various coated zinc particles. A paint was prepared by mixing the coated particles with a solution of Dow Corning 805 silicone resin in xylene (50% solids content). Approximately 30 g of resin were used for each 100 g of coated zinc particles.

Test panels were prepared by painting the test paint onto one side of sheet aluminum 0.030" thick and 1 ft². The aluminum sheet was cleaned (degreased) before painting. After xylene solvent is evaporated, which occurs rather rapidly, the coating is cured by heating it above 120°C for at least an hour. This can be effected in the sun if desired. The opposite side of the aluminum test panel was painted white.

The test panel was mounted in an insulated box with the black surface exposed and subjected to stagnation temperature testing. The insulated boxes had a transparent (glass or Plexiglas) front cover and a white painted sheet aluminum back cover. The test panels were supported at a distance of 1" from each cover. When exposed to summer sunshine the stagnation temperature was a maximum of 250°F.

As a standard for comparison, stagnation temperature of a panel painted with a conventional black paint was obtained. The conventional black paint is a commercially available spray paint (Rustoleum). Improved selectivity is demonstrated by the increase in temperature obtained at peak temperature around midday with the selective blacks of the process over that obtained with the nonselective black of the standard panel.

The effectiveness of zinc particles coated with copper oxide (Sample C) is shown by a stagnation temperature of 199°F, which is 13°F more than 186°F stagnation temperature obtained with the standard panel. This is 13% improvement (temperature increase above temperature of standard panel divided by temperature increase of standard panel above ambient temperature). For further comparison, a commercial selective black, by Alcoa, gave a stagnation temperature of 193°F, only a 7°F increase over the standard panel. A new selective black obtained from Alcoa gave a 13% improvement. These commercial blacks are electrodeposited coatings and are relatively expensive.

In tests with zinc particles coated with CuS + PbS (Sample No. F), an increase of 13°F over that of the standard panel was obtained. However, the color gradually changed from black to brown over a period of about 30 days with a resultant decline in stagnation temperature. The temperature difference stabilized at 8°F over that of the standard panel.

## ANODIZED ALUMINUM-SILICON ALLOY AS ABSORBER

The collection of solar radiant energy requires an energy absorbing panel or material that can withstand high temperatures without physical change, and all types of weather conditions without surface deterioration. Probably the best type collecting surface is described as a black body, but ordinarily these are laboratory test units, and are not suitable for exposure to weather conditions for long time periods. If a solar energy absorbing material were available that approached the absorptive characteristics of a black body, which had excellent mechanical characteristics so that it could be exposed to the weather elements without deterioration, and which transferred the surface radiant energy to the energy transport fluid, to be used subsequently for the extraction of its heat energy, one of the main problems for the use of solar energy would be solved.

The process of *G.W. Streander; U.S. Patent 4,002,541; January 11, 1977; assigned to Design Systems, Inc.* provides an anodized article which may assume any physical configuration on its metallic base, i.e., sheet, rod, tube or the like. The article in one form comprises an alloy layer of aluminum containing up to about 18% by weight of silicon having a matrix of aluminum oxide formed on at least a part of its surface and including crystals of silicon dioxide grown from the alloy extending through, bound in and supported by the aluminum oxide matrix.

The properties of the article are determined by the silicon concentration in the alloy since the concentration determines the spacing of the silicon dioxide crystals projecting through the aluminum oxide matrix. For use as a thermal mechanical surface, and specifically a solar energy absorbing article, for example, silicon contents in the range from 10 to 18% by weight are preferred. Articles made from relatively high silicon content alloys are very smooth and nonabrasive, exhibit low thermal conductivity but high transmission of radiant energy because of their optical characteristics, low specific heat, low coefficient of thermal expansion, high dielectric strength, very high melting point, high tensile strength and modulus of elasticity and high surface hardness.

The process or method for making the article involves the steps of cleaning the surface of an aluminum-silicon alloy, etching the alloy for a time sufficient to expose virgin alloy and particularly atomic silicon, and anodizing the etched alloy to grow silicon dioxide crystals therefrom and to form an aluminum oxide supporting matrix around the crystals.

*Example:* An example of an aluminum-silicon alloy used to make an anodized article with this process comprises an aluminum alloy 3003 core having a thickness of about 63 mils double clad with 6 mil aluminum alloy sheet containing 7.5% silicon by weight.

In the anodizing step the exposed silicon surfaces and etched aluminum surfaces are anodized to grow silicon dioxide crystals from the exposed silicon crystals and an aluminum oxide supporting matrix layer from the etched aluminum surfaces so that the silicon dioxide crystals are embedded in and protrude from a surface of the composite matrix layer.

Figure 5.1 illustrates a section through a sheet of an anodized article **10** showing the spatial relationships between the individual grown crystals **12**, the silicon particles **18**, the anodized layer **14**, and the base alloy **16**. As depicted, the anodized layer contains a mixture of grown crystals and silicon particles.

In an experiment performed to measure the absorptivity and emissivity of the anodized article a plate with the aluminum oxide-silicon dioxide layer on the aluminum-silicon supporting base and a plate the same size with a coating material as near as possible to a black body were mounted on an insulated test stand.

## FIGURE 5.1: ANODIZED ALUMINUM-SILICON ALLOY AS ABSORBER

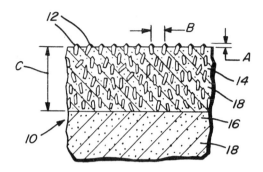

Source:   U.S. Patent 4,002,541

Measurements showed that losses from conduction through the insulation were essentially zero. Calibrated thermocouples were placed on the backs and fronts of the test plates, and connected to graphic recorders for the temperature measurements. The test stand was inclined at an angle to obtain the maximum insolation, for the time of year, which was measured with a pyroheliometer to provide a value of the incident solar energy. From the temperature measurements the values of absorptivity and emissivity of radiant energy by the surfaces may be calculated parametrically from a derived equation. The results indicated that the article of the process as an energy absorber was similar to the black body plate.

## OXYGEN-DEFICIENT $PbO_2$ PANEL COATING

About one-fifth of the fuel consumed in the United States is used for heating and cooling of buildings so that it would be desirable to use solar energy instead of energy derived from fossil or nuclear fuel sources. Many known devices are not efficient and require large expanses of collector surface area to operate. As a result, known collectors and equipment are expensive because of the required size with resultant high investment. Prior art less costly low temperature (approximately 220°F) installations use flat plate collectors, and the more expensive type (above 400°F.) use concentrators before collection of the energy. The collectors involve a tube or panel which absorbs the incident solar radiation and heats a fluid circulating thereby.

*F.J. Schmidt; U.S. Patent 3,958,554; May 25, 1976; assigned to Ametek, Inc.* describes a panel coated with oxygen-deficient $PbO_2$, such as $\alpha$-$PbO_2$ or $\beta$-$PbO_2$, heat being absorbable thereby and transferable to a liquid for operating heating or cooling systems.

The black coating of the panel of the collector is of the most importance inasmuch as it determines the two most important parameters of the collector. The solar absorptivity, or $\alpha$ value, should be as high as possible, the limit thereof being that of a theoretical black body or 100%. The $\alpha$ is measured at the solar spectrum which peaks at 0.5 $\mu$ wavelength. The emissivity, or $\epsilon$ value, is the reradiated heat loss which should be as low as possible. $\epsilon$ is measured at the collector temperature or for 220°F at around 8 $\mu$ wavelength. According to the Stefan-Boltzmann law, $\epsilon$ increases with temperature until an equilibrium temperature is reached where the reradiated energy equals the absorbed solar energy. The equilibrium temperatures corresponding to various $\alpha/\epsilon$ ratios, $\alpha/\epsilon$ being a surface property, are shown in the following table.

| $\alpha/\epsilon$ | °F* |
|---|---|
| 6.0 | 470 |
| 5.0 | 430 |
| 2.0 | 250 |
| 1.0 | 135 |
| 0.5 | 40 |
| 0.2 | -60 |

*Approximate values

Typical $\alpha/\epsilon$ representation values for various materials are shown in the following table.

| | $\alpha$ | $\epsilon$ | $\alpha/\epsilon$ |
|---|---|---|---|
| Al, freshly evaporated | 0.10 | 0.025 | 4 |
| Au | 0.16 | 0.02 | 8 |
| Ag | 0.07 | 0.01 | 7 |
| Ta | 0.59 | 0.02 | 29 |
| $Al_2O_3$ | 0.16 | 0.75 | 0.21 |
| Lampblack | 0.99 | 0.97 | 1 |
| White paint, 1 mil | 0.15 | 0.94 | 0.16 |
| Black paint, 1 mil | 0.97 | 0.94 | 1.03 |
| Clear varnish on Al, 1 mil | 0.20 | 0.80 | 0.25 |
| Clear varnish on Al, 0.24 mil | 0.20 | 0.10 | 2.0 |

It was ascertained that by using a coating of $\beta$-$PbO_{1.98}$ on the collector plate, an unobvious result of decidedly improved solar collection was reached. The coating is infrared transparent, that is, has a low $\epsilon$, and is dark gray in the solar or visible range. The $\alpha$ was measured to be about 90%, and the $\epsilon$ about 0.15 and the ratio of $\alpha/\epsilon$ to be 6. Such is very much in contrast to the values for other substances shown in the preceding table.

It is seen therein that some material, such as bare metals, have good $\alpha/\epsilon$ ratios, but the absolute value for $\alpha$ is low so that most of the incident energy is reflected $(1-\alpha)$ and only a small portion (the $\alpha$) is absorbed which results in a very low efficiency. Black paints or organic coatings in general have high $\alpha$ values but the ratio $\alpha/\epsilon$ is not much above unity so that they remain cool.

The collector surface can be plated by electrodeposition to obtain a semiconductor-type $PbO_2$. At a $O_2$/Pb ratio of 1.98, the coating is an oxygen-deficient, n-type metal oxide with high electron mobility which is several orders higher than for other oxides of this type, e.g., ZnO, $In_2O_3$ or $SnO_2$. One manner of applying the aforementioned $\beta$-$PbO_{1.98}$ coating is as follows. The plating bath composition contained 0.6 M (200 g/l) lead nitrate (obtained by dissolving 135 g lead monoxide in 79 cc of nitric acid, SG 1.415, and adding water to bring the volume to 1 liter), 1.5 g wetting agent (Tergitol, nonionic) and 5 g copper nitrate (latter is used to plate out on the cathode, instead of lead, to conserve the lead in the bath). Beta-lead dioxide deposited on the anode under the following strict conditions: pH 1 (range 0.5 to a maximum of 2) and temperature, 75°C (range 60°C to boiling). Copper plate cathodes were used. The workpiece was the anode.

For agitation, the critical current density (CD) was 10 to 20 asf on the anode. Above 20 asf the stresses cracked up the coating. Below 10 asf there was no uniform plating. Optimum CD was 17 asf. The thickness of the coating after twenty minutes was 0.0003". Other oxygen-deficient lead dioxides or semiconductor-type lead dioxides can be used.

It was further found that the infrared absorption within the oxygen-deficient $PbO_2$ film was further decreased by decreasing the thickness of the film. For example, by applying 0.00003" coating, the $\alpha/\epsilon$ ratio increased to 11. The oxygen-deficient $PbO_2$ can be obtained in the ranges of $PbO_{1.66}$ to $PbO_{1.99}$, such as recognized in the paper "Electrical Properties of Electrodeposited $PbO_2$ Films" by W. Mindt, *Journal Electro-Chemical Society*, Vol. 116, No. 8, pp. 1076 to 1080.

## BLACK NICKEL COATING

*J.R. Lowery; U.S. Patent 3,920,413; November 18, 1975; assigned to the U.S. Administrator of the National Aeronautics and Space Administration* describes a panel for selectively absorbing solar thermal energy comprising a metallic substrate, a layer of bright metallic material carried on the substrate, and a solar thermal energy absorbing coating carried on the bright metallic material.

The phrase "solar energy absorbing coating" as used herein means a heat absorptive coating characterized by a high $\alpha$ value (making it a good absorber) and a low emittance value because of its extreme thinness (making it a poor thermal emitter). The thickness of the solar energy absorbing coating is preferably of the order 1500 A thick. The solar energy absorbing coating is applied by an electroplating step for the period of time required to produce a thin layer of alloy which is grey to black in appearance.

The preferred method for making the coated metal substrate which selectively absorbs thermal energy comprises the steps of cleaning an aluminum substrate, applying a thin film of zinc of about 1500 to 2000 A on which to plate first bright nickel and then black nickel. Conditions for the zincating of aluminum consist of immersing the clean aluminum surface into a bath containing about 13 oz/gal of zinc oxide and about 70 oz/gal of sodium hydroxide for 30 sec to 1 min at a bath temperature of around 75°F.

Conditions for the anodization of aluminum are selected in accordance with the particular aluminum alloy used. For Al-Cu-Mg alloys, such as AA 2,014 and 2,024, the preferred bath composition contains between about 300 and 400 g of phosphoric acid per liter of water. However, a particularly preferred bath composition contains on the order of 350 g of phosphoric acid per liter of water. The relatively pure aluminum alloys, e.g., AA 1,100, preferably are anodized in a bath containing from about 400 to 600 g of phosphoric acid per liter of water, most preferably about 500 g of phosphoric acid per liter of water. The preferred bath for the nickel brightening layer contains from 30 to 50 ounces of nickel(II) sulfate hexahydrate, from 5 to 10 oz of nickel(II) chloride hexahydrate, and from 3 to 7.5 oz of boric acid per gallon of aqueous solution. The plating bath also contains up to about 5% by volume of one or more brightener compositions, such as brightener No. 7 and brightener No. 2-WL, and up to about 1.0% by volume of nonpitting agent, such as nonpitting agent No. 22. Each of the aforesaid materials is a product of the Udylite Corporation.

The most preferred bath composition is of the order of 40 oz of nickel(II) sulfate hexahydrate, 8 oz of nickel(II) chloride hexahydrate, 5.5 oz of boric acid, 0.125% by volume of brightener No. 2-WL, 2.0% by volume of brightener No. 7 and 0.5% by volume of nonpitting agent No. 22 per gallon of solution. The pH of the solution is thus from 3.5 to 4.8.

Application of the bright nickel layer is preferably done at a current density from 15 to 25 asf at a bath temperature in the range of from 120° to 140°F for a time sufficient to apply a coating from 0.00025 to 0.00075 inch in thickness. For the application of a coating 0.0005 inch in thickness, 30 minutes of plating at a current density of 20 amp/in² is required.

The preferred bath for application of the black nickel solar thermal energy absorbing coating contains from 5 to 15 oz of nickel(II) ammonium sulfate hexahydrate, from 4 to 6 oz of zinc sulfate hexahydrate, from 1 to 3 oz of sodium thiocyanate and 10 oz of nickel sulfate hexahydrate per gallon of solution.

Preferred operating conditions for this bath include a pH of 5.6 to 5.9 at room temperature and a current density between about 0.5 and 4.0 asf. Using 4.0 asf produces a coating with better optical properties (higher $\alpha$ values without much sacrifice in increased emittance) than the lower current density. The time for plating is preferably that which produces a coating which exhibits a solar absorptance, $\alpha$, of at least about 0.90 and a thermal or infrared emittance, $\epsilon$, of not more than about 0.06. At a current density of 0.5 asf, about 5 minutes of plating time are required. At 4 asf, a 30-second plating time is required.

It will be understood that the significance of the $\alpha/\epsilon$ ratio, where $\alpha$ is solar absorptance and $\epsilon$ is emittance, is that a high ratio indicates a high efficiency in terms of collecting solar thermal radiation. When conventional black nickel coatings are prepared on aluminum, such coatings are dark black, relatively thick, and have a high solar absorptance as well as high emittance, so that the ratio approaches unity or less. Thus, it is imperative that the black nickel solar absorber layer be very thin, preferably of the order of 1500 A. The efficiency of the selective solar layer decreases to the extent that it would not be considered suitable for collecting solar energy outside of a thickness range of between 800 and 5000 A.

# STORAGE DEVICES

## LIQUID STORAGE MEDIUM

### System with Two Tanks in Fluid Communication

A system is described by *N.B. Saunders; U.S. Patents 4,018,214; April 19, 1977 and 3,952,947; April 27, 1976* for storing near infrared heat energy of the sun for use in a building including at least one glazing panel for transmitting the light and near infrared heat energy of the sun into the building. The system comprises a first tank capable of being completely filled with a heat absorbing fluid and positioned relative to the glazing panel so as to be exposed to at least a portion of the heat energy transmitted through the glazing panel and so that the heat absorbing fluid in the tank absorbs at least a part of the portion of the energy.

A second tank is in fluid communication with the first tank and disposed above the first tank. The system also includes conduit means connecting the bottom of the first tank and the second tank so that fluid disposed on the bottom of the first tank will flow into the second tank when the fluid in the first tank expands, and so that fluid disposed in the second tank will flow into the first tank when the fluid in the first tank contracts.

Figure 6.1 shows the wall of building **20** which is exposed to solar radiation. The wall of building **20** comprises windows having an inner glazed panel **22** and an outer panel **24**. Both panels are made of material which is transmissive to both light and near infrared heat energy and opaque to middle and far infrared heat energy, such as glass or the like. The panels are preferably sealed in place at their top and bottom edges in the heat insulated sills **26** in a manner well-known in the art. The building may also include curtains **140** which may be provided if privacy is desired.

Curtains **140** are spaced from the inner surface of panel **22** so that air along the surface will be stagnant, moving generally in neither an upward or downward direction when winter insolation is striking the curtain. For example, for standard eight foot high curtains, the latter are spaced from the panel **22** about 0.1 meter. The rod **142** is spaced from the ceiling a distance depending on how much top lighting is desired. The spacing at the bottom of the curtain and the floor is made approximately half the spacing to the panel **22** in order to provide a path for circulating air. It is noted that the curtain, when used on a wall minimally exposed to solar energy, may extend all the way to the floor in order to help keep the heat within the building.

Curtains **140** preferably should be made of material which is opaque and absorptive to the visible and near infrared portion of the spectrum, but transparent or reflecting to all other infrared, (i.e., heat in the building). For example, cellophane or other completely transmissive sheets containing small grains of silicon, germanium, thallium, bromide-iodide or similar materials opaque in the visible and near infrared but transmissive and highly reflective to all other infrared are satisfactory. An example of the dimensions of a finished sheet would be a sheet having an overall thickness of between 25 and 100 micrometers and the grains from 5 to 25 micrometers in diameter.

**FIGURE 6.1: SYSTEM WITH TWO TANKS IN FLUID COMMUNICATION**

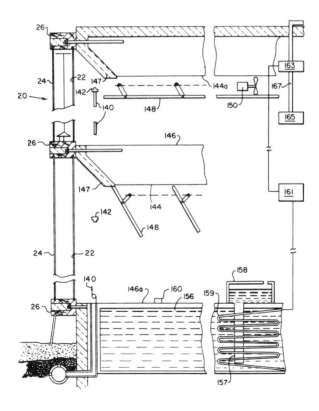

Source: U.S. Patent 4,018,214

The floors **146** and ceiling **144** preferably are made of material which has a high heat capacity and heat conductivity, such as concrete or the like. Where the floor is covered, such a covering must be made of a thin and high thermally conductive material. The floors and ceilings are well insulated from the sills **26** in a manner well-known in the art. The portion **147** of the ceiling adjacent the window is inclined at an angle, e.g., 45° and is preferably heat reflective. Insulating panels **148** are pivotally supported from each ceiling **144** so that in a closed position they form a duct therebetween, and in an open position, expose the ceiling to the interior rooms.

The panels may be made of any heat insulating material such as foamed polystyrene or the like, and preferably are surfaced to be reflective to the full infrared spectrum. A fan **150** which may be thermostatically controlled is placed between the panels **148** and ceiling **144** so as to draw air from the interior portion of the building near the window, through the building and circulate the air therein as will be described in greater detail hereinafter. This is particularly desirable when the building is provided with interior partitions.

In the preferred embodiment, a thermal delay and heat sink is incorporated into the building structure for storing a portion of the sun's energy entering through panels **22** and **24** so that this energy can be released at a later time into the building. The thermal delay and heat sink are in part provided by the intermediate concrete floor slabs. For example, if these floors are made 0.2 meter thick, the midafternoon heating of the bottom of the slabs produces a maximum heat release on the topside about dawn the next day when heat is usually most needed. In the preferred embodiment this heat sink is in part provided by the tank **156**. The latter is filled with a heat absorbing fluid such as water or the like.

It is preferred that the fluid completely fill the tank **156** since an air gap would act as a heat insulator and thus inhibit heat flow between the floor **146a** and the fluid in the tank. An expansion tank is preferably provided on the bottom floor which is in fluid contact with the tank **156** to hold the overflow from the latter. A pipe **157** is also provided wherein one end is placed near the bottom of the tank **156** and the other is placed in the bottom of the expansion tank **158**. Since the coolest portion of the fluid is on the bottom of the tank **156**, this portion will flow through pipe **157** into the expansion tank **158** when the fluid expands from heat input and fluid will flow back through pipe **157** into the tank **156** from tank **158** when fluid in tank **156** contracts.

This structure utilizes the physical properties of water to maintain deaeration. However, a float or needle valve **160** may further be provided to let air out in order that the fluid will come into contact with the top of tank **156** when the latter is filled. If desired, the heat storing capabilities of the tank can be improved by making the bottom floor **146a** transmissive to the visible and near infrared and the bottom of the tank radiant heat energy absorptive, in which case the pipe **157** and expansion tank may be eliminated and tank **156** need not be completely filled with fluid.

Tubing **159** is connected from the tank **156** to a compressor **161**. Tubing **159** is coiled in the fluid of tank **156** so as to provide an evaporator during warm weather and a condenser during cold weather. The compressor **161** is also connected to heat exchanger **163**. The latter is attached to or secured in the top ceiling **144a.** Tubing **157** and exchanger **163** function to provide heat to the tank **156** in the winter and carry heat from tank **156** in the summer. The heat exchanger **163** forms part of the heating and ventilation system which also includes blower **165** which is connected to the exterior portion of the building through pipe **167.**

When it is desirable to utilize the insolation received to heat the interior of the building, the energy will be transmitted through the glazed panels **22** and **24** whereupon it will strike each floor **146.** The visible and near infrared energy of the insolation absorbed will be mostly conducted to the floor **146** only a small portion of which will be reradiated as energy in the far infrared region of the electromagnetic spectrum. Insolation energy will also be transferred from the floor **146** into the fluid in tank **156.**

On days of exceptionally high insolation, the curtains **140** are drawn. During cold days when the curtain is drawn the warm air moving up both sides of curtain **140** will move along the underside of ceiling **144,** where heat is transferred from the air to the ceiling. Fans **150** may be used to air the transfer. The cool air returns along the floor and enters the space between the curtain **140** and panel **22.** Since the curtain **140** and panel **22** are spaced to minimize motion of air adjacent the panel **22,** the air passing between the panel and the curtain will be heated by heat transfer from the curtain with a minimum heat loss to the panel. Heat is stored in the ceiling during the day. During this time panels **148** may be pivoted to their closed position so as to substantially block heat transfer from the ceiling into the room.

The heat stored in the ceiling during this time is transferred to the top of the slab **146** by the next morning. The remainder of the stored heat can be released directly into the room below either by natural heat convection or thermostatically by opening the panels **148.** When the sun is not shining and the interior begins to cool, the heat absorbed in the floors will be convected and reradiated into the rooms to provide heat.

## EUTECTIC SOLUTIONS

### Heat Storage Cylinder for Roof Installation

*P.S. Hepp; U.S. Patent 3,996,919; December 14, 1976; assigned to Sun Oil Company of Pennsylvania* describes a system for collecting and storing solar energy which includes solar panels which are installed between the joists of the roof so that the collector surface of each panel acts as part of the roof of each panel, and also includes a heat storage system connected to the back side of each panel. Each heat storage system has a plurality of heat storage cylinders containing a phase change, heat storage mixture and a heat pipe for conducting the heat collected by the collector surface to the heat storage material.

The containers of heat storage material extend into ductwork connected to a conventional forced air heating system so that the air is heated when it is circulated around the heat storage cylinders. The heat storage system can be used with a flat solar collector surface as well as with a parabolic reflector for focusing sunlight on the end of the heat pipe. Each solar collector panel has a heat absorbing plate **10** and its own heat storage system which includes a plurality of heat storage cylinders mounted on the back side of heat absorbing plate **10** as illustrated in Figure 6.2a. A transparent cover **11** helps to protect the surface of heat absorbing plate **10** from deterioration as well as to reduce convection losses. The bottom side of absorbing plate **10** is covered with a layer of insulation, **12**, to prevent heat loss.

### FIGURE 6.2: HEAT STORAGE CYLINDER FOR ROOF INSTALLATION

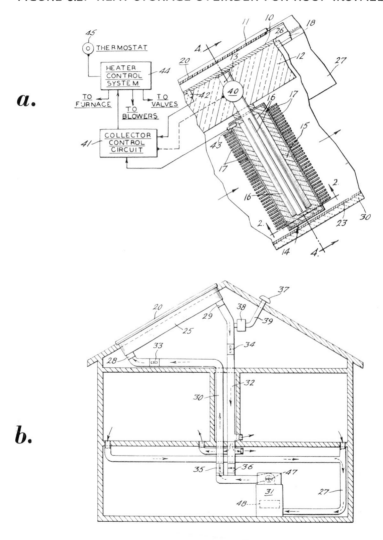

(a)  Partial section of heat storage cylinder with schematic
       diagram of control system
(b)  Method of connecting collector panels to conventional
       forced air heating system

Source:  U.S. Patent 3,996,919

A heat pipe **13** is mounted to the underside of heat absorbing plate **10** to transfer the heat collected to heat storage cylinder **14**. Heat pipe **13** can have one of many designs which are currently available. The construction and operation of the heat pipe are well known. The heat pipe provides an extremely efficient method of transferring the heat absorbed by plate **10** to heat storage cylinder **14** since its thermal conductance can range from several hundred to more than a thousand times the thermal conductance of copper. The heat pipe has other advantages which make it particularly applicable in such a solar collector and storage system. It can transfer heat with a small temperature drop and can transfer a relatively large amount of heat with respect to its size and weight. It operates automatically, is noiseless, and has a long life with minimum loss in efficiency.

Heat storage cylinder **14**, in which the cooling end of heat pipe **13** is embedded, can contain a phase changing material such as a eutectic salt mixture, which has a high heat absorption to volume ratio. A plurality of fins **16** extend longitudinally along the outside surface of heat pipe **13** and into heat storage material **15** to provide more efficient distribution of the heat conducted from heat absorbing plate **10**. The outside surface of cylinder **14** also has a plurality of fins **17** for better transfer of heat to the air circulated around the cylinders.

The entire collector panel system can be installed in a building in many ways. One design for installation with a forced air system which can be used for retrofitting a building as well as in a new building, is illustrated in Figure 6.2b. For this design, only the installation of an extra duct, **30**, from the exhaust end of the existing furnace **31** to inlet manifold **28** of the collector panel bank is required for retrofitting. Outlet manifold **29** of the collector panels would then be connected to the central heat duct **32** for the existing system. Valves **33**, **34**, **35** and **36** are used to control the direction of the air forced through the system depending upon whether or not there is sufficient heat to use the solar collectors and may be of the type which can be actuated by a solenoid control. A vent **37** is connected to duct **32** through heat sensitive valve **38** and duct **39** so that if the heat within the duct system builds up to a certain temperature, the vent will allow it to escape.

When using heat pipes to conduct the heat absorbed from the sun away from the solar collector a problem arises when the temperature of the collector absorber plate falls below the temperature in the heat storage cylinder, since the heat pump will now begin to operate in a reverse direction, conducting the heat stored back to the collector. One solution to this problem is to use a valve, **40**, located in the heat pipe, which is closed when the temperature on the collector absorber layer falls below that in the heat storage cylinder or falls within a predetermined temperature difference.

The valve control system for control valve **40** of heat pipe **13** includes a collector control circuit **41** which is connected to temperature sensors **42** and **43** for monitoring the temperature of heat absorbing plate **10** and heat storing material **15**. Control circuit **41** can be programed to turn valve **40** off when there is not enough heat being absorbed by heat absorbing plate **10** to significantly contribute to the supply of heat in heat storage cylinder **14**, thereby preventing reverse flow of heat through heat pipe **13** during periods of limited sunlight or at night. The operation of the solar collector panel and heat storage system in conjunction with a conventional backup heating system will now be described.

On a day with sufficient sunlight, heat absorbing plate **10** will become quite hot due to the sunlight falling on its surface. This heat will cause the working fluid in heat pipe **13** to boil and flow to the opposite, cooler end where it will be condensed and the heat storage material, **15**, will absorb the heat given off by the condensation. During this process, collector control circuit **41** has sensed that the temperature of heat absorber plate **10** is above that in heat storage material **15**, which causes heat pipe valve **40** to remain in its open position. Once the sun sets or is sufficiently covered by clouds and the temperature of absorber plate **10** falls below that in heat storage material **15**, heat pump valve **40** will then be closed to prevent the loss of heat from heat storage cylinder **14**.

When heater control system **44** receives a signal from collector control circuit **41** which indicates that a sufficient quantity of heat is stored in the heat storage system, valve **35** is placed in the open position and valve **36** is placed in the closed position. While no air is being circulated through the collectors, valves **33** and **34** remain closed to minimize heat loss from the air around the heat storage cylinders **14**. The furnace control is also conditioned so that when thermostat **45** turns blower **47** on, heat element **48** does not turn on. When blower **47** is turned on, valves **33** and **34** are opened and air is circulated up duct **30**, in inlet manifold **28**, through the heat storage system for each collector panel, out through outlet manifold **29**, and into each room through duct **32**. Air returns to blower **47** through return duct **27**.

If collector control circuit **41** indicates not enough heat is stored in the heat storage system, heater control system causes valves **33**, **34** and **35** to close and valve **36** is opened. When blower **47** is turned on by thermostat **45**, heater element **48** is also turned on and hot air is forced into the rooms through duct **32**.

### Solution in Thermally Insulated Tank

Many prior systems have used solar heating panels but problems with such limited systems arise due to the fact that the heating capacity is only available during the daylight hours when heating to increase the temperature of the house is least required. Attempts to overcome these problems have included various systems for storing heat but the usual storage material is water or other similar materials which have a limited heat storage capacity. Eutectic salts which melt in the range of 200° to 700°F provide a heat storage capacity of as much as ten times that of water. The advantages of material having such a large heat storage capacity are apparent.

*H. Switzgable; U.S. Patent 3,991,936; November 16, 1976* describes a heat transfer system including a thermally insulated tank defining a chamber therein which contains eutectic salt material for retaining high volumes of heat. The chamber inside of the tank is airtight with respect to the atmosphere. A conduit such as a pipe passes through the walls of the tank at two locations to provide a winding within the chamber such that as heated fluid is passed through the conduit, heat is retained by the eutectic salt material within the chamber. A portion of the walls of the tank have protruding sections which extend inward into the eutectic salt solution. The system includes a heat sink adapted to be placed in thermal communication with the walls of the protrusions to withdraw heat selectively from the eutectic salt solution, a pump and sump system for recirculating the heated fluid from the conduit through a solar panel for heating and a blower and plenum area for passing air over the heat sink to provide a source of heated air.

The process may be more fully understood with reference to Figure 6.3, which is a schmatic drawing of a preferred embodiment of the heat storage system.

FIGURE 6.3: SOLUTION IN THERMALLY INSULATED TANK

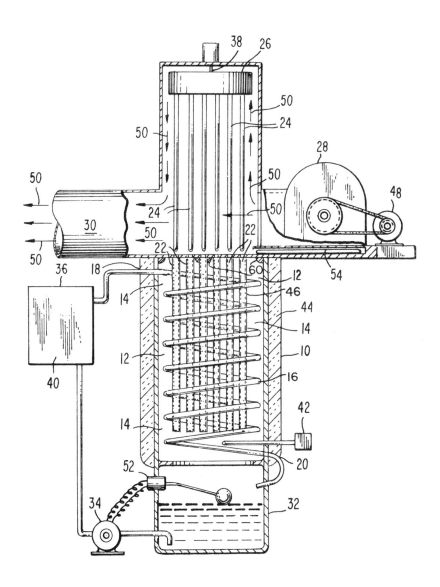

Source: U.S. Patent 3,991,936

This system includes a tank or similar structure **10** which has walls having thermally insulating sections **44** and thermally conductive sections **46**. The tank **10** defines therein a chamber **12** having heat storage material **14** such as eutectic salt or the like located therein. The chamber interior **12** is a sealed system such that fluid flow communication between the chamber and the external environment is prohibited by the airtight walls of tank **10** and by seals **60**.

To provide heat to the heat storage material, a conduit means **16** is positioned to thermally communicate with the heat storage material. Conduit means **16** includes an inlet **18** and an outlet **20**. Heated fluid material flows in through the pipe shaped conduit means **16** at inlet **18** and flows about through the conduit means which is configured to pass through the eutectic salt material to provide heat thereto before the heated fluid material passes through outlet **20**. To facilitate thermal conduction between conduit means **16** and the heat storage material, the conduit means can be configured to wind throughout the interior of chamber **12** to provide a maximum amount of surface area in which the surface of the conduit means **16** contacts the heat storage material to provide an increased amount of thermal flow therebetween. As the cooled fluid flows out of outlet **20** it may be collected in sump **32**.

To withdraw heat from the eutectic salt solution a plurality of protrusions **22** are configured in the thermally conductive sections **46** of tank **10**. Similarly a plurality of rod members **24** are positioned to selectively be placed adjacent protrusions **22** such that heat flow from the heat storage material through the thermally conductive sections **46** into the protrusions **22** will continue into the rod members **24**. Then the rod members will be in thermal communication with the heat sink **26** which is in the form of a small radiator type assembly.

When the rod members and the heat sink are withdrawn from the protrusions, motor **48** will operate to actuate blower means **28** which causes air to flow along the paths shown by arrows **50**. In this manner, the air traveling along these directions will be heated by contacting the rod members and the heat sink and this heated air will then be blown through plenum area **30** and provide a convenient source of heat for the household or other required usages.

To facilitate operation of the system, the regeneration of the heat supplying fluid can be provided by the use of a pump means **34** which is responsive to the level of fluid within the sump **32** through a standard level sensing means **52** to cause the pump to be actuated. When actuated, pump **34** will pump fluid from the sump into a heating means **36** such as a solar panel **40** or the like. During the daylight hours the solar panel will heat the fluid and thereby cause it to flow through inlet **18** to heat the eutectic or other heat storage material **14**.

During periods of limited solar activity an alternate electrical heating element **42** may be positioned in abutment with the eutectic salt solution within the chamber to temporarily continue the operation of the entire system until solar heating is again available. Also a windmill or other windpower system can be used to operate electric heater **42** or to heat fluid passing through inlet **18**.

One of the primary advantages of the system is the very close and accurate control of heat output which is available by the use of the rod members **24** and the heat sink **26**. A push rod means **38** can be used as shown in this particular embodiment to urge the heat sink and rod members downward into protrusions **22**.

This push rod means **38** can be responsive to the required heat such that the elements **24** will be placed at varying distances into the protrusions **22** to vary the amount of heat flowing upward therefrom. At the same time this control of the amount of heat drawn from the eutectic solution will also control the amount of surface area available to the blower to conduct heating air along lines **50** and out through plenum area **30**. To increase the efficiency of the transfer of heat from the protrusions **22** to the heat sink **26** the rod members **24** can be configured in the forms of heat pipes. Heat pipes are commonly known in the field of heat transfer art to be sealed devices having a fluid therein which by a phenomenon of continuous condensing and evaporating will convey heat at a greater rate than heretofore possible.

To minimize the amount of heat lost through the protrusion **22** a cover **54** may be utilized to be selectively placed over the protrusion areas to provide a double wall structure in the area of the thermally conductive sections **46** such that the heat flow out of the protrusions during periods when the push rod means **38** has completely withdrawn the rod members **24** from the protrusions **22** will be minimized. The heat loss from eutectic salts and other heat storage material **14** will be very slight since the other areas of the walls of tank **10** will consist of the thermally insulated sections.

One of the primary advantages of this process is the greatly increased total heat storage capacity which is available by the sealed tank and chamber system in which eutectic salts are positioned therein. Eutectic salts such as sodium hydride and various other sulfur compounds have a great amount of heat storage capacity. This system provides an apparatus for intimately securing contact between the heat input conduit **16** and the heat output protrusions **22** and the eutectic salt materials **14**. Prior systems have had great difficulty in having a very close contact between these three elements in order to maximize thermal conductivity therebetween while at the same time allowing a close and accurate control of the amount of heat drawn therefrom. The apparatus can be especially adaptable for use with a standard home having large roof surface areas for holding solar panels **40**.

## USE OF STONES OR CRUSHED ROCK

### Triangular Storage System

The solar heating apparatus of *J.H. Keyes, C.I. Strickland and R.G. Strickland; U.S. Patent 3,987,786; October 26, 1976; J.H. Keyes, C.I. Strickland and R.G. Strickland; U.S. Patents 3,946,944; March 30, 1976; 3,946,721; March 30, 1976; 3,946,720; March 30, 1976; and 3,894,685; July 15, 1975; all assigned to International Solarthermics Corporation* is self-contained in an elongated housing preferably of triangular transverse cross-sectional configuration. This configuration has been found to allow a maximum quantity of heat-retaining material, such as gravel, to be stored in the apparatus with a minimum of structural reinforcement. The housing is basically constructed of two rectangular top panels, a rectangular bottom panel and two triangular end panels which are interconnected to define an enclosed storage chamber for the heat–retaining material.

The panels are each laminated in such a manner as to give both structural strength and the required insulating qualities for maintaining the temperature of the heat-retaining material in the storage chamber. A collector unit is mounted upon one of the top panels of the housing so as to be inclined relative to the vertical in a position to receive the maximum heat from the winter sun.

The collector unit is designed to absorb solar radiated heat and retain the heat by converting the heat waves, which will readily pass through transparent glass or plastic panes on the collector face, into long wave heat radiation which will not readily pass back through the glass or plastic panes on the face of the collector. The solar heat is absorbed on a base panel of the collector which emits relatively long wave heat radiation that becomes trapped in the collector.

The base panel of the collector has a plurality of forwardly opening cups which serve to increase the heat absorption and emission capability of the collector. Depending upon the material from which the cups are made, they usually will not retain the heat imparted thereto by the solar radiation for extended periods of time; accordingly, air is circulated through the collector to transfer the heat absorbed by the cups into the storage chamber of the apparatus where the gravel material not only absorbs the heat carried by the air but also retains the heat for extended periods of time due to inherent heat-retaining characteristics of gravel and its inherent restriction of convection.

The air which passes through the collector and into the storage chamber is re-circulated through the collector so as to continuously transfer heat, when desired, from the collector to the storage unit. For purposes of the process, this circulating air will be referred to as conditioning air. Since it is important to the optimum operation of the unit that the conditioning air be equally exposed to the entire base of the collector, a series of baffles are provided in the collector to direct the air stream through a series of reversing bends. Similarly, baffles are provided in the storage chamber to direct the conditioning air throughout the entire quantity of gravel in the storage chamber.

A conditioning air pump is positioned within the storage chamber to effect the desired conditioning air flow. The air is passed from the storage chamber to the collector and back into the storage chamber through inlet and outlet ducts which are positioned at an elevation below both the storage chamber and the collector so that when the pump is not in operation, the hot air which is lighter than cold air, and therefore urged to the top of the respective components of the apparatus, will not be able to freely flow between the components so that the ducts establish thermal traps that avoid the necessity of relatively expensive valve means to accomplish the same purpose.

A reflector panel is hinged to the framework of the housing along an edge of the collector unit so that by opening the reflective panel, the solar heat radiation being absorbed by the collector unit is increased. This reflective panel is designed so that in a closed position it overlies the collector unit and thereby protects the relatively fragile glass from detrimental environmental elements such as hail, sunlight in summer months, and the like.

The heat retained by the heat-retaining material in the storage chamber is transferred into an adjacent building structure or the like by a utility pump which may also be positioned within the storage chamber and connected to the building structure by suitable insulated duct work having outlets for selectively distributing the hot air through the building structure. This air flow, which will be hereinafter referred to as the utility air flow, is circulated back through the storage chamber in a manner so as to obtain a maximum heat transfer from the heat retaining material to the air and in a manner such that the utility air is not short circuited and directed through the collector with the conditioning air unless both pumps are operating simultaneously. This is accomplished by positioning the inlet and outlet ducts for both the conditioning air circuit and the utility air circuit on appropriate sides of the baffle members within the storage chamber.

The unit is ideally suited for connection to an existing forced air heating system in a building structure so as to serve as an auxiliary unit to the forced air heating system even though in many instances, the solar heating unit is sufficient in itself to provide the necessary heat for the building structure.

According to the process, heat is first absorbed from the sun on a collector surface where the collector surface is insulated from the ambient environment and internal air is passed across the collector surface in a heat transfer process so that the heat absorbed by the collector surface is transferred to the internal air. The air is then passed through a duct which is lower than the collector surface into a raised storage chamber where it is directed through heat absorbent and heat retaining material in the storage chamber so that the heat in the hot air is transferred to the material in the storage chamber. The heat retained by the material in the storage chamber is transferred into a building structure by directing a utility stream of air through the material in the storage chamber and into the building structure where it is distributed as desired throughout the structure.

The collector unit is of a size substantially the same as the top panels of the housing and is mounted directly on the outer face of the top panels. The collector unit includes an outer peripheral rigid frame, a front insulating glass portion and a back heat accumulator portion. The insulator glass portion and heat accumulator portion are separated by a plurality of baffle members which serve to circulate air uniformly through the collector.

The peripheral frame abuts the inner surfaces of the extensions of the end panels beyond the top panel so as to be insulated along the associated two sides from the ambient environment and an elongated wedge shaped insulating block lies across and is attached to the top portion of the peripheral frame to insulate the top portion from the ambient environment.

The insulating glass portion of the collector unit consists of three spaced layers of glass with each layer of glass having two coplanar glass or plastic panels separated at the longitudinal center of the collector by a center plate. Each glass or plastic panel is separated from the glass panel in the next adjacent layer by a rubber sealant strip which extends around the periphery of the panel.

The heat accumulator portion of the collector unit includes a planar back plate, preferably a sheet of black coated metallic coil or the like which lies against or is affixed to the outer plywood sheet of the top panel. A plurality of forwardly opening cups preferably of cylindrical configuration and made of aluminum and coated black, are positioned upon the black aluminum back sheet and define spaces therebetween which expose the back sheet. The cups may be loosely disposed upon the back plate or could be secured thereto if desired. It will be appreciated that the cups enlarge the surface area of the heat accumulator and thus the solar thermal energy capturing ability of the apparatus.  The forward extent of the accumulator cups is rearwardly spaced from the insulator glass defining an open space or passage therebetween through which air can freely pass. Baffle members are positioned within this space to direct the conditioning air currents along a predetermined path which fairly uniformly covers the entire array or matrix of accumulator cups whereby a complete and effective transfer of heat from the accumulator cups to the air can be effected.

Illustrative diagrams of the collector, relative to a dwelling, are shown in Figure 6.4.  A detailed description of the heating system and additional diagrams are included in the patents.

## FIGURE 6.4: TRIANGULAR STORAGE SYSTEM

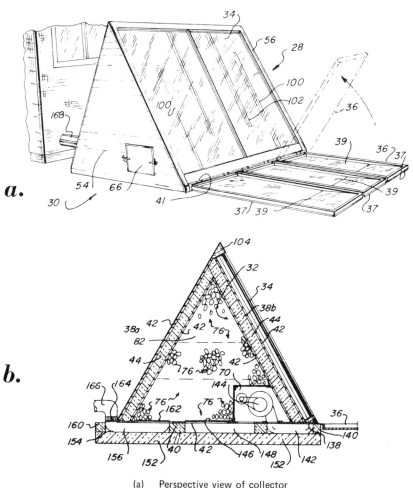

(a)    Perspective view of collector
(b)    Vertical section of collector

Source:  U.S. Patent 3,946,720

## Multiple Compartment System

The process of *H.E. Thomason and H.J.L. Thomason, Jr.; U.S. Patents 3,980,130; September 14, 1976; and 3,983,929; October 5, 1976* includes a number of features regarding storage of heat and cold (technically, storage of heat at higher and lower temperature levels). One of the important features is the use of an air conditioner compressor for its normal chilling, drying function during the hot summer, using it as a heat pump during variable autumn and spring weather to heat one bin while chilling another and using it as an auxiliary heat source for long cloudy spells during the winter when solar energy is not adequate, thereby eliminating the furnace. Dry air passing through the system during the winter may be humidified as needed to keep the home from feeling so dry and cold. The heat or cold may be supplied to various zones of the home, winter or summer.

U.S. Patent 3,983,929 teaches the use of two (or more) storage containers. They are used for storing heat at two levels at the same time (warm and cool), or for storage of heat in both containers, or for storage of coolness in both containers. Preferably the main source of heat is solar energy and the source of coolness (and dryness) is an air conditioning compressor although other sources could be used for either, or both. The compressor is operated during the hot summertime, primarily at night.

In U.S. Patent 3,980,130, the air conditioning compressor serves the function set out above, and more, as follows:

(1) During the winter the compressor serves as a heat pump to provide auxiliary heat when solar heat is inadequate. Therefore, it eliminates the need for a furnace for a back-up heating system.

(2) Further, during winter, in another mode of operation, the compressor serves as a heat pump to pump heat from the low temperature container to the high temperature container. That yields dual desirable results:

(a) Fluid from the low temperature container is circulated to the solar heat collector and that low temperature fluid picks up heat with increased efficiency of solar heat collection.

(b) The warmer container provides more heat for the home per minute of operation. Therefore, the blower does not have to operate as much of the time. The net result is that more of the total heat load for the building is supplied by solar energy.

(3) Still further, during variable springtime and autumn weather, the compressor keeps one container charged with heat while the other is charged with coldness, or coldness and dryness. Therefore, for chilly days or cold nights out-of-season, stored heat is available from the warm container. Similarly, for warm or warm muggy days out-of-season, stored coldness, or coldness and dryness are available from the cool container.

Referring to Figure 6.5a, heat or cold storage apparatus **10** comprises two or more compartments **11, 12** with liquid storage containers or tanks **13, 14** and stones, containers or heat-of-fusion storage material, or other illustrated at **15**. A wall **16**, of insulating material, is preferably constructed between the compartments.

Warm liquid, from a solar heat collector **17a** for example, or other source of heat flows into tank **14**, near its top, by way of conduit **17** and flows out, from near its bottom, by conduit **18**. From **18** the liquid may pass through line **19** directly to valve **20**, or may flow through line **21** to near the top of tank **13** and then, from near the bottom, through line **22** to valve **20**. Pump **23** draws liquid from tank **14** or tank **13**, depending on the setting of valve **20** and sends the liquid through line **24** to solar heat collector **17a** or other source of heat such as off-peak heat producing equipment, a heat pump, or other.

Air from spaces to be heated or cooled is drawn, by blower **28** in at **25** through filter **26** and heating-cooling coils B and C (**27** and **27'**). Moisture condensing out of the air drips into condensate troughs **27"** from which it drains, is pumped, or otherwise, preferably over to outside coil A to help cool it when it runs as a hot coil. Blower **28** is preferably one of the multispeed, multicapacity type. Air from blower **28** passes multiposition damper **29** and enters the storage compartments as follows. With damper **29** in position A, the air flow is directed to compartment **12**, or in position B the air flows to compartment **11**, or in position C the air flows to both compartments.

The air flows through one or both of compartments **11** and **12** where it is warmed (or cooled) and passes out through ducts **30, 31** and **32**. Multiposition damper **33** may be set in position A to direct the warmed or cooled air primarily to **Zone 1**; for example, the living room, dining room and kitchen of a home. Or, damper **33** may be set in position B to direct the air to **Zone 2**, the bedrooms of a home for example. Or, damper **33** may be set in position C to allow the air to flow to both zones.

Bypass line **34** and damper **35** permit recirculation of air at times. For example, during the cooling cycle the air may be recirculated at times through coil **27**(B), or through both coils **27** and **27'** (B and C) for further cooling and dehumidification of the materials in the storage compartment or compartments. (Of course if air is to be recirculated through one coil only, say coil B only, then a bypass and damper must be provided for that side of the apparatus. If desired a similar bypass and damper may be provided for the other side and coil C). Whether using one side or both sides the apparatus permits greater storage of coolness and dryness at times when there is very little or no need for cooling of the home, such as late at night during chilly hours near dawn.

As another example, during the heating cycle, the air may be recirculated through coils **27** and **27'** operating as hot coils, with compressor **36** pumping heat in from **37** (coil A) operating as a cold coil. This could be in operation during warm winter days for keeping the home warm on cold winter nights when stored heat is needed in large quantities. As still another example, during cloudy periods, at night, etc., heat can be pumped from coil B (**27**), operating as a cold coil, to coil C (**27'**) operating as a hot coil; this cools container **11** while warming container **12** to provide additional heat for the home. Then, cooled liquid from tank **13** is more efficient for picking up heat from the solar heat collector when the sun begins to shine.

FIGURE 6.5: MULTIPLE COMPARTMENT SYSTEM

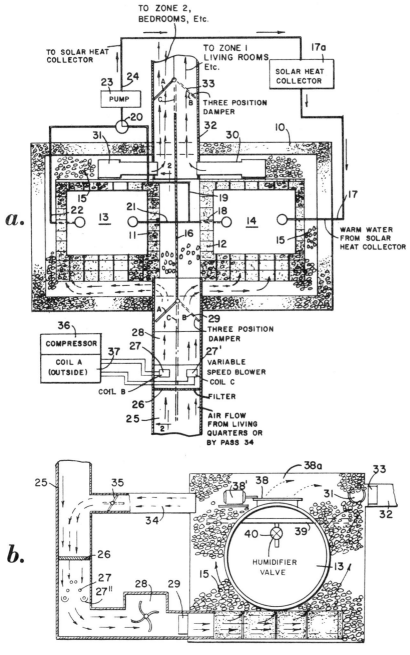

(a)   Diagrammatic illustration of plan view
(b)   Diagrammatic illustration along line 2–2 of Figure 6.5a

Source:  U.S. Patent 3,980,130

As still another example, during variable spring and autumn weather, container 11 may be kept cool and dry to supply coldness and dryness to the home on hot muggy days out of season while container 12 is kept warm to supply heat during cold snaps out of season. Of course free heat from the sun is usually available if the system is used in conjunction with a solar heat collector. Therefore, the heat pumped out from cold coil B (27) could be discharged through Coil A (37) instead of Coil C (27') if desired.

It should be noted that air flow through coils B (27) and C (27') is downwardly. This is an important feature when one or both are operating as cold coils to cool and dehumidify. As explained in U.S. Patent 3,812,903, the moisture condensing out of the coils is whisked out by the combined downward force of gravity plus downward air flow. That keeps the coils from becoming wet and clogged with water as often happens when air is blown upwardly as in most home furnace-air conditioning combinations. By keeping the coils dry and unclogged the air is dried and cooled with greater efficiency. Also, the air flows more freely, thereby eliminating back pressure and wasted power trying to force air through partially clogged wet coils. The air moves faster through the home, thereby making it feel cooler. When operating at night, the cool night air takes heat away from coil A faster, resulting in colder coils B and C, with even more dehumidification as well as greater efficiency of the system for cooling and drying.

A manhole or other opening may be provided at 38. A motor device 38' may be used, if desired, to open and close a cover as described below. A humidifier at 39, such as a spray pipe or drip pipe may be controlled by humidifier valve 40. Then, during dry cold winter weather moisture may be added to the air through storage material 15 by opening valve 40 to permit water or pleasant smelling liquid to drip from tank 13 or 14 or both as desired. If desired liquid or perfumed fluid with the aroma of roses or orchids could be supplied to pipe 39 from a source outside of tank 13 or outside of container 11. Valve 40, or cover 38 as operated by motor device 38' or both, may be opened and closed automatically by a humidistat. That allows liquid or vapor 38a to enter the air flowing through the container(s) in a manner as will be obvious to those skilled in the art.

In Figures 6.5a and 6.5b heat and cold from coil B (27) and coil C (27') are fed directly, by the flowing air stream, to the storage containers 11 and 12. In that manner much of the heat, or cold, or both, is stored as it is being produced. The heat or cold that is produced passes into bins 11, 12 where much of it is absorbed and the remainder (with damper 35 closed) is directed to the living quarters of the home, or other space to be heated or cooled. That results in heating or cooling of the home but at a fairly slow rate. At times it may be desirable to obtain quick heating or cooling (e.g., when a family returns home on a cold day after a vacation trip). If desired a storage bin bypass, or two, could be installed, bypassing container 11, or container 12, or both. It should preferably be connected downstream from the blower (or blowers) 28 adjacent to damper 29 and running directly to outlet 32.

A damper in the bypass, (or dampers in the bypasses) could be opened to permit direct use of the heat, or cold, or both, instantly, for quick heating or cooling of the living quarters. The dampers would be closed for normal use, while heat (or cold) is being stored or recovered from storage. Inasmuch as this type of operation would be infrequent and perhaps never used in some homes, the damper(s) could be manually operated for simplicity and low-cost. Earlier versions of related storage apparatus have been described in U.S. Patents 3,254,702, 3,369,541 and 3,812,903.

## OTHER STORAGE MEDIA

### Heat Sink Encapsulated in Resin Matrix

*J.S. Best and W.J. McMillan; U.S. Patent 4,003,426; January 18, 1977; assigned to The Dow Chemical Company* describe a heat or thermal energy storage structure comprising a crosslinked polymeric resinous matrix having a plurality of substantially unconnected small closed cavities and a heat sink material encapsulated within the cavities. The structure is characterized in that the heat sink material forms an essentially stable dispersion in the uncured polymeric resinous matrix when mixed therewith before the matrix is crosslinked. The structure can beneficially be used in conjunction with low level heat or thermal energy collector means and heat transfer means to provide a space heating or cooling apparatus.

Referring to Figure 6.6, a heat or thermal energy storage structure **10** is illustrated. The storage structure **10** comprises a crosslinked polymeric resinous matrix **12** having a plurality of substantially unconnected small closed cavities encapsulating a heat sink material which may be in a liquid state, as shown by numeral **14**, or in a solid state, as shown by numeral **16**, after releasing its heat of fusion to the adjacent environment.

**FIGURE 6.6: HEAT SINK ENCAPSULATED IN RESIN MATRIX**

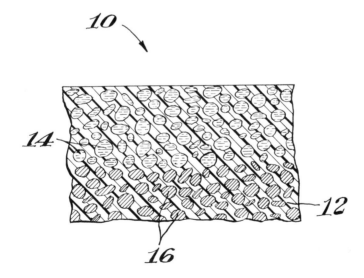

Source: U.S. Patent 4,003,426

The heat or thermal energy storage structure which can be utilized in space heating or cooling apparatus can be formed with a matrix of any crosslinked or thermoset polymeric resinous material provided the heat sink material will form an essential stable dispersion in the uncured polymeric resinous matrix before the matrix is crosslinked. Particularly suited crosslinked polymeric resinous matrixes are selected from the group consisting essentially of polyesters, polyvinyl esters, and epoxies. Beneficially, the crosslinked polymeric resinous matrix comprises as low as 25 weight percent but preferably 35 weight percent or more of the heat or thermal energy storage structure.

The heat sink materials useful in forming a heat or thermal energy storage structure should be selected to take advantage of their relatively large latent heat capacity at their melting and freezing phase change which supplies heat to or removes heat from the heat or thermal energy storage structure. The heat sink materials are characterized in that they should form an essentially stable dispersion in the uncured polymeric resinous matrix when mixed therewith before the matrix is crosslinked. Depending on the service requirements to be met, the heat sink materials forming the heat or thermal energy storage structure useful in space heating or cooling apparatus should beneficially melt between 5° and 100°C and should not supercool more than about 5°C below the melt temperature of the heat sink material. The heat sink material can comprise up to 75 weight percent and beneficially comprises up to 65 weight percent of the heat or thermal energy storage structure.

Particularly suited as heat sink materials are inorganic hydrates such as barium hydroxide octahydrate, zinc nitrate hexahydrate and aqueous organic hydrate compositions such as illustrated in U.S. Patent 3,834,456.

To insure against long-term loss of the heat sink material from the heat or thermal energy storage structure, the structure may beneficially be enveloped in a gas or vapor barrier material. For example, after the heat or thermal energy storage structure has been formed it can be sealed in an envelope of metal foil such as aluminum foil or in a thermoplastic resinous barrier material. A wide variety of thermoplastic barrier materials may also be employed in the envelope. Particularly suited are combinations of vinylidene chloride polymers, vinyl chloride polymers, vinylidene fluoride polymers and mixtures thereof.

*Example:*

| Composition | Parts by Weight |
|---|---|
| Vinyl ester resin* | 300 |
| Pinacol hexahydrate | 900 |
| Benzoyl peroxide | 0.88 |
| Dimethyl toluidine | 0.72 |

*Derakane 470

In forming the heat or thermal energy storage structure of this example, the vinyl ester resin and the pinacol hexahydrate (melting point 45°C) were preheated to about 52°C. The benzoyl peroxide was then dissolved in the vinyl ester resin with vigorous agitation. Next, the pinacol hexahydrate was slowly added while continuing agitation to form an emulsion. Thereafter, the dimethyl toluidine was added while mixing to form the final composition which was then poured into a mold. The composition set up quickly in the mold (within about 5 minutes) and was removed after about 2 hours in the form of a rigid structure with the pinacol hexahydrate dispersed therein. The heat or thermal energy storage structure provided in accordance with this process is useful in forming an apparatus for space heating and cooling when combined with a low level heat or thermal energy collector means and heat or thermal energy transfer means. For example, when the utilization of solar energy for heating purposes is desired, the heat collector means comprises a radiant energy heat transfer device having at least one radiant energy transferring face adapted to absorb incident solar energy in the form of heat.

In addition, the heat or thermal energy storage structure described in the process is cast around a heat exchange circulating coil in any desired form such as a wall structure for a building and the heat transfer means is interconnected to the collector means, storage structure and a space the temperature of which is to be controlled whereby heat would be transferred from the collector means to the storage structure and to the space when the space is being heated and from the space to the storage structure and to an alfresco environment when the space is being cooled.

### Granular Polyvinyl Chloride Heat Sink

A thermal bank described by *R.L. Rudd; U.S. Patent 3,780,262; December 18, 1973* is comprised of a granular mass of polyvinyl chloride which surrounds a heating mechanism such as a conduit containing heated fluid. The granular polyvinyl chloride mass is formed by treating commercial dry flaked polyvinyl chloride with a small amount of stabilizer which causes the powder to form granules having interstices therebetween. The granular polyvinyl chloride mass not only serves as a high temperature insulator but also serves as an excellent heat storage system. A metallic foil surrounds the polyvinyl chloride mass and serves as a radiation shield, and an air impervious outer cover surrounds the foil and prevents convection losses from the mass. The thermal bank may be constructed as the primary storage center for heating a building structure deriving its heat from solar energy during the day and releasing it gradually during the night.

Commercial polyvinyl chloride is generally available in a dry, usually flake condition. It is desirable to change the flake condition of polyvinyl chloride into a granular particulate form to increase the interstices or air spaces between individual particles. The heat insulating properties of the polyvinyl chloride resides in its granular condition.

The dry commercial polyvinyl chloride is therefore treated with a suitable commercial stabilizer such as Adbastab (Advanced Chemical Co.) or Mark WK-6 or Mark 649-A (Argus Co.). Typically, approximately eight quarts of the stabilizer is added to a 55 gallon drum of polyvinyl chloride in a mixer or blender and the polyvinyl chloride is thoroughly mixed. When treated with the stabilizer, the dry flake polyvinyl chloride assumes a granular characteristic similar to sugar.

Referring to Figures 6.7a and 6.7b, the thermal bank **30** is thereshown. The thermal bank includes a heating mechanism which is in the form of a conduit or pipe through which is circulated a heated fluid such as hot water. The hot water may be heated by a solar heating system **32** and the water heated by solar energy is directed to the heat pump **29** which extracts the heat from the water and directs high temperature water into the heating pipe **31**. The pipe or conduit **31** may be coiled and disposed in contact with a primary heat sink member **31a** formed of a suitable metal. It is also pointed out that the heating conduit or pipe may be shaped into a heat sink member which is provided with a passage through which the heated water flows, the heat sink member having any desirable shape or configuration and being formed of a suitable metallic material.

## FIGURE 6.7: GRANULAR POLYVINYL CHLORIDE HEAT SINK

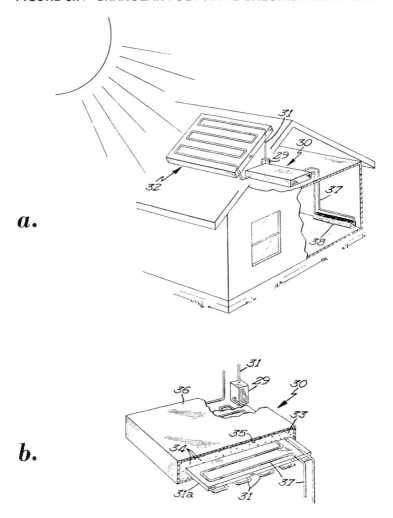

a.

b.

(a)    Perspective view of thermal bank used as heat
        dispensing means for a house
(b)    Cross sectional view of thermal bank of Figure 6.7a

Source: U.S. Patent 3,780,262

The heating conduit and primary heat sink member are surrounded by a granular mass **33** of polyvinyl chloride in which the individual particles of polyvinyl chloride have interstices **34** therebetween. The thermal bank is provided with an inner foil cover **35** which covers the mass of polyvinyl chloride and which serves as a radiation shield. The radiation shield or cover **35** is preferably formed of aluminum having a reflective inner surface and is in turn covered by a fluid impervious outer cover **36** preferably formed of polyethylene or the like. The polyethylene cover serves as a convection shield.

A coiled heat transmission conduit **37** is positioned within the mass of polyvinyl chloride and is connected to any heat dispensing means such as radiators **38**, so that the water heated by the polyvinyl chloride mass will be circulated between the radiators and the thermal bank. With this arrangement, the thermal bank is heated by heat from a solar heating system and the heat is very effectively stored for use as desired. It will be appreciated that the quantum of heat will be dependent upon the size of the polyvinyl chloride mass.

## UNDERGROUND DEVICES

### Heat Storage Tank

Solar energy heat collectors have been developed which are quite efficient. However, in order to make practical use of them, it is necessary to have some kind of a heat storage system to maintain the heating of the house during nights and periods of cloudy, sunless days.

The process of *H. Harrison; U.S. Patent 4,010,731; March 8, 1977; assigned to Halm Instrument Co., Inc.* provides a heat storage tank which is connected to a solar heat collector to provide sufficient heat storage to obtain practical use of the solar heat collector.

The process provides a storage tank which is sunk into the ground. An outer liner of incompressible insulating material is provided. A water impervious liner tank is mounted against the insulation. A top rests on the contents of the tank and the tank is divided into center and side portions by at least one insulating barrier extending from the tank top to a point near the bottom of the tank. Hot water from the heat collector is brought into the center portion. The tank is substantially filled with heat storage material such as gravel and stones and water.

The hot water will collect and circulate in the center portion of the tank. Domestic hot water may be heated in a heat exchanger mounted in the upper center portion. Cooler water is pumped from a side portion to the input of the solar heat collector. Some of the heat storage material may be layers or pockets of finer material, such as sand. The gravel and stones have sufficient voids between them to provide for good heat exchange fluid circulation. The heat exchange fluid is preferably water, but other fluid may be used. The heat storage tank provides adequate heat storage with a minimum of materials.

Referring to Figure 6.8a, the heat storage tank is preferably mounted in a pit **1**, in the ground. The sides and the bottom of the pit are lined with incompressible insulation **2**, which may be a foam material of polystyrene or polyethylene.

## FIGURE 6.8: HEAT STORAGE TANK

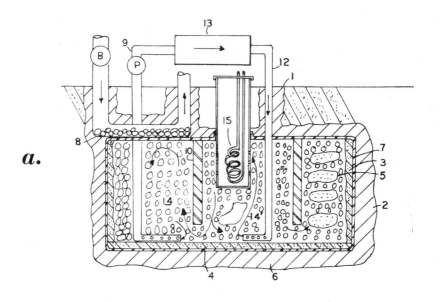

*a.*

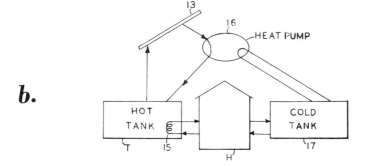

*b.*

(a)    Side sectional view of storage tank
(b)    Schematic diagram illustrating use of storage tank

Source: U.S. Patent 4,010,731

If the soil is dry and the bottom of the pit is at least several feet above the water table the bottom portion **6** of the foam insulation may be omitted as the soil itself will provide sufficient insulation. Inside the insulation is mounted a water impervious liner tank **7**, which may be of plastic, for instance, of vinyl or polyethylene. The plastic tank liner does not have to have any appreciable structural strength since it is supported by the surrounding earth and the contents of the tank. To prevent puncturing the liner **7** when the tank is being built, a layer of sand **4**, a few inches thick is spread on the bottom. Protection for the sides may be a layer **3** of sand, or alternatively of mastic or plastic foam. The top of the tank is covered by a portion of the liner tank **7** and may have a layer of stones **8** which provides an extended heat transfer surface for heating warm air. An insulating barrier **10** extends down from the top, leaving only sufficient space at the bottom for free passage of water. The barrier **10** separates the tank into a center portion and a side portion.

The tank is substantially filled with gravel and stones **14** of reasonably uniform size so that there will be sufficient void spaces between them for a good circulation of water. Finer materials which permit less water circulation may be clumped in layers or pockets **5** which are surrounded by gravel. Earth taken from the pit **1** can frequently be used for filling the tank after it has been screened to develop water circulation voids.

A hot water intake pipe **12** extends down to the bottom of the center portion of the tank. A cold water out-take pipe **9** extends from the bottom side portion up to the top of the tank. A pump **P** is connected to the out-take pipe to pump cool water to a heat source **13** which may be a solar heat collector which heats the water. The water then flows down through the pipe **12** and out into the center portion of the tank as shown by the arrow **14'**. In the center portion of the tank, the hottest water will rise to the top where it will come in contact with the heat exchange device **15** which will extract the heat for the purpose of providing hot water and heat to the house.

The insulating barrier **10** tends to trap the hottest water in the center portion. The coolest water in the center portion flows under the barrier **10** into the side portion. The warmest portion of this water rises to the top, where its heat may pass into the heat exchange rock layer **8** by conduction, there it warms house-heating air circulated by blower **B**. The tank for a well-insulated one family dwelling may be approximately 20 x 30 feet and about 5 feet deep. This size tank stores enough heat so that heat collected in summer can be used for winter heating.

For maximum economy, it may be desired to bond at least some of the contents of the tank together with cement. This creates a porous monolithic concrete block with sufficient strength to serve as the foundation for a house. The house is then erected directly on top of the heat storage reservoir. If the tank actually extends below the water table in the ground it would be desirable to have an additional plastic liner on the outside of the insulation. The high temperature water is horizontally stratified since it is trapped at the top of the center portion where it is extracted by the heat exchanger.

Figure 6.8b illustrates the use of the storage tank **T**, in a complete system. The heat storage tank **T** is connected to the heat collector **13** and is connected to the house **H** by means of heat exchanger **15**. The heat pump **16** circulates the heating water. A complete system preferably has a cold storage tank **17** which is connected to the heat pump **16** and the house **H** for providing cooling services such as air conditioning.

### Storage Tank Combined with Two Energy Exchange Tanks

A thermal energy storage system including a thermal energy storage tank and a pair of thermal energy exchange tanks disposed in a different horizontal plane than the thermal energy storage tank is described by *D.M. Jardine; U.S. Patent*

*4,008,709; February 22, 1977.* Each tank contains a heat exchange medium
and is in fluid communication with the other tank for circulation of the heat
exchange medium between the exchange tanks and the storage tank by convection. The exchange tanks contain a heat exchange coil which is in fluid
communication with a first heat exchanger for heating or cooling the medium
in the exchange tank.

The storage tank is in fluid communication with a second heat exchanger for
the transfer of the heat exchange medium therebetween to heat or cool a structure. The system is disposed beneath the ground adjacent the structure being
heated or cooled and an envelope of noncoherent material is disposed about the
system to provide a corrosion resistant barrier between the tanks and the adjacent earth and to act as a conduit for the transfer of thermal energy between
the system and the surrounding earth.

As illustrated in Figures 6.9a through 6.9g, the process is embodied in a heating
system where the heat source is solar derived. As is more specifically shown in
Figure 6.9a, a structure **10** is provided with a roof top heat exchange panel **12**
suitably located for exposure to the rays of the sun. The heat exchange panel
**12** comprises heat exchange coils **14** which are formed of a suitable heat conductive material for transmitting solar energy to heat exchange fluid contained
therein. The heat exchange coils **14** are preferably utilized in conjunction with
solar collectors, not shown, of conventional design for focusing the rays of the
sun on the coils.

Heated fluid is led by line **16** to an underground heat storage system shown generally at **18** and cooled heat exchange fluid is led back to the heat exchange
panel **12** through line **20** for reheating. A pump **22** in the line **20** provides the
necessary pumping action for the circulation of the heat exchange fluid between
the heat exchange panel **12** and the heat storage system **18**.

A line **24** leads from the heat storage system **18** to a conventional heat exchanger,
such as a heat pump, illustrated schematically at **26**, for circulating heat exchange
fluid from the storage system to the heat pump for the removal of heat therefrom and for the distribution of the heat within the structure **10**. A line **28**
provides return circulation to the heat exchange system **18** and suitable pumping means, not shown, may be provided for the circulation of the heat exchange
fluid as described. Similarly, a line **30** leads water, which has been heated in
the heat storage system **18** to a hot water storage tank **32** for domestic use or
other use within the structure and a line **34** returns cool water from the tank to
the heat storage system for reheating.

As is shown in Figures 6.9a and 6.9b, the heat storage system **18** comprises a
pair of exchanger tanks **36** and **38** which are spaced apart and disposed in substantially the same plane and a hot fluid storage tank **40** disposed in a plane
above the exchanger tanks. The exchanger tanks **36** and **38** are in fluid communication with each other by means of lateral conduits **42** and are in communication with the hot fluid storage tank **40** by means of downcomers **44**
which communicate between the lateral conduits and the hot fluid storage tank
and by means of risers **46** communicating between each of the tanks **36** and **38**
and the hot fluid storage tank **40**. The heat storage system **18** is preferably disposed in an underground location adjacent the structure **10** so that energy stored
in the hot fluid tank **40** and the exchanger tanks **36** and **38** is conducted through

the walls of the tanks and retained in the surrounding earth for retrieval when the temperature of the tank falls below that of the surrounding earth. In this manner the storage capacity of the system **18** is substantially increased. The dimensions of the tanks **36, 38** and **40** can be varied depending upon well understood determinants such as for example, the type of structure, the heating load, the type of heat exchange, and the like. The embodiment illustrated is designed for heating a single family residence in a severe winter climate and the tanks have a diameter of 36 inches and a length of 20 feet so as to provide a maximum heat exchange medium capacity of about 424 cubic feet.

The system **18** is disposed in the earth below the frost line and preferably at a point where the ambient temperature of the earth remains substantially constant. The exact depth of the system is not critical and will vary depending upon the local climatic conditions. It has been found that a depth of on the order of 10 feet below the surface is adequate for most conditions encountered in the United States. An envelope **48** of particulate, noncoherent, noncorrosive material is disposed about the heat storage system and between the tanks **36, 38** and **40**, so as to provide a barrier between the heat storage system and the surrounding earth.

Preferably, the envelope has an apparent coefficient of thermal conductivity (k) of at least that of the surrounding earth so as to not interfere with the energy transfer between the heat storage system **18** and the earth. Good results are achieved when the thickness of the envelope **48** between the heat storage system **18** and the earth ranges between about 8 to 24 inches. The thickness of the envelope **48**, however, may be varied depending upon soil conditions, the climatic conditions and the dimensions of the storage system **18**.

FIGURE 6.9: STORAGE TANK COMBINED WITH TWO ENERGY
EXCHANGE TANKS

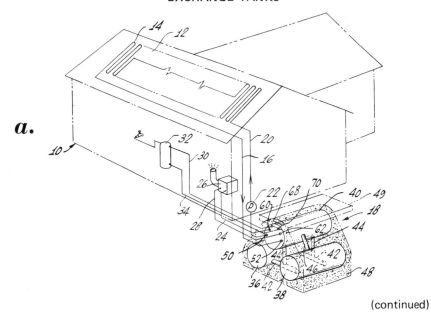

(continued)

## FIGURE 6.9: (continued)

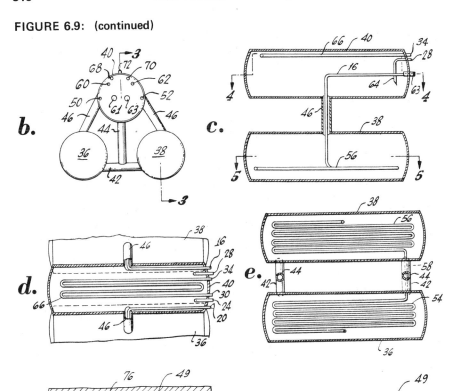

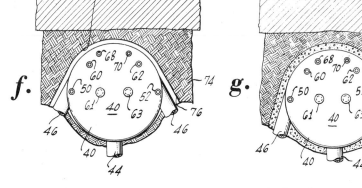

(a)   Partially diagrammatic partially isometric view of complete heating system

(b)   Enlarged front elevation of heat storage system

(c)   Sectional view taken through line 3—3 of Figure 6.9b

(d)   Sectional view taken through line 4—4 of Figure 6.9c

(e)   Sectional view taken through line 5—5 of Figure 6.9c

(f)   Enlarged front elevation of hot fluid storage tank disposed in earth

(g)   Enlarged front elevation of hot fluid storage tank having a quartz envelope

Source:   U.S. Patent 4,008,709

Under normal operating conditions, it has been found that a zone of heated earth will extend from the system **18** about 65 feet. Accordingly, it is preferred practice to provide a substantially horizontal layer of insulating material **49**, over-lying the heat storage system to prevent heat loss to the surface. The material forming the envelope **48** is noncorrosive to the system **18**, is noncoherent and has a (k) not less than that of the surrounding earth. Good results are achieved using finely crushed quartz as the material of the envelope **48**. It is preferred that the particle size of the quartz range between about 0.5 to 2.0 mm.

As is more specifically shown in Figures 6.9b through 6.9e, openings **50** and **52** are provided in the end wall of the hot fluid storage tank **40** for the extension therethrough of inlet lines **20** and **16** respectively for the circulation of heat exchange fluid between the storage system **18** and the solar panel **12**. The line **16,** which carries the heat exchange fluid from the solar panel **12**, extends through a portion of the interior of the tank **40**, downwardly through the riser **46** and leads into a series of heat exchange coils **56** (Figure 6.9e) disposed in the lower portion of the interior of the tank **38**.

A corresponding series of heat exchange coils **54** are similarly disposed in the tank **36** and communicate with the heat exchange coils **56** by a lateral line **58** extending between the coils **54** and **56** through the lateral conduit **42**. The out-let line **20**, which conducts heat exchange fluid back to the solar panel **12**, leads from the heat exchange coil **54** through the riser **46** back to the hot fluid storage tank **40** and exits therefrom through the opening **50**.

Openings **60** and **62** are provided in the end wall of the hot fluid storage tank **40** for the extension therethrough of the lines **24** and **28** respectively for the cir-culation of heat exchange fluid between the heat storage system **18** and the heat pump **26**. In the embodiment illustrated, the heat exchange fluid is withdrawn directly from the hot fluid storage tank **40** for circulation to the heat pump **26** and returned to the tank **40** for reheating. As an aid to the proper flow of heat exchange fluid, the return line **28** terminates in a downwardly turned portion **64** within the tank **40** for directing the returned cooled heat exchange fluid toward the downcomers **44**.

In place of direct use of heat exchange fluid, the lines **24** and **28** can communi-cate with a heat exchange coil, not shown, for the transfer of energy from the heat exchange fluid within the tank **40** to a heat exchange fluid within the heat exchange coil if direct use of fluid from the tank **40** is not desired.

Hot water for domestic purposes is heated in the hot fluid storage tank **40** by means of a heat exchange coil **66** located in the upper portion of the hot fluid storage tank **40** to which the lines **30** and **34** are connected for the circulation therethrough of domestic water. The lines **30** and **34** extend through openings **68** and **70**, respectively, which are provided in the end wall of the hot fluid stor-age tank **40**.

The hot fluid storage tank **40** is vented to the surface at **72** for the relief of pres-sure caused by the expansion and contraction of the heat exchange fluid con-tained in the heat storage system **18**. However, if higher energy storage capacity is desired, the storage system **18** may be pressurized by the incorporation of an expansion tank and pressure relief valve, not shown, as is conventional in the art.

As is more specifically shown in Figure 6.9f, the storage of heat energy in the tank **40** will cause it to expand resulting in the compression of a layer **74** of the earth surrounding the tank wall. Should the temperature within the tank **40** fall below the maximum temperature, the tank wall will contract while the layer **74** of earth, due to its coherent nature, will not expand at the same rate. As a result an air film **76** would be formed between the wall of the tank **40** and the earth. The air film would act as an insulative boundary because of the very low (k) coefficient of air and the quantity of heat energy in Btu/hr which can be transferred between the tank and the earth would be substantially decreased. It should be clear that a similar effect would occur around the walls of the exchange tanks **36** and **38**.

As is more specifically shown in Figure 6.9g, the envelope **48** of quartz sand surrounding the wall of the tank **40** being noncoherent does not take a permanent set when subjected to the radial compression of the tank wall and acts to absorb the compression so that the earth layer **74** is not itself compressed. Accordingly, formation of the air film **76** is avoided. The quartz sand envelope **48** additionally aids in the conduction of heat energy between the wall of the tank **40** and the adjacent earth. For example, where clay comprises the surrounding earth, the coefficient of heat transfer is on the order of 27 times greater when the quartz sand envelope **48** is provided about the system **18** than the system about which no envelope is provided.

The foregoing ratio assumes a ground temperature of 50°F and a rise in the internal temperature of the system to 180°F. Without the envelope **48**, an air film will be formed about the heat storage system **18** due to expansion of the tanks **36**, **38** and **40**. In a cooling mode, the position of the fluid storage tank and the exchanger tanks is reversed and the fluid storage tank is disposed in a horizontal plane below that of the exchanger tanks.

### Hot and Cold Storage Ground Wells

*R.K. Petersen; U.S. Patent 3,965,972; June 29, 1976* describes an environment heating and cooling system comprising a solar collector, heat storage ground well, cold storage ground well and a heat exchange apparatus. Water from a cold storage ground well is heated in the heat exchange apparatus by solar heating fluid heated in a solar collector. The heated water is stored in a heat storage ground well. Water from the heat storage ground well heats the ambient environment when the solar collector requires supplementation. Water from the cold storage ground well is used to cool the ambient environment. In addition, water from both ground wells serves ordinary household purposes as drinking, bathing and the like.

Referring to the drawing, there is shown in Figure 6.10a a structure **10** capable of receiving solar radiation **11**. The environment control system of the process has a solar heating system shown generally at **12**. Structure **11** has a roof **13** supporting a solar collector **14**. In the northern hemisphere during the summer months, collector **14** is preferably mounted on the roof **13** facing due south or slightly west from due south. At 40° north latitude, the preferred angle of tilt from horizontal is 50°-60°. The solar collector can be a movable solar heat collecting device which can be positioned to take maximum advantage of the sun. The collector **14** comprises a glazing **15** which may be one or more sheets of glass or diathermanous plastic. A collector plate **16**, preferably a selective or dull black surface, is located below glazing **15** for retaining solar energy and transferring heat to a solar heating fluid which is circulated through solar heating system **12**. The solar heating fluid is preferably water with an antifreeze additive such as ethylene glycol. Insulation **18** between collector plate **16** and roof **13** greatly reduces the loss to roof **13** and structure **10**.

The solar heating fluid flows downwardly over the collector plate **16** into a collecting manifold **19**. From collecting manifold **19**, the solar heating fluid proceeds through piping **20A** to heat exchange apparatus **21**, preferably located in the basement **22** of structure **10**. Leaving heat exchange apparatus **21**, the solar heating fluid is returned upwardly through piping **20B** by a pump **23** to a distributing manifold **24** located at the top of the solar collector **14**. Manifold **24** distributes the fluid over collector plate **16** whereby the solar energy elevates the temperature of the fluid. The fluid in system **25** is water. For example, fluid as water in the solar collector **14** is elevated to a temperature of 190° to 200°F on a bright sunny day.

## FIGURE 6.10: HOT AND COLD STORAGE GROUND WELLS

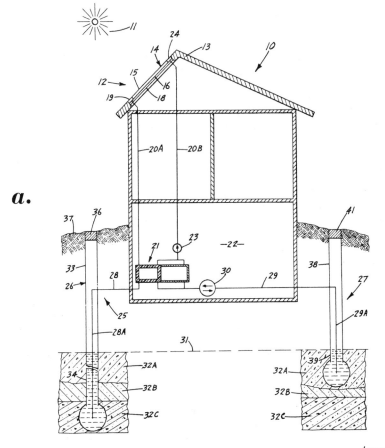

a.

(continued)

FIGURE 6.10: (continued)

**b.**

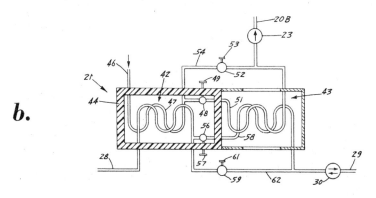

(a)    Vertical sectional view of structure and heating and
       cooling system
(b)    Vertical sectional view of heat exchange apparatus

Source:  U.S. Patent 3,965,972

A fluid supply system indicated generally at **25** interacts with solar heating system **12** through heat exchange apparatus **21**.  A heat storage ground well **26** receives hot water from heat exchange apparatus **21** and stores the hot water in the ground.  The temperature of the hot water introduced into well **26** is preferably 150°-200°F.  This hot water increases the temperature of the water and ground materials in the zone around the lower end of well **26**.

A second cold storage ground well **27** retains water at ground ambient temperature.  The cold water may be used to cool structure **10** or for drinking and the like.  Wells **26** and **27** are preferably constructed at sufficient distance from one another so that any significant heat transfer between them is prevented.  Wells **26** and **27** can also be at different levels.  Hot well **26** is shown as extended down through a sand and gravel layer or aquifer **32A**, a clay layer or aquiclude material **32B** and into a second sand or gravel layer or aquifer **32C**.  Cold well **27** extends into first layer or aquifer **32A**.  In some locations there is only a single aquifer so that both wells **26** and **27** extend into this aquifer.

Other locations may have numerous water bearing earth formations.  The wells **26** and **27** can then be extended into separate aquifers.  When more than one aquifer is present, a single well having tapped or separated openings to separate aquifers can be used for the hot water and cold water.  Separate lines are used in the same well casing to carry the hot water and cold water.  Piping **28** joins hot well **26** and heat exchange apparatus **21**.  A pipe or line **29** joins cold well **27** with heat exchange apparatus **21**.

When water is to be heated, it is drawn from cold ground well **27** through piping **29** by a pump **30**.  Pump **30** can be driven in a reverse direction to move hot water from well **26** to well **27**.  Entering heat exchange apparatus **21**, the ·water receives heat energy from the solar heating fluid after which it proceeds to hot well **26** via pipe **28**, displacing the cooler water already present in hot well **26**. Below the water table represented by line **31**, aquifer **32C** surrounding hot well **26** is gradually heated by conduction of heat from warmer to cooler water and from warmer to cooler soil, by heat transfer from water to the soil, and by convection as warmer water enters the aquifer nearest the well outwardly displacing cooler water. In this manner, a gradual temperature gradient is created in the aquifer **32C** proximate to the lower end of the well **26**. This achieves superior heat retention as compared, for example, to underground water contained within a tank or pipe. Since ground water flow is laminar, there is very little mixing of hot and cold water layers. The hot water displaces the cold water in hot well **26**.

When hot water is needed for space heating, it is drawn by pump **30** from hot well **26** through piping **28** to heat exchange apparatus **21** from which its heat is released to structure **10**. The water is discharged in well **27**. Ground well **26** has a vertically disposed casing or pipe **33** extending from the surface **37** of the ground below the water table **31**. The casing **33** has a lower end **34** located a considerable distance below the water table **31**. The depth of the well can vary in accordance with the characteristics of the earth and water bearing earth materials. The top of casing **33** is closed with a removable plug **36**. Pipe **28** leading from the heat exchange apparatus **21** has an elongated portion **28A** which extends down through casing **33** and terminates at the lower end **34** of the casing.

Cold ground well **27** has a generally upright casing **38** extended into the ground. Casing **38** has a lower end **39** located below the water table **31** so that there is a reservoir of cold water always present adjacent the lower end of casing **38**. Pipe or line **29** has a downwardly directed section **29A** which extends down in casing **38** and terminates at the lower end of casing **38**. Wells **26** and **27** can be the conventional wells wherein a plurality of end-to-end casings are driven into the ground until they reach water bearing rock, gravel, sand or other like earth material.

Figure 6.10b, an enlarged sectional view of heat exchange apparatus **21**, shows a first heat exchanger **42** connected to a second heat exchanger **43**. The interior walls of first heat exchanger **42** are padded with thermal insulation **44** to minimize heat loss to structure **10**. Conversely, second heat exchanger **43** is designed to allow heat flow to and from structure **10** and thus functions as a radiator to heat or cool structure **10** directly or in cooperation with forced air, gravity, fluid circulation or other heat circulation means. For example, heat exchanger **43** can be located in the duct system of a forced air heating arrangement.

The solar heating fluid enters heat exchange apparatus **21** at inlet **46**. Within heat exchange apparatus **21** piping **47** is preferably coiled or otherwise arranged to maximize exchange of heat. Flow of solar heating fluid is directed by valve **48** with valve control means **49** located on primary line **51**. A valve **52** with valve control means **53** is located on bypass line **54**. With valve **48** open and valve **52** closed, the solar heating fluid flows along primary line **51** through second heat exchanger **43**. With valve **48** closed and valve **52** open, the solar heating fluid flows along bypass line **54** avoiding second heat exchanger **43**. Similarly, flow of water through heat exchange apparatus **21** is directed by valve **56** with valve control means **51** located on primary water line **58**. A second valve **59** with valve control means **61** is located on water bypass line **62**. Water is directed to flow through second heat exchanger **43** or to avoid second heat exchanger **43** in the manner of solar heating fluid control explained above. Within heat exchange apparatus **21**, piping **28** is preferably coiled or otherwise arranged to maximize the exchange of heat.

### Liquid Aquifer Storage Method

*W.B. Harris and R.R. Davison; U.S. Patent 3,931,851; January 13, 1976* describe a liquid aquifer energy storage method by which hot water is collected and stored in underground aquifers during the summer months and made available for heating during winter months. The liquid aquifer energy storage method also allows for the storage of cold water during the winter months for use in cooling during the summer months. The liquid aquifer energy storage method includes heating water and hot and warm zones within the aquifer or aquifers for storage of hot and warm water, respectively. Additionally, the method includes cooling water and cold and cool zones in the aquifer or aquifers for storage of cold and cool water.

The term aquifer is used herein in its commonly accepted sense, i.e., a water-bearing bed or stratum of permeable rock, sand, or gravel capable of yielding considerable quantities of water to wells or springs.

Hot water produced by a solar heater or cold water from a cooling pond is pumped into an underground porous formation. The hot or cold water which is pumped into the formation displaces any water whch already exists in the formation until a large hot or cold zone is created. The first time this is done, a significant quantity of heat or cold will be used to change the temperature of the rock formation. In subsequent cycles, the amount of heat or cold lost to the heating or cooling of the surrounding core rock will be reduced significantly. In most instances, the operation of the system will require two zones in the water-bearing formations for both the heating and cooling portions of the system as will be discussed below.

Referring to Figure 6.11a, the operation of the cooling cycle will be considered. During the winter season, cold water is produced in a cooling pond, spray pond, cooling tower, etc. **1**, by contact with the cold air as well as by nocturnal radiation. As the cold water is produced, it is pumped into the cold zone **2** through a pipeline **3**. In the summer, as cooling is required, the cold water is withdrawn and distributed to the houses and buildings **4** in pipelines **5**, much as city water is delivered, except that the pipelines **5** are insulated for protection from heat gain. Within the buildings **4**, the cold water flows through suitable heat exchangers (as may be selected by those skilled in the art) so that the building air is cooled and the water is warmed.

If the water is warmed to a temperature which is still below the normal formation temperature, it may be delivered to the cool zone **6** for storage by means of pipelines **7**. When the temperature of the water is being lowered during the winter, the water may be withdrawn from the cool zone **6**, pumped to the chilling area, pond, etc. **1**, by means of pipeline **8** and finally pumped into the cold zone **2**. In this process, no net amount of water is withdrawn from the formation except for that which is evaporated during winter cooling. Even if the water is salty, or otherwise contaminated, it may be used since all of the water is returned to the formation.

## FIGURE 6.11: LIQUID AQUIFER STORAGE METHOD

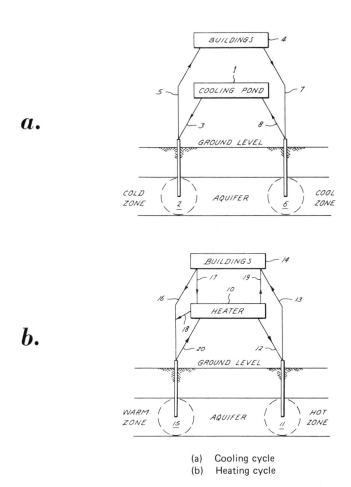

a.

b.

(a)    Cooling cycle
(b)    Heating cycle

Source:   U.S. Patent 3,931,851

The hot water system, as shown in Figure 6.11b, is similar in operation to the
cold water system.  The hot and cold water may be distributed to the houses
and buildings by either the same or parallel water distribution systems.

During the summer, hot water is produced by a solar heater **10** and pumped into
the hot zone **11** of an aquifer by means of a pipeline **12**.  It is withdrawn in the
winter and circulated through pipes **13** to buildings and houses **14** in which it
is sent through a suitable heat exchange device for heat exchange with air of the
building or house **14** and the water itself is cooled.  The resulting warm water
is returned to the warm zone **15** by means of pipeline **16**, or if solar conditions
are good, the warm water may be sent to the heater **10** by means of pipeline **17**
for partially reheating before being returned to the warm zone **15** by means of

pipeline **18**. On sunny days, the water might be sufficiently reheated to recycle directly by piping **19** to the buildings **14** rather than using stored hot water. During the summer, the water in the warm zone **15** is sent, by means of pipe-line **20**, to the heater **10** for reheating and then is pumped into the hot zone **11**. As in the case of the cooling system, no net withdrawal of water results in the heating system except for that which may be evaporated during summer heating.

While the process is suitable for a single dwelling, its cost factors are such that it can readily be adapted for large scale use.

# HEATING AND COOLING SYSTEMS

## LIQUID CIRCULATION SYSTEMS

### Reciprocating Piston Heat Engine

*J.D. Ruff and P.R. Wheeler; U.S. Patent 4,018,581; April 19, 1977* describes a heating system using heat derived from solar collectors to operate a reciprocating piston heat engine which provides operating power to drive a heat pump, and with additional capability to operate as a heat pump with electric motor drive, and with separate inlet valves for heat engine and heat pump operation.

*Heating with Solar Powered Engine:* Figure 7.1 shows solar collector panel **1** through which pump **2** causes water (or any other suitable liquid) to flow. This water is heated by solar radiation as it flows through the panel, and water heated in this manner flows through pipe **3** to provide heating of boiler **4**. Return water flows through pipe **5** back to pump **2**.

Boiler **4** is thus maintained at a temperature high enough to provide pressure for heat engine operation. This temperature can be above 200°F (with high solar output) for high engine output. But at temperatures as low as 100°F (with poor solar output) some useful engine output can still be maintained. For a working medium, a quantity of liquid refrigerant (typically Freon 12) is maintained in boiler **4**. When this refrigerant boils in boiler **4**, refrigerant vapor at pressure travels through boiler pipe **6**, through primary inlet valve **7**, to exert pressure on the underside of piston **8**, which moves in cylinder **9**.

The topside of piston **8** is exposed to the pressure existing in crankcase enclosure **10**, which is connected by equalizer pipe **11** to suction line **12**, which connects to evaporator **13**, in which the pressure is less than the pressure in boiler **4**. Then, since the top side pressure on piston **8** is less than the underside pressure, it will tend to move upward in cylinder **9** in a power stroke. Piston **8** is connected by rod **14** to crankshaft **15** which is caused to rotate by the power stroke. Flywheel **16** maintains momentum, and after top dead center, piston **8** goes downward in an exhaust stroke and pushes vapor through exhaust (discharge)

327

valve **17**, through discharge pipe **18** to condenser **19** which is cooled by a flow of inside air, which is generally at a temperature around 72°F. The temperature of condenser **19** is thus maintained lower than the temperature of boiler **4**, so the condensing pressure is thus always lower than the pressure in boiler **4**. Consequently the power produced in the power stroke is greater than the power absorbed by the exhaust stroke.

Thus the power and exhaust strokes are repeated in a continuous cycle, and rotation of crankshaft **15** continues as power is developed in a heat engine function. Valves **7** and **17** are controlled by cams **20, 21** so that primary inlet valve **7** is only open during the power stroke, and exhaust (discharge) valve **17** is only open during the exhaust stroke. Secondary inlet valve **22** is a poppet valve with valve spring **23**. Since the pressure in cylinder **9** is greater than the pressure in suction line **12** (during engine operation) valve **22** remains closed. Refrigerant vapor condenses in condenser **19** and the liquid (refrigerant) drains into receiver **24**, then through line **25** to injector pump **26**, which injects liquid into boiler **4**. The injector pump is a reciprocating pump activated by cam **27** on crankshaft **15**, but could alternately be a gear pump or any other suitable type of pump.

FIGURE 7.1:  RECIPROCATING PISTON HEAT ENGINE

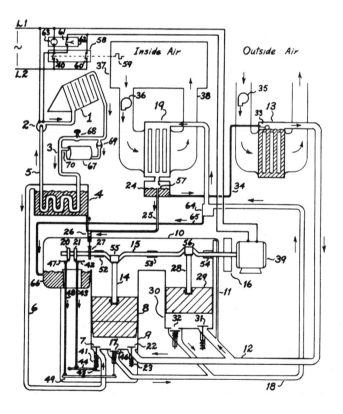

Source:  U.S. Patent 4,018,581

Crankshaft **15** through rod **28** actuates compressor piston **29** in cylinder **30**. Piston **29** draws vapor on its upward (suction) strokes through inlet valve **31**, through suction line **12** from evaporator **13**. On downward (compression) strokes piston **29** forces the vapor through discharge valve **32** into discharge pipe **18**, where it mixes with vapor discharged from cylinder **9** through exhaust (discharge) valve **17**. This vapor mixture travels to condenser **19**, to condense and furnish heat, to heat the inside air. Evaporator **13** is of the flooded type and float valve **33** maintains the liquid level by supplying liquid refrigerant through liquid line **34** from receiver **24**.

Circulating fan **35** pulls air from the outside heat sink and this outside air is passed through evaporator **13** and provides heat of vaporization. Evaporator **13** is thus maintained at a temperature close to (but a little below) outside ambient. Air then flows from evaporator **13** back to the outside heat sink. Circulating fan **36** pulls inside air from within the heated space **37** and moves it through condenser **19** where it picks up heat and is then discharged through duct **38** to provide heating of space **37**. Motor **39** is coupled to crankshaft **15**, and any time that heat engine operation is to be commenced (after having been stopped), motor **39** is energized (when thermostat switch points **40** are closed).

This causes motor **39** to rotate shaft **15**, and rotation of the heat engine is commenced. After rotation is commenced, motor **39** can be deenergized and the rotor of motor **39** continues to turn during heat engine operation, though the motor is deenergized. Automatic control of stopping and starting of motor **39** is shown later.

Primary inlet valve **7** is a poppet valve with valve spring **41** tending to pull it closed. Pressure in boiler pipe **6**, greater than the pressure in cylinder **9**, pushes valve **7** open against the pressure of valve spring **41**, thus admitting high pressure vapor from boiler pipe **6** into cylinder **9** for the (upward) power strokes of the heat engine. But during the (downward) exhaust strokes, valve **7** must be kept closed; so during these (downward) exhaust strokes, cam **21** pushes downward on cam follower **42**, which pushes on push-rod **43**, which pushes on rocker **44**, which applies pressure to flange **45** on the stem of primary inlet valve **7** to hold it closed. During the (upward) power strokes cam **21** does not exert pressure to keep valve **7** closed, but valve **7** is allowed to open under the influence of pressure in boiler pipe **6**.

Exhaust (discharge) valve **17** tends to remain closed under the pressure of valve spring **46**. But during the (downward) exhaust strokes, with primary inlet valve **7** being kept closed by pressure from cam **21** (as already described), piston **8** generates pressure in cylinder **9** greater than the pressure in discharge pipe **18**. This pressure pushes exhaust (discharge) valve **17** open and the vapor in cylinder **9** is thus exhausted into discharge pipe **18** during these (downward) exhaust strokes of heat engine operation. But during the (upward) power strokes, valve **17** must be kept closed to prevent incoming vapor escaping directly into discharge pipe **18**; so during the (upward) power strokes, cam **20** pushes downward on cam follower **47**, which pushes on pushrod **48**, which pushes on rocker **49**, which applies pressure to the stem of valve **17** to hold it closed. During the (downward) exhaust strokes cam **20** does not exert pressure to keep valve **17** closed, but valve **17** is allowed to open under the influence of pressure in cylinder **9**.

The operation of the system, as described above, provides the advantage that with all the heat originating in solar collector panel **1** being dispersed through condenser **19**, additional heat absorbed from the outside heat sink (in evaporator **33**) is dispersed also through condenser **19** in the function of a heat pump. This additional heat is considerable and in conditions of mild outside temperature more than 100% increase in heat output is obtained.

*Controls:* Control of the system is achieved by two stage thermostat **58** with sensing element **59** located in space **37**. Typical settings for thermostat **58** are for first stage points **40** to close on drop of temperature at 72°F and open on rise at 73°F; and for second stage points **60** to close on drop at 71°F and open on rise at 72°F.

*Operation* — With space temperature above 73°F, points **40** and **60** are open and electric power for **L2** does not reach pump **2** or motor **39**, so the system does not function. When temperature in space **37** drops to 72°F, first stage points **40** close and pump **2** is energized. Also current flows through the normally closed points **61** of timer **62** to energize motor **39**. Conductor **L1** is connected permanently to pump **2** and motor **39** to complete the electrical circuit. As hot water is pumped through boiler **4**, vapor pressure is generated, and with motor **39** causing starting rotation of crankshaft **15**, heat engine operation is commenced. At the time when points **40** closed, coil **63** of timer **62** also was energized. After a preset time (typically 2 min) timer points **61** open and motor **39** is deenergized, but with heat being supplied to boiler **4**, heat engine operation continues.

When temperature in space **37** rises to 73°F thermostat **58** is satisfied, and points **40** open. Pump **2** is deenergized and with no hot water going to boiler **4**, heat engine operation stops.

*Heat Pump Operation:* At times the water pumped through boiler **4** is not hot enough to provide sufficient heat and pressure in boiler **4**, to provide sufficient heating of space **37**. This occurs during cloudy weather, at night, or in very cold weather. Temperature then drops in space **37**. At 71°F, second stage points **60** close and motor **39** is energized continually and drives crankshaft **15** to actuate piston **29** in cylinder **30**, to draw vapor from evaporator **13** and compress it into condenser **19** in the heat pump function already described.

In addition, with crankshaft **15** actuating piston **8** in cylinder **9**, vapor flows from boiler **4** through primary inlet valve **7**, into cylinder **9**, during upward strokes, and out through exhaust (discharge) valve **17**, during downward strokes to condense in condenser **19** and add to the heating output. This continuous energization of motor **39** is often employed at times when the solar heated water flowing from pipe **3** into boiler **4** is still warmer than condenser **19**.

In this case some heat engine power is developed at piston **8**, and this power assists motor **39**. When the water temperature deteriorates to a temperature below that of condenser **19**, piston **8** derives power from crankshaft **15** and functions as a heat pump compressor, drawing vapor (during upward strokes) through primary inlet valve **7**, from boiler **4** (which acts as an evaporator heat source). Piston **8** compresses the vapor (during downward strokes) and discharges it through exhaust (discharge) valve **17**, into discharge pipe **18** to condense in condenser **19** and add to the system heating output, thus functioning as a solar heat pump.

At times when motor **39** is energized continuously and there is no solar heating output from collector panel **1**, (such as at night or overcast days) the temperature of the water flowing through boiler **4** drops below the temperature of the outside heat sink. Then the pressure in boiler pipe **6** is lower than the pressure in suction line **12**. So, as piston **8** starts to rise on upward strokes (after bottom dead center), secondary inlet valve **22** opens to admit vapor from suction line **12**, and primary inlet valve **7** does not open (since there is insufficient pressure in boiler pipe **6**).

Operating in this manner pistons **8** and **29** are both drawing vapor from evaporator **13**, through suction line **12**, through secondary inlet valve **22**, and inlet valve **31** respectively, during their upward strokes; compressing this vapor during their downward strokes, and discharging it through exhaust (discharge) valve **17** and discharge valve **32**, through discharge pipe **18** to condense in condenser **19**. This function is as an electrically driven air to air heat pump, with the outside heat sink furnishing heat to evaporator **13**, with motor **39** driving pistons **8** and **29** to compress vapor drawn from evaporator **13**, and discharge it into condenser **19**, which heats circulated air, to heat space **37**.

When the temperature in space **37** rises (due to the heating effect) second stage points **60** in thermostat **58** open and motor **39** is deenergized and system operation stops. Should solar output have resumed while second stage points **60** were closed, pressure would build up again in boiler **4**, and then when second stage points **60** open, the heat engine operation would continue until either first stage points **40** open to shut the system down, or second stage points **60** close again to energize motor **39**.

The function of primary inlet valve **7** and exhaust (discharge) valve **17** is similar in heat engine and heat pump operation, in that during both types of operation primary inlet valve **7** is open only during upward strokes of piston **8**, and exhaust (discharge) valve **17** is open only during downward strokes of piston **8**. These valves open (against their respective valve springs) only under the influence of pressure, and for this reason primary inlet valve **7** does not open at all when the pressure in boiler pipe **6** is less than the pressure in suction line **12**. In this case secondary inlet valve **22** is the operating inlet valve. Conversely, when the pressure in boiler pipe **6** is greater than the pressure in suction line **12**, secondary inlet valve **22** does not open and primary inlet valve **7** is the operating inlet valve.

In related work by *J.D. Ruff and P.R. Wheeler; U.S. Patent 3,960,322; June 1, 1976* the system can be used for cooling by switching the flow of outside air to the system condenser and passing inside air over the evaporator.

### Combination Heat Pump and Low Temperature Collector

*H.B. Ramey; U.S. Patent 4,005,583; February 1, 1977* describes a combination heat pump and low temperature solar heat collector which includes a compressor and lines having a restrictor for forming vapor and condensate sections. The collector comprises containers for liquid, which may be water, mixed with substances for lowering the freezing point and for darkening the liquid or for influencing the heat conductivity. The heat pump has a reversing valve to convert the evaporator tubes, winter setting, to condenser tubes, summer setting. Solar radiation or ambient air restores heat to the cooled water.

FIGURE 7.2: COMBINATION HEAT PUMP AND LOW TEMPERATURE
COLLECTOR

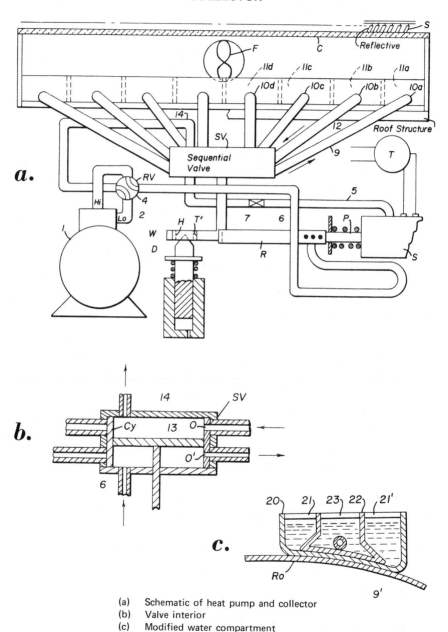

(a)    Schematic of heat pump and collector
(b)    Valve interior
(c)    Modified water compartment

Source:  U.S. Patent 4,005,583

Figure 7.2 shows a compressor **1** having a low pressure line **2** and a high pressure line.  Reversing valve **4** is shown in the position used in cold weather.  High pressure refrigerant fluid flows through valve **4** (also marked **RV**) to coil **5**, to line **6**, through restrictor **7**, into the distributor valve and out into line **9** to an outside tube functioning as evaporator tubes.  The refrigerant fluid evaporates in the tubes, cooling, and/or freezing the water in compartments **11a** and **11b**.  The refrigerant is then returned through line **12** to the valve cavity above divider **13**, Figure 7.2b.  Line **14** leads to the low pressure side of compressor **1**.

After an appropriate period of time, timer **T** operates the electrical device **S** which moves plunger **P** to the right causing spring ratchet **R** to move ratchet wheel **W**.  The ratchet engages teeth **T**, and a reciprocating motion of the plunger revolves the ratchet wheel.  Spring pressed detent **D** is received in hole **4** to position a rotary cylinder **Cy** so that its openings **O** and **O'** register with the inlets or outlets of appropriate tubes leading to the water compartments.

After the timer **T** has caused the valve **SV** to sequentially supply all the tubes with vaporized refrigerant fluid, it will again supply tubes **10a** and **10b**.  Meanwhile, the compartments previously cooled have been warmed by solar radiation passing through the transparent cover **C**.  The heat restored to the water in compartments **10a** and **10b** is available for transfer by the heat pump to coil **5** for space heating purposes.  When compartments **11a** and **11b** contain ice, heat transfer from tubes **11a** and **11b** to the ice is slow.  Therefore, to provide for heating during sub-freezing weather, salt or some other antifreeze must be added to the water to keep it in the liquid state.  If the temperature is low and the sun is not shining, the low temperature brine or ice can, nevertheless, be warmed by air furnished by fan **F**.

In colder climates each compartment **11** may be divided into smaller channels, as shown in Figure 7.2c.  Channel member **22** divides the space inside channel member **20** into channels **21, 21'** and **23**.  Channel **23** contains water having its freezing point low enough so that ice will freeze in channels **21** and **21'** before it freezes in channel **23**.  In extremely cold weather ice may remain in channel **21** and channel **21'** most of the time, the water in channel **23** freezing periodically.  When no sunshine falls on the water compartments, air may be forced over the ice or water to restore the heat taken out by the evaporator tubes.

It should be noted that while the ice is being frozen the temperature remains constant.  Consequently, the temperature difference between the evaporator tubes and the freezing liquid remains constant until all the heat of fusion has been removed.  The low temperature solar collector formed by the water compartment walls, which may be blackened, and the water, which may contain a colored suspension, restores heat to the ice without creating an unfavorable temperature gradient across transparent cover **C**.

In warm weather the valve **4** may be turned to reverse the flow of refrigerant so that the tubes **10** become condensers, giving up heat to the water which cools itself by evaporation and, at night, radiation from the compartment bottoms and walls to the atmosphere and to space will also remove heat and form a sink into which heat can be transferred from the inside to the outside of the enclosure by the heat pump.  Shutters S may be provided as a sun shield and may be formed of reflecting material to direct sunlight into the water compartments.

Figure 7.2c shows the tray resting on an arched member **Ro** which could be the roof of a trailer type dwelling.

### Plate Absorber Freezes or Heats Water Sheet

*H.B. Ramey; U.S. Patent 3,991,938; November 16, 1976* describes a combination heat pump and solar heat absorber which includes an outside conduit acting as an evaporator and heat absorber in cold weather and as a condenser and heat dissipator in warm weather. The heat absorber is exposed to the sun, and a spray device enables the heat absorber to freeze a sheet of ice and further cool the ice so that ice also absorbs heat from the atmosphere and is then melted by the sun's rays. The melted material is further heated and returned to the inside of the house to the condenser of the heat pump and is heated thereby and used as a heat exchange fluid for home heating.

Figure 7.3 shows a house having rafters **1**, sheathing, and shingles **3**. The usual gutter is shown at **4**. The building may have a brick wall **5** and studding **6**. The heat pump includes a compressor **10** having a high pressure line **11** and a low pressure line **12**, these lines being connected to a reversing valve **13** having passageways **13a** and **13b**. The valve, as shown, is set for the heating cycle and allows the refrigerant fluid to enter the condenser **18** and to leave the condenser by line **28** which leads to a flow restrictor **44** and on to an evaporator tube **35** having a return line **17**. Tubes **35** and **17** are soldered or welded to a plate **7** which is shown in section and which runs along the crest of the house.

### FIGURE 7.3: PLATE ABSORBER FREEZES OR HEATS WATER SHEET

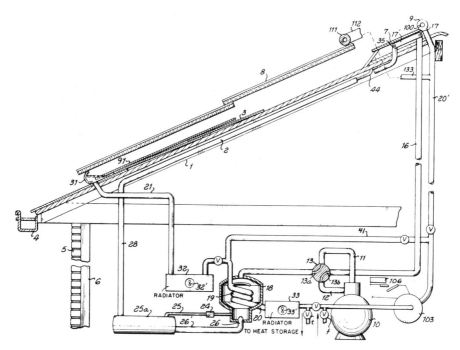

Source: U.S. Patent 3,991,938

The plate is exposed to the ambient atmosphere and to the rays of the sun. A transparent cover shown at **8** transmits solar radiation to the shingles **3** and to the materials falling from the plate **7**. A water spray tube **9** having apertures **100** emits water onto plate **7**.

The water freezes losing heat to plate **7** which is cooled by tubes **35** and **17**. At certain intervals the valve **13**, which may be conventionally controlled, reverses, heating plate **7**, and the ice on the plate then slides onto the shingles **3** to be melted by the sun's rays, and the resulting water is further heated and delivered to gutter **31** and line **21** through a house heating radiator **32** having an air circulator **32'** and to condenser coils **19**. The radiator reduces the temperature of the water to near room temperature and thus prepares it for its function in condenser **18** where tubes **19** aid in condensing the refrigerant and picks up heat from the condensing refrigerant fluid and delivers the heat to an additional radiator **33** having an air circulator **33'**. The cooled water is then returned by pump **103** and line **20'** to the spray tube **9**.

During dark days the water circulator may be short circuited through line **44** and the plate **7** used to absorb heat in the manner known to those familiar with the conventional heat pump. In case of snow, the defrosting cycle will remove the accumulation periodically. It should be noted that the plate **7** is reduced to extremely low temperatures and absorbs heat from the surrounding air. Additionally on sunny days the plate transduces radiant energy to sensible heat. The ice and water on the roof also absorb heat recoverable in the condenser **18**.

Materials may be added to the water to reduce its freezing point and/or increase its heat conductivity. However, if the material added is lamp black or the like, some source of high pressure water other than line **20'** should supply nozzle **111**, and an additional cover **91** should be placed over shingles **3**.

### Modular Building with Tubular Frame

A building construction is disclosed by *R.E. Diggs; U.S. Patent 4,000,850; Jan. 4, 1977* wherein a prefabricated, tubular frame is used through which liquid is circulated to heat and/or cool the building, and in which a plurality of rigid, insulated, prefabricated panels are secured to the frame on the roof and walls thereof to form the building, and with solar panels supported on top of the roof through which a heat exchange fluid is circulated to absorb solar energy and then used to obtain the desired temperature in the fluid circulated through the frame of the building.

With reference to Figure 7.4, a building is indicated generally at **B** which comprises a frame **F** having substantially vertically extending wall columns **10** and inclined roof beams **11** connected to and supported on the upper ends of the columns **10**. A plurality of substantially identical wall panels **W** are secured to the columns **10** to form the walls of the building, and a plurality of substantially identical roof panels **R** are supported on the roof beams **11** to form the roof of the building. Further, a plurality of solar panels **P** are supported on the roof panels for absorbing solar energy to heat a fluid heat exchange medium for use as desired.

A first fluid circulating system **12** is connected with the frame **F** of the building for circulating a heat exchange fluid therethrough to either heat or cool the building as desired, and a second fluid circulating system **13** is connected with the solar panels **P** to collect and circulate a heated fluid medium to a means for conversion of the heat energy into a desired form, as for example, to heat or cool the fluid circulated through the frame **F**.

In order to simplify construction of the building, and in order to reduce the cost thereof, the wall columns **10** and roof beams **11** are substantially identical in construction, with the columns and beams being made in standard, predetermined lengths, as desired, for construction of buildings or portions of buildings of different size.

The primary fluid flow system **12** includes the tubular columns **10** and roof beams **11** and the eaves connectors **29** and beam connectors **22** and pipes **32**. Further, the first fluid flow system includes an elongate header pipe **33** embedded in the floor of the building, as for example, in the concrete slab **20** or the like, and running the length of the building. A plurality of substantially equally spaced apart pipes **34** are connected with the header pipe **33** and extend outwardly to the bottom ends of the columns **10**, and are connected with the columns through pipe fittings or elbows, which project upwardly from the floor **20** and into the sides of the channels of the columns.

A substantially vertically extending fluid return pipe **36** is connected with the pipes **32** and extends downwardly from the peak or ridge of the building to adjacent the floor thereof, and is connected at its lower end with a pair of outwardly extending branch return pipes **37** and **38**, which are in turn joined through elbows with a pair of longitudinally extending return pipes **39** and **40** at opposite sides of the building, which extend to a fluid reservoir **41**.

### FIGURE 7.4: MODULAR BUILDING WITH TUBULAR FRAME

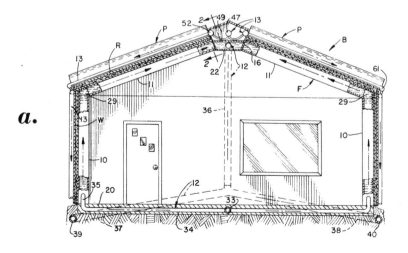

*a.*

(continued)

FIGURE 7.4: (continued)

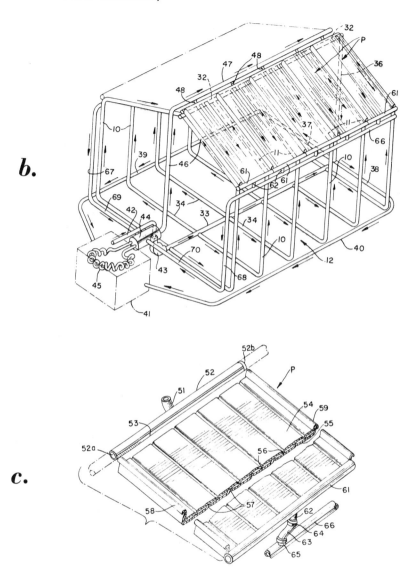

*b.*

*c.*

(a)   Transverse, sectional view of building
(b)   Schematic, perspective view of fluid systems of
        building
(c)   Enlarged, perspective view of solar panel

Source:  U.S. Patent 4,000,850

Fluid is supplied to the first fluid circulating system through an inlet pipe **42**
connected with the fluid reservoir **41** near the upper end thereof, and connected
with the inlet of a circulating pump **43**. The header pipe **33** is connected with
the outlet of pump **43**, whereby upon operation of the pump, fluid from the
reservoir **41** is caused to circulate through header pipe **33** and outwardly through
the supply pipes **34** to the columns **10**, and then upwardly through the columns
and roof beams **11** to the beam connectors **22** and pipes **32** and then downwardly through return pipes **36, 37, 38, 39** and **40** back to the reservoir **41**.

The fluid circulated through the first fluid circulating system may be heated or
cooled as desired to maintain a desired temperature in the building by means
utilizing the energy developed through use of the solar panels **P**. This means
includes a heat pump **44** having a heat exchange coil **45** associated therewith,
with the heat exchange coil disposed in the fluid in fluid reservoir **41** to effect
the desired temperature change thereof. The heat pump and coil are part of
the second fluid circulating system, including the solar panels and the heat pump
is connected with an outlet riser or supply pipe **46** extending upwardly to a
supply header pipe **47** extending along the peak or ridge of the building above
the beam connectors **22**, and having a plurality of outlet bosses **48** thereon corresponding with the approximate center location of respective adjacent solar
panels.

Short lengths of Teflon hose or other suitable flexible fluid conduit means **49**
are secured at one of their ends to the bosses **48** by means of hose clamps and
are similarly secured at their other ends to bosses **51** on supply manifold pipes
**52** connected with the upper ends of the panels **P**.

As seen best in Figure 7.4c, the manifold pipes **52** have elongate slots **53** extending along the side thereof opposite the bosses **51**, and the panels **P** are
welded to the slot. The opposite ends of the pipes **52** may be closed with caps
**52a** and **52b**, if desired.

As seen in Figure 7.4c, the panels **P** each comprise an upper sheet **54** of aluminum
or other suitable material, and a lower sheet **55** of aluminum or other suitable
material. The top sheet or panel **54** has a plurality of elongate, substantially
parallel ribs or protrusions **56** formed therein, and the bottom sheet or panel **55**
has a plurality of similar ribs or protrusions **57** formed therein, such that when
the sheets or panels are assembled, the ribs of the respective sheets engage the
opposite sheet to hold the sheets or panels in spaced apart relationship to define
a fluid flow passage or plurality of parallel fluid flow passages between the top
and bottom sheets or panels.

In a typical embodiment, the ribs have a depth of approximately $3/16$ of an inch.
The sheets or panels **54** and **55** may be formed at high speed on a roll mill or
the like, if desired. Further, the upper panel **54** is coated with a special black
finish (Olin Co.) which absorbs almost 97% of the solar energy striking the panel.

### Multiple Heat Pump System

The process of *M. Meckler; U.S. Patent 3,996,759; December 14, 1976* relates
to a hydronic heat pump and air conditioning system assisted by the environment in which it operates. Referring to Figure 7.5a, water source heat pumps
**A** are employed that operate with a water source of determined heat range such
as, for example, 55° to 90°F.

FIGURE 7.5: MULTIPLE HEAT PUMP SYSTEM

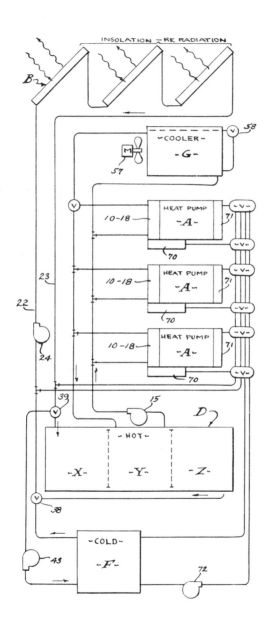

(continued)

FIGURE 7.5:  (continued)

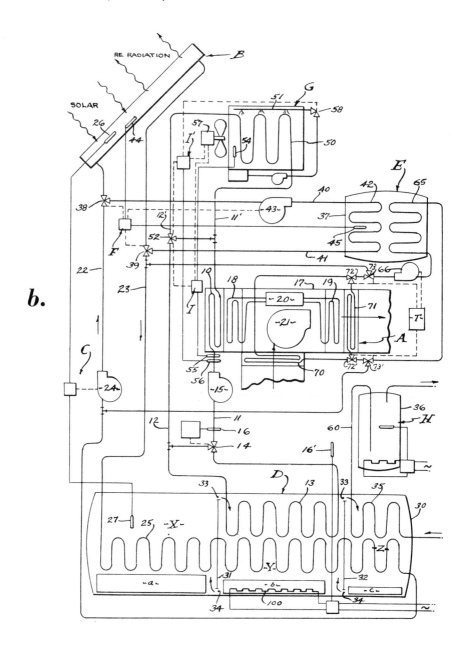

b.

(a)     Block diagram of system
(b)     Detailed diagram of system

Source:   U.S. Patent 3,996,759

Heat exchange means **B** is employed, preferably in the form of solar heat collectors, which may vary widely in form and construction, and which are primarily operative to collect heat energy into liquid or water up to 250°F, more or less; and differential control means **C** is provided to circulate solar heated water therethrough when it is at a higher temperature than the thermal mass to be increased in temperature thereby.

A first stratified thermal mass **D** is provided in the form of a compartmented reservoir comprised of a high heat range section **X** associated with the heat exchange means **B**, a moderate heat section **Y** associated with the water source heat pump or pumps **A**, and a low heat range section **Z** associated with auxiliary needs such as to apply residual heat to preheating of domestic hot water. A second thermal mass **E** is provided in the form of a cold reservoir; and differential control means **F** is provided to circulate cooled water therethrough when it is at a lower temperature than the thermal mass to be decreased in temperature thereby.

A heat absorption means **G** is provided for applying and/or removing heat from the heat pump water source circuit, and a residual heat transfer means **H** is provided for preheating the domestic hot water supply.

As shown in Figure 7.5b, the heating pump **A** is of the water source type that requires a supply of 55° to 90°F liquid, preferably water, to and from which heat is transferred by a refrigerant to source water heat exchanger coil **10** at the heat pump. The coil is a closed loop water source circuit comprised of a delivery line **11** and a return line **12** extending from a heat exchanging coil **13** immersed in the moderate heat range section **Y** of the thermal mass **D**. The thermal mass temperature in section **Y** is, at most times, expected to be in excess of the maximum 90°F of the water source, and to this end a proportioning valve **14** is provided in the delivery line through which the source water is circulated by means of a pump **15**, the valve being controlled by a temperature responsive means **16** in the line.

The heat pump **A** is comprised, generally, of a housing **17** in which reversely operable heat exchanger coils **18** and **19** operate as evaporator and condenser elements of a mechanical refrigeration system which includes a compressor unit **20** with flow directive means and expansion valve means to condition the same for heating or cooling as may be required. That is, the flow directive means operates in the refrigeration mode by expanding refrigerant into the coil **19** as an evaporator in which case the coil **18** acts as a condenser. Conversely, in the heating mode the evaporation takes place in coil **18** while condensing takes place in coil **19**.

The heat exchange means **B** is shown primarily as a solar heat collecting panel that collects solar heat energy by insolation into a closed loop heat transfer circuit comprised of a delivery line **22** and a return line **23** extending from a heat exchanging coil **25** immersed coextensively throughout the high to low heat range sections **X**, **Y**, and **Z**.

The means **B** is primarily for the absorption of solar heat by means of insolation, and they are secondarily for the dissipation of heat by means of terrestrial reradiation as will later be described. The collector or collectors of means **B** are associated with the stratified thermal mass, the temperature in section **X** expected to be at a lower temperature than the collectors per se through which heat

transfer liquid or water, preferably water-glycol solution, is circulated by a pump
24 through the lines 22 and 23, the pump being operated by a differential control means C with temperature responsive means 26 and 27 at the means B and
thermal mass D respectively. The control means C is set so that the pump 24
is operated only when the collector temperature is greater than the thermal mass
temperature within section X thereof.

The stratified thermal mass D is provided to distribute heat throughout the
several sections X, Y, and Z and to separate higher temperature thermal mass
from lower temperature thermal mass, according to the requirements of heat
pump operation, the residual heat above ambient being used for auxiliary needs
such as to preheat a domestic hot water storage heater.

As shown, there are three sections in a liquid storage tank 30 having vertically
disposed partitions 31 and 32 separating the tank into a high heat range section
X, a moderate heat range section Y and a low heat range section Z. In Figures
7.5a and 7.5b, the tank 30 is horizontally disposed and filled with a liquid mass
such as water, in which case the partitions are provided with upper and lower
liquid or water transfer ports 33 and 34 for the convection flow or thermal
syphon effect of heated and/or cooling waters from one compartmented section
to the other.

Thus, cooler waters from section Y will enter into section X through lower ports
34 while hotter waters discharge from section X into section Y through the
upper ports 33, and independently, cooler water from section Z will enter into
section Y through lower ports 34 while hotter waters discharge from section Y
into section Z through the upper ports 33. In carrying out this process, and in
practice, a normal operational temperature range for section X is 70° to 190°F,
for section Y is 70° to 120°F, and for section Z is 70° to 100°F; however, it is
to be understood that these temperature ranges will vary greatly dependent upon
the availability of solar heat, and the use to which the system is put.

Should there be insufficient heat captured by solar insolation and/or from ambient surroundings, an immersion electric heater 100, or any suitable available
auxiliary heat source, is thermally conductive with the thermal mass (and mass
b later described) so that if for any reason temperature sensed at sensor 16 (and
with sensor 16' in outside air below a predetermined setting) falls below 55°F
at any time, heater 100 will be activated to maintain this temperature level.

Immersed in the low heat range section Z is a heat exchanging coil 35 comprising the residual heat transferring means H conducting domestic water from a
public utility water supply or the like and to a domestic water storage heater
36. Alternately, the compartmented separation can be effected by a vertical
disposition of the tank 30, with or without the partitions 31 and 32, and wherein the hottest liquid or water rises upwardly toward the top portion of the tank
by means of the convection flow or thermal syphon effect.

The coextensive heating coil 25 is complementary to the aforesaid heat range
stratification, having its hottest portion within section X, its moderate heat portion within section Y, and its low heat portion within section Z, all of which
advantageously employs the maximum temperature differential available within
the thermal mass D. It will be apparent, therefore, that there is a high heat
range, a moderate heat range and a low heat range portion of the thermal mass

that is stored in the tank **30**, and each associated with heat transfer coils **25**, **13**, and **35**, respectively, that induce the aforesaid heat range differentiations by their induction, conduction and dissipation of heat. As is indicated, supplementary masses **a**, **b** and **c**, are installed residually in each of the sections **X**, **Y** and **Z** respectively, and each communicatively capable of holding heat according to the section in which it resides, such as solid insoluble material of selectively high heat retaining capabilities.

The second thermal mass **E** is provided to separate a lower temperature thermal mass according to the dissipation availability with respect to terrestrial reradiation and the like. In other words, the thermal mass **E** is a cold reservoir from which heat energy is removed. Accordingly, the mass **E** advantageously utilizes the aforesaid heat exchange means **B** which is secondarily a dissipator of heat by means of terrestrial reradiation, since the outside environment is at nighttimes often lower than the thermal mass temperature in the reservoir of means **E**. To these ends, the means **E** involves a liquid storage tank **37** filled with a liquid mass such as water, preferably the same water-glycol solution that is circulated through the collector **B**, to be stored at low temperatures below 70°F.

The thermal mass **E** is associated with the stratified thermal mass **D** through the aforementioned delivery and return lines **22** and **23** that are tapped by diverting valves **38** and **39** which alternately direct the collector flow through delivery and return lines **40** and **41** and through heat exchanging coils **42** within the tank **37**. The pump **43** is operable to circulate the low temperature water when required as controlled by a differential control means **F** with temperature responsive means **44** and **45** at the collector and thermal mass **E** respectively.

The control means **F** is set so that the pump **43** is operated thereby only when the collector temperature is less than the thermal mass temperature within the tank **37** up to some predetermined minimum temperature to be maintained at all times in tank **37**. A heat exchanging coil **65** is immersed in the tank **37** of thermal mass **E**, and through which liquid heat transfer media is circulated by a pump **66** on demand of any one of the water source heat pump units and responsive to the thermostat **T** controlling the same in each instance.

The heat absorption means **G** is a heat exchanging device comprised principally of heat exchanging coils **50**, installed out of doors, and operable either to dissipate or to absorb heat. To this end the coils **50** suffice for operation of means **G** in a heat mode, and evaporation means **51** is combined with the coils for operation of the means **G** in a cool mode.

It is significant that the heat absorption means **G** is associated with the stratified thermal mass **D** through the aforementioned delivery and return lines **11** and **12** that are tapped by a diverting valve **52** which alternately directs the flow of lines **11** and **12** through the coil **50**. The pump **15** is operable to circulate the water as required. The heat mode is put into effect, by turning on a fan **57**, for example, when the water sources temperature is near or below the minimum 55°F and the outside air is of higher temperature, by a differential control means **I** with temperature responsive means **54** and **55** at the outside air and in the water source loop respectively. The cool mode is put into effect by opening a valve **58**, for example, when the water source temperature is near or above the maximum 90°F, by a control means **I'** with temperature responsive means **56** in the water source loop. Operation of either the heat or cool mode actuates the valve

**52** to extend the water source loop through lines **11'** and **12'** and through the coil **50**, and simultaneously to energize the motor **57** of an air circulating fan. During operation of the cool mode actuation of a water valve **58** may be required to apply moisture over the coil **50** and achieve additional capacity by means of evaporative cooling. The evaporative cooling and heat absorption means **G** is, therefore, a two-way or dual purpose means that tempers the closed loop water source by extending the same for heating or cooling as circumstances require.

The heat pump **A** is assisted in each instance in both the heating mode and the cooling mode, as determined by a multirange thermostat **T**. The thermostat **T** is temperature responsive within a zone to be air conditioned and controls assistance from either the heat exchange means **B** or the cold thermal mass **E**, by directing hot and cold fluid selectively through heat exchanging coils **70** and **71** at the return inlet and useful air outlet, respectively, of the water source heat pump **A**. Valves **72** and **72'** controlled by thermostat **T** determine flow through heat exchanging coils **70** or **71**, while valves **73** and **73'** controlled by the thermostat **T** determine flow from the heat exchange means **B** or the thermal mass **E**.

In the heating mode, the valves **72** and **72'** are open only through the heat exchanging coil **70** and through the valves **73** and **73'** directly assisted through the heat exchanging means **B** acting as a solar heat collector, via the lines **22** and **23**; and only in the event that the assistance is insufficient, the water source heat pump **A** is operated in the heat mode. In the cooling mode, the valves **72** and **72'** are open only through the heat exchanging coil **71** and through the valve **73** and **73'** directly assisted through the cold thermal mass **E** acting as a direct cold source; and the water source heat pump **A** operated in the cooling mode.

In the event that the effect of load transfer on supply air delivered through coil **71** will not permit the predetermined zone space temperature to be maintained with water source heat pump **A** operative, then the flow to coil **71** is shut off so that all of the available capacity of the water source heat pump **A** can be utilized for cooling of its respective zone. However, if the latter unassisted operation of the heat pump **A** remains insufficient, only then does the thermostat **T** operate the valve **72** to open and direct flow to heat exchanging coil **70** for lowering the temperature at the inlet of return air, at the point of greatest thermal differential. Thus, the water source heat pump **A** is automatically assisted by direct hot or cold sources, as circumstances require.

The residual heat temperature means **H** is associated with the stratified thermal mass **D** to absorb heat from the low heat range section **Z** thereof. It is the domestic water storage heater **36**, or a like utility such as a pool heater, that is in a line **60** through coil **35**, by which means water is preheated to a temperature not to exceed the 140°F or thereabouts available in the section **Z**.

## System Utilizing Alternatively Solar or Fuel Energy

*V. Bearzi; U.S. Patent 3,977,601; August 31, 1976; assigned to Sunlife SpA, Italy* provides a direct utilization solar thermal system for a house, which is constructively simple and operates even when the temperature difference between the end user and the solar heat source is a minimum, with consequent optimum efficiency. A further object is to supplement the required services by an auxiliary source of heat of traditional type, operationally separate from the solar energy system.

The system considered in Figure 7.6a comprises a radiant solar energy collector or absorber **1** which is a solar energy exploiting fluid heating circuit, preferably in the form of a tube bundle plate with an inlet pipe and outlet pipe offset on opposite sides with respect to its longitudinal axis and the outlet pipe situated at a higher level than the inlet pipe.  The collector **1** heats a fluid, nonfreezing if necessary, which by way of a delivery pipe **2** and a pump **3** arrives directly at a user device or heat exchanger utilization means **4**, such as a radiator or a bank of radiators or radiating panels having an input and an output pipe, and then returns through a pipe **5** to the collector **1**.

A heat storage tank **6** is connected into the fluid circuit downstream of the heating means **4** in parallel with a by-pass pipe **7**, by way of a three-way motorized valve **8** sensitive to the temperature of the fluid leaving the heating means **4**, which connects in the tank **6** when this latter temperature exceeds a predetermined value and shuts it off when this temperature is lower than said value.  A pump **9** feeds hot fluid from the tank **6** to the utilization means **4**.  The system is automatically controlled by thermostats **10** and **13** and probes **11** and **12**.

It will be appreciated that the thermostats **10, 13** and the probes **11, 12** as well as the differential temperature integrator constitute temperature responsive control means for controlling the pumps **3** and **9** and the setting of the valves **3a** and **8**.

## FIGURE 7.6: SYSTEM UTILIZING ALTERNATIVELY SOLAR OR FUEL ENERGY

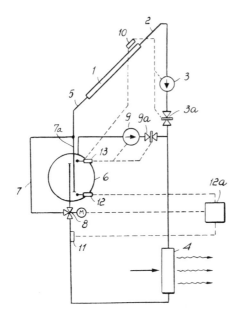

*a.*

(continued)

FIGURE 7.6: (continued)

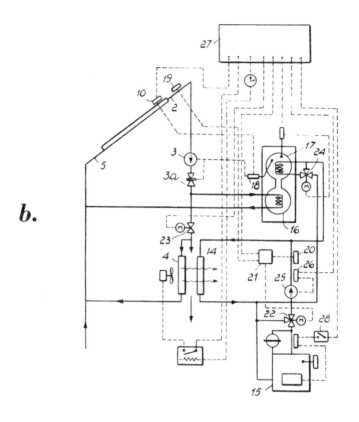

*b.*

(a) Solar system alone
(b) Solar system plus auxiliary system

Source:  U.S. Patent 3,977,601

The system heretofore described has been considered for the purpose of underlining the principle of the process.  In practice, and leaving out of consideration special climatic conditions, a system according to the process can completely satisfy requirements only if used in conjunction with a traditional heating installation which comes into operation when the direct or stored solar radiant energy is insufficient for requirements, by which the overall system leads to considerable economy of fuel, electricity or any other source of energy usually adopted in heating installations.

A practical fuel energy exploiting system is shown in Figure 7.6b, in which the storage tank for the excess heat is not shown in order not to complicate the drawing, but which may be used.  In this embodiment the means **4** are associated with means **14**, such as a normal radiator traversed by the hot water of a fuel energy exploiting boiler **15**.  The heat exchanger utilization means **4** and **14** are operationally separate and independent, but may be enclosed in the same thermo-ventilator or may consist of radiant panels mounted on a wall or the ceiling and/or in the floor, according to known methods. The solar energy system also feeds a hot water tank 16 coupled to a second hot water tank 17 associated with the boiler 15, a thermostat 18 being provided for protection against superheating of the hot water tanks.

The pipes which convey the fluid to the heat exchanger of the hot water tank 16 are sized so as to give precedence to its use in environmental heating. The hot water tank may be connected by known methods to bathroom and/or kitchen radiators, to give better use of the storage in the hot water tank 16 and better comfort conditions without operating costs between seasons. A sensor 19 connected to the delivery pipe 2 of the absorber 10 constitutes the pilot probe having the function of a master pilot probe, and a second sensor 20 constitutes the subpilot probe having the function of a submaster pilot probe of an adjustable control 21 which processes the data supplied by 19 and 20 and acts on a three-way motorized valve 22 associated with the boiler 15 by way of a switch 28.

The system is completed by a two-way motorized valve 23 for shutting off the means 4, which can be used for example in summer when the system needs only to supply hot water for consumption; a motorized three-way valve 24 associated with the hot water tank 17; a pump 25 connected in the delivery pipe from the boiler 15 together with its relative thermostat 26; and a control relay unit 27. The thermostats are calibrated so that the radiant solar energy is first utilized and the auxiliary and supplementary boiler 15 comes into operation only when this is absent or insufficient for requirements. The supplementary boiler 15 is always maintained at a temperature (which is subordinated to summer or winter conditions) or preset to exclude the auxiliary system.

## Heating and Cooling System for Dome-Shaped Structure

*R.G. Reines; U.S. Patent 3,949,732; April 13, 1976* describes a solar heated building of generally hemispherical shape which supports on its surface solar heat collectors. The solar heat collectors are in the shape of spherical sectors and cover an arcuate area defined by the receipt of usable solar heat energy; consideration being given to the diurnal and seasonal positions of the sun.

Heat collecting fluid is passed in thermal contact with the solar heat collectors and is in circulation with a heat storage reservoir. Air is passed in thermal contact with the solar heat collector to prevent overheating when the heat collecting fluid is cut off or to provide hot air when the heat storage reservoir is fully heated or when the solar heat collector is warmer than ambient but not hot enough to supply heat to the heat storage reservoir. The solar heat collectors are segregated by the heat collecting fluid circulation system piping into discrete arrays each covering about 15° of azimuth arc and each such array is controlled by one or more valves which admits or blocks heat collecting fluid flow.

Each of the solar heat collector arrays and the heat reservoir is provided with a temperature sensor. A temperature comparison device compares the temperature of each of the solar collectors with the temperature of the heat reservoir to automatically open the valves to only such arrays as will supply heat to the heat reservoir. The air circulation system through the solar heat collectors is automatically activated for cooling when the solar heat collectors are not being used for heat storage. When air is passed through the solar heat panels, the heated air may be used to directly provide hot air for space conditioning or other purposes and thereby conserve the stored heat. The dual-mode capability of air-fluid operation enables the system to extract the maximum amount of solar energy for usable purposes.

The dome shaped building 15 is shown in Figure 7.7a, with portions shown in Figures 7.7b, 7.7c and 7.7d, includes an outer hemispherical shell 16 constructed of interlocking sector panels 17 to which is attached an inner wall of insulation 19. Each sector panel has on both its elongated edges a reentrant channel for interlocking with adjacent sector panels. Each sector panel also has an outwardly projecting middle rectangular reinforcing rib 20 along its vertical median line. Each of the sector panel vertical edge reentrant channels when assembled to adjacent sector panels provide outwardly projecting rectangular ribs 22 and 24 similar in configuration to the middle rectangular rib 20.

Shell sector panels along an arc profitably exposed to the sun, such as on the southeastern and south exposures of the building are utilized as the heat collecting members for solar heat collectors 21.

The assembled shell rests on and is anchored to a foundation or footing 23 of any suitable material such as concrete. One practical method for securing the shell to the foundation utilizes bolt-hooks 25 shown in Figure 7.7c which engage an annular metal ring 28. Ring 28 is constricted by a turnbuckle or the like (not shown) against the outer surface of footing 23.

The top end of the frusto-sector panel portions utilized as an element of the heat collecting panels is sealed by a hood or upper end closure plate 38 shown in Figure 7.7d.

For thermal insulation, three or four inches of in situ applied insulation foam 19 is attached to the inside surface of the building shell. An economical, safe and very effective insulation is sprayed and hardened foaming material upon which is applied an inner coating 33 of fire preventive material. A layer of reflecting material like aluminum foil 34 may be used to enhance the insulation effect.

To the end that the disproportionate expansion and contraction of the exterior shell sectors relative to the wall of insulation will not cause buckling of the shell or detachment between the shell sector panels and the insulation, the engagement between adjacent panel sectors must be slidable to a compensating degree. Proximate the top of the dome, a ventilating cap 39 is affixed. A rain shield 41 is affixed to the outer surface of the ventilating cap 39 thereby providing with ventilating cap apertures 42, passages for ventilating air, as shown in Figure 7.7e.

Solar energy collecting panels 21 are shown in cross section in Figures 7.7c, 7.7d and 7.7f. The heat collecting fluid flows downward over the surface of panel 43. Panel 43 differs from nonheat collecting panels in that its outer surface is coated with black heat absorbing paint. The amount of fluid passed over the panel surface is limited by the fluid temperature desired and the rate of heat collection by the panel. The fluid, if liquid, is generally a very thin sheet if it covers the entire width of the heat panel. With such a very thin sheet of fluid, it is very difficult to prevent channeling; that is, the fluid tends to convert from a sheet to rivulets which have inadequate thermal coupling with the surface of the panel. To the end that the stream of fluid be a continuous sheet of adequate width to give good thermal coupling with the panel, vertical confining and guiding dams **45** and **47** are affixed to the surface of the panel. The dams shown in Figure 7.7f may be plastic material magnetic strips of a type commercially available.

Referring again to Figure 7.7f, the solar energy collecting panels are covered with two transparent sheets **49** and **51**. Such materials have a high temperature coefficient of expansion compared with the metal heat absorbing panels. To the end that the transparent sheets can differentially expand and contract, the sheets are firmly, but slidably mounted on the heat collecting panel ribs. Sheet **49** rests on nonsticking gasket strips **53** which in turn rest on and are affixed to panel ribs **20**, **22** and **24**. All the transparent sheets are provided with projecting sidewise locating tabs **55**.

Adjacent heat panel transparent sheets **52** overlap the edges of sheet **49**. In the overlapping areas, nonsticking gaskets **61** are provided between the sheets to permit relative shifting. Over the top surface of transparent sheets **52** in the overlap zone with sheet **49**, another set **63** of nonsticking gaskets are provided.

FIGURE 7.7: HEATING AND COOLING SYSTEM FOR DOME-SHAPED STRUCTURE

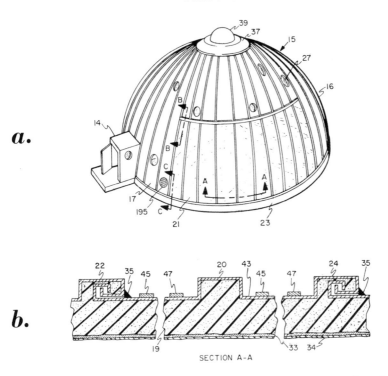

SECTION A-A

(continued)

FIGURE 7.7:  (continued)

**c.**

**d.**

**e.**

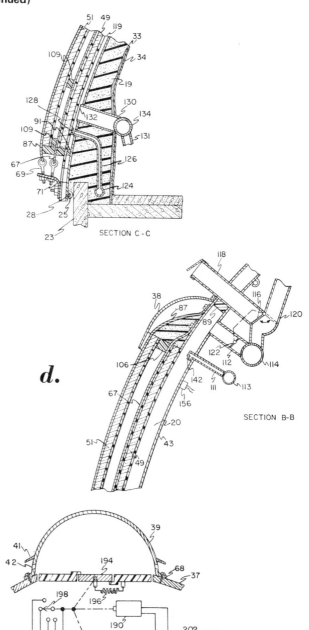

SECTION C-C

SECTION B-B

(continued)

**FIGURE 7.7:** (continued)

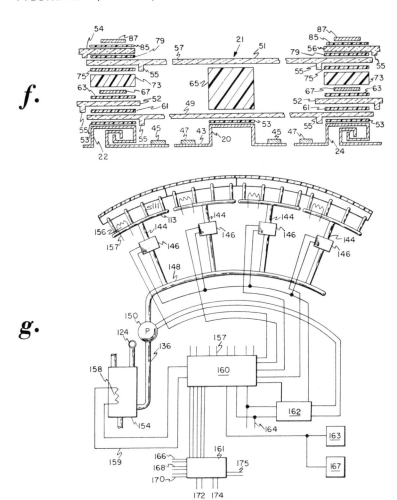

*f.*

*g.*

(a)  Side perspective view of dwelling
(b)  Horizontal cross section taken along section **A—A** of Figure 7.7a
(c)  Vertical diametric cross section taken on section **C—C** of Figure 7.7a
(d)  Vertical diametric cross section taken on section **B—B** of Figure 7.7a
(e)  Vertical diametric cross section of central part of roof, ventilation cap and ventilation structure
(f)  Horizontal cross section collecting panel with details disproportionately enlarged
(g)  Schematic drawing of collecting panel tracking details

Source:  U.S. Patent 3,949,732

Each edge of the first or inner layer of transparent sheets is held in place and hermetically urged together and to the panel ribs by tensioned metal strips or bands **67** shown in Figure 7.7c. Bands **67** are anchored to the panel ribs **22** and **24** at the top end as shown in Figure 7.7d. At the bottom end, the bands **67** are connected to a tensioning bolt-eye **69**. Bolt-eye **69** threads bracket **71** which in turn is secured to base bolt **25**. Bands **67** are drawn tight enough to provide adequate radial pressure between the transparent sheets, gaskets and rib tops.

The second assembly of transparent sheets **51, 54** and **56** is made in a manner similar to the first assembly. Spacer blocks **73** are set in place over tensioning bands **67** over ribs **22** and **24**. A thicker spacer block or strip **65** is set over transparent sheet **49** over rib **20**. On top of blocks **73**, nonsticking gaskets **75** are set in place. Transparent sheet **51** is installed in contact with gaskets **75** and spacer blocks **73** and **65**.

Nonsticking gaskets **79** are set over the edge zones of transparent sheet **51**. Next, transparent sheets **54** and **56** are set in place. Nonsticking gaskets **85** are placed over the edge zones of transparent sheets **54, 56** and tensioning bands **87** are installed in a manner similar to tensioning bands **67**. At the top and bottom of each solar heat collector panel as shown in Figures 7.7c and 7.7d, filler blocks **89** and **91** respectively are affixed to the collector panel **43** between the ribs to seal the ends thereof. Cross blocks **109** are placed between the transparent panels transversely of the lengthwise direction of the solar heat collector panels to prevent warpage of the plastic material.

Each solar heat collector panel is constructed to heat a heat conducting fluid which is liquid and/or air. Referring to Figure 7.7d, the upper end of each heat panel **43** (shown without the inside insulation), between each pair of ribs, is provided with an inlet fluid pipe **111** and an outlet air duct **112**. The air duct **112** is provided with a gate **122** and is connected to a plenum **114** and a three-way valve **116**. The three-way valve communicates with a duct **118** which is ported to the outside and a duct **120** which may be connected to household accessories such as clothes dryers, or to a room register for direct space heating. Temperature sensing means **156** on the solar heat collecting panels automatically opens gate **122** when a heat collecting panel exceeds a selected upper limit of temperature.

Gate **122** is normally closed in order to block the air passage when the solar heat collector panel is utilized to heat the heat transport liquid. The flexibility of the arrangement allows gate **122** to be partially opened while heat transport liquid is flowing to generate moist environmental air when needed for the interior of the building. In addition, gate **122** may be opened and gate **116** closed to the outside for heating the interior when heat transport liquid is not flowing. This means of heating results in the ability to use those heat panels which are not hot enough to supply heat to the heat storage reservoir but are hot enough to directly provide usable hot air for space heating or other purposes.

Referring to Figure 7.7c, hot heat transport liquid collection manifold **124** communicates with the solar heat collector via pipe **126**. The hot liquid traveling down the solar heat collector panel **43** encounters dam **128** and is diverted to exit pipe **126**. An inlet air duct **130** communicates with the space between the heat collector panel ribs and is provided with a projecting lip **132** which prevents the ingress of liquid into the air duct. Air duct **130** is connected to a common manifold **134** which in turn is coupled via pipe **131** to the interior of the building or to the exterior to preheat fresh air.

The heat transport liquid is conveyed from heat storage reservoir **154** shown in Figure 7.7g through a pump **150** and pipe **136** to electrically operated valves **146** which in turn are connected by pipes **144** to manifolds **113**. It has been found that approximately 15° of arc of heat panels supplied with heat collecting fluid through one controlled manifold allows for effective sun tracking. Accordingly one tube **111** with one or more orifices communicates with the top portion of each solar heat collecting panel liquid channel shown diagrammatically in Figure 7.7g.

To the end that the solar heat collecting panels will be activated only when they can supply heat to the reservoir, a temperature sensing device **156**, such as a thermistor is attached to at least one solar heat collecting panel in each array. A similar temperature sensing device **158** is in thermal contact with the liquid in the heat storage reservoir **154**. The solar heat collecting panel temperature sensing device **156** in each solar heat collecting panel array, and the temperature sensing device **158** in the reservoir are electrically connected through leads **157** and **159**, respectively, to electronic temperature comparitor **160** using circuitry well known in the art.

Comparitor **160** automatically generates energizing current for opening valves **146** in one or more solar heat collecting arrays at some selected temperature differential hotter than the reservoir. All other array supply valves **146** remain closed. The solar heat collecting panel liquid supply pump **150** is energized by current responsive relay **162** whenever any one or more of valves **146** are activated by temperature comparitor **160**. The electrical current for both valves **146**, pump **150** and any other electrically associated devices is supplied from any available source whether commercial or in situ generated when connected to electrical connections **164**.

Further details of this system and its adaptation to conventional structures are included in the patent.

### Open-Cycle System

Efficiency of an open-cycle air conditioning apparatus for heating and cooling is improved in the method of *W.F. Rush, J. Wurm and R.J. Dufour; U.S. Patent 3,889,742; June 17, 1975; assigned to Gas Developments Corporation* and the economy of external power is increased both with respect to cost and energy consumption by providing a combination of a low temperature heater and a high temperature heater for regenerating the desiccant means in the air conditioning apparatus. The power source for the low temperature heater can utilize solar energy, waste energy, and the like. The power source for the high temperature heater, when needed, can be an open flame burner or the like.

A particularly preferred air conditioning system embodying the process and utilizing solar heat is illustrated in Figure 7.8a. Enclosed space such as home **22** is provided with solar energy storage tank **23** containing heat transfer fluid **24**, solar energy collector means **25** and conduits **26** and **27** which provide communication between collector means **25** and tank **23**.

FIGURE 7.8: OPEN-CYCLE SYSTEM

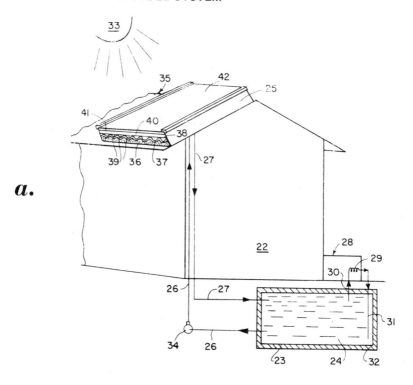

*a.*

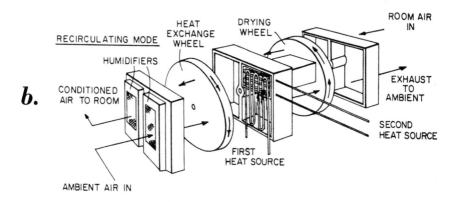

*b.*

(a)   Schematic representation showing use of solar heat
(b)   Schematic representation of open-cycle apparatus
        showing full recirculating mode

Source:  U.S. Patent 3,889,742

Home **22** is heated or cooled, as desired, by air conditioning apparatus **28** which is of the general type shown in Figure 7.8b. Heater means in open-cycle air conditioning apparatus **28** comprises heat exchange coil **29** (equivalent to first heat source in Figure 7.8b) through which heat transfer fluid **24**, e.g., water, water-ethylene glycol mixtures, or the like, is circulated via conduits **30** and **31**. Heat loss from tank **23** is minimized by means of insulating layer **32** which surrounds tank **23**.

In operation of this solar energy recovery system, radiant solar heat from source **33**, the sun, is utilized to raise the temperature of heat transfer liquid **24** in tank **23**. Liquid **24** is circulated by means of pump **34** via conduit **26** from tank **23** up to and through solar collector means **25** situated on roof **35**, and then returned to tank **23** at a relatively higher temperature. Pump **34** is operated only during times at which the solar transfer fluid in the collector means **25** is at a temperature higher than the temperature of the heat transfer liquid **24** at the upper portion of tank **23**. For operating the low-temperature heater means of air conditioning apparatus **28**, relatively hotter heat transfer fluid is withdrawn from tank **23** via conduit **30** at an upper level and relatively colder heat transfer fluid is returned to tank **23** via conduit **31** at a lower level thereof.

Solar energy collectors suitable for use in the system can be of two general types: (1) concentrating type, or (2) nonconcentrating type.

The concentrating type solar energy collector is capable of developing higher temperature by concentrating the radiation emanating from the sun and to achieve a relatively higher collector efficiency by using a smaller heat absorption area with attendant smaller heat losses. However, the concentrating type of collector must use the direct component of sunlight, thus there can be no heat collection on cloudy days. Moreover, the mirrors and/or lenses that follow the direct component of sunlight are guided by a relatively complex and costly tracking system.

The nonconcentrating solar collectors collect both the direct and the diffuse components of sunlight, and are operable on cloudy or overcast days as well, They are less costly and no tracking systems are required. Nevertheless, heat transfer liquid temperatures as high as about 230°F are readily achievable, which temperatures are sufficiently high for these purposes. A suitable noncentrating solar collector is shown in Figure 7.8a.

Collector **25** comprises insulated base **36** on which is placed a sandwich comprising corrugated aluminum plate **37** and flat aluminum plate **38**, together defining a plurality of passageways **39** through which a heat transfer fluid is circulated. The exposed face **40** of plate **39** may be coated with a selective coating which reduces infrared emission from the collector surface. Spaced transparent cover sheets **41** and **42** are situated over exposed face **40** to reduce convective heat losses as well as to provide protection from the elements, windblown debris, and the like. A polyvinyl fluoride film, glass or the like, reinforced with a wire or fabric mesh is suitable for this purpose.

Any type of solar collector which will raise the temperature of the heat transfer fluid to over about 180° to 200°F is suitable for use in the process.

## Heating and Cooling of Proposed Skyscraper

*D.W. Pulver; U.S. Patent 3,935,897; February 3, 1976* provides a method of
solar heating and cooling in a building of the type having insulated opaque and
vision glass areas, including orienting the vision glass so as to avoid solar exposure,
while shading the vision glass with a series of heat collecting panels and circulating fluid in absorbent communication with the collectors for use in winter heating and summer cooling systems. The method is distinguished both in its orienting of shading, according to latitude, as well as blocking or cutting off of
circulating fluid from the collectors, except under conditions of solar exposure.

In a typical 35 story office building, a controlled interior climate may be achieved
by the following:

(1) Minimization of heating and air conditioning requirements by
respectively minimizing heat loss in winter through the exterior wall by means of maximum insulation in opaque areas,
double glazing in vision areas, and by minimizing solar heat
gain in the summer by orienting vision glass to the north on
the north facade, north-northwest on the west side, and completely shading vision glass on the south side by means of angled
solar collectors and;

(2) Collection of all solar energy striking the building facade and roof
by means of double or triple glazed clear glass covered collectors made of coated copper or aluminum plates, with integral
or attached fluid-carrying channels, connected to pipes, containing a liquid (e.g., water or water and ethylene glycol) which
is heated to optimum temperature, returned to a central location at the base of the building, then redistributed through the
building where needed for heating in the winter, and used to
operate an absorption cycle or other such known system operable
upon heat exchange with a heated fluid, amply illustrated by the
prior art for refrigeration equipment in the summer. An insulated storage tank in the basement stores excess hot liquid for
nighttime cooling or heating; any excess hot liquid can be sold
to neighboring buildings;

(3) The integration of the above two principles results in a design
which, with the exception of energy for lighting, can be a net
exporter of energy, meaning that the excess of solar energy collected on sunny and mildly overcast days vs that needed for
heating and cooling the subject building can be exported in a
quantity greater than that needed to be imported (gas, oil, steam
or electric backup) on a day or days when solar energy is not
available in adequate quantities to heat or cool subject building.

Figure 7.9a is a perspective view of proposed building, showing southern and
western facades.

Figure 7.9b is a perspective of the north and west facades.

Figure 7.9c is a fragmentary enlarged view of the west facade, showing angular
orientation of the heating panels and north-northwesterly orientation of the double glazed vision areas.

Figure 7.9d is an enlarged rear elevation, showing the south facade and adjacent
west facade with opaque solar energy collecting panels used
complementally as shading for the vision areas.

Figure 7.9e is a top plan showing the northwesterly and northeasterly orientation of the west and east vision areas.

Figure 7.9f is a fragmentary section taken along section line **6—6** of the south
      facade and showing the opaque roof-top heat collector, as well as
      lower collectors superposed at a 45° angle as a shield or shade for
      the vision areas.

Figure 7.9g is a fragmentary vertical section taken as shown in Figure 7.9e and
      showing angular orientation of the heat collecting panels on the
      east facade, as well as the northeasterly orientation of the vision
      glass.

Figure 7.9h is an enlarged transverse section of Figure 7.9g and showing the
      positioning of the double vision glass, the collector plate and cir-
      culating liquid channels, as well as backup insulation.

Figure 7.9i is a schematic view of a suggested building heat recovery and storage
      system.

In Figure 7.9a a multistory office building generally designated as **20** is illustrated
as having inclined southern rooftop opaque collecting area **22**, southern facade
**26** and western facade **24**. In Figure 7.9b the buildings northern facade **28** is illustrated as having conventional double pane vision areas **34** and opaque insulated
panels **32**.

**FIGURE 7.9: HEATING AND COOLING OF PROPOSED SKYSCRAPER**

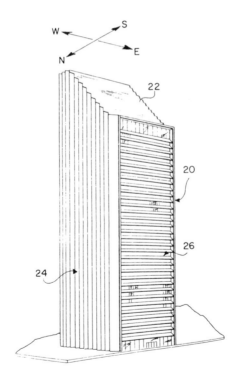

*a.*

(continued)

FIGURE 7.9: (continued)

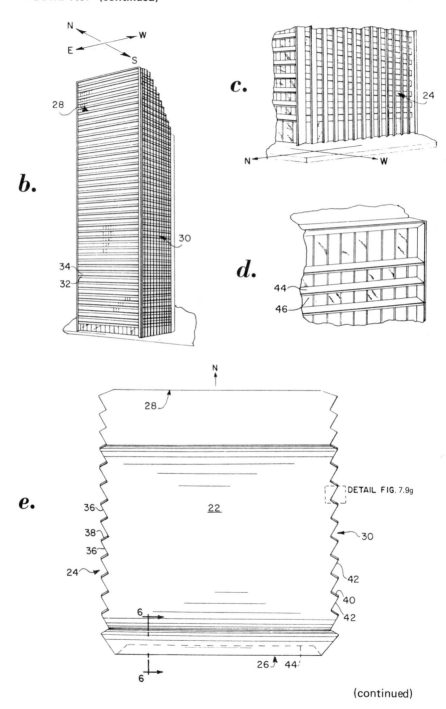

(continued)

FIGURE 7.9: (continued)

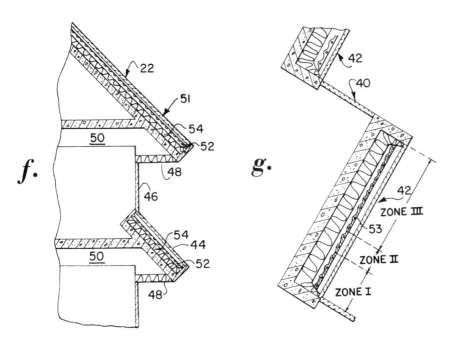

*f.*

*g.*

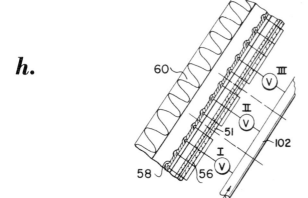

*h.*

(continued)

FIGURE 7.9: (continued)

*i.*

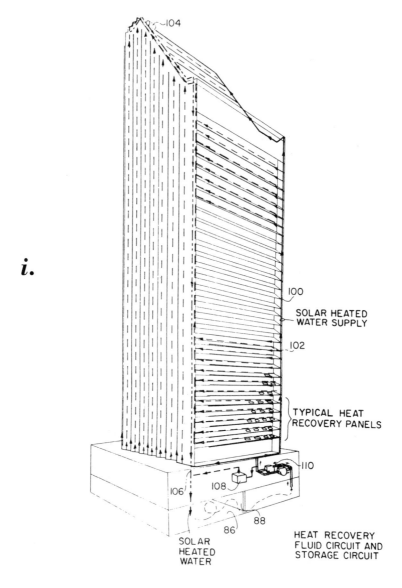

Source: U.S. Patent 3,935,897

In Figure 7.9d the southern facade is further illustrated as having double pane horizontal vision areas **46** shaded by angularly superposed disposed opaque collector panels **44**. In Figure 7.9e the building layout is generally illustrated. West facade **24** has its vision areas **38**, north-northwesterly disposed with adjacent opaque collector panels **36** exposed to the prevailing sun.

Similarly in the eastern facade **30** the vision areas **40** are north-northeasterly oriented intermediate opaque, angularly disposed or staggered collector panels **42**. In the south facade vision areas **46** are shaded by horizontally disposed opaque collector panels **44**. Manifestly, the angle of the windows on east and west facades, as well as the angle of the collector panels may be varied, according to the sun latitude. Similarly, the angle of the shading collector panels **44** may be varied so as to prevent the winter sun exposure to the vision area.

In Figure 7.9f the rooftop collector panel **22** is illustrated fragmentarily and superposed with respect to collector panels **44** which shade the respective vision areas **46**. The rooftop and east-west collector panels may be constructed similarly to include a clear and insulated clear glass cover **51**, a collector plate **52**, with integral liquid channels **53** and a back-up insulation member **60**. Insulation **48** may be interposed intermediate the bottom of the collector panel and the building wall, so as to enclose a circulating plenum or duct **50**.

In Figure 7.9h the east-west facade collector panel is illustrated in enlarged detail. The collector plate may have a selective surface coating and may be a flat metal plate clad with formed metal plate. Alternatively, the collector panel may include a flat metal plate with welded attached tubes or other combination.

In Figure 7.9g the collector panels on the east facade are disposed at a 30° angle; however, this angle may be varied, according to latitude. The individual panels may have disconnect zones **I, II, III** or the like which may be circuited to cut out of the system when shaded from the sun.

In Figure 7.9i a heat recovery and storage system is illustrated as including storage tank **86** having a median baffle **88**, heat recovery pumps **110** and auxiliary stand-by heater **108**, communicating with solar heating water return **106**. The heat recovery pumps communicate with solar heating water supply **100**, as well as solar heating water reverse return **102**. An expansion tank **104** may be positioned at the building rooftop.

### Home Heated by Water Circulated from Swimming Pool

The process of *W.E. Saypalia, Jr.; U.S. Patent 3,910,490; October 7, 1975* describes a system installed in a private home so as to provide heat or coolness which is powered by solar energy, the system incorporating an aboveground swimming pool, a collector and aluminum foil reflector which are struck by the sun's rays, water from the swimming pool circulating through the collector and back to the pool, the pool thus becoming warmed so to run through a hot water system of a house, the system additionally including reflector curtains, double layer glass air insulation, and other components.

Referring to Figure 7.10, reference numeral **10** represents a solar energy heating and cooling system according to the process which includes an aboveground swimming pool **11** from which swimming pool water is drawn through piping **12**, through a filter and pump **13** and then through a collector **14**. From there the water moves through piping **15** back into the swimming pool. In this form of the process, the swimming pool and collector are exposed to the sun's rays. Additionally an aluminum foil reflector **16** is provided which also is exposed to the sun's rays **7**. As the water is circulated through the collector, it is heated by the sun's rays. As a result the water reentering the pool becomes sufficiently heated so that it can be circulated through a hot water system **17** of a house **18**. Such water is then caused to be passed through a pump **19** and the furnace **20** of the house. The entire heating equipment comprising the pool, the collector and foil reflector are located behind a double layer glass **21** or a polyethylene plastic that is transparent. An air insulation is provided between the layers **21** so that the sun's rays enter the area without heat escaping therefrom.

Reflector curtains **22** are also provided adjacent the interior side of the double layer glass, the reflector curtains being adaptable to be pulled out and thereby enclose the entire interior area surrounded by the double layer glass. A fan **23** is located within the interior **24** surrounded by double layer glass, the fan serving to circulate air throughout the interior. The example illustrated shows the collector being positioned so that the sun's rays come from the south in order that a maximum amount of rays can effect the collector **14**. Alternately, the collector can be placed on swivels so that the elevation thereof can be changed in order to follow the path of the sun as the seasons change.

When the system is intended for operation in summer, the double layer glass wall and curtains are removed or rolled to the roof. A pump in the greenhouse **25** is utilized to circulate water from the pool to the collector at night. Evaporation of water from the surface of the pool and the collector as well as exposure to the cooler night air functions to chill the water. The chilled water is pumped as needed through the heating system in the house to cool the interior. A dehumidifier is preferably installed in an appropriate place in the house to remove water from sweating pipes and the radiators. In some locations, solar cooling and heating may be sufficient by itself.

**FIGURE 7.10: HOME HEATED BY WATER CIRCULATED FROM POOL**

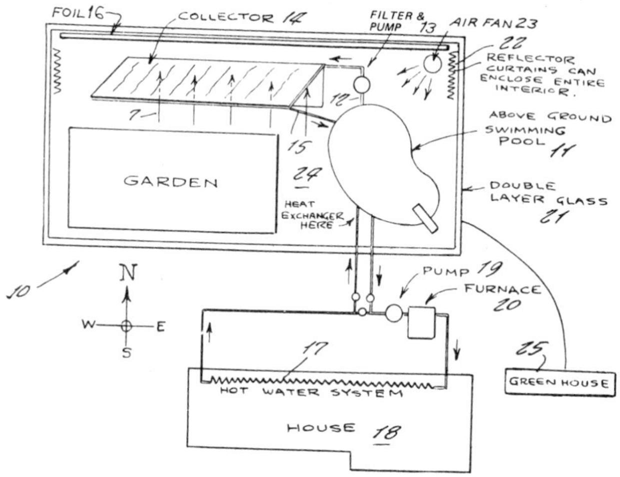

Source:  U.S. Patent 3,910,490

## GAS CIRCULATION SYSTEMS

### System Using Daytime Solar Heat and Electric Resistance Heat at Night

*D.W. Pulver; U.S. Patent 3,994,276; November 30, 1976* describes a system in which, during daylight hours, solar heated air is circulated as a heating supplement or substitute for furnace heated air in the existing forced air supply ducts. At night the solar heat collecting panel is shut off from the furnace system and electric resistance heated air is circulated to the exclusion of oil and gas consumption.

In Figures 7.11a, 7.11c, and 7.11d the solar collecting panel **12** is illustrated as including a solar heated air plenum **86** having insulation **84** at its bottom, a corrugated top collector panel **88** and a flat collector panel **90** both advantageously of fiberglass, for defining a separate closed insulating plenum **92**. A solar collector fan **44** may be employed to enhance the removal of solar heated air from the plenum **86** and the delivery of solar heated air into central return duct **30**. During summertime, auxiliary vent **40** having damper **42** may be opened such that the solar heated air is advantageously vented exteriorly of the roof surface either by natural convection through the assistance of fan **44**, thus further serving to remove an unwanted solar heating loading. Bottom vents **91** and **93** covered during winter by panel **95**, hinged at **97**, may be provided for this purpose.

**FIGURE 7.11: SYSTEM USING DAYTIME SOLAR HEAT AND ELECTRIC RESISTANCE HEAT AT NIGHT**

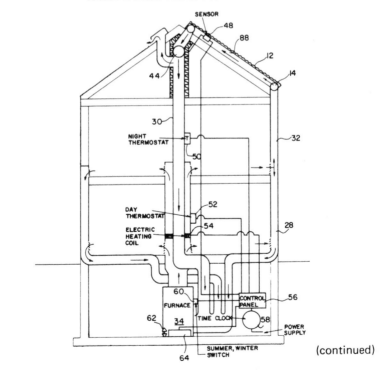

*a.*

(continued)

(continued)

FIGURE 7.11: (continued)

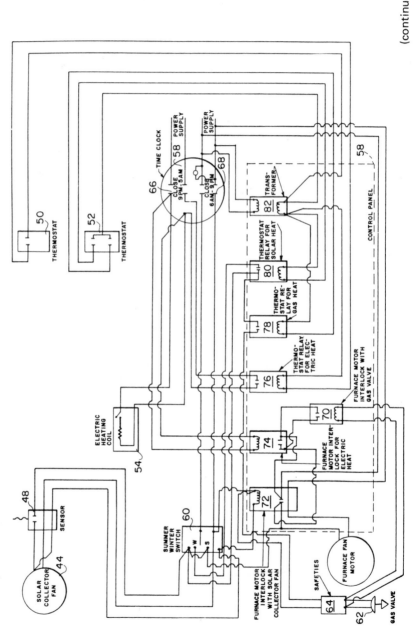

*b.*

FIGURE 7.11: (continued)

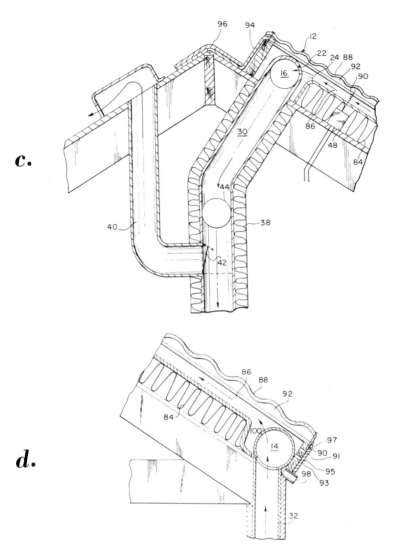

c.

d.

(a) Transverse section, showing schematically the night and day thermostats, positioning of the sensor, the electric heating elements, a time clock and controls within a household system

(b) Wiring diagram according to Figure 7.11a

(c) Enlarged, fragmentary section of the collector panel at the top

(d) Enlarged, fragmentary section of the bottom of the panel

Source: U.S. Patent 3,994,276

A plurality of weep holes **98** may be employed to permit flow of condensation from the plenum. Flashing **94** may extend from between the panels **88** and **90** for securement under ridge shingles **96**. Conventional insulation **38** may line top central return duct **30**, so as to eliminate heat loss in nonliving areas, such as the attic. Top panel **88** may be of fiberglass corrugated for strength with another transparent sheet **90** to define the plenum's upper boundary for insulation.

In Figure 7.11b solar collector fan **44** is illustrated as controlled by means of temperature sensor **48** mounted within plemum **86**, so as to activate fan **44**, as the desired temperature is reached. Also, a night thermostat may be placed in night sleeping areas, such that the electric resistance heating elements are turned on by means of relay **76** and furnace motor interlock **74** for circulating resistance-heated air through the sleeping rooms at night. A day thermostat **52** may be employed in the daytime living areas, so as to switch on for gas heat relay **78** as appropriate. A transformer **82** may be employed, as well as the respective thermostat relays for solar heat **80**, electric heat **76** and gas heat **78**.

Also provided are furnace motor interlock with solar collector fan **72** and a furnace motor interlock **70** with gas valve **62**. A suitable gas turn-on valve **62** may be employed with suitable safety devices **64**. A time clock **58** may be employed, e.g., with a daytime close-out switch **68** activating the conventional oil fired furnace during the daylight hours of 6 AM to 9 PM and a nighttime switch **66** activating the electric heating coil **54** during the nighttime hours of 9 PM to 6 AM. Also, as illustrated in Figure 7.11a and 7.11b a summer-winter switch **60** may be employed to activate sensor **48** and fan **44** only during the winter months, shutting them off in the summer months.

### Air Circulated Through Channels in Planes of Building

*K.N.A. Nilsson; U.S. Patent 4,006,856; February 8, 1977; assigned to AB Svenska Flaktfabriken, Sweden* describes an arrangement for use in the utilization of solar energy for the heating of a building comprising a number of preferably planar building parts in the form of floor, outer walls and roof and enclosing a number of rooms.

The arrangement is characterized primarily in that the floor, outer walls and roof of the building are constructed so as with each other to form channel spaces which communicate relative to each other. They are sealed toward the surrounding atmosphere in such a manner that they form in at least one cross section of the building a closed channel system for an air stream circulating therein. In one or more channel spaces a preferably plane solar heat absorbing body is located, which channel space enclosing the body is provided with at least one passageway extending in the circulation path of the air stream along the body, so that the channel space(s) and/or the body are covered by a layer of a material pervious to solar energy in the form of heat rays.

The closed channel system also includes, separated from the channel space, a separate channel space, which includes a heat-accumulating magazine passed by the circulating air stream. An expedient embodiment of the arrangement is characterized in that the channel space including the solar heat absorbing body is covered by one or more layers of a material preventing heat reflection from the body.

Figure 7.12a shows a cross section of a building with the basic structural design, comprising the closed channel system, the solar energy absorbing body and the heat accumulating magazine and Figure 7.12b shows a corresponding cross section of the building, which is equipped with means for mechanical ventilation and jet nozzles connected to a compression air source for guiding and increasing the circulation in the closed circuit.

**FIGURE 7.12: AIR CIRCULATED THROUGH CHANNELS IN PLANES OF BUILDING**

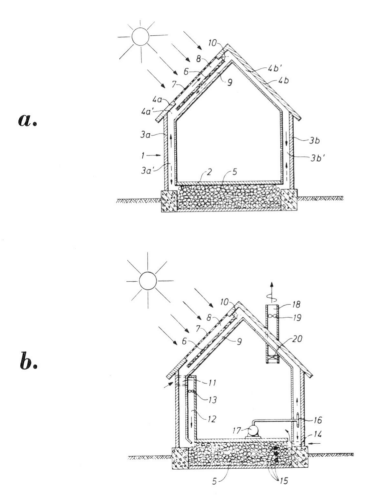

Source: U.S. Patent 4,006,856

In the drawings, **1** designates the building, **2** designates its floor, and **3a**, **3b** designate the outer walls. **4a** and **4b** designate a roof facing to the south and, respectively, a roof facing to the north. The channel spaces in the outer walls are designated by **3a'** and **3b'**. Corresponding spaces in the roof are designated by **4a'** and **4b'**. The designation **5** stands for a magazine, i.e., a channel space beneath the floor **2** and located, from the viewpoint of air flow, in a part of the closed channel system which lies substantially directly in front of **4a'**. **6** designates a solar heat absorbing body, and **7** designates a layer which air-tightly covers the channel space **4a'** and constitutes a part of the roof surface **4a** in the embodiment shown. **8** designates a channel in front of the body **6**, i.e., between the body and the layer **7**, and **9** designates a corresponding channel behind the body, which channel is a by-pass.

**10** designates a check valve, which according to the process is intended to substantially reduce and brake the air stream through the channel **8** upon absent or strongly reduced heat radiation of the body **6**. On such an occasion the temperature of the forward surface of the body **6** decreases while the rearward surface of the body will show a lower temperature first after a longer period of absence of solar heat radiation. According to the process, the self-circulation through the channel **8** is caused to substantially cease by means of the check valve **10** when closed and, instead, the self-circulating air stream is then caused to pass through the aforesaid by-pass.

**11** designates a supply air opening for ventilation air to the interior of the room(s) from the atmosphere, and **12** and **13** designate a duct and, respectively, a fan for the supply air supplied through a supply air opening **14** to the interior of the room(s). The corresponding spent air duct and spent air fan are designated by **18** and, respectively, **19**. The spent air fan, of course, may in known manner be equipped with a heat exchanger, which is designated by **20**.

**15** designates electric heat cables, which preferably are intended for operation during the low-load periods (at night-tariff), **16** designates jet nozzles connected to a fan, air pump or compressor **17**. By means of the jet drafts supplied through the jet nozzles it is possible to ensure by simple means guidance of the air stream, which circulates or, at special operation cases, is reversed, and to bring about an optimum increase of the closed circuit through the different channel spaces and the magazine **5**.

**Automatic Air Flow Control System**

*G.F. Mason; U.S. Patent 3,997,108; December 14, 1976* describes an automatic air flow control system for a solar heating installation wherein thermostatically controlled dampers are associated with such solar heating elements as the collector and the storage area, and with the rooms to be heated, the thermostats being presettable to program their operations, with minimal supervision, in response to variable heat supply at the collector and variable heat demand in the rooms to be heated.

Since the specific details of air circulation within a house, to and from one or more rooms thereof, will vary according to the size and design of each individual house, Figure 7.13a shows only ducts which supply air to a house and receive air from a house, regardless of any additional ducting in the house. The location of the heating system elements will be indicated below. Referring to Figure 7.13a, the system includes a solar heat collector **10**, of any effective type, designed to receive solar thermal energy and to transfer it to an air stream which may be circulated through the collector.

As shown, the collector has an inlet end **11**, a series of baffles **12** causing the air to follow a serpentine path, and an outlet end **13**. The dimensions and shape of the collector may vary widely but it will normally include one or more flat black surfaces (plastic or painted metal) for solar heat absorption and one or more air passages adjacent to the surfaces. It must, obviously, be placed in a location where its heat absorbing area is exposed to direct sunlight for as many hours a day as possible, and at the most favorable average angle or angles. Any exposed adjacent ducting may also be made of black material to supplement the heat absorption in the collector.

A storage unit is essential if the system is to be operative at times when the sun is not shining on the collector, as at night or on a cloudy day. The storage unit **15**, shown herein, may be of any suitable type, but the rock type is preferred. In the air circulation path shown, the collector outlet **13** is connected by a duct **16** to a first damper **17**, **17a** having an alternative inlet **18** from the house and an outlet **19** to a duct **20** containing a fan **21**. From the fan the air path goes to a second damper **22**, **22a** having an outlet **23** to the house and an outlet **24** to the inlet **25** of the storage unit **15**. The storage outlet **26** connects with a third damper **27**, **27a** having an outlet **28** to the house and an outlet **29**, connected by the duct **30** to a fourth damper **31**, **31a** which has an inlet **32** from the house and outlet **33** to the inlet end **11** of the collector.

FIGURE 7.13: AUTOMATIC AIR FLOW CONTROL SYSTEM

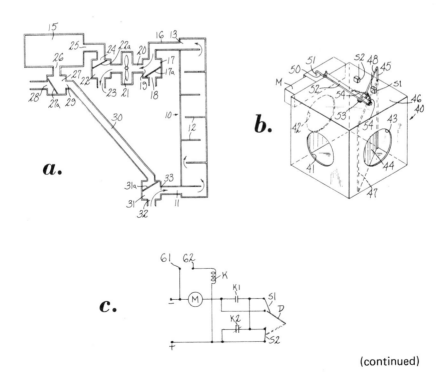

(continued)

FIGURE 7.13: (continued)

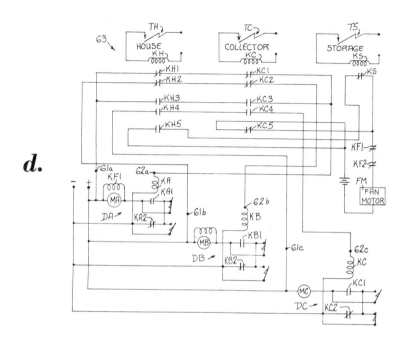

*d.*

(a)   Elements of heating system with dampers set to circulate warm air
      from the collector through the house
(b)   Isometric projection of damper
(c)   Damper circuit
(d)   Circuit diagram showing the pertinent elements for automatic control
      of the system

Source:  U.S. Patent 3,997,108

A suitable damper construction is shown in Figure 7.13b wherein the housing
**40** is in the form of a rectangular box having a vent opening **41** in one end wall,
vent openings **42, 43** in two side walls and a vane or flap **44** fixed to a vertical
axle **45** pivotally mounted adjacent the end wall **46**. The vane or flap is of a
size to swing freely with minimum clearance between the bottom and top walls
and its free edge may desirably be provided with a resilient sealing strip **47** such
as a rubber weather strip to seal tightly against each side wall and to muffle the
sound of coming in contact with the respective wall.

A lever arm **48** is fixed to the upper end of the axle and extends across the top
of the damper, parallel to the vane or flap, between upwardly projecting limit
switches **S1, S2**. Actuation of the vane or flap is effected by a small motor **M**
driving gears (not shown) to rotate a crank **50** on the gear shaft **51**. The crank
is connected to the lever arm by a long link **52**, and, preferably, a short link **53**
which is centered by springs **54**, the effect of which is to permit closing of the
damper vane or flap against either side wall with a yielding contact or squeezing

action, whereby precise adjustment of the throw of the crank **50** is not required. In Figure 7.13a, the air circulation path is indicated by arrows and flow lines. The condition illustrated in Figure 7.13a is that wherein the collector **10** is receiving thermal energy, by exposure to the rays of the sun, and is therefore capable of collecting heat either for use or for storage. The house is cool enough so that its thermostat **TH** calls for heat. In response to this call, the damper vane **17a** opens the passage through ducts **16** and **20** to the fan **21**, the damper vane **22a** closes the outlet **24** (to storage) and opens the outlet **23** to the house, and the damper vane **31a** opens the return passage between inlet **32** from the house through outlet **33** to the inlet end **11** of the collector.

Cool air from the house is drawn in through inlet **32**, passed through the collector and returned to the house as warm air through the outlet **23**, this circulation continuing until the house thermostat **TH** stops calling for heat (or the collector thermostat **TC** indicates that no more is available from the collector). At the completion of the house heating cycle, just described, and assuming that the sun is still shining on the collector, the control circuit (described below) shifts the dampers to other conditions as needed. Diagrams showing damper settings necessary to obtain other circulation paths are included in the patent.

A typical control circuit for a damper is shown in Figure 7.13c and comprises a damper motor **M**, a relay **K** having controlled contacts **K1** and **K2** and limit switches **S1** and **S2**.. Relay **K** will be energized when a circuit is closed between terminals **61** and **62**. The limit switches are normally closed, but are opened by contact by the damper arm **D** (**48** in Figure 7.13b). As shown in Figure 7.13c, the motor **M** is not energized since both switch **S1** and contact **K1** are open. If relay **K** should be energized, contact **K1** is picked up and contact **K2** is dropped out. This circuit arrangement provides a circuit through motor **M** by way of switch **S2** and picked-up contact **K1**. Motor **M** will then operate to drive damper arm **D** to the opposite position.

When the damper arm opens the switch, the circuit to motor **M** is opened and movement of the damper is halted. The circuit will remain in this condition and the damper arm in the position holding **S2** open until relay **K** is deenergized. When this occurs, the contacts return to the position shown in Figure 7.13c and another circuit is established to motor **M** through contact **K2** and switch **S1**. The motor will then operate until the damper arm returns to the position shown, to open switch **S1** breaking the circuit to motor **M**.

Three damper controls **DA**, **DB**, and **DC** are utilized and are shown in Figure 7.13d. The damper controls are identical to the circuit shown in Figure 7.13c, except that controls **DA** and **DB** include fan control relays **KF1** and **KF2**. The relays **KA**, **KB**, and **KC** are energized or deenergized in response to the condition of a controller circuit **63** which is further responsive to the settings of thermostats **TH**, **TC**, and **TS**. Thermostat **TH** senses the temperature of the house, and is normally open if the house is up to a predetermined temperature.

If thermostat **TH** closes, it energizes a relay **KH**. Thermostat **TC** senses the temperature in the collector and is open when the collector is above a predetermined temperature. If relay **TC** should close, it energizes a relay **KC**. Thermostat **TS** senses the temperature in storage and if the temperature falls below a predetermined value it will energize the relay **KS**. Relay **KH** controls a plurality of contacts **KH1** through **KH5**, Relay **KC** controls contacts **KC1** through **KC5**. Relay **KS** has one control contact **KS1** in circuit with fan motor **FM**. The fan motor may be energized through normally closed contact **KC5**, or through normally opened contact **KH5** when contact **KS1** is closed.

### Collector with Maze of Air Passageways

A solar heat converter described by *D.L. Pyle; U.S. Patent 3,902,474; Sept. 2, 1975* comprises a box of any convenient size with a maze of air passageways within the box. The passageways are partially filled with shredded heat conductive material, preferably having a black color. The heated air is forced through the passageways by means of fans or pumps, and the interior of the box is exposed to sunlight by a covering of thermal glass. In operation, the solar heat converter collects heat which is measured by an internal thermostat. The fans are operated to force heated air through an area to be heated in response to temperatures set on this and another thermostat in the area.

The principal elements of a solar energy converting module 20 (Figure 7.14) comprise an electrical control circuit 21, and a maze 22 connected to a more or less conventional forced air heating or cooling system 23, and any suitable supplemental appliance 24. The solar energy converter 20 may be made of any suitable material and in any convenient size. However, in one embodiment, it is made from materials and in sizes which are compatible with conventional building structures and practices. Thus, the outer perimeter panels 30, 31, 32, 33 of the box may be made from insulation or wooden boards, or plastic panels, about an inch thick, six to ten inches wide and two to four feet long.

In one particular case, the box was 40 inches long and 28 inches wide. The back 34 of the box may be made from a sheet of any material having suitable strength which may be joined to the sides 30, 31, 32, 33 in an airtight manner. The entire outside of the box may be insulated to reduce or preclude a loss of heat to the surrounding air.

### FIGURE 7.14: COLLECTOR WITH MAZE OF AIR PASSAGEWAYS

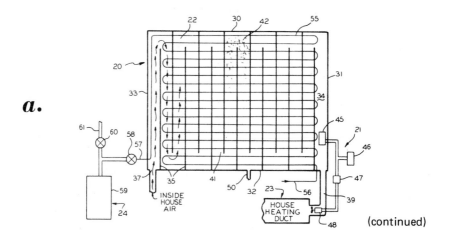

*a.*

(continued)

FIGURE 7.14: (continued)

b.

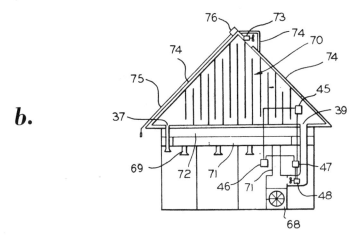

    (a)   Collector module
    (b)   Collector of Figure 7.14a built into house

Source:  U.S. Patent 3,902,474

Inside the box are any suitable number of baffles or partitions **35** arranged to form a maze or tortuous air passage. Thus, air entering the box at **37** must follow the path indicated, in part, by arrows until it leaves the box at outlet **39**. In the above-cited example of a 40-inch by 28-inch box, there are 13 baffles, each being about 24 inches long, arranged to form fourteen air passageways, one of which is numbered **41**. This arrangement forms a maze having a folded air passage which is about 28 feet long, and perhaps 2 inches by 8 inches in cross section.

All of the baffles inside the box, whether insulated or not, are covered by aluminum foil or other material having a good heat conductive material, which may be painted or otherwise colored black. The air passageway inside box **20** contains at least some shredded black aluminum foil or wire **42** in a sufficient quantity to provide a maximum amount of heat exchange, without seriously impeding the air flow inside the passageway.

A thermostat **45** is positioned inside the box near the outlet thereof and adjusted to close an electrical heating control circuit at a predetermined high temperature and to open the circuit at a predetermined low temperature. A thermostat **46** is positioned in a house, appliance, or other area to be heated by the solar energy converter. This thermostat **46** is connected in series with the thermostat **45** and is arranged to close the heating control circuit at a selected low temperature and to open it at a related high temperature.

The two thermostats **45, 46** cooperate to control a relay or other device **47** in order to demand heat when the house or other area is colder than the temperature selected by thermostat **46**, if there is a sufficiently high level of heat in the solar energy converter **20**. A circuit which is completed by relay **47** operates a fan **48** which draws air from the house through inlet port **37**, the maze inside the box, and the outlet **39** to the fan **48**. A conventional forced air heating system conveys the heated air through the house and back to inlet port **37**. If the temperature in the solar energy converter **20** is not then hot enough, thermostat **45** is not closed, and relay **47** does not operate. A conventional furnace is then turned on in a normal manner by the thermostat **46**. It is thought that such a supplementary use of a conventional furnace would be required only on extremely overcast and very cold days. A water drain **50** is formed in the bottom of the box to drain off condensation.

Any suitable number of the solar energy converters **20** may be formed into a mosaic by connecting their inlets **37** to their outlets **39**, either in series or in parallel, to thereby form a single passageway from the house through one inlet **37** and out a final outlet **39**.

Supplementing the air flow may be a fluid system comprising a pipe **55** which follows a serpentine path through the box. Thus, the fluid may be pumped through piping **55** to a point where it collects and stores heat generated by the solar energy falling on the converter. By way of example, the drawing shows an input connection **56** for leading the pipe to a city water supply, which furnishes suitable fluid pressure. The output end **57** of pipe **55** is coupled through a valve **58** to a hot water tank **59**. As an alternative, a valve **60** may also provide means for drawing water directly from the city water supply **61** and into the hot water tank. The hot water in the tank may be for any use, such as the normal hot water supply, for example.

For an existing house, a plurality of the modules of Figure 7.14a may be placed in a mosaic assemblage on top of the roof. For new housing, the solar converter may be constructed as taught in Figure 7.14b. In greater detail, the maze **70** is preferably built into the attic area or between roof and ceiling of a house to provide a folded air passage, much as described above in connection with Figure 7.14a. The air passage folded into the maze is connected into the normal duct work **71** of a forced air furnace **68** having a blower and room vents **69**. The flow of air through the duct is controlled by fan **48** and thermostats **45**, **46**. Insulation **72** is interposed between the maze in the attic and the living space in the house.

For summer months, an exhaust fan **73** may draw hot air from the attic maze and vent it through an open insulated door **74**, which is normally closed during the winter months. Also, at least a part of the roof **74** of the house is covered by thermal glass to expose the maze to the sun during the winter months and thereby heat the air. To cover the thermal glass during summer months a light reflective awning **75** may be unrolled from a box **76** permanently mounted on the roof.

### Solar Heated Patio Area Enclosed in Building Structure

*R.F. Schmitt and E.A. Schmitt; U.S. Patent 3,894,369; July 15, 1975* provide a building structure in which most or all of the exterior glass area is exposed to an outdoor area which is enclosed during cold weather and has a transparent roof permitting passage of solar energy therethrough for heating the enclosed area and thereby minimizing the loss of heat through the exterior glass area without sacrifice to natural lighting or outdoor viewing. A fire in the enclosed area is readily visible from virtually every room in the structure and may be used to provide supplemental heat to the enclosed area at night or during poor solar days in cold weather. Sliding glass doors and the like may also provide easy access to the enclosed area from virtually every room in the structure, and because of the solar heating effects on the enclosed area, it may be used for various outdoor patio activities substantially the year around.

The particular building structure **1** illustrated in Figure 7.15 is generally in the shape of a U, providing a central outdoor patio or court area **2** enclosed along three of its sides by the walls of the house and along the fourth side by an insulated wall **3** having large glass portions **4** which may be opened or removed for a purpose to be subsequently described. The two wings or sides **5** and **6** of the house **1** may have separate roof portions **7** and **8**, respectively, whereas the connecting portion **9** of the house between the two sides and the patio area **2** may be covered by a single gable roof **10**.

Thus, there is formed a building structure in which most or all of the exterior glass area is exposed to an outdoor area that is enclosed under a transparent roof with insulated wall enclosure during cold weather to create a greenhouse effect which substantially reduces or completely eliminates the loss of heat through the exterior glass area depending on the temperature differential between the enclosed outdoor area and the interior space exposed to the outdoor area. If the temperature of the enclosed solar heated area is only slightly less than the interior temperature, there will be very little heat loss through the exterior glass area, whereas if the temperature of the enclosed solar heated area is higher than the interior temperature an interior heat temperature gain will result by the heat passing directly through the exterior glass area or by opening the glass area to permit transmission of the heat by convection.

### FIGURE 7.15: SOLAR HEATED PATIO AREA ENCLOSED IN BUILDING STRUCTURE

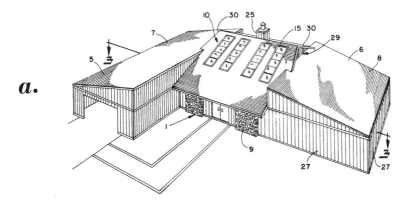

(continued)

**FIGURE 7.15:** (continued)

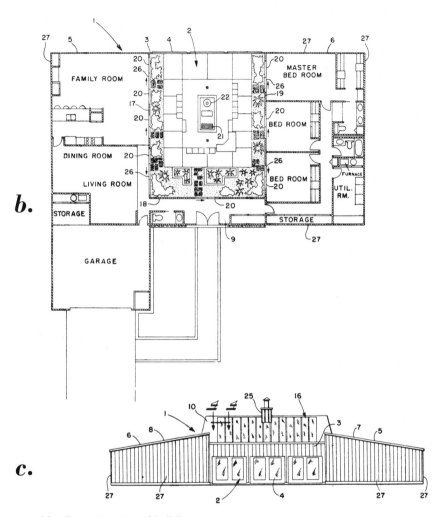

*b.*

*c.*

(a) Perspective view of building structure
(b) Horizontal section taken on the plane of the line 3–3 of Figure 7.15a
(c) Rear elevation view

Source: U.S. Patent 3,894,369

By eliminating most or all of the exterior glass area along the exterior walls of the structure not exposed to the enclosed solar heated area, the major source of heat loss through the building structure is eliminated with little or no sacrifice to natural lighting and outdoor viewing. In fact, the enclosed outdoor area provides an excellent patio setting which may be used for outdoor patio activities and to grow flowers and other plants the year around in colder climates because of the solar heating effects on the area. Supplemental heating for the entire structure may also be obtained from the patio area on cold nights or during poor solar days by providing a fire in a fireplace and/or potbellied stove in the patio area. In addition to the heating effects, a patio fire may be used for outdoor cooking, and there are also the psychological benefits obtained from the patio fire which is visible from virtually every room in the house. A patio fire also eliminates the heat loss from a fire in a conventional interior fireplace and its unbalancing effect on the house heating system, and a patio fire is also much safer since it is not near any combustible materials.

During warm weather, the solar heating effects on the patio area may be minimized by opening large glass doors or windows in the insulated wall of the patio area and large louvers in the gable ends of the glass covered roof area and vented openings at the bottom of the front roof slope glass area which create a chimney effect inside the patio area for continuously removing excess heat in the summer. Insulating panels may also be installed over the patio glass areas to assist in keeping the patio area cool in warm weather and also minimize heat loss through the patio glass area during cold weather when the sun is not shining.

## SYSTEMS INCLUDING STORAGE MEANS

### Heat Storage Fluid Used for Heating and Cooling

The system of *K.A. Alkasab; U.S. Patent 4,007,776; February 15, 1977; assigned to Universal Oil Products Company* provides a solar energy powered heating and cooling system which is simple in design, which is easily switched from a heating to a cooling mode, which produces cooling from the relatively low temperature water supplied from a flat plate solar collector and which provides storage capacity for both heat and cold and uses both for cooling to limit the requirement for auxiliary power.

In the system, solar energy is collected by a collector device such as a simple flat plate collector mounted on the roof of a residence. A collector circuit circulates water or other fluid from a heat storage tank through the solar collector by means of a collector pump. After the water is heated by the solar collector it is returned to the heat storage tank to raise the temperature thereof. Temperature sensors in the heat storage tank and within the solar collector sense the fluid temperature and the temperature of the absorption surface of the collector and are utilized in a control device to prevent the collector pump from operating when the water in the storage tank is hotter than the absorption surface in the solar collector. In order to insure sufficient hot water in the storage tank when there are long periods without sunshine, an auxiliary heating element is provided in the heat storage tank.

A heat exchanger located within the heat storage tank has inlet and outlet tubes which carry circulating water which is heated indirectly by the fluid in the tank. Depending on whether the system is in its heating mode or its cooling mode, a set of 3-way valves is selectively actuated to direct the water to either heat exchange means for warming the space to be heated or to a refrigerant boiler. In the heating mode, the house thermostat can control the pump which circulates the water to the heat exchange means. The space heating and cooling heat exchange means can be located centrally and can be connected to a central blower and air ducts or can be located in individual rooms. If desired, separate heat exchangers could be used for heating and cooling. When the 3-way valves are actuated in the cooling mode, the heat storage tank heat exchanger is directly coupled with a heat exchanger in a refrigerant boiler to circulate heated water from the heat storage tank to the boiler so as to heat the refrigerant therein. Preferably, a refrigerant having a relatively low boiling point is used since flat plate solar collectors have a relatively limited heating capacity. Refrigerant R-11, which evaporates at 75°F at atmospheric pressure, is an example of a suitable refrigerant.

As the refrigerant boils, the vapors formed in the boiler travel to an ejector where they expand and produce a vacuum which lowers the boiling point of liquid refrigerant in an evaporator and draws additional refrigerant vapors from the evaporator into the ejector. The combined vapors or gases then pass to a fan-cooled condenser where they are cooled and condensed into liquid. A refrigerant pump in the refrigerant circuit pumps a portion of the refrigerant liquid back to the boiler and a portion back to the evaporator. The evaporator is positioned in a cold storage tank in heat exchange relation with a quantity of brine therein. The evaporator serves to cool the brine by drawing heat from it to replace heat lost by the refrigerant as it boils in response to the lowering of its vapor pressure by the vacuum in the ejector.

A heat exchanger in the cold storage tank is placed in series with the heat exchange means in the space being cooled to circulate cold water to it as an incident of operating the aforementioned 3-way valves. The circulating pump is controlled by the house thermostat. To prevent freezing of either the brine in the cold storage tank or the circulating water, a temperature sensor is placed in the brine and used to control the operation of the refrigerant pump, the condenser fan, and the boiler pump which circulates hot water to the boiler from the heat storage tank.

Referring to Figure 7.16, the heating and cooling system is indicated generally at **10** and includes a solar collector **12** which has an absorption surface **13** from which heat may be collected by water **14** which is circulated to the solar collector from the heat storage tank **16** by means of an inlet circulating line **18** and an outlet circulating line **20**. The flow of water, or any other heat transfer fluid, is caused by circulating pump **22** positioned in the inlet line **18**. Preferably, an expansion tank **24** is located in the outlet line **20**. It is desirable to prevent the circulation of water through the solar collector when the water leaving the collector would not be as hot as the water already in the storage tank.

For this purpose, a water temperature sensor **26** is located in the heat storage tank and a collector temperature sensor **28** is located in contact with absorption surface **13**. The temperature readings produced by the aforementioned sensors are compared in a heat controller **32** in a conventional manner and used to control the operation of circulating pump **22**. When the temperature of the water in the storage tank is less than a predetermined minimum, such as 150°F, a heater switch **36** operated by the heat control unit **32** is actuated to energize auxiliary heating element **38** located in the heat storage tank. In order to minimize the operation of the auxiliary heating element the switch **36** is preferably deenergized by the controller **32** when the water in tank **16** reaches a temperature of approximately 160°F.

## FIGURE 7.16: HEAT STORAGE FLUID USED FOR HEATING AND COOLING

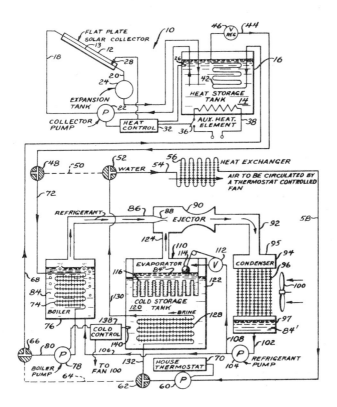

Source: U.S. Patent 4,007,776

Located within the heat storage tank **16** is a heat exchange coil **42** having an outlet line **44** which contains a flow regulating valve **46** for controlling the rate of flow in the line and thus the rate at which heat can be transferred from the water **14** in the storage tank. When the system **10** is to be used for heating, the fluid in the line, which may be water or other suitable heat transfer medium, passes through 3-way valve **48** which is actuated in the heating mode to direct the fluid through line **50** to a second 3-way valve **52** from whence it flows through line **54** and through a heat exchanger **56**.

The heat exchanger preferably has air passed through it by a circulating fan (not shown) for warming the space to be heated and may be either a central type unit such as found in conventional heating and air conditioning systems or an individual room unit. After losing heat in the heat exchanger, the cooled fluid flows through line **58**, heat exchanger circulating pump **60**, 3-way valve **62**, line **64**, 3-way valve **66** and back through line **68** to the heat exchange coil **42** in the heat storage tank to be reheated. A thermostat **70** controls the operation of circulating pump **60** to control the amount of heat available to the heat exchanger.

In the cooling mode the 3-way valve **48** is actuated to the position so that the hot fluid in line **44** will pass through line **72** into a heat exchange coil **74** positioned within the refrigerant boiler **76**. As the cooled fluid exits from the heat exchanger **74** it passes through boiler pump **78**, line **80**, 3-way valve **66** and back through return line **68** to the heat exchange coil **42**. The refrigerant boiler **76** contains a refrigerant **84** such as refrigerant R-11 which boils at atmospheric pressure at approximately 75°F. As the refrigerant is boiled in boiler **76** by the heat produced by the heat exchange coil the vapors produced pass through ejector inlet tube **86** and through nozzle **88** in the ejector **90**. As the vapor or gases leave the nozzle their pressure is greatly reduced so as to create a vacuum condition within the ejector.

The gases then leave the ejector through an ejector outlet tube **92** from whence they pass to a condenser **94** having an inlet gas manifold **95**, heat exchange tubes **96** and an outlet gas manifold **97**. The gases entering the inlet manifold are cooled as they pass through the heat exchange tubes by a fan **100** and are condensed into liquid **84'** by the time they reach the outlet manifold. The condensed liquid then passes through liquid line **102** and refrigerant pump **104**. A portion **84** of the liquid is then returned through boiler refrigerant inlet line **106** to the boiler. The remaining portion **84''** of the liquid condensate leaving the condenser passes through the evaporator refrigerant inlet line **108** into the evaporator indicated generally at **110**.

The flow of liquid into the evaporator is controlled by valve **112** in response to the liquid level of fluid **84''** as sensed by float member **114**. The evaporator includes a plurality of evaporator heat exchange tubes **116** which contact the refrigerant liquid **84''** on their external surfaces while contacting the brine solution **120** with their internal surfaces. The brine solution is contained in a large cold storage tank **122**. A suction line **124** connects the evaporator to the vacuum region of the ejector produced by the venturi effect of the nozzle. Accordingly, the surface of the liquid **84''** in the evaporator is subjected to a much lower surface pressure than the liquid **84** in the boiler. The lower pressure reduces the boiling point of the liquid **84''** in the evaporator and thereby cools the liquid **84''** as heat is extracted from it to boil off vapors which are drawn into the ejector.

The brine is also cooled as heat is extracted from it by the heat exchange tubes to replace the heat removed from the refrigerant **84''**. The cold stored in the storage tank **22** is transmitted to the residence heat exchange means **56** by a heat exchange coil **128** filled with water or other suitable heat exchange fluid positioned in the brine, outlet line **130**, 3-way valve **52** and line **54**. The warmed fluid is returned to tank **122** by line **58**, pump **60**, 3-way valve **62**, and return line **132**. The flow of cold fluid through the heat exchanger is controlled by the residence thermostat **70** which is connected to the circulating pump.

In order to prevent the cold storage tank **122** from getting too cold and freezing up, a cold control **138** is provided which includes a temperature sensor **140** immersed in the brine **120**. When the brine drops to a temperature of approximately 35°F the cold control **138** turns off the boiler pump **78**, the refrigerant circulating pump **104** and the condenser cooling fan **100**.

## Conduits in Rock Layer Below Concrete Floor Slab

In the system of *V. Heilemann; U.S. Patent 4,000,851; January 4, 1977,* rotatably adjustable elongated cylindrical solar collector plate cells, rotatable around the elongated axis thereof for adjusting angle of incidence of exterior light rays from the sun to the surface of the collector plate, are mounted upon a roof with water flow therefrom being channelled below an insulated ceiling downwardly for alternate flow as between parallel flow paths alternating selectively to and through concrete slab conduits having copper tubing directing heated water therethrough. The parallel flow conduits are situated through a layer of rocks beneath the concrete slab. The concrete slab is a part of the floor structure of the dwelling and the layer of rocks is a reservoir sink therebeneath.

Flow is directed dependent upon differential temperature of the upper floor surface of the concrete slab, such that space within supporting wall room space defined between the ceiling and the floor is economically heated devoid of excessive room temperatures and with substantially level and constant ambient temperature ranges as desired and preset within the room space over extended periods of time for and throughout a heating season of the year. The system may be inoperative and nonfunctional when heat is not desired, and includes further a hot-water heating provision embodied within an intermediate heat exchanger located between the solar cells fluid circuit and the concrete slab heating circuit.

With reference to Figures 7.17a and 7.17b, a system of solar cells **5** is arranged along a roof **57**, with individual cells lying substantially horizontally along the surface of the roof extending lengthwise of the roof, having cell inlet pipes **7a**, **7b**, **7c** and cell outlet pipes **8a**, **8b**, and **8c** collectively channelled through collector pipe **9** and into down-pipe **11** into the reservoir tank **12**.

## FIGURE 7.17: SYSTEM WITH ROOF-MOUNTED COLLECTOR

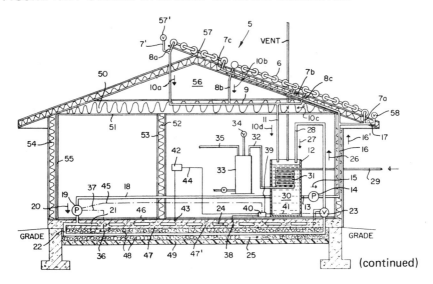

(continued)

FIGURE 7.17: (continued)

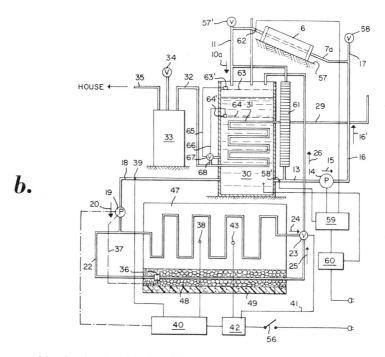

(a)  An elevation side view of house
(b)  Diagrammatic flow and circuitry diagram of the process

Source:  U.S. Patent 4,000,851

The reservoir tank has space **30** with hot-water heating coils **31** to be heated
thereby to heat cold water entering through source water pipe **29** with an outlet to the hot water tank **33** by the outlet pipe **32**.  From the water within
space **30**, outlet **13** leads cooler water from the tank to pump **13** delivering water by up-pipe **16** in direction **16'** to the safety valve mechanism **17** and to the
inlets **7a, 7b,** and **7c**.  Also from the tank space outlet pipe **18** leads the water
to pump **19** in direction **20** through one or both alternate flow-path pipes **21**
and **22**, the extent of flow through the pipes being controlled by the flip or
butterfly valve **23** which is controlled by thermostat **40** as dependent upon the
temperature of the concrete slab **47** as sensed by sensor **38** as well as dependent
upon the temperature of the water in pipe **18** as sensed by sensor **39**.

Thermostatic sensor **38** causes the valve to direct all or more flow through pipe
**21** when the upper surface of the concrete slab drops below a predetermined
set temperature, and causes the valve to direct more or all flow to flow through
the pipe **22** after the upper surface temperature at thermostatic sensor exceeds
a predetermined value whereby heat becomes stored in the rocks **48** preferably
of large gravel size, typically, and the peripheral insulation **49**, which typically
is urethane foam or the like, prevents any significant heat loss in a downward

direction to an exterior of the building structure, as water flows in direction 25 until valve 23 again shifts flow to pipe 21 for flow in direction 24. The thermostat (differential thermostat) 40 also in part controls the pump 19 turning it on whenever thermostatic sensor 38 senses a predetermined low and also thermostatic sensor 36 turning on the pump whenever the temperature of the rocks 48 is below a predetermined minimum. Pump 19 is off only when both the sensors are switched to off, whereby the pump remains running when flow is shunted from pipe 21 to pipe 22.

Thermostatic sensor 43 is a safety sensor which causes switch 42 to break circuit if and when the temperature of the concrete upper portion exceeds a predetermined dangerous or hazardous temperature, thereby turning off power to the system and shutting down the pump. Downflow through the down-pipe 11 in direction 10d results in a heating of water in the tank to a predetermined temperature at which the pump 14 shuts down as controlled by the differential thermostat 59 which responds differently to the signals from thermostatic sensors 58 and 62, and turns on the flow when that temperature differential drops, as compared to the temperature of outflow water from the solar cell 6 as typically shown in Figure 7.17b.

The water tank 33 has the conventional safety vent valve 34 and house-water outlet pipe 35. Sight-glass 61 permits visual inspection of the water level within the tank 30. Sensors 63' and 64' sense respectively the turn-off water level 63 and the turn-on water level 64 and these sensors jointly control the off-on valve 67 through leads 65 and 66, controlling inlet flow through inlet pipe 68 into the space 30.

While the primary utility of the process concerns the concept of the combination of low-temperature utilizable water to adequately heat the living spaces of the building by virtue of solar energy supplying only low temperatures during most of the day and/or evening hours, in conjunction with the floor-heating unit thereby eliminating the problem of prior art systems of solar heat units which have relied solely upon conventional radiators, baseboard heat and the like, the utility is further enhanced by heavy ceiling insulation and preferably also both outer and inner-walls insulations 50, 54, and 53, respectively, of the ceiling 51, outer walls 55 and inner walls 53 as typically identified, retaining acquired heat.

In related work by *V. Heilemann; U.S. Patent 3,991,937; November 16, 1976* there is provided a dwelling structure which includes a floor heating structure including copper piping embedded within a concrete slab having insulation thereunder. The system has hot water circulated to the concrete slab conduits from a solar cell unit arranged along an upright outer wall of the dwelling at an elevation substantially beneath the floor heating structure and the system also has a hot water-containing reservoir vessel located at an elevation substantially above the floor heating structure in flow series in closed circuit for flow from the vessel to the floor heating structure downwardly to a lower portion of the solar cells and upwardly from an upper portion of the solar cells to the reservoir vessel, by heat convection flow.

The solar cells are arranged substantially along the upright outer wall of the dwelling, and the individual cells are cylindrical rotatable cells rotatable around the elongated axis thereof, adapted such that the angle of incidence of sunlight rays is adjustable intermittently, with the solar cells extending with the longitudinal elongated axes substantially horizontal, but preferably with the outlet end being at least slightly elevated above the inlet end thereof, thereby enhancing heat convection flow therethrough. A diagrammatic elevation side view of the system is shown in Figure 7.18.

## FIGURE 7.18: SYSTEM WITH UPRIGHT COLLECTOR

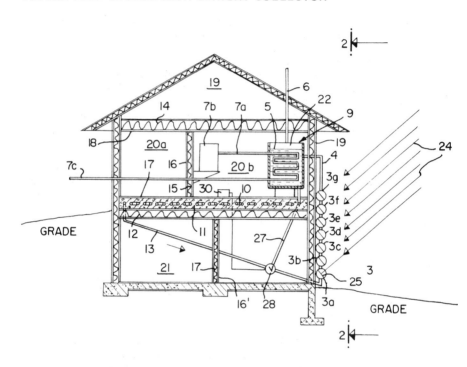

Source:   U.S. Patent 3,991,937

### System with Three-Bridged Control Circuit

*R.J. Schlesinger; U.S. Patent 3,986,489; October 19, 1976* describes a system for transferring thermal energy from a solar energy collector to a storage tank by pumping water from the tank through the heat exchanger and back into the tank. Two temperature-sensitive thermistors sense respectively the temperature of the water as leaving the heat exchanger or as being held therein, and the temperature of the water in the tank or as leaving the tank; these thermistors are included in bridge circuits which provide control signals representing the collector and tank temperatures and the differences of these temperatures for controlling water circulation, collector heating and/or dumping of the water, for collecting thermal energy and for preventing the circulation from freezing or boiling.

The control circuit providing the control operations is a simple one. It consists essentially of two thermistors respectively placed at or near the outlets of collector and water tank (for monitoring water temperatures) and (electrically) connected in a bridge circuit whose diagonal voltage represents merely the monitored temperature differential and controls a solid state device which in turn turns the pump on and off in accordance with the temperature differential, so that pumping of water will result in a flow of thermal energy in the desired direction only.

Figure 7.19a shows a relatively large, flat plate collector **10**, having a large black surface exposed to the radiation of the sun and mounted, e.g., to the south side roof of a dwelling. Meandering duct **11** is provided directly underneath the black surface in good thermal conductive relation therewith or even constituting part thereof. Water flows through the collector duct **11** which is fed thereto by a pipe **12** and discharged therefrom via a pipe **13**.

Water is pumped up in pipe **12** by an electrically controlled pump **15**, drawing water from a storage tank **16**, particularly from the bottom thereof. Water flows into the tank through pipe **13** simply by force of gravity as the tank is presumed to be in a lower portion of the building. There is no inherent necessity for this spatial relation, but that will simply be the result of considerations of practicality. A check valve **14** prevents backflow of water in the path, when pumped. The pipe **13** (or **12**) has a portion **13a**, which is of reduced cross section, throttling the rate of flow. The rate is quite small as will be shown shortly. However, reference numeral **13b** denotes a by-pass of normal cross section, and being operative only when a valve **19** is open. That valve is normally open but closed under control of circuit **20** when the pump maintains a circulation of water through the collector for preventing freezing.

A heat exchanger **17** may be included in tank **16** for feeding the heating system **18** of the building. However, the water of the tank itself could be circulated through the heating system; on the other hand, temperature control and constant water temperature in the user circuit is more readily obtained when the circulations are kept separately. This way, the collector-tank circulation can accumulate as much thermal, solar energy as the collector can gather on a day by day basis and as weather conditions permit. That amount of energy may differ from day to day.

The pump **15** is controlled by the circuit **20** operating in such a manner that water is permitted to descend through pipe **13** only when the collector water is hotter than the water in the bottom portion of the tank **16**. Then and only then will it pump cooler water from the tank up to the collector for being heated before return to the tank. The valve **19** opens the by-pass for this operation. For normal operation, control circuit **20** operates the pump **15** on the basis of the temperature differential between collector temperature and tank temperature. The temperature differential is detected by measuring the temperature of the water in the collector (transducer **21**) and by measuring the temperature, e.g., at the outlet of or otherwise near the bottom of tank **16** (transducer **22**).

The control circuit **20** processes the signals provided by transducers **21, 22** for controlling pump **15**. One will preferably use thermistors as temperature sensing transducers. The circuit **20** shown in Figure 7.19b includes a sensing bridge **25** with DC bias circuit **30** for the bridge circuit which includes the two thermistors

21 and 22 establishing two of the four branches; two resistors 26 and 28 are the other two branches, one of the resistors being actually a potentiometer, 28, to change the balance between branches 22 - 28.

## FIGURE 7.19: SYSTEM WITH THREE-BRIDGED CONTROL CIRCUIT

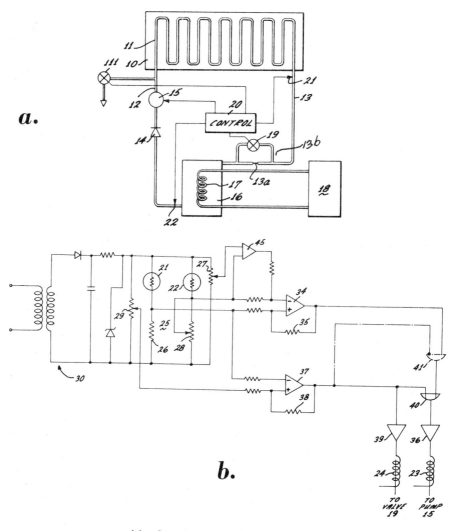

(a)     Schematic illustration of system
(b)     Circuit diagram of the control circuit

Source:   U.S. Patent 3,986,489

The DC bias is applied to the junction between the thermistors and the junction between the resistors. The bridge diagonal voltage is taken between the potentiometer 28 tap and the junction between thermistor 21 and resistor 26. The diagonal voltage is applied to a differential amplifier 34, which is used as comparator with positive feedback for hysteresis.

The potentiometer together with positive, zero-output feedback by resistor 35 determines the differential in temperature, which sets the pump 15 into motion. Specifically, if the two thermistors exhibit a particular difference as to their respective temperature dependent resistance, commensurate with the temperature differential adjustment as per potentiometer setting, amplifier 34 will respond. The amplifier may control a relay driver 36 which in turn operates a pump relay 23 to turn pump 15 on when the collector temperature exceeds the tank temperature by the value as set by the potentiometer.

While the pump is working, the collector heats water which is being pumped up, and the heated water flows back into the tank. Since the capacity of the collector is smaller than that of the tank, the water temperature of the tank will rise slower, but it will rise. Nevertheless, the temperature differential between collector and tank will remain sufficiently large to keep the pump working. Thus, as the tank water is being heated, the resistance of thermistor 22 drops also but that drop will not have any effect on the control as long as the collector water remains hotter than the tank water.

It may be advisable, e.g., to set the potentiometer to a level so that a relatively large spread in temperature is needed to set the system into motion in the morning (e.g., 20°F). The temperature must change, so that the voltage at the junction between the two thermistors will rise to a particular value before the pump is turned on. The circuit has a built-in hysteresis, so that a decline in collector temperature following turn-on will not turn the system off. The amplifier circuit has positive feedback (resistance 35) for this purpose.

Eventually the temperature of the collector will begin to decline, e.g., in the late afternoon the collector will be heated to a lesser extent than around noon or in the early afternoon, and the temperature differential will diminish; the resistance of the two thermistors will tend to equalize. However, the system should continue as long as the water leaves the collector warmer than it entered. The bridge voltage drops below the value as set by 28 and 35 when the temperature differential is quite small again, whereupon the pump is shut down. Subsequently, the residual water in the collector will cool further but that causes a change in the input of amplifier 34 in a direction away from the pump turn-on level. When the sun comes up, the cycle will start anew.

Turning now to the nighttime problem, thermistor 21 monitors collector temperature. Accordingly, a second potentiometer 29 is provided and connected across the DC bias circuit 30 to establish a second bridge which shares elements 21, 27, and 28 with the first-mentioned bridge. Potentiometer 29 is adjusted so that an amplifier 37 is operated when the thermistor indicates that the collector threatens to freeze. Amplifier 37 operates a relay driver 39 which in turn operates a relay 24 for control of the valve 19. Positive feedback resistor 38 introduces a hysteresis also here to prevent shunting of the protective control.

The illustrated circuit shows a logic circuit interposed between amplifiers **34**, **37** and relay drivers **36**, **39**. But for the logic circuit the latter drivers were not needed. The and/or circuit **41/40** makes sure that either the response of amplifier **34** (tank temperature sufficiently below collector temperature) or amplifier **37** (collector temperature close to freezing) will turn the pump **15** on. Response of both amplifiers **34**, **37** (tank and collector temperature close to freezing) constitutes an error condition and is used logically to prevent the pump from being turned on.

If the water in the tank **16** is not too warm, and ambient conditions are severe, the tank temperature may drop and now suddenly the differential in signals between **21** and **22** may again drop but from the opposite direction. That condition could be sensed separately to control turn off of pump **15** while dump valve **111** opens for emptying the collector **11**. Instead of maintaining a low rate circulation, the response of freeze control amplifier **37** could be used directly to open the dump valve. In this case, and/or structure **41/40** and constriction **13a** could be omitted; a by-pass is likewise not needed in this case. Moreover, the relay drivers **36** and **39** may likewise not be needed if the amplifiers **34** and **37** have sufficient gain to drive relays. The two circuits are completely decoupled.

In lieu of dumping water or maintaining a slow rate warm water circulation, the response of amplifier **37** can be used to turn a heater on in collector **11**, sufficient to heat the collector. The heating of the collector could be used directly, without pump, so that circuit **40** and **41** can be omitted also in this case. Thermistor **21** could be used additionally as thermostatic control for the intensity of the heating or, if the heating is rather strong, one may operate in alternating on-off cycles.

The circuit includes a third bridge, composed of bridge branch **22**, **28** and a potentiometer **27**. Thermistor **21** senses tank temperature, and potentiometer **27** is set at a value to cause the voltage derivable from this third bridge to change polarity when the temperature in the tank approaches and exceeds a danger point, such as 211°F or thereabouts, depending on response of the system. This bridge voltage is monitored by a differential amplifier **45** which when responding and providing a nonzero output changes the balance on the input for circuit **34** to obtain pump shut down.

### Combination Water Heater and Chiller

This process of *R.J. Rowekamp; U.S. Patent 3,886,998; June 3, 1975* relates to a method and an apparatus which can be used either to heat or cool water through solar technology merely by the addition or removal of a few materials from a basic structure, thus making it possible to expose water to sunlight in winter so as to provide hot water for heating buildings, or to chill water by exposing it to cold night air during summer so as to cool the same buildings.

The basic object is to reduce the cost of hot and cold water thus produced by using what is essentially a water chiller as a basic structure, and then adding to it during winter, a glass panel at the top and an insulating panel at the bottom so the device can be converted into a solar water heater. Also provided are ways for heating or cooling several small houses or one very large building through the use of automatic controls, large storage tanks, and an enclosed collector area located in the backyard and in the midst of several houses so that it is not necessary to mount the devices on the roofs of the buildings themselves, as has been the practice in most solar energy projects.

Wood dividers **11** serve as a structural support for four thin gage, narrow, shallow, and uncovered aluminum pans **12** shown in Figure 7.20a. Wood bottom supports **13a** and **13b** are shown which brace the aluminum pans from the bottom. The four pans each have a supply pipe **14** running into them so they can be filled with water **16**; on the opposite side of the chiller **9** is a drain pipe **15** so water can be removed after it is either heated or chilled. In Figure 7.20a is shown how drain pipe **15** is constructed so that water can be drained out of all the pans by a suction pump, thus eliminating the necessity of welding a pipe to the bottom of the pans to accomplish drainage.

**FIGURE 7.20: COMBINATION WATER HEATER AND CHILLER**

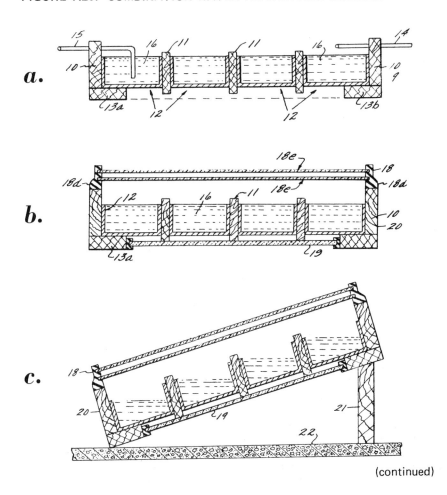

(continued)

**FIGURE 7.20:** (continued)

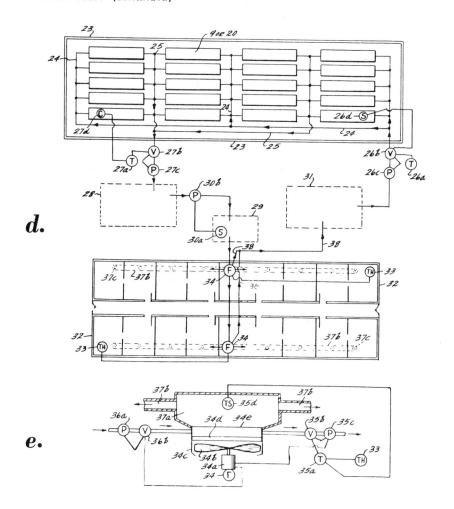

**d.**

**e.**

(a)   View in section of solar water chiller
(b)   View in section showing solar water heater
(c)   Schematic view in section showing solar water heater
(d)   Schematic view of group of combination solar water heaters and chillers
(e)   Enlarged detail view of fan unit shown in 7.20d

Source:  U.S. Patent 3,886,998

Pans **12** will be made from thin gage aluminum sheet or coil that contains 2% silicon and 1% manganese alloyed with it, so the light shiny metal will turn black as described in U.S. Patent 3,314,414.  Figures 7.20b and 7.20c show a solar water heater **20**, which was created by adding glass panel **18** and insulating panel **19** to the water chiller **9** shown in Figure 7.20a.  All the components of the water chiller serve to help heat water by sunlight; as the sun shines through the glass panel **18**, its infrared rays are absorbed by the black color which has been oxidized on the shallow, narrow, thin gage aluminum pans **12**; the wood frame **10**, wood dividers **11**, and bottom supports **13a** and **13b** brace the aluminum pans so they can hold their shape and contain the water **16**. Insulating panel **19** and glass panel **18** help prevent heat losses from the solar water heater **20**. Figure 7.20c shows how the solar water heater can be tilted toward the sun in winter when it is far off in the southern skies; this is accomplished merely by placing a wood block **21** under the bottom support **13a**; the front portion of the water heater will rest directly on the earth **22**. Figure 7.20c clearly illustrates the practicality of the narrow aluminum pans that were designed for the water heater; if only one wide pan were used to cover the entire bottom and sides of the water heater, little water could be held in it because the steep pitch would make it overflow at the lower end; but, as designed, about three times as much water can be exposed to sunlight, and more energy can be collected.

Figure 7.20d shows a group of combination solar water chillers **9** or water heaters **20** enclosed within a fenced area **23**; only a few devices are shown on the drawing, but under field conditions as many as a thousand might be so enclosed. The chillers or heaters will be filled with water by supply pipe **24**, and emptied of water by drain pipe **25**. Automatic controls will be used to fill and drain the solar devices and to assure that the maximum amount of water will be heated or chilled within a day's time.

To provide for ample storage of energy in the form of hot or chilled water, two large tanks and one small tank will be provided. Heated or chilled water will be drained into a large water storage tank, hereinafter called energy storage tank **28**, capable of holding 25,000 to 100,000 gallons of energized water, so that a large group of homes in a subdivision or a large commercial building can be made comfortable in winter and summer; after this heated or chilled water has been used to accomplish its purpose, the water will be recycled to another large storage tank, hereinafter called deenergized water storage tank **31** for reuse in the system.

A small tank **29** will be connected to energy storage tank **28** containing the heated or chilled water, and its purpose will be to act as a temporary storage near the building so that the heated or chilled water will not be standing in piping where it will dissipate all its energy into the ground instead of into the buildings. Figure 7.20d also shows an office building **32** having several offices to be heated and cooled. The comfort system for the building will consist of a fan unit and automatic controls, which will supply hot or cold water to the fan unit and periodically drain or refill it so that a continuous flow of hot or cold air can be made by the fan unit and be distributed to the offices by an air duct system.

Figure 7.20d shows how the chiller **9** or water heaters **20** will be automatically filled and drained through the use of automatic controls. A valve **26b** and a pump **26c** are installed in the main trunk of supply pipe **24**, thus making it possible to fill all the solar devices within fenced area **23** through the use of one pump and one valve. Timer **26a** will be connected to both valve **26b** and pump **26c**; and, depending upon the season, will be set to pump in new water from deenergized water storage tank **31** twice to several times a day or night. When the chillers or water heaters are filled, a float switch **26d**, located in one master solar unit, will close valve **26b** and shut off pump **20c**.

Next, the water in all the solar devices will be either heated or cooled, depending upon the season; after this has been accomplished, timer **27a** will open valve **27b** and start suction pump **27c**, which will remove all the heated or chilled water from the solar devices through drain pipe **25**, and pump it into energy storage tank **28**. If it is winter, timers **26a** and **27a** will be set to fill and drain the solar devices about twice a day, starting with one batch around 9 o'clock in the morning, draining it around noon, putting in a second batch shortly after noon, and draining it again around 4 o'clock in the afternoon. If it is summer, the timers will be set to fill and drain the solar devices at two hour intervals; and each time the temperature of the water will reach 45° to 65°F or whatever the night temperature happens to be.

If it is cloudy or rainy or snowing in winter or if it is too hot in summer and one of the batches is not brought to a useable temperature, temperature sensor **27d**, located in one master solar unit, will not permit timer **27a** to function until the designated temperature is achieved.

Figures 7.20d and 7.20e show how the office building **32** will be heated and cooled through the use of automatic controls. Hot or cold water will remain in the energy storage tank until the thermostat **33** in the office building calls out for heating or cooling. The thermostat is tied in with fan unit **34** and all the controls which move energized water into the radiator **34e** and out into deenergized storage tank **31**; it also controls, indirectly, pump **30b**, which takes water out of energy storage tank **28** and pumps it into small storage tank **29**; a float switch **30a** in the small storage tank starts pump **30b** after pump **36b** has nearly emptied the small storage tank by moving energized water into radiator **34e**.

It is estimated that to cool office building **32**, which, for example, is a structure of 35,000 square feet, that 9,000 gallons of chilled water per hour will have to be pumped through fan unit **34**, which is comprised of a motor **34a**, a fan **34b**, a fan shroud **34c**, a filter **34d**, and a radiator **34e**; this means that the radiator would have to be quite large and that, actually, several of them would be required to dissipate the chill in 9,000 gallons of cooled water every hour of a summer day; it also means that frequent changes of water will be required each hour.

Such an undertaking will be accomplished in the following fashion. As long as the temperature set on the thermostat is not satisfied, timer **35a** will remain energized, and it will pass through one cycle after another; first, to open and shut valve **35b** and start and stop pump **35c** to drain all the water out of the radiators **34e**; next, it will start motor **34a**, which blows air through filter **34d** and radiator **34e**; almost simultaneously with the starting of the fan unit, timer **35a** will open valve **36b**, and start pump **36a**, which will pump chilled water from small storage tank **29** into radiator **34e**; when this has been accomplished, the timer cycle will automatically close valve **36b** and stop pump **36a**.

The fan unit will take perhaps a minute to dissipate all the chill in the water up into the plenum **37a**, from thence into ducts **37b**, and finally out into the offices through diffuser **37c**. At this point, timer **35a** will start passing through another cycle such as described above; this will occur when a temperature sensor **35d**, located in the plenum, says that the air passing by it is too warm; and will then energize the timer so it will start its cycle. Water is now removed from the radiator **34e**, as described above, and passes through drain pipes **38** into deenergized storage tank **31**, where it will remain until the next day or night when it will be pumped into the solar devices in the fenced area **23**, where it will be heated or chilled, depending upon the season of the year.

## HYDRATION-DEHYDRATION SYSTEMS

### Dehydration of Calcium Hydroxide

*R.L. Collie; U.S. Patent 3,955,554; May 11, 1976* describes a solar heating method and apparatus including a system for storing solar heat provided for heating a house, building, or other area. A chamber is filled with calcium oxide which is fed on demand to a tank of water where it converts to calcium hydroxide releasing energy which heats the water. Heat from the water is removed through a heat exchanger for heating a building, or the like, and the calcium hydroxide is dewatered utilizing a solar heater which converts the calcium hydroxide back to calcium oxide. The calcium oxide is transferred back into the calcium oxide storage container. The solar heat collector used in the process is a parabolic mirror which reflects sunlight onto a center mirror which redirects the light into a light tunnel where it is absorbed into a solar heating chamber. Figure 7.21 is a diagram of the system.

**FIGURE 7.21: DEHYDRATION OF CALCIUM HYDROXIDE**

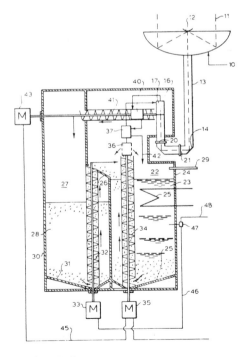

Source: U.S. Patent 3,955,554

### Vaporization of Lithium Chloride Solution

In a process by *R.R. Stubblefield; U.S. Patent 3,894,528; July 15, 1975; assigned to Broyles & Broyles, Inc.* a dilute solution of lithium chloride having a vapor pressure greater than that of relatively dry air is exposed to sunlight to vaporize water from the solution into a body of air, this concentrates the solution and lowers its vapor pressure while increasing the vapor pressure of the air-water vapor mixture. The moist air and concentrated solution are separately conveyed to a chamber where they are mixed and the water vapor is absorbed by the concentrated solution, giving up its latent heat of vaporization, and the solution is thus diluted and heated. Heat is then removed from the solution as converted solar energy and the air and cooled dilute solution are recycled in a continuous process.

In Figure 7.22, numeral **2** designates a solar collector generally in the form of a container, preferably of shallow dimension but covering a substantial horizontal area and provided with a transparent cover **4** through which sunlight may penetrate. Preferably, the bottom and side walls of the container are opaque and may be provided with either heat absorbing or heat reflective inner surfaces. A conduit **6** is arranged to direct a dilute aqueous solution of lithium chloride into the bottom of the container adjacent one end thereof and an outlet conduit **8** is arranged to drain solution from the other end of the container.

### FIGURE 7.22: VAPORIZATION OF LITHIUM CHLORIDE SOLUTION

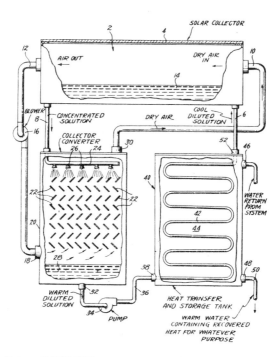

Source: U.S. Patent 3,894,528

An inlet duct **10** is arranged to direct air into the container **2** above the bottom thereof and at the end corresponding to the inlet conduit **6**. Likewise, an outlet duct **12** is arranged to receive and remove air and water vapor from the container at the same end thereof as the outlet conduit **8**. In operation, the level of the lithium chloride solution in the container will be substantially below the transparent cover **4**, so that only a relatively small volume of the container is occupied by the solution **14**. As stated, the lithium chloride solution introduced into the container is dilute, i.e., it is sufficiently diluted so that its vapor pressure is greater than the vapor pressure of the relatively dry air introduced through the inlet air duct.

As the sunlight traverses the transparent cover, the heat thereof is trapped within the container and causes vaporization of water from the solution, thus rendering the solution more concentrated and lowering its vapor pressure as it flows from inlet **6** toward outlet **8** and the heat thus absorbed is essentially only the necessary heat of vaporization and the materials do not exhibit an appreciable rise in temperature but the vapor pressure of the air increases as it entrains the water vapor.

A suitable blower or pump **16** in the outlet duct withdraws air and water vapor from the container and directs the same to an inlet **18** of a second or collector-converter container **20**, adjacent but spaced upwardly from the bottom thereof. As shown, the second container **20** is provided with a multiplicity of baffle plates **22** therein and the outlet conduit from the container directs concentrated solution from the container to a header **24** in the upper part of container **20**. The header is provided with a multiplicity of downwardly directed nozzles **26** through which the concentrated solution from the container **2** is sprayed to cascade downwardly over the baffle plates and the air and water vapor introduced through inlet **18** rises upwardly in countercurrent scrubbing relation to the solution moving downwardly over the baffle plates.

The air introduced at **18** contains a considerable amount of water vapor and its vapor pressure is thus quite high relative to that of the concentrated lithium chloride solution introduced into container **20**. As is known, under these conditions, the concentrated solution will reabsorb water vapor in the form of water and the same is condensed therein, thus releasing the latent heat of vaporization, to effect a rise in the sensible temperature of the solution and this also effects a dilution of the lithium chloride solution. A heated dilute solution then gathers in the bottom of the container, as shown at **28**. The dried air leaves the container at outlet **30** and is recirculated to inlet **10** of the first container **2** for recycling.

The heated dilute solution at **28** leaves the container **20** through its bottom outlet **32** and pump **34** causes flow thereof along conduit **36** to the inlet **38** of a heat exchanger designated generally at **40**. The heat exchanger may be any suitable type, e.g., it may contain internal coils **42**, preferably of the externally finned type, surrounded by a body of water at **44** in the heat exchanger tank, which water is in heat exchange relation to the coils. Water is circulated through the space **44** from an inlet **46** to an outlet **48**. As is obvious, the water circulating through the space will absorb heat from the heated solution in the coils and will thus extract the converted solar energy and may be directed through conduit **50** to any suitable place for storage or use. For example, the water could be circulated through the heating system of a residence but obviously could be used for any other heating purpose. The cooled diluted solution leaves the heat exchanger **40** through outlet **52** which leads directly to the inlet conduit **6** previously described and, thus, the lithium chloride solution is continuously circulated as is the solvent water, and the body of air serving as a carrier gas for the water vapors.

# DOMESTIC HOT WATER SYSTEMS

## WATER HEATER WITH SPHERICAL LENSES

*K. Nonaka; U.S. Patent 3,587,559; June 28, 1971* describes an apparatus for heating water by solar rays in which a plurality of spherical lenses are used to enable solar rays to be converged whenever there is sunlight present. The apparatus also incorporates a super-heat-resisting carbon-impregnated cloth to cover that area of metal which is subjected to the intensive heat of the focused rays.

Referring to Figure 8.1a, the apparatus comprises a box 1 covered by a glass 2 which functions to trap solar energy. The box is placed at an appropriate angle in an elevated position, for example, on the southern slope of a roof. The box in this example consists of two units, but the number of units may be decreased or increased according to the need. As seen from Figures 8.1b and 8.1c, the box is partitioned by a partition plate 3 having a plurality of regularly spaced holes 4 in rows. Each of these holes receives a hemispherical member 5 having at its mouth a brim 5a which is welded to the partition plate.

## FIGURE 8.1: WATER HEATER WITH SPHERICAL LENSES

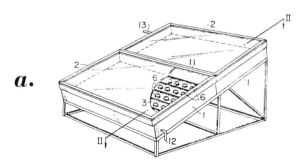

*a.*

(continued)

FIGURE 8.1:  (continued)

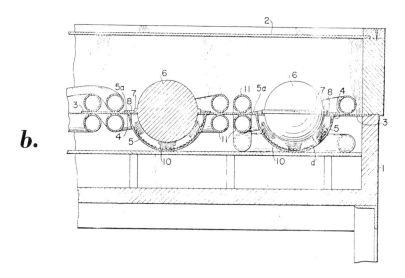

**b.**

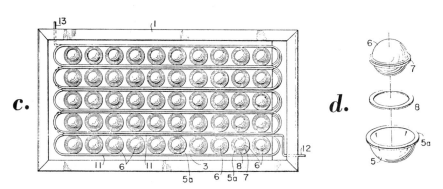

**c.**

**d.**

(a)   General perspective view of apparatus for heating water by
      solar rays according to this process (two units being
      combined)
(b)   Partially enlarged section view of apparatus at line II—II
      of Figure 8.1a
(c)   Plan view of part of apparatus (a single unit)
(d)   Perspective view of spherical lens, ring for supporting lens,
      and hemispherical member

Source:  U.S. Patent 3,587,559


A spherical lens **6** may be made of glass and formed with a flange-like projection
along its largest diameter.  This flange-like projection sits on a ring **8** which is
placed on the brim **5a** of the hemispherical member **5**.  The diameter of the lens
is smaller than that of the mouth of the hemispherical member so that the face

of the lower hemisphere of the lens 6 and the inner face of the hemispherical member 5 are spaced at such a distance d that the solar rays passing from the lens focus on the surface of a super-heat-resisting carbon-impregnated cloth 10 which lines the inner face of the hemispherical member.

The focused rays heat the carbon-impregnated cloth to high temperatures which in turn heat the hemispherical members and the partition plate 3. A continuous water pipe 11 is arranged in convolutions enclosing each row of the hemispherical members at both sides of the partition plate. Water is supplied to the water pipe from a water inlet 12 and is discharged via an outlet 13. As water passes through the water pipe, it absorbs the heat from the partition plate within the box 1 and is thereby heated to a high temperature.

If the space between the opposite faces of the hemispherical member and the lens is predetermined at an appropriate distance d (for example, 8 mm for a lens having a diameter of 40 mm), it is possible to constantly focus the rays on a portion of the carbon-impregnated cloth which lines the inner face of the hemispherical member and subject intensive heat thereto. The focal distance remains the same even when parallel rays incident on the lens come from an oblique angle, as would happen just after sunrise and just before sunset. Therefore, as long as the sun is shining, that is from sunrise to sunset, the rays passing through the lenses focus at some portions on the carbon-impregnated cloth on the hemispherical member.

If there is no such heat-resisting cloth at the points where the rays focus, a material forming the hemispherical member would be damaged at such area. If the material used is aluminum whose melting point is 658°C, the focused rays would burn holes in such material. The carbon-treated cloth used in the process is that which is made by impregnating carbon therein and giving heat treatment thereto. Such a carbon-treated cloth has the property of superheat resistance and can therefore withstand temperatures as high as 3000°C. Thus, even when the focused rays passing from the spherical lens result in as high a temperature as 1400°C, which is possible on summer days, the carbon cloth used therein withstands such heat without being burnt. Thus the heated carbon cloth may be raised to a high temperature which is transmitted to the air inside the hemispherical member and the intensive heat is conducted to the partition plate.

Since the water pipe, arranged in convolutions at both sides of the partition plate, could have a continuous length of some 30 meters, the water contained in or circulating through the pipe is effectively heated. The heating efficiency could be increased according to the need by combining two or more units of this apparatus. In such a case, the water heated in the first unit may be further communicated to the second unit. The heated water discharged from the outlet 12 is led to an appropriate hot water storage tank which is not shown in the drawings.

## CLOSED SYSTEM FOR THIN FILM HEATING OF HEAT TRANSFER FLUID

*H. Meier, Jr.; U.S. Patent 3,987,782; October 26, 1976* describes a closed-system, solar heat holder for thin-film heating of heat transfer fluid in a tank. Solar energy, passing through an insulated glass cover, is trapped between the glass cover and an absorbing surface to heat the absorbing surface and thereby a thin film of heat transfer fluid passing between the thin-film spacing provided by the absorbing surface and a parallel-disposed, insulated baffle with a bimetallic thermostat valve controlling the passage therethrough of such heat transfer fluid which, when heated, in turn gives up heat to fluid flowing through a heat exchanger, thereby cooling such heated heat transfer fluid.

Another insulated baffle is disposed parallel to the first baffle and the cooled heat transfer fluid moves downwardly between the baffles to the bottom of the tank. A pneumatic container in the tank contracts to relieve the tank of pressure resulting from the heating and expansion of the heat transfer fluid. Mirrors disposed between the glass cover and absorbing surface reflect solar energy onto the absorbing surface during variations of solar energy incidence when the sun's rays are not perpendicular to the glass cover.

In Figures 8.2a and 8.2b, reference numeral 1 generally refers to the apparatus. A trough-shaped, double-walled, watertight, metal tank 3, sandwiching therebetween suitable insulation 5, has a flat-bottomed, upstanding rear wall 9, sidewalls 11, a lower wall 13 projecting from bottom 7 and upper wall 15 projecting from the rear wall, as shown. It should be noted that the metal tank is double-walled throughout.

The shoulder portions formed in the sidewalls receive in mounting relationship a transparent, insulated glass cover 19 composed of a pair of spaced-apart glass plates 21 and 23 held in place by suitable glazing compound 25.

Radiant energy absorbing surface 27, disposed parallel to the cover, has upstanding end portions 29 received in recesses 31, and suitably sealed, formed in the lower and upper walls, respectively, and joined to the sidewalls such as by brazing. The absorbing surface preferably is blackened metal plate such as copper.

An insulated baffle 35, of marine plywood, impervious to water, and disposed parallel to the absorbing surface, has its lateral edges received in fixed mounting relationship within U-shaped channel members suitably fixed, such as by screws, to the sidewalls. Spacers 41, carried by screws disposed through copper plate 27 and engaged with baffle 35, maintain an approximate 1/16" spacing between the copper plate and the baffle. It should be noted that the spacing depicted between the copper plate and the baffle is shown exaggerated for purposes of clarity.

Shown in its closed position in Figure 8.2b is a bimetallic thermostat valve 45 whose one end is suitably fixed to the baffle and whose other operative end engages the copper plate. As would be viewed if shown in Figure 8.2a, the valve extends the full width of the copper plate absorbing surface.

A second baffle 47, similar to and disposed parallel to baffle 35, has its lateral edges received in fixed mounting relationship within U-shaped channel members suitably fixed, such as by screws, to the sidewalls.

A perforated bracket member 53, tansversely disposed relative to the rear wall and having holes formed therethrough, has its adjacent lateral edges 57 received in fixed mounting relationship within U-shaped channel members 59 suitably fixed, such as by screws, to the rear wall and sidewalls. An angle 61 is suitably fixed to baffle 47 and the bracket member to join them.

FIGURE 8.2: CLOSED SYSTEM FOR THIN FILM HEATING OF HEAT
TRANSFER FLUID

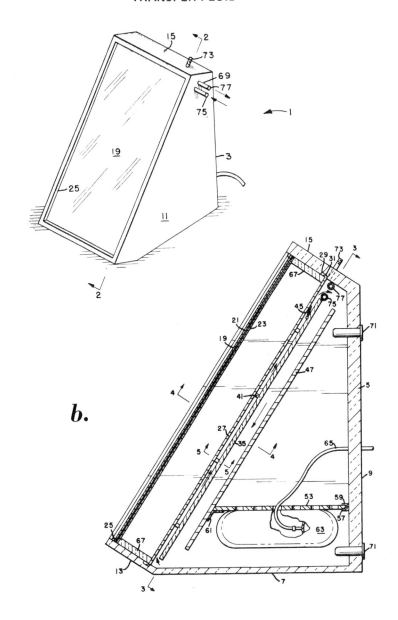

(a)    Perspective view of solar heat holder
(b)    Sectional view taken in the direction of arrows 2–2 in Figure 8.2a

Source:  U.S. Patent 3,987,782

A suitable, pressure-relieving, pneumatic container 63 has a pressure hose 65, disposed in suitable sealed relationship through rear wall 9, which communicates with the container to regulate the amount of air under pressure in the container that can be maintained, released, or introduced from an external supply (not shown).

Disposed between glass plate 23 and copper plate 27 are two reflecting surfaces 67, such as mirrors, that extend the full width of the lower wall and the upper wall, and are suitably fixed thereto. A heat exchanger 69 of U-shaped tubing is suitably mounted in fixed relationship by sidewall 11 and is suitably sealed in watertight relationship therewith.

Interiorly projecting wells 71 are suitably fixed to the rear wall. Such wells are adapted to mount and receive therein suitable conventional sensing or control devices to monitor the temperature of the heat transfer fluid in tank 3 and to control the flow of fluid through the heat exchanger in cooperation with other conventional means (not shown) for such control.

The solar heat holder is appropriately disposed in use such that the maximum solar energy will impinge upon the glass cover with the sun's rays being perpendicular to the glass cover and hence perpendicular to the copper plate absorbing surface. The filler and vent 73 is suitably utilized to fill the tank with a sufficient quantity of heat transfer fluid such as water containing ethylene glycol to prevent freezing.

For reasons of the variations in incidence of the sun's rays from early morning to late afternoon, the mirrors are employed to reflect the sun's rays during such variations onto the absorbing surface when the sun's rays are not perpendicular to the glass cover so that maximal amounts possible of such radiant heat energy will impinge upon the absorbing surface.

The radiant energy passing through insulated glass cover 19 and the air space between the glass cover and the absorbing surface is trapped therebetween and heats absorbing surface 27 and thereby the thin film of heat transfer fluid between the absorbing surface and baffle 35. Solar heating of a thin film of heat transfer fluid in a solar heat holder appears to be the most efficient utilization thereof in today's technology. Heating of such thin film of heat transfer fluid causes its temperature to rise appreciably along with expansion of its volume.

The heated heat transfer fluid will rise between the absorbing surface and the baffle with the closed bimetallic thermostat valve 45 opening by its operative end being disposed upon the baffle. So long as the heated heat transfer fluid passing over the valve is of a certain temperature, the valve will remain open. Otherwise, if such heat transfer fluid is less than such certain temperature, the valve will close.

As such heat transfer fluid is heated, it rises and passes over the heat exchanger and into the tank. After the solar heat holder 1 has been in operation, all the heat transfer fluid in the tank will have become heated. Since the system utilized herein is a closed system, such heating of the heat transfer fluid results in the exertion of pressure therefrom because minimal room for fluid expansion is provided for in the tank.

Were it not for the pressure-relieving, pneumatic container **63** incorporated in this closed system, the tank would eventually burst from the pressure exerted by such heat transfer fluid. Such spatial expansion of the heat transfer fluid and the resulting pressure same exerts in this closed system is accommodated and relieved by the container which contracts from such pressure exerted by such heated and expanded heat transfer fluid. The fluid to be heated in heat exchanger **69** can be water for domestic purposes or for heating a home, etc.

## COLLECTOR WITH INFLATABLE ELASTIC MEMBER FOR USE AT FREEZING TEMPERATURES

In any region where freezing weather occurs, the liquid in a collector can freeze, and when it freezes it expands and can damage exposed pipes. Various ways of overcoming this problem are known. For example, the collector may be drained when low temperatures are expected or when sun heat is not being collected. This requires a reliable valve system and a heat exchanger to isolate the collector from the pressurized domestic water supply. Alternatively, the collector may employ a heat exchange fluid like ethylene glycol which does not freeze at winter temperatures, but then double-barrier heat exchangers must be used to keep these poisonous liquids out of the potable hot water systems. Additional heat exchangers are known to reduce the efficiency of a solar heat collection system substantially.

Another known way to prevent freezing is to circulate warm water through the collector during times of freezing temperatures. This requires a more complex control system which can reliably respond to outdoor temperature and preferably a flow-control circulating system to keep wasted heat no greater than required. Still another solution to the freezing problem is to make the collector and associated exterior piping freeze-tolerant, so that repeated freezing will not cause any permanent damage to the system. This is the preferred approach.

*H. Harrison; U.S. Patent 3,989,032; November 2, 1976; assigned to Halm Instrument Co., Inc.* provides a system for solar heating of water in combination with a domestic hot water system having a hot water storage tank having an inlet and an outlet, and a controllable heater arranged for heating water for storage within the storage tank.

The system comprises a solar heat collector having a surface which absorbs sunlight to produce heat; a heat exchange passage for water in heat-conductive relation with the absorbing surface; piping and pump means connected to the collector and the tank for circulating water from the tank outlet through the heat exchange passage to the tank inlet; an inflatable elastic member extending substantially the entire length of the collector passage; and means to maintain air within the inflatable member at a higher hydrostatic air pressure than the static hydrostatic water pressure in the passage whereby the collector is rendered tolerant to freezing.

With reference to Figure 8.3, in usual domestic hot water heating systems, an insulated tank **K**, receives cold water from a source of supply, which may be city water mains, heats the water by means of a fossil fuel burner or an electric heater **H**, to a temperature **T**, which is controlled by a thermostat **23**, and delivers it to a domestic hot water piping system.

FIGURE 8.3: SCHEMATIC EMBODIMENT OF PROCESS IN HOME
INSTALLATION

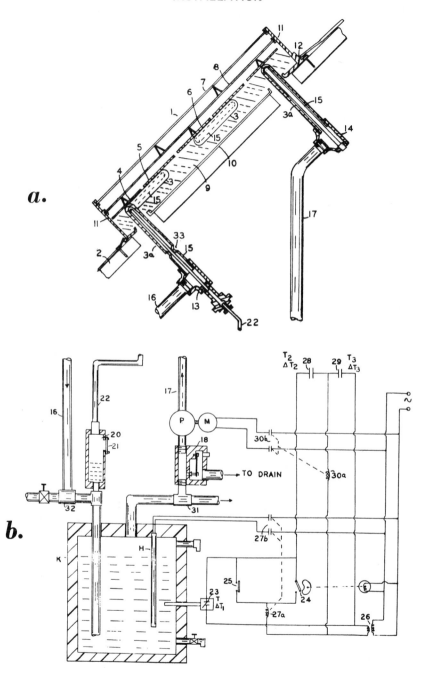

Source: U.S. Patent 3,989,032

The hot water tank **K** is generally located on a lower floor or in the basement. A pressure-actuated safety valve is preferably provided to protect the tank from damage. The auxiliary solar heating system is joined to the usual water heating system at tee fittings **31** and **32**, and a substitute electrical control circuit is inserted between the thermostat and the heating unit of the tank.

A solar heat collector panel **1**, is mounted on a sloped generally south-facing roof **2**, of the house. The collector consists of a serpentine tube **3** bonded to a series of sunlight-absorbing metal fins **4, 5** and **6**. The collector is insulated in front of two transparent covers **7** and **8**, spaced apart from the fins and secured to them by small, slender tripods, cemented to the surfaces. The bottom of the heat collector is nested in an insulating pad **9**, which may be fiberglass. Below the insulating pad and secured to it by cement is a two-layer moisture-resistant plastic backing **10**. A weather-resistant extended flexible member **11** seals the edge of the transparent covers, the receiver, and the insulating pad.

An edge of the flexible member tucks between the two layers of the plastic backing. A portion of the lowest plastic layer projects beyond the edge of the collector, forming a tab which is nailed to the roof to secure the collector in place. The roofing material and a flashing strip **12**, are assembled with the collector in conventional layered relation substantially as shown to prevent rain water from entering under the collector. The ends **3a**, of the serpentine tube are bent at right angles and pass through the roof through holes bored for the purpose. They are ended with adapter tee fittings, **13, 14**, which are each soldered to the tube on one arm and tapped for threaded pipes on the other two openings.

The receiver fins' surface preferably may be coated with a selective coating such as copper oxide, which efficiently absorbs sunlight, but does not radiate much heat. The two transparent covers may be of fiberglass-reinforced polyester, which reflects glare diffusely, transmits sunlight well, withstands typical temperature extremes, cements adequately, and toughly conforms to normal rough handling in mounting, without breakage. The tripods may be molded of thermoset glass-reinforced plastic which cements well with silicone rubber cements, withstands the maximum temperatures attained, and conducts little heat through the slender legs. Other spacers, such as paper cones, wire forms, or blocks of foam glass can be used. The extruded edge strip may be of silicone rubber or another elastomer compounded to resist ultraviolet and ozone aging.

Inside the serpentine collector tube, extending from one end fitting to the other, is an air-filled rubber tube **15**. This tube has relatively thin walls so it may be easily collapsed by a small extra pressure on the outside. It may have longitudinal reinforcing cords or wires embedded in the wall of the tube which prevent it from stretching lengthwise. The two ends of this tube are secured on barbed adapters screwed into the tee adapter fittings which terminate the collector tube.

Water-circulating connection pipes **16** and **17** are threadedly assembled in the fittings **13** and **14**, bringing water up from the hot water side of the tank at fitting **31** and returning it to the cold water side at fitting **32**. A pump **P** preferably near the bottom of the pipe **17** as shown, causes water to circulate through the collector when the collector is hot enough. A temperature-responsive relief valve **18** is mounted on the pipe **17**, and set to discharge water to a drain if unsafe water temperatures are reached. Also mounted on a tee-branch from the return line is a small trapping air reservoir **20** with a sight glass **21**, to check that there is air in it, and a vent plug screw to assist in draining excess water. The air in the reservoir communicates with the inside of the rubber tube in the collector via a small rigid tube **22** threadedly coupled to the fitting **13**. The other end of the rubber tube, at fitting **14**, is plugged.

The electrical control for the electric tank heater shown consists of a low voltage contact thermostat **23**, a fixed time interval manual override switch **25**, a transformer **26** to provide low voltage, and a relay **27a, 27b**, to interrupt the heater current, connected as shown. The electrical control for the pump motor **M** includes the tank thermostat, the contact **28**, which closes at temperature $T_2$ of the collector in series with it, the contact **29**, operating at a higher collector temperature $T_3$, and the relay **30a, 30b**, which interrupts the motor current, connected as shown.

The operation of this system is as follows. When the tank is cold and the collector is cold and no hot water demand is expected soon, neither the electric heater nor the pump is working, and the water remains cold. The rubber tube inside the collector being pressurized by air at the hydrostatic pressure near the bottom of the system and surrounded by water at the hydrostatic pressure at the top of the system, is inflated to occupy a substantial part of the metal collector tube. When the outdoor temperature is below freezing, some or all of the water in the collector tube may freeze and expand, but since the rubber tube provides an easily deformable surface, the metal tube will not be subjected to damaging stress.

When the temperature of the solar heat collector reaches $T_2$ while the tank is below the temperature $T_1$, low voltage current will flow through contact **28** to the coil **30a** and actuate relay contact **30b**, and power will flow to the circulating pump motor. Water will be circulated through the collector, picking up heat and delivering it to the tank **K**. $T_1$, $T_2$, $T_3$ and $T_4$ are predetermined temperatures. The pressure produced by the pump is sufficient to overcome the hydrostatic head pressure and collapse the rubber tube, which therefore cannot prevent flow from taking place. Any gross amount of water which may have diffused or seeped into the rubber tubing will be squeezed out toward the air reservoir line, so that the tube will always be in an empty condition to prevent freezing damage.

## MULTIELEMENT SEMICYLINDRICAL COLLECTOR

The collector system of *H.S. Robertson; U.S. Patent 3,990,430; November 9, 1976* comprises a multielement collector combined with an optical radiation concentrator system, which system is designed to permit optimization of the energy collection process by proper sequential flow of a heat transfer fluid through the elements of the collector system.

With reference to Figure 8.4, in which like reference characters designate like or corresponding parts throughout the various views, and with particular reference to Figure 8.4a, a typical bank of solar energy collector devices is illustrated at **10** in any appropriate type of fixed frame **12**, illustrated in broken lines. Three of the devices **14, 16** and **18** are illustrated; however, in practice any required number thereof may be included in the bank.

# FIGURE 8.4:  MULTIELEMENT SEMICYLINDRICAL COLLECTOR

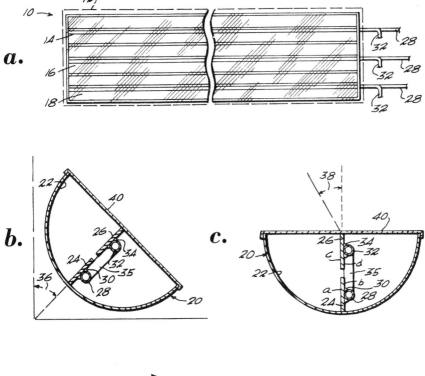

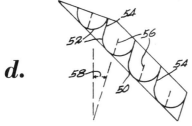

(a)  Semischematic plan view of bank of collector devices
(b)  Transverse sectional view through collector assembly
       angled away from vertical
(c)  Transverse sectional view through a collector indicating
       a typical angle of light incidence
(d)  Schematic illustration of collector bank on roof

Source:  U.S. Patent 3,990,430

With reference to Figure 8.4b, the collector system comprises a semicylindrical member **20** having a mirror inner surface **22**. A split collector plate means **24** and **26**, thermally insulated from each other by an air space therebetween, bisects the area within the semicylindrical member. The collector plates are designed to heat a fluid such as water, oil, air, or some fluid used in a refrigeration cycle, more efficiently than can be done with a flat plate collector, and much more simply than is ordinarily possible with a focusing collector. A fluid conduit **28** is fixed in any conventional manner, as by soldering **30**, to the lower collector plate **24**, and a similar conduit **32** is similarly fixed at **34** to the upper plate **26**. The conduits are interconnected at **35**.

The bank **10** of Figure 8.4a is longitudinally mounted in an east-west disposition and the angle **36** of Figure 8.4b approximately equals the latitude of the installation. The angle **38** of Figure 8.4c designates a typical angle of incidence of light rays. The angle of incidence will change with the time of day. A calculatable fraction of the light incident on the left half of the mirror surface will be collected on surface **a** of collector plate **24** and the balance of surface **c**, and similarly for the right half of the mirror surface on surfaces **b** and **d**.

For clear days at noon, the annular angular excursion of the sun is plus or minus 23.5°, and the system will produce an average concentration of 70% of the radiation on the **a–b** surface combination, for east-west alignment of the mirror axis at the elevation angle **36**, equal to the latitude. But because of the mirror surface properties, for angles of incidence up to 45°, there is more radiant energy concentrated on plate **24** than on plate **26**. Thus, if the heat exchange fluid passes through the system twice, first down pipe **32**, and then back through pipe **28**, it is heated more effectively than is possible with a flat plate collector, and higher conversion efficiencies are possible.

As illustrated in Figures 8.4b and 8.4c, the open top of the semicylindrical member is sealed by a transparent cover **40**, of glass or of any appropriate synthetic material. Figure 8.4d illustrates the orientation of a bank of solar energy collector devices of the process, oriented to a nonoptimum roof pitch. Numeral **50** designates the roof pitch, **52** the basic reflector member, **54** a supplementary plane reflector, **56** the split collector plate, and **58** the correct collector angle.

In practice the direction and sequential flow of the heat transfer fluid through successively hotter parts of the conduit means is coordinated with the angle of tilt of the collector system and the angle of incidence of the radiant energy from the sun on the collector so as to permit optimum energy collection.

For small, virtually maintenance-free installations, the collector array and optical system should be sealed in an insulated box with a clear glass cover. The collector array can consist of two or more fluid channels attached to metal collector strips, with the fluid circulated through the channels in order of increasing energy input.

For most installations, it is most convenient to store the heated fluid in an insulated tank at ground level, rather than at the usual roof-top level of the solar collector system. Therefore it becomes necessary and convenient to use a sensor-controlled fluid pump to circulate the heat exchange fluid appropriately. Many standard, simple circuits exist for comparing the fluid temperatures in the tank and collector, and causing the pump to act only when it is beneficial for it to do so.  Particular advantages of this program are evident for the retrofitting of a solar water heater to an existing hot water system.

## SINGLE-LEVEL STORAGE-TYPE HEATER

A storage-type solar water heater comprises essentially a collector which is heated directly by solar radiation, and a storage tank to which heat is conveyed from the collector by forced or natural circulation of a heat exchange liquid, commonly water.  Such heaters are widely used in certain hot regions of the world that receive considerable quantities of sunshine, and are used primarily for obtaining low-grade heat for domestic use or for use in hotels and hospitals. The heated water may be drawn directly from the storage tank, or the water to be heated may be passed through a tubular heat exchanger mounted in the storage tank and so heated indirectly.

Solar water heaters which rely upon forced circulation of liquid employ a pump and a differential temperature-responsive control system for controlling the pump operation.  Such units have the important advantage that they are convenient to install, but they are very costly, frequently inefficient, and tend to be unreliable in operation.  Solar water heaters which rely upon natural circulation are generally inconvenient to install, since the storage tank must be placed at a higher level than the collector; hitherto it has not been feasible to place the collector and storage tank adjacent one another at the same height, for although such an arrangement would operate efficiently in the daytime, it would operate in reverse at night when the stored heat would be reradiated into the atmosphere.

The process of *I.V. Wikholm; U.S. Patent 4,003,367; January 18, 1977* relates specifically to a compact, unitary heater construction which relies on natural circulation of the heat exchange liquid, and in which reverse flow of liquid at night is prevented.

A solar water heater in accordance with the process comprises a unitary housing structure providing a liquid-tight storage compartment and a liquid-tight heating, or collector, compartment of substantially smaller volume than the storage compartment, the housing structure providing a thermally insulating enclosure for the storage compartment, which enclosure includes a frontal wall portion separating the compartments.

The two compartments are interconnected by first and second liquid flow passages extending through the frontal wall portion of the insulating enclosure, forming therewith a thermosiphon responsive to absorption of solar radiation by the collector; one of the liquid flow passages extends between an inlet communicating with the storage compartment in the lower portion thereof and an outlet communicating with the heating compartment in the lower portion thereof, the passage providing a first duct portion extending upwardly within the insulation of the frontal wall portion from the inlet, a second duct portion extending upwardly within the insulation of the frontal wall portion from the outlet, and an intermediate duct portion interconnecting the first and second duct portions.

Heating means communicating with the intermediate duct portion of the liquid flow passage are provided for inhibiting reverse flow of liquid when the liquid in the heating compartment is cooler than the liquid in the storage compartment. The heating means may be a conductive heat exchanger extending between the intermediate portion of the liquid flow passage and the upper portion of the storage compartment. The conductive heat exchange means may be constituted by a metallic tube, for example a copper tube, lining the first liquid flow passage, or at least the intermediate duct portion thereof, a portion of the tube extending into the storage compartment. Alternatively, the heating means may simply be an electric heating element in the intermediate portion controlled thermostatically or by a timer.

Heated water may be drawn directly from the storage compartment in the conventional manner. Alternatively, and preferably, a tubular heat exchanger may be mounted in the storage compartment, the heat exchanger providing water flow connections for the passage of water to be heated therein.

Referring to Figure 8.5a and Figure 8.5b, the solar water heater is of unitary construction, and comprises a unitary housing structure **10** having a rigid outer casing **11** of glass-fiber-reinforced synthetic resin. The casing forms a flat base **12**, a rear wall **13** which slopes upwardly and rearwardly from the base, and having a forwardly inclined upper portion **14** which merges with the top **15** of the casing. The base, top and side walls of the casing terminate in a longitudinally ribbed flange **16** which defines a rectangular opening at the front of the casing.

## FIGURE 8.5: SINGLE-LEVEL STORAGE-TYPE HEATER

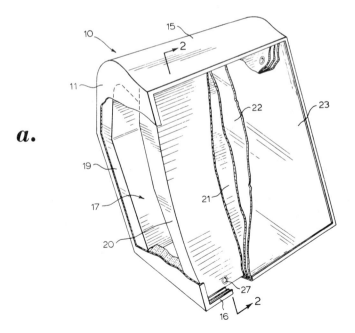

*a.*

(continued)

FIGURE 8.5: (continued)

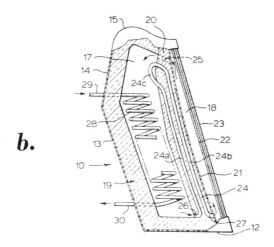

**b.**

(a)   Perspective view
(b)   Sectional elevation taken on line II—II of Figure 8.5a

Source:  U.S. Patent 4,003,367

The housing structure **10** provides a liquid-tight interior storage compartment **17**, and a liquid-tight interior heating compartment **18**, which is of substantially smaller volume than the storage compartment. The storage compartment is totally enclosed by a thermally insulating enclosure **19** of polyurethane, the latter being internally lined, for example by a glass-fiber-reinforced synthetic resin, to prevent seepage of water from the storage compartment into the insulation.

The thermally insulating enclosure lines the whole of the interior of the casing, and includes a frontal wall portion **20** which slopes upwardly and rearwardly with respect to the base. The exterior surface **21** of the frontal wall portion is also lined with a glass-fiber-reinforced synthetic resin, and is blackened or otherwise treated so as to make it nonreflective to solar radiation, this surface providing the heat absorption element of the collector of the heater.

Two rectangular transparent panels **22, 23**, which may be of glass or plastic, are retained by the flange **16** and peripherally sealed to the frontal portion of the housing to form a window which is transparent to solar radiation. The two panels are spaced apart to provide an intermediate air space, the interior panel **22** being spaced forwardly from the nonreflective surface **21** so as to define the heating compartment which is confined between them.

The window slopes upwardly and rearwardly with respect to the base, at an angle suitable for the latitude in which the heater is used, so as to transmit the maximum solar radiation when the heater is facing southwards. It is important that the window panels should be of a material which is not only transparent to solar radiation, but has a higher transparency to solar radiation than to infrared radiation which is reradiated from the collector surface **21**, glass being the most convenient material for this purpose. Alternatively, the interior panel **22** may be of a thermally conductive material, such as copper, having a nonreflective exterior face.

The storage compartment **17** and heating compartment **18** are interconnected by a first liquid flow passage **24** and a second liquid flow passage **25**. The passage **24** comprises a copper tube which is shaped to provide a first duct portion **24a** extending upwardly within the insulation of the wall portion **20** from an inlet **26** communicating with the lower portion of the compartment **17**, a second duct portion **24b** extending upwardly within the insulation from an outlet **27** communicating with the lower portion of the compartment **18**, and an intermediate duct portion **24c**, which is defined by a portion of the copper tube extending into the upper portion of the storage compartment.

The second liquid flow passage is a short passage extending rearwardly and upwardly through the frontal wall portion between an inlet communicating with the upper portion of the heating compartment and an outlet communicating with the upper portion of the storage compartment. The passages form with the compartments a thermosiphon responsive to absorption of solar radiation transmitted via the window **22, 23** into the heating compartment, the absorbed heat being carried by convection into the storage compartment.

Heated water may be drawn directly from the storage compartment. However, in the embodiment described, water to be heated is passed through a tubular heat exchanger **28** mounted in the storage compartment, the tubular heat exchanger providing a pair of external water flow connections **29, 30**. It should be mentioned that the water must be heated indirectly by means of a heat exchanger in any system where the water supply pressure is greater than the housing structure would otherwise withstand.

In operation of the heater, solar radiation is transmitted through the window and is absorbed by the collector surface, the water in the heating compartment being heated and caused to rise. Water from the heating compartment flows through the passage **25** into the upper portion of the storage compartment, cooler water being displaced from the bottom portion of the latter into the duct **24**. Cooler water enters the lower portion of the heating compartment, and is in turn heated, a thermosiphon thus being started and continuing for as long as the heating receives direct solar radiation.

At night, when there is a tendency for the collector surface to reradiate, the water in the heating compartment falls to a lower temperature than the water in the storage compartment. This would normally cause a reverse flow of water, and consequent loss of stored heat. The purpose of the conductive heat exchanger constituted by the copper tube is to equalize the temperature of the stored water and the water in the duct portion **24a**. If this is achieved, reverse flow will be inhibited.

Actually, since a heat exchanger will always have a loss, what happens is that the heat exchanger heats the upper portion of the duct portion **24a** rapidly, when normal circulation stops, to a few degrees below the temperature in the top of the storage tank. A very slow reverse circulation will then start and displace the hot water slowly down the duct portion **24a**, the colder water from duct portion

**24b** flowing slowly into the first duct portion and being heated. This process continues until all of the first duct portion is filled with hot water, a few degrees below the temperature in the top of the tank. At this point an equilibrium is reached and reverse circulation ceases.

## CLOSED SYSTEM WITH HEAT TRAP

A solar water heating system of the closed type which comprises a solar collector, a water storage tank, and water lines therebetween is described by *E.L. Chayet; U.S. Patent 4,010,734; March 8, 1977; assigned to Solar Energy Dynamics Corporation.* The solar collector preferably comprises a continuous length of tubing coiled in a helical array of closely adjacent turns, having a water inlet communicating with the outermost turn and a water outlet communicating with the innermost turn. Comparatively cold water is taken from a water outlet adjacent the bottom of the storage tank and is pumped through a line to the water inlet of the solar collector, and heated water is supplied from the solar collector water outlet, together with cold water from an external supply, to a common inlet adjacent the top of the storage tank.

The water line between the hot water outlet of the solar collector and the cold water inlet adjacent the top of the storage tank includes, moreover, a heat trap taking the form of a U-shaped line section which extends from the hot water solar collector outlet past the top of the tank on its exterior to a position substantially level with the bottom of the tank, and then extends vertically upward to the water inlet adjacent the top of the tank.

The water at different levels in the heat trap adjacent the tank tends to assume the same temperatures as the corresponding levels of water within the tank itself and, since hot water cannot flow downward, hot water is prevented from flowing out of the tank when the solar collector is cooler than the heated water within the tank. This extremely important feature assures that there is no loss of heat from the tank due to radiation or due to the natural rise of heated water during a cool evening or under inclement weather conditions, and accomplishes this heat retention without the need for solenoid valves, check valves, or other devices that would impede water flow and increase the cost of the overall system.

Referring to Figure 8.6, a solar heater of the closed system type comprises a solar collector **10** which may be mounted on the roof **11** of a house, or at some other appropriate location, and which is operative to admit solar radiation to heat a supply of water.

The solar collector includes a housing **10a** of generally rectangular configuration, having a width and depth of substantially 5' each and a height of approximately 4", the housing being preferably fabricated of an insulating material, e.g., fiber glass having a urethane base, and provided with one or more transparent panes **10b** disposed in spaced substantially parallel relation to the bottom of the housing and in sealed relation to the sides of the housing to create a heat pocket within the housing immediately beneath the transparent face. The face or panes are preferably fabricated of window glass having a low iron content since this type of glass captures the long rays of the light spectrum and tends to retain heat inasmuch as such long rays will not reflect back through the glass.

## FIGURE 8.6: CLOSED SYSTEM WITH HEAT TRAP

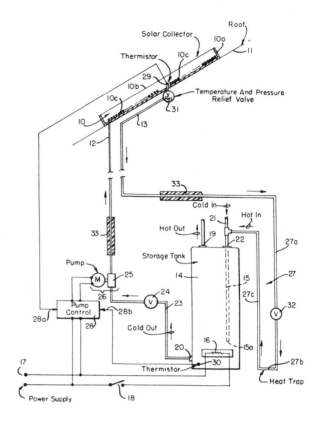

Source:  U.S. Patent 4,010,734

The interior of the solar collector comprises a continuous length of tubing which is coiled in a helical array **10c** of closely adjacent contiguous turns disposed in a plane substantially parallel to the bottom of housing **10a**. The helical array and the entire interior of the housing is preferably covered with black paint of high carbon content to maximize heat adsorption by the solar collector. The outermost turn of the helical array communicates with a water inlet line **12** while the innermost turn of the array communicates with a water outlet line **13**.

Water fed into the array via the inlet line thus flows from the exterior to the interior turns of the array and preferably exits under the helix to a point near the point of original entry. While the outlet line is illustrated in the figure as being disposed below the bottom of the housing, in a preferred form of the process it is preferably disposed within the housing immediately below the array so that the inlet line and the outlet line pass through the housing walls at points closely adjacent to one another near one of the upstanding sides of the housing.

The actual quantity of water which passes through the array **10c**, and the temperature to which it is heated, is dependent upon the dimensions of the tubing used in the helical array. In a preferred embodiment, the helical array may comprise substantially 250' of ½" diameter copper tubing forming the outer turns of the array, connected in continuous flow sequence to approximately 150' of ⅜" diameter tubing forming the inner turns of the array, and due to the differing diameters of the two portions of the array, the overall helix exhibits two elevations, i.e., an elevation of substantially ½" adjacent the outer turns, and an elevation of substantially ⅜" adjacent the inner turns.

The copper tubing is coiled so that each turn is in full engagement with the adjacent turns to cause the tubing itself to act as an absorption plate, thereby eliminating need for an additional absorption plate which has been commonly employed heretofore. A solar collector having the dimensional considerations discussed herein for the helical array is capable of producing substantially 15 to 20 gph of water heated to substantially 170°F.

The solar collector **10** is associated with an insulated hot water storage tank **14** disposed at an appropriate location within the residence, preferably at a position significantly below the solar collector. The storage tank may comprise the conventional hot water tank already located in a residence, having a filler tube **15** therein and an associated electrical heater **16** adapted to be energized from the home power supply **17**.

When such a standard hot water heater is used for storage purposes, a switch **18** is preferably placed in series with the heater so that the heater is normally deenergized but can, by closure of the switch, be energized to supplement or replace the hot water heating effects of the solar collector under prolonged conditions of inclement weather. In addition, the filler tube in such a preexisting storage tank is cut short at its bottom within the tank so that the outlet **15a** of the filler tube is positioned at an intermediate position in the tank, below the hot water outlet **19** which is located adjacent the top of the tank and above the bibdrain **20** at the bottom of the tank.

Cold water is supplied to the tank from an external supply line **21** which is connected to tank inlet **22** communicating with the filler tube. Cold water within the tank is in turn taken from the tank outlet adjacent the bottom of the tank and fed through a line **23** past an opened shut-off valve **24** by the impeller **25** of a pump **26** when the pump motor **M** is energized.

Such cold water is then fed to inlet line **12** of the solar collector, forcing heated water out of the collector via outlet line **13** through a heat trap **27** (to be described) to a tee coupled to cold water inlet line **21** to cause the hot water to also enter through the cold water inlet **22** of the tank. The heated water so entering the tank is thoroughly mixed with the cold water in the tank due to the fact that the cold water and heated water are admitted through the same tank inlet to the same interior point in the tank, and the heated water tends to rise to the top of the tank where it may be withdrawn as needed via the hot water outlet.

The pump is normally deenergized but may be selectively energized by pump control **28** which is coupled to the power supply and which operates, under the control of signals supplied to input lines **28a** and **28b** to provide energization to pump motor **M**. Line **28a** is coupled to a thermistor **29** mounted adjacent the innermost turns of helical array **10c** to provide a signal input to pump control **28** related to the temperature of the heated water in solar collector **10**. Input **28b** is coupled to a thermistor **30** located on the outside of tank **14** near its bottom, or in the cold water outlet line therefrom, to provide a further input signal related to the temperature of the cold water at the bottom of the tank.

The pump control is responsive to the difference in the temperatures being monitored by the thermistors and operates to energize pump **26** when the water in the solar collector is hotter than that at the bottom of the storage tank by a predetermined quantity, e.g., 5° or 10°F. When such a temperature difference is detected, energization of the pump motor drives impeller **25** to pump water from the bottom of the tank through lines **23**, **12** into the outermost turns of the helical array, to force hot water from the innermost turns of the helical array via line **23** and heat trap **27** into the cold water inlet of the tank.

Outlet line **13** includes a temperature and pressure relief valve **31** which is set to open at predetermined parameter values such as 150 psi and 210°F, and line **13** preferably also includes an additional shut-off valve **32** having a structure and function similar to that of valve **24**.

In order to avoid undesirable loss of heat, all of the water lines to and from solar collector **10** and the tank are insulated throughout their length as represented diagrammatically at **33**. In addition, outlet line **13** leading from the solar collector to the cold water input of the tank includes the aforementioned heat trap comprising an elongated line section **27a** passing vertically from the solar collector past the top of the tank to a line section **27b** located at a level corresponding to the bottom of the tank, and then extending vertically upward as at **27c** to the cold water inlet at the top of the tank.

This U-shaped line section prevents heat dissipation from the heated water within the tank when the solar collector is not operating, e.g., at night or in inclement weather, ensures against the loss of heat due to radiation or the natural rise of heat under such conditions, and accomplishes these purposes without the provision of solenoid valves, check valves, or other devices which would increase the cost of the overall system and which would have the disadvantage of impeding water flow.

It will be appreciated that hot water rises to the top of the tank. If the heat trap were not provided, and line **13** from the solar collector extended directly to cold water inlet **22** of the tank, then when the coil **10c** in the solar collector cooled, the hot water located adjacent the top of the tank would tend to rise through line **13** to the coil, and the heat in the water would be dissipated by radiation from the coil.

By using the heat trap, however, the water standing in vertical lines **27a** and **27c** tends to assume the same temperatures at various levels as are exhibited by the corresponding levels of the water within the tank itself, i.e., the water adjacent line section **27b** will have a temperature corresponding to the temperature of the cold water near the bottom of the tank, whereas the water in lines **27a** and **27c** at levels adjacent the top of the tank will have temperatures corresponding to the heated water near the top of the tank. These temperature gradients within the legs of U-shaped heat trap prevent hot water located near the top of the tank from flowing out of the tank to solar collector **10**, even though the temperature of the solar collector is significantly lower than that of the water within the tank **14**.

## FLEXIBLE DOMED COLLECTOR SYSTEM

*H.J. Vroom, W.R. Bolle, H. Schneider and B. Swerdling; U.S. Patent 4,015,586; April 5, 1977; assigned to Grumman Aerospace Corporation* provide a system which adds to a structure a solar collector means for heating a storage tank connected between a water inlet and a hot water tank by means of a controllable system of circulating a water/glycol fluid therebetween.

With more particular reference to Figure 8.7a there is shown a closed water/glycol system having two solar collectors **10** and **12** connected in parallel for supplying solar-heated fluid via line **14** having check valve **16** to a heat exchanger **18** about (it could be within but there is less chance of fluid commingling as shown) a glass-lined storage tank **20**. As shown the line **14** is equipped with a relief valve **22** and a fill port **24** to permit addition of the water/glycol fluid into the system.

From the heat exchanger, actually a thin-walled tube-like structure having a substantial contact area with the liner of tank **20** to effectuate efficient heat exchange, a line **26** connects to a pump **28** that is connected by line **30** to the collectors. Line **26** as can be readily seen is tapped first to provide a drain port **32** and secondly to connect in the closed circuit an expansion tank **34**.

## FIGURE 8.7: FLEXIBLE DOMED COLLECTOR SYSTEM

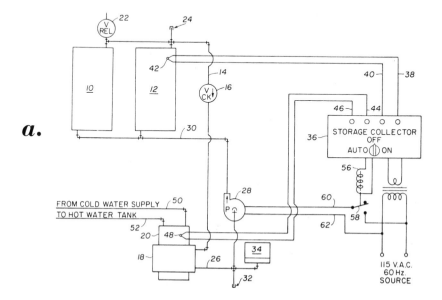

(continued)

FIGURE 8.7: (continued)

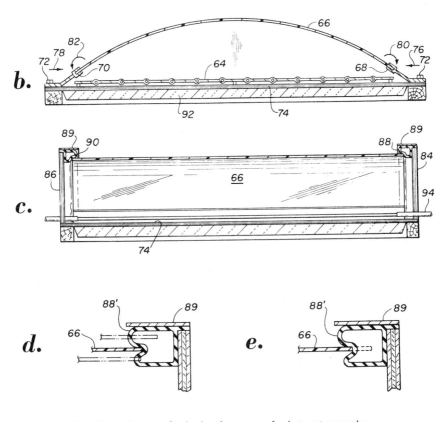

(a)    Block diagram of solar heating system for hot water supply
(b)    Cross section of the middle portion of collector
(c)    View in cross section of collector
(d)(e)  Partial cross-sectional views of end seal employed with the
        dome

Source:  U.S. Patent 4,015,586

Completing a general description of the elements of the system is the temperature control **36** connected by leads **38** and **40** to a temperature sensor **42** in the
solar collector system and leads **44** and **46** to a temperature sensor **48** in the
storage tank for monitoring the difference in temperature between the water in
the storage tank and the fluid in the solar collector.  Cold water inlet of preheating storage is connected to supply pipe **50** and the heated water outlet pipe **52**
from the tank leads to the normal hot water heater.

The sensors known to the art are connected in an appropriate circuit to control
operation of the pump **28** whenever the temperature difference is such that circulation of the fluid will heat the water in the tank.  Thus, a relay-operated
switch **58**, connected between the power source and the pump, will energize or

deenergize pump **28** as required. In a system that has been constructed the relay **56** closes switch **58** whenever a temperature difference of 20°F or greater exists between sensors **42** and **48** and opens the switch as soon as that difference drops below 3°F. However, it is readily recognizable that those temperature limits could vary as required.

With reference to Figures 8.7b and 8.7c, the solar collectors have aluminum collector plates **64** under an acrylic dome **66**. Transparent dome configurations for flat plate solar collectors have thus far generally been permanently shaped. As such they have involved expensive heat molding. With this process, however, it has been found that one can avoid these costly heat-forming methods. This is done by bending or springing the film, sheet or plate transparent material in the cold state directly into an arched shape and then mechanically restraining such developed shape.

Actually edge extrusions **68** and **70** which extend the length of the dome are mechanically fastened by bolts **72** to a base plate **74** to provide forces in the directions of arrows **76** and **78** and moments **80** and **82** for given values of the width between the edge restraints and perimeter length therebetween to produce the desired shape of the dome.

The aforesaid domed collector is placed within end frames **84** and **86** that are fastened to the base plate to provide end closures for the collector housing that is sealed by hollow elastomeric gaskets **88** and **90**.

Thermal installation requirements for the collectors **10** and **12** are provided by the sealed air gap above the plate and below it, the material/thickness selected for the base plate and the material/thickness selected for an insulating blanket **92**. The inlet/outlet provisions **94** for liquid collectors are provided by appropriate holes or slots cut in the end frames to allow passage of the associated plumbing. Finally while it has been mentioned that the dome is acrylic it will be readily understood that the plastic/elastomeric materials which can be used are defined as transparent outdoor weather-resistant grades.

Figures 8.7d and 8.7e show the thermal expansion principles of the restrained transparent dome. The neutral position shown by solid lines is defined as that material state existing at cold forming of the dome and installation with the edge restraints. As the solar collector temperature increases the arched shape changes between the edge restraints and the length changes. The flexure of the restraints allow the former and the hollow gaskets the latter.

Actually Figure 8.7d depicts a hollow elastomeric gasket **88'** at the center of the dome closure serving as a compression seal. Increased and decreased temperature positions are depicted by the dash line attitudes above and below respectively, the neutral position shown. Figure 8.7e shows the same compression seal simulating a wiper-type seal as it approaches the edge constraints. The end frame cap strip **89** fastens the hollow elastomeric gasket in place and constrains the gasket and end frame **84** to perform as depicted. In other words the caps stabilize the seals and integrate the end frames with the seals to the dome to increase the structural integrity of the housing.

The collector plate is coated with a solar-absorbing material which maximizes absorption and retention of the incident solar energy. As may be familiar to those skilled in the art the upper surface of plate **64** may be blackened or coated with a selective surface. In one embodiment the effective absorbing surface area of each collector was 25.4 ft². The base is of exterior-type plywood and the edge restraints aluminum extrusions. Insulating blanket **92** was adequate when fabricated from 1" thick fiberglass insulation with a vinyl vapor barrier on one side. In this construction the end frames were also of exterior-type plywood. The use of a wood construction aids in insulation and ease of assembly and disassembly and repairing.

Further construction details thus far known have the storage tank **20** being an 82-gallon glass-lined steel tank. The tank preferred is equipped with a magnesium anodic rod which is attached to the top of the tank and extends therewithin. Appropriate bosses are provided to connect lines **50** and **52** and, if necessary, a pressure relief and temperature sensor connection.

A rolled aluminum jacket heat exchanger **18** is attached to the outer circumference of the storage tank. Prior to this installation a layer of suitable thermal grease is applied to the outer circumference of the tank. The grease increases the thermal conductance between the heat exchanger and the storage tank. Preferably the conductance is on the order of 20 Btu/hr/ft²/°F. After completing the plumbing connections insulation is wrapped about the tank and heat exchanger.

In order to accommodate the expansion of the solar collector working fluid, a pressurized diaphragm expansion tank **34** is installed in the system. This tank has means such as a diaphragm stretching across the inside diameter of the tank to separate it into chambers, one of which it is preferred to pressurize with air. This enables minimizing the size of an expansion tank.

Finally check valve **16** has a very important function in the system by eliminating thermosiphoning which could occur whenever solar collectors **10** and **12** are colder than tank **20**; i.e., gravitational flow to a higher point caused by the difference of fluid densities, the latter being due to a temperature difference. Such may be normal at night without check valve **16**.

## DIFFERENTIAL AMPLIFIER CONTROL FOR WATER HEATER

*C.A. Frazier and M.L. Cunningham; U.S. Patent 4,019,495; April 26, 1977* provide a system for controlling the flow of a liquid through a solar heating system of the type having the output of a solar energy collector coupled to the input of a storage tank and having a circulating pump interposed along a return liquid pipe coupled between the recirculating output of the storage tank and the input of the solar energy collector. A first element senses the temperature of the liquid adjacent to the output of the solar energy collector and generates a first signal responsive thereto.

A second element senses the temperature of the liquid at a second location within the solar heating system and generates a second signal responsive thereto. A first comparator is coupled between the first and second elements for generating a run signal responsive to the difference between the first and second signals exceeding a predetermined level. The control system further includes an actuating element for powering the circulating pump responsive to the run signal, whereby the liquid is circulated within the solar heating system. A freeze protection mechanism may also be in the system.

A control system, shown generally as **10** in Figure 8.8a, will be described for a solar heater **12** of the type having a solar heating collector for heating a liquid **16** (such as water) therein. A typical solar heating collector **14** has a plurality of water passageways serpentined therethrough and is fabricated having a black surface facing the sun to maximize the absorption of solar radiation. The solar heating collector has an input **18** thereto and an output **20** therefrom. The output from the solar heating collector is coupled by a hot water pipe **22** to an input **24** of a storage tank **26**.

A second hot water pipe **32** is coupled from the first hot water pipe to the input **34** of a second storage tank **36** of the type having an auxiliary heating unit **38** coupled thereto. The second hot water pipe includes a first auxiliary valve **30** therein for controlling the flow of the hot water therethrough. The first storage tank **26** includes a first relief valve **40** coupled thereto and the second storage tank includes a second relief valve **42** coupled thereto. The first storage tank includes a cold water input **44**.

The first storage tank further includes a hot water return line **50** (liquid return line) which is coupled therethrough adjacent the bottom section thereof. The cool water return line **50** is coupled to the input of a circulating pump **52**. The output of the circulating pump is coupled by another cool water return line **54** to the input **18** of the solar heating collector. A second cool water return line **56** is coupled to the second storage tank adjacent the bottom section thereof. A second auxiliary valve **58** is interposed along the second cool water return line. The second storage tank further includes a main hot water output line **60** coupled adjacent the upper section thereof.

A first thermistor (or first temperature sensing means) **62** is attached to the solar heating collector adjacent to the output **20** thereof for sensing the temperature of the water flowing therefrom and for generating a first signal responsive thereto. The first thermistor may be coupled to the output pipe **20** rather than through the heating collector. The first signal from the first thermistor is coupled by a first signal line **64** to a plus input **66** of the first comparator **70**.

A second thermistor or second temperature sensing means **72** is coupled to the first storage tank adjacent to the lower section thereof. This second location for the second thermistor is normally located immediately adjacent to the cool water return line **50** or attached thereto. The second signal generated by the second thermistor responsive to the temperature thereof is coupled by a second signal line **79** to a minus input **68** of the first comparator.

The first comparator generates a run signal whenever the first signal present at the plus input is less than the second signal present at the minus input by a predetermined level. The run signal is coupled from the output **76** of the first comparator through a control line **78** to the input of a timer **80**. The output of the timer is coupled by another control line **82** to the input **84** of an actuating means or actuator **86**. The output of the actuator is coupled by another control line **88** to supply power to the circulating pump **52**.

(continued)

FIGURE 8.8:  DIFFERENTIAL AMPLIFIER CONTROL FOR WATER HEATER

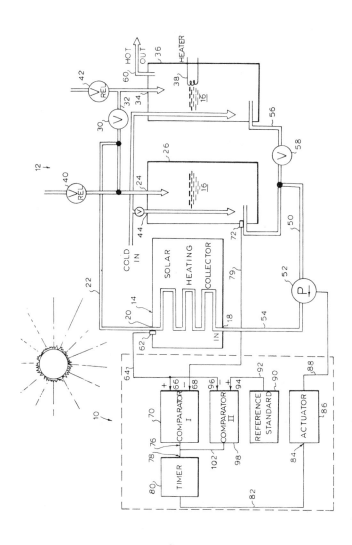

*a.*

**FIGURE 8.8:** (continued)

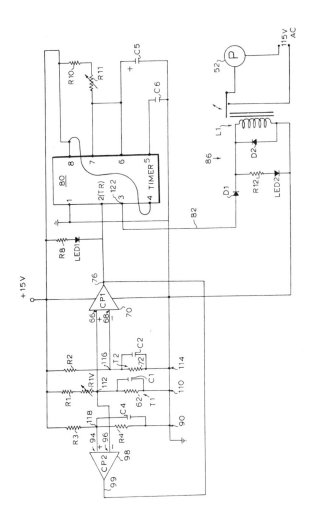

*b.*

(a)   Block diagram showing the control system
(b)   Circuit diagram for the differential amplifier
       control system

Source:   U.S. Patent 4,019,495

A reference signal generated by a reference standard **90** is coupled through a reference signal line **92** to the plus input **94** of a second comparator (or second comparator means) **98**. A minus input **96** of the second comparator is coupled to the first thermistor **62** by the first signal line **64**. The output of the second comparator is coupled to the input of the timer **80** by another signal line **102**.

With reference to Figure 8.8b, the first thermistor **(T1) 62** together with a first reference resistor **R1** and a first variable reference resistor **R1V** form a first leg **110** of a bridge circuit. A first sampling point **112** is included at the junction between the first variable reference resistor and the first thermistor. If a variable temperature function is not desired, then the variable resistor may be omitted. The second thermistor **(T2) 72** together with a second reference resistor **R2** comprises a second leg **114** of the bridge circuit. A second sampling point **116** is located between the series connected second reference resistor and the second thermistor.

A third leg **90** of the bridge circuit includes a third reference resistor **R3** in series with a fourth reference resistor **R4**, with a third sampling point **118** included at the intersection thereof. The first thermistor is bypassed by a first bypass capacitor **C1**, the second thermistor is bypassed by a second bypass capacitor **C2**, and the fourth reference resistor is bypassed by a fourth bypass capacitor **C4**. The first and second thermistors have a nominal 5 kohm value at a nominal 25°C. Both first and second thermistors have known precision resistance over a temperature variation of 0° to 100°C and have a negative temperature coefficient.

The first sampling point is coupled to the plus input **66** of the first differential comparator **70**. Likewise, the second sampling point is coupled to the minus input **68** of the first comparator. The first comparator may comprise a LM 311 voltage comparator, for example. When the voltage at the plus input of the first comparator is less than the voltage at the minus input thereof, the output **76** is in a low state or zero volts. When the voltage at the plus input of the first comparator is greater than the voltage at the minus input thereof, the output **76** of the first comparator is a positive voltage thereon (the off signal).

The operation of the control system is as follows. The water **16** within the solar heating collector **14** will be heated by solar radiation. The temperature of the water therein will be sensed by the first temperature sensing means which is the first thermistor. The temperature of the cooler water within the first storage tank **26** will be sensed by the second temperature sensing means **72** or the second thermistor. When the temperature of the first thermistor is greater than the temperature of the second thermistor plus the predetermined offset level (determined from the difference, in ohms, of **R1** and **R2**) the output voltage **76** of the first comparator will drop low.

Otherwise the output voltage of the first comparator will remain high. When the low output voltage from the first comparator is coupled to the input of the timer, the output of the timer will go high, thus energizing the relay coil **L1** of the actuator **86**. The closing of the relay responsive to the voltage across the relay coil will supply power to the circulating pump **52**, thereby pumping the hot water from the solar heating collector through the hot water pipe **22** and into the first storage tank. Of course, a portion of the cold water within the first storage tank will be recirculated through the cool water return lines **50** and **54** by the circulating pump **52**. If the output **76** of the first comparator **70** goes low only temporarily, the output **122** of the timer **80** will remain high for a minimum period of time determined by the values of resistors **R10** and **R11** and capacitor **C5**. When hot water **16** is demanded from the main hot water output **60**, hot water within the first storage tank **16** will be drawn from the first storage tank **26** through the hot water output pipe **32** into the second storage tank **36**. The auxiliary heating unit **38** within the second storage tank may be utilized to heat the water therein on days when sufficient solar heating is not available.

Under cold weather conditions, or under periods of low solar heating, the temperature of the water within the solar heating collector **14** may approach the freezing level. Under these conditions, the temperature of the first thermistor **62** (or **T1**) will be compared to a reference standard **90** by the operation of the second comparator **98**. When the voltage across the first thermistor, which is coupled from the first sampling point **112** to the minus input **96** of the second comparator, goes more positive than the positive voltage from the reference standard, the output **99** of the second comparator will drop from the normal high voltage to a low voltage output designating the approach of a freezing condition.

The output **99** of the second comparator is coupled to the input of the timer in a manner similar to the output **76** of the first comparator. Thus, as the temperature of the water within the solar heating collector approaches within several degrees of the freezing level, the output **99** of the second comparator will actuate the timer thereby energizing the relay coil **L1** and closing the relay to power the circulating pump.

Therefore, the circulating pump will pump the warmer water within the first storage tank into the solar heating collector, and the cooler water from the solar heating collector into the first storage tank. This method of circulating the cold water will be sufficient to prevent freezing for short durations of cold weather. However, longer durations of cold weather will require the water within the solar heating collector to be drained to prevent the freezing thereof. In the alternative, the heater **38** can be used to heat the water which is then circulated.

## SOLAR ABSORBERS AT DIFFERENT TEMPERATURE LEVELS

The standard domestic solar water heater in Australia is used both with and without electric or fuel boosting, depending on climatic conditions. The collectors are manufactured typically in units 1,220 mm by 610 mm (0.75 m$^2$ in area), and incorporate a selective absorbing surface with a single glass cover. A selective absorbing surface is one which has a higher absorptance than emittance at the radiation wavelength concerned. Such surfaces may be produced by special black oxide coatings and may typically have an absorptance of 0.8 but an emittance of 0.1 to 0.15 at wavelengths of 0.2 to 2 microns.

Such heaters are typically used to heat water from 15°C and losses are about 75 Wm$^{-2}$. At higher water temperatures the losses are normally twice this figure. By using more insulation and double glazing these losses could be reduced but the collector would then cost more and would be less efficient at low temperatures because of the reduction in insolation reaching the absorber plate of the collector. Since low-temperature collectors are unsatisfactory at high temperatures and high-temperature collectors are both more expensive and less efficient at low temperatures, there will be an optimum operating temperature range for each design of collector.

The process of *R.N. Morse and E.T. Davey; U.S. Patent 4,021,895; May 10, 1977; assigned to Commonwealth Scientific and Industrial Research Organization, Australia* provides for solar heating of a fluid in stages involving solar heaters which maintain good thermal efficiency to differing maximum temperatures in order to provide effective heating over a temperature range wider than could be effectively dealt with by any one type of solar heater. More particularly the process provides a method of heating a fluid comprising passing a fluid successively through a plurality of solar heaters which are exposed to solar radiation and are capable of operation with substantial thermal efficiency over incremental temperature ranges extending to successively greater operating temperatures.

The system shown diagrammatically in Figure 8.9a comprises four independent solar heaters denoted generally as **1, 2, 3, 4** each consisting of a bank of individual collector units connected in series. These heaters are connected to a common columnar storage tank **5** at different levels to give four temperature zones within the tank.

The solar collector units of the four heaters are of different types. Heater **1** has collectors which are designed for high-temperature operation and which will be referred to as Type 1; heater **2** has collectors which are designed for medium-high-temperature operation and which will be referred to as Type 2; heater **3** has collectors which are designed for medium-temperature operation and which will be referred to as Type 3; and heater **4** has collectors which are designed for low-temperature operation and which will be referred to as Type 4.

FIGURE 8.9: SOLAR ABSORBERS AT DIFFERENT TEMPERATURE LEVELS

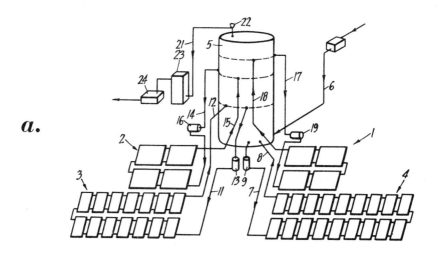

*a.*

(continued)

FIGURE 8.9:  (continued)

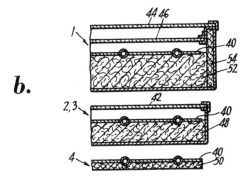

**b.**

(a)    Diagrammatic layout of an installation
(b)    Cross section of high-, medium-high-, medium- and
          low-temperature collectors included in the installation

Source:  U.S. Patent 4,021,895

The cross-sectional details of the four types of collectors are shown in Figure 8.9b.  The Type 3 collectors are standard commercial rectangular units with copper absorber plates **40** treated to provide a selective surface and fitted with single glass cover **42** and having 50 mm of insulation **48** to the rear thereof. The selective surface may have an absorptance of 0.8 but an emittance of about 0.1 to 0.15 at wavelengths between about 0.2 to 2 microns.  The Type 2 collectors are of similar construction but each unit has twice the area making it square.

The Type 1 collectors are similar to Type 2 except for double glazing **44, 46** and extra edge insulation **52** and with extra rear insulation **54** of 75 mm thickness.  The Type 4 collectors have no glass cover or case and consist merely of a standard absorber plate **40** with matt black finish and 12 mm of insulation **50** on the rear only.  The matt black collector surface may have an absorptance of 0.95 at wavelengths of between about 0.2 to 2 microns but also an emittance of about 0.95 at the same wavelengths.

Cold water is supplied to the bottom of tank **5** via supply pipe **6** and the four solar heaters are connected to the tank at different heights to give four temperature zones within the tank.  More particularly the low-temperature heater **4** is connected to the bottom part of the tank via an outflow pipe **7** and a return flow pipe **8**.  The outflow pipe is fitted with a pump **9** to circulate water from the bottom of the tank through the collectors of heater **4** and then back into the bottom of the tank.  Similarly, heater **3** is connected to the tank at a higher level by an outflow pipe **11** and return flow pipe **12**, the outflow pipe being fitted with a circulation pump **13**.

Heater **2** is connected to the tank at a yet higher level by an outflow pipe **14** and return flow pipe **15**, the outflow pipe being fitted with a circulation pump **16**.  Heater **1** is connected to the tank at a higher level near to the top of the tank by an outflow pipe **17** and a return flow pipe **18**, the outflow pipe being fitted with a pump **19**.

Since the flow and return connections for each heater are at the same level in the tank, circulation through the four heaters generates a substantially uniform water temperature in each of the four zones thus defined in the tank.

The four heaters may be designed to produce temperature rises of 15° to 20°C each and thus provide an overall rise of 75°C. As shown in Figure 8.9a heated water is drawn from the top of the tank via an outlet pipe **21** fitted with an air eliminator **22** and is passed through a boiler **23** to boost the water temperature to any desired temperature. The flow of water may be measured by passage through a flow-measuring tank **24**.

## COLLECTOR-AWNING DEVICE FOR MOBILE HOME

A combination solar heat collector and awning is described by *J.A. Lanciault; U.S. Patent 3,973,553; August 10, 1976* as an attachment for a travel trailer or mobile home wherein the heat collector panel is extendable to an awning position overlying the wall of the vehicle which should be facing toward the sun. The heat collector panel has water pipes extending therethrough which provide heated water to a tank mounted on the roof of the vehicle and connected to the domestic hot water system of the trailer or to heat radiators as desired.

The heat collector panel is extendable and retractable with a cable system which is selectively motor-operated or hand-operated. The total unit when in stored position or in position of use has a relatively low silhouette and permits passage of the vehicle through normal roadways.

Referring to Figures 8.10a through 8.10d, the reference numeral **10** indicates generally a combined solar water heater and retractable awning unit for attachment to travel trailers and mobile homes. The unit includes a base **11** having a pair of spaced-apart parallel longitudinally extending frame members **12, 13** connected by a plurality of generally horizontal cross members **14**.

A front end wall **15** extends between the frames and projects upwardly therefrom. A cog track **16** and a second cog track **17** extend longitudinally in spaced parallel relation and are secured to the cross members between the side frames. The rear ends of the cog tracks are curved upwardly in a generally U-shaped end portion **18, 19** respectively.

The base member is secured to the roof of the vehicle **20** by means of adhesive **21**. A tank support trestle **22** is mounted on the side frames supporting an insulated elevated hot water tank **23** above the base. A conduit **24** extends downwardly through a fitting **25** in the roof of the vehicle to provide hot water to the domestic system (not shown) within the vehicle. A vacuum valve **26** on the tank permits air to enter the tank as water flows outwardly therefrom through the conduit.

A heat collector panel **27** includes a metal box **28** having a flat rectangular bottom wall **29** and upstanding side walls **30** including a horizontal flange **31** at its upper edge thereof. A generally rectangular plate or fiberglass window **32** is supported on the flanges (see Figure 8.10d).

FIGURE 8.10:  COLLECTOR-AWNING DEVICE FOR MOBILE HOME

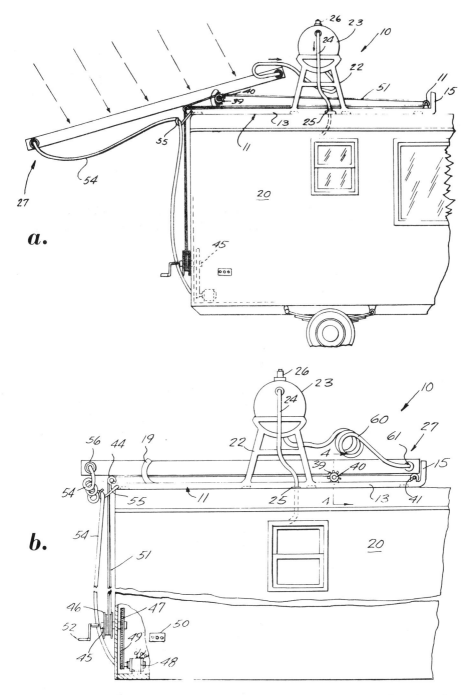

(continued)

FIGURE 8.10: (continued)

**c.**

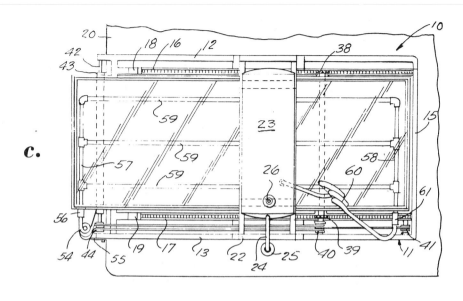

**d.**

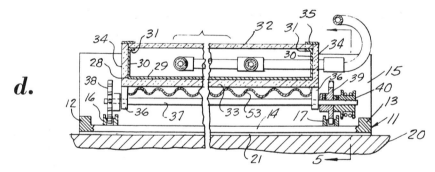

(a)   Side elevation shown in extended position
(b)   View with the unit in stored position
(c)   Top plan view of the apparatus in stored position
(d)   Enlarged fragmentary vertical sectional view on line 4—4 of Figure 8.10b

Source:  U.S. Patent 3,973,553

An insulation panel **33** is beneath the bottom wall and secured thereto.  Insulation panels **34** are secured to all of the side walls **30** and the insulation panel **33**.  A retainer frame **35** is secured to the insulation panels **34** and extends over the edges of the window to secure the window in place.

Brackets **36** extend downwardly from opposite sides of the box **27** and have an axle **37** journalled therein and extending transversely of the unit **10**.  The axle has a spur gear **38** rigidly secured to one end thereof and meshing with the cog track **16**. A spur gear **39** is rigidly secured to the opposite end of the axle meshing with the cog track **17**. A drum **40** is rigidly secured to the outer end of the axle **37** adjacent to the spur gear **39** for reasons to be assigned.

A drum **41** is journalled in the base member **11** adjacent to the front wall **15** as can be seen in Figure 8.10b. An elongate shaft **42** extends between the rear ends of the longitudinal members **12, 13** and is journalled therein. A roller **43** is mounted on the shaft and has pulleys **44** secured thereto and turning therewith. The pulleys and drums are all arranged in longitudinally aligned relation. A shaft **45** extends through the rear wall of the vehicle and has a drum **46** mounted on its outer end and a drive pulley **47** mounted on its inner end.

A battery-operated electric motor **48** is connected to the pulley **47** by a belt **49** and the motor is controlled by push-button controls **50**. An endless cable **51** is wrapped around the drum **46** several turns with both ends then passing up and over the pulleys **44** and forwardly where one leg is wrapped around the drum **40** while the opposite leg extends directly forwardly and around the drum **41**.

Rotation of the drum **46** either by the electric motor or the hand crank **52** will move the cable and cause the spur gears to rotate with the shaft **37** so as to move the spur gears along the cog tracks. As the spur gears reach the U-shaped end portions **18, 19** of the cog tracks they will climb the cog tracks so as to elevate the forward end of the box **27** with the rear end of the box extending outwardly over the end of the vehicle to provide an awning thereover. A ribbed plastic panel **53** is secured to the underside of the insulation **28** to provide a firm support therefor.

A flexible hose **54** extends from the box to a source of cold water or to the outlet of heating radiators in the vehicle. A hook **55** secured to the frame member **13** supports the hose to prevent its becoming entangled. The flexible hose is secured to a fitting **56** forming a part of a header **57** within the box. A second header **58** at the opposite end of the box is connected to the header **57** by a plurality of longitudinally extending conduits **59**. A flexible hose **60** extends from a fitting **61** on the outer end of the header to the bottom of the hot water tank **23**.

In the use and operation of the apparatus the unit **10** is secured to the top of the vehicle with which it is to be used and the connections to extend through the vehicle walls are made. Water pressure controlled by a pressure regulator (not shown) then enters the unit through the conduit **54**. The box is moved to its rearward position rolling on the roller and also supported by the spur gears. As the box reaches its rearmost position the spur gears climb the U-shaped end portions of the cog tracks. This permits the outer end of the box to move downwardly to assume the desired angle for collecting heat therein.

Moving the cable **51** in the opposite direction will move the box forwardly until only a minor portion thereof overlaps the rear of the vehicle **20**. The water entering the box will be heated and moved through tank **23** under convection currents. As water is used from the tank by domestic water usage or by radiator usage the water will be replenished and the cycle will be continuous. The conduits **57** and **59** can be cemented or otherwise secured to the bottom wall **29** if desired for conductance of heat.

Another modification of a water heating device for use with a mobile home is provided by *J.A. Lanciault; U.S. Patent 3,823,703; July 16, 1974.* In that system a self-storing solar heater is installed on a house trailer with the heater being extendable over a portion of the roof of the trailer to receive the rays of the sun during the day and is stored in a heated compartment on cold days and nights to prevent the water in the solar heater from freezing. A thermostatically controlled motor-driven reel retracts the solar heater into the heated storage compartment and a pulley system actuated by the same motor extends the solar heater when heating rays are available from the sun.

# SWIMMING POOL APPLICATIONS

## POOL SURFACE SYSTEMS

### Floating Ball Blanket

As is known to those skilled in the floating ball blanket art, the floating ball blankets of the prior art are typically comprised of a plurality of spherical, hollow plastic balls used to cover liquid surfaces such as the liquid surface of a typical controlled temperature bath. Such typical controlled temperature baths may include acid pickling, plating, rinsing, dyeing, anodizing, phosphating and food processing tanks containing liquids, or semiliquids, generally maintained at elevated temperatures.

Such floating ball blankets comprised of the generally hollow spherical floatable balls of the prior art are reputed to help control the temperature by limiting the surface area exposed to air thereby limiting liquid loss by evaporation, heat loss by such evaporation, and heat transfer (either loss or gain) by convection from the surface of the covered liquid.

As is further known, the spherical floatable balls of the prior art, due to their spherical configuration are engageable only in point-to-point contact, and hence provide a floating ball blanket having a plurality of gaps, between the spherical floatable balls which gaps leave open space for liquid loss by evaporation, heat loss by such evaporation, and heat transfer by convection from the surface of the liquid.

Unlike the spherically shaped floatable ball known to the prior art, the floatable ball of the process of *F.J. Fuchs and D.J. Fuchs; U.S. Patent 3,998,204; December 21, 1976* is a modified spheroid provided with a predetermined number of flat surfaces around its equator whereby a plurality of such modified spheroids are engageable in flat surface-to-surface engagement at the equators thereof to provide a gapless or uninterrupted floating ball blanket. The gapless or uninterrupted floating ball blanket substantially prevents liquid loss by evaporation, heat loss by such evaporation, and heat transfer (either loss or gain) by convection from the surface of the liquid.

Further, the floatable ball of the process may further include means for orienting the floatable ball upon being floated such that the flat surfaces provided at the equator thereof are disposed horizontally and are presented for flat surface-to-surface engagement with the flat surfaces of other floatable balls of the process similarly configured and similarly oriented. Still further, the floatable ball may be constructed so as to absorb radiant energy and transfer the absorbed radiant energy to the liquid covered by the floating ball blanket.

Referring now to Figure 9.1a, of the drawings, there is shown a typical temperature controlled bath **10** with the leftward surface thereof being covered with a floating ball blanket comprised of a plurality of spherical floatable balls known to the prior art, and the rightward portions of the surface being covered with a floating ball blanket comprised of a plurality of floatable balls of the process.

## FIGURE 9.1: FLOATING BALL BLANKET

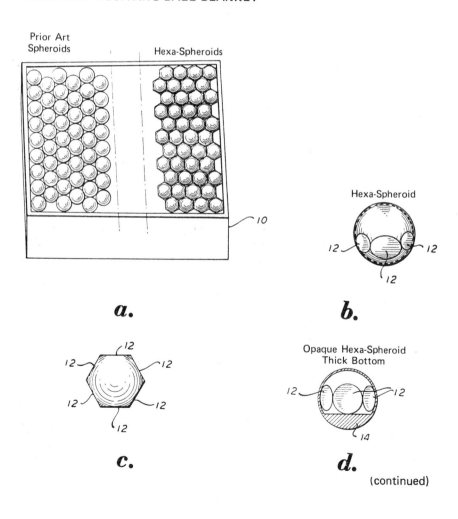

(continued)

FIGURE 9.1: (continued)

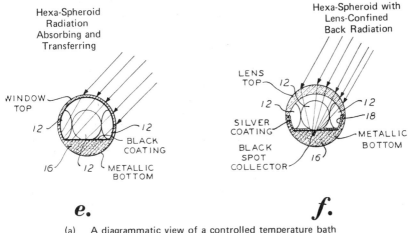

Hexa-Spheroid Radiation Absorbing and Transferring

Hexa-Spheroid with Lens-Confined Back Radiation

e.    f.

(a)   A diagrammatic view of a controlled temperature bath covered with floating ball blankets of the prior art and the process

(b)(c)  Figure 9.1a and 9.1b perspective side and top view of floatable ball embodiments

(d)   Side view, in cross section, illustrating means for orienting the ball

(e)(f)  Side views, in cross section, of embodiments for absorbing and transferring radiant energy

Source:  U.S. Patent 3,998,204

It will be noted that the prior art floating blanket of spherical floatable balls includes a plurality of gaps between the balls which do not come into flat surface-to-surface contact, but instead, due to their spherical configuration, come into point-to-point engagement. To the contrary, the floating ball blanket comprised of a plurality of floatable balls of the process which are provided with a plurality of flat surfaces around the equators thereof, provides a floating ball blanket which is gapless and thereby eliminates the liquid loss, heat loss and heat transfer by convection from the surface of the liquid caused by the gaps in the prior art floating ball blanket.

Referring now to Figures 9.1b and 9.1c there are shown floatable balls which are provided with a predetermined number of flat surfaces 12 around the equator thereof. As may be noted from Figure 9.1c, which provides a top view, the flat surfaces provided around the equator provide the modified spheroid with an equatorial cross section, the outline of which is a closed plane figure comprised of a plurality of interconnected straight lines equal in number to the respective number of flat surfaces. Thus the embodiment of the floatable ball shown is a modified spheroid provided with six flat surfaces 12 around its equator.

Accordingly, upon a floating ball blanket being comprised of a plurality of floatable balls such as the embodiment shown in Figures 9.1b and 9.1c, and as illustrated in the rightward portion of Figure 9.1a, the floatable balls upon floating upon the surface of a liquid are engageable in flat surface-to-surface contact or engagement with the respective flat surfaces in engagement, thereby providing a gapless or uninterrupted floating ball blanket.

Referring now to Figure 9.1d, there is shown a further embodiment wherein the floatable ball is provided with means for orienting the ball when floating such that the flat surfaces 12 are disposed horizontally and are presented for flat surface-to-surface engagement with the flat surfaces of other similarly configured and oriented floatable balls. More specifically, the floatable ball may be substantially hollow and comprised of a generally thin, plastic wall and wherein the means 14 for orienting the floating ball comprises a bottom wall portion which is thicker and hence heavier than the top and side wall portions and which will cause the ball to rotate and orient itself upon the liquid being slightly agitated such that the heavier portion assumes the bottom orientation thereby assuring that the flat surfaces 12 are disposed or oriented horizontally for flat surface-to-surface engagement with the flat surfaces of other similarly configured and oriented floatable balls. Further, it will be understood that no rolling or ballpoint pen action can occur.

As shown in Figure 9.1e, the top half of the modified spheroid may be made of clear plastic and the bottom half may be made of metal-filled black plastic or, as shown, metal, the top surface of which is provided with a black coating for absorbing radiant energy.

Referring now to Figure 9.1f of the process, a further embodiment of the floatable ball of the process is shown for absorbing and transferring radiant energy wherein the top upper wall portion of the modified spheroid is shaped, as shown, to provide a generally semispherical convex lens for focusing radiant energy on the radiant energy absorbing and thermally conductive materials 16. The bottom half or portions of the modified spheroid is comprised of metal and is provided with a top inner surface which is substantially flat and circular and which top inner surface also includes an integrally formed annular side wall portion which side wall portion extends upwardly and outwardly to a predetermined height as shown.

Further, the top inner surface of the metal 16 may be covered with a black coating for absorbing radiant energy and may further include a silver coating having a generally centrally formed aperture as shown for confining the surface exposure of the black coating and for lessening any tendency of the metal 16 to reradiate the radiant energy absorbed upwardly. The centrally formed aperture of the silver coating covering the black coating provides a black spot radiant energy collector.

Referring now to Figure 9.1f, a further embodiment is shown wherein the top upper wall portion of the modified spheroid is shaped to provide a generally semispherical convex lens for focusing radiant energy on the radiant energy absorbing and thermally conductive material 16. The bottom half or portion of the modified spheroid is comprised of radiant energy absorbing and transferring material such as metal which may be provided with a top inner surface which is substantially flat and circular and which top inner surface also includes an integrally formed annular side wall portion 18 which side wall portion extends upwardly and outwardly to a predetermined height as shown. Further, and in accordance with the teaching of the process, the top inner surface of the metal may be covered with a black coating for absorbing radiant energy and may further include a silver coating having a generally centrally formed aperture as shown for confining the surface exposure of the black coating and for lessening any tendency of the metal to reradiate the radiant energy absorbed upwardly. The centrally formed aperture of the silver coating covering the black coating provides a black spot radiant energy collector.

One attractive and beneficial use of such floatable balls is to heat swimming pools. The floatable balls can be drained off into a storage tank when the pool is in use and can be poured or delivered back onto the surface of the pool by a suitable valve arrangement attached to the filtering system typically associated with the swimming pool. Clearing the swimming pool and recovering the floatable balls in this manner would take only a few minutes and would provide no undesirable interruption of pool use. Further, all white balls could be substituted for composite floatable balls at night with a similar ball handling system and such white floatable balls would prevent heat loss to the cold night sky by radiation.

### Loop-Shaped Panel Assembly

*C.S. Forman and R.K. Gerlach; U.S. Patent 3,984,882; October 12, 1976; assigned to CaTel Manufacturing Inc. and R.K. Gerlach; U.S. Patent 3,984,881; October 12, 1976; assigned to CaTel Manufacturing Inc.* describe a solar panel unit comprising a loop-shaped plastic frame, bounding an open zone, the frame having a channel section; a plastic sheet extending across the open zone; and insert means retained in the channel section and holding the sheet to the frame. The sheet has woven construction and defining air filled interstices distributed over the sheet area across the open zone.

The sheet may typically include a colored plastic filler applied to the woven construction, the filler defining the air-filled interstices and being exposed at upper and lower sides of the sheet; and the filler may be dark colored at one side of the sheet to absorb light and produce heat, and light colored at the opposite side of the sheet to reflect heat from the water body when the solar panel is inverted.

Further, the frame may be toroidally twisted about 180° to tension the sheet edge portions back over the insert means so as to retain it in the frame channel section preventing inadvertent pull-out of the sheet from the frame; and the insert means may comprise an elongated flexible bead constructed to interact with the channel section to firmly and positively retain the sheet edge portion in the frame. For example, interference shoulders may be provided to engage and retain the sheet. Finally, the frame may include interfitting portions that cooperate to retain the sheet in position, and the panel units may be constructed to nest and stack for ease of shipment, the units having different diameters for this purpose.

Referring first to Figure 9.2a, panel units **10** are shown deployed on the surface of a body of water **11** such as is contained by swimming pool structure **12**. The floating units **10** are generally circular in shape, and function to intercept solar radiation and to transfer solar heat by conduction to the pool water; in addition, they act to prevent heat loss from the pool due to evaporation.

FIGURE 9.2: LOOP-SHAPED PANEL ASSEMBLY

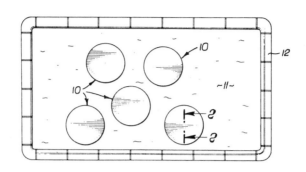

a.

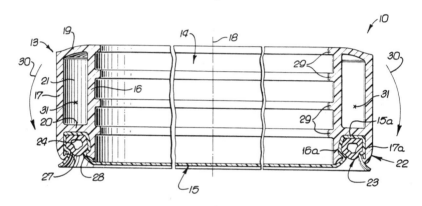

b.

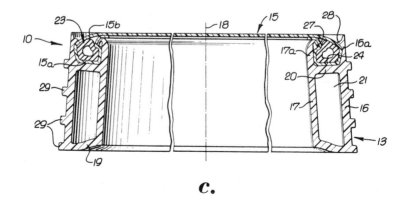

c.

(continued)

FIGURE 9.2: (continued)

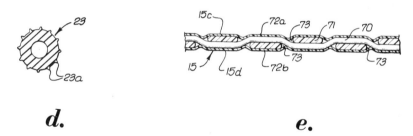

**d.**                                    **e.**

(a)  Plan view of swimming pool with panels
(b)  Enlarged section through panel frame and cover
(c)  Like Figure 9.2b, but showing frame and
     cover assembly after toroidal twisting
(d)  Enlarged section through insert bead
(e)  Enlarged section through panel cover

Source:  U.S. Patent 3,984,882

Each unit **10** basically comprises a loop-shaped plastic frame, one example being shown at **13** in Figure 9.2b and bounding an open zone **14**; a plastic sheet **15** extending across zone **14**; and insert means retained in a channel section of the frame and holding the sheet to the frame.  The frame **13** includes radially spaced walls **16** and **17** which extend generally parallel to the central axis **18** of the unit **10**, and axially spaced walls **19** and **20** bridging between walls **16** and **17**.

Walls **16, 17, 19** and **20** form an enclosed hollow **21** extending about axis **18** so that the frame is buoyant and tends to float on the water body **11**.  Walls **20** together with annular cantilever extensions **16a** and **17a** of walls **16** and **17** form a channel section **22** to receive the insert element **23** for holding the sheet **15** to the frame.  Element **23** may advantageously comprise an elongated, flexible elastomer or plastic bead sized to tightly fit within the recess **24** defined by the channel shaped section **22** along with an edge portion **15a** of the sheet **15**, as shown.

The unflexed insert bead may have generally circular cross-section as seen in Figure 9.2d, and define lengthwise extending surface serrations **23a** which project outwardly and which are spaced circularly about the bead cross-section. Accordingly, the serrations cooperate with the sheet edge portion, and with the inner wall surfaces of the section **22**, and with the inwardly projecting tongues **27** and **28** integral with and at the free ends of wall extensions **16a** and **17a**, to tightly hold the sheet to the frame.

Note that tongues or lips **27** and **28** are caused to yieldably grip the sheet edge portion **15a**, due to the resilient cantilever bending capability of the annular wall extensions **16a** and **17a,** and the yieldable compressibility of the insert bead or spline **23**.  The four axially spaced annular ridges **29** integral therewith as shown stiffen the frame.

Following assembly of the sheet **15** to the frame as described, the frame is twisted toroidally by manual or other application of forces as indicated by arrows **30** acting about an annular axis **31** of the frame (i.e., generally about the annular hollow **21**), to displace the frame inside out, i.e., through about 180° of rotation about axis **31**. The resultant configuration appears in Figure 9.2c, with the sheet **15** now tensioned and extending at **15b** back over the insert bead in tight overlapping relation therewith proximate the mouth of the recess defined by the arm extensions **16a** and **17a**.

Accordingly, the bead is held in position in the recess, preventing its pull-out by the sheet **15** which was initially held to the frame by the bead in Figure 9.2b. Further, the sheet edge portion **15a** including extension **15b** extends all the way around in the bead in Figure 9.2c. Toroidal twisting presents the four axially spaced annular ridges **29** on wall **16** in an outward direction, so that they may mesh or interdigitate with similar ridges on adjacent floating panels, preventing stacking of the panels in a pool when the wind blows.

In Figure 9.2e the sheet **15** is shown to have woven construction, as defined by enlarged warp and woof solid plastic strands **70** and **71**. The plastic itself may advantageously consist of polypropylene, polyethylene or other suitable plastic, and the frame preferably consists of ABS plastic material. Further, air-filled interstices or voids are distributed over the sheet, and act to load with water to increase the weight of the sheet in a pool, thereby diminishing any tendency for the panel to be wind blown up off the water surface.

The sheet may include a colored plastic filler such as plastic (similar to that listed above) paint or film applied to the woven construction, to define the upper and lower surfaces **15c** and **15d**. Such filler is indicated at **72a** (upper) and **72b** (lower). The filler may define, with strands **70** and **71**, the air filled voids or interstices as at **73** and into which water tends to seep via the porosity of the film. Woven construction or strands **70** and **71** may advantageously consist of clear (uncolored or transparent or translucent) polypropylene, whereas upper filler layer **72a** may have a dark color (blue, for example), and lower filler layer may have a light color (white, for example), all for the purpose of absorbing downward solar radiation at the upper surface **15c** to heat the pool during the day or to reflect heat radiation away from the pool when surface **15d**, faces the sky to minimize heat transfer to the pool. This condition would exist as in desert areas with very hot daytime sunshine.

### Inflatable Raft

*M. Pelehach, R.W. Kress and R.J. Larson; U.S. Patent 3,949,095; April 6, 1976;* describe a solar heating device for swimming pools comprising an inflatable raft having a thermally reflective bottom surface and a thermally transparent top surface, and means for elevating at least a fraction of the reflective surface above the swimming pool surface during periods of diminished solar radiation to reduce heat loss from the water.

The main component of this process is an air cushion raft preferably of a size easily handled by one person. It may be about 3' x 6' and can be compared to the floats used for recreational purposes in swimming areas. The raft consists of two layers of plastic separated by an air pocket. One of the layers is covered on the outside by a highly reflective aluminized surface. On the inside, this same layer is covered by a dull black heat absorptive surface. The second plastic layer on the other side of the air pocket is transparent. When used for pool heating, the raft is floated on the surface of the pool, aluminized side down. Incoming solar radiation is transmitted essentially undiminished through the transparent layer to the black layer where the heat is absorbed and conducted to the pool through water contact with the aluminized surface on the other side of the black layer.

The heating principle as described has been used by others for similar applications. The pool cover described in U.S. Patent 3,072,920 is such an example but does not show the separate individual rafts which provide a measure of flexibility.

The major point of departure of the process from prior art lies in the provision of additional means of raising the aluminized surface above the water during periods when heat input to the water body is absent. If the aluminized surface is held out of water contact, heat will not be lost from the water by conduction through that aluminized surface, and any heat loss from the water by radiation is reflected back to the water. Such means for raising the aluminized surface may be automatic, semiautomatic or manual, as desired.

With reference to Figures 9.3a and 9.3b, a preferred embodiment of the solar heating raft **10** is shown in an elevated condition where the bottom of the raft is raised above the surface of the water **11**. The raft **10** comprises a top transparent layer **12** of pliable plastic material and a lower pliable plastic layer **13**, which are sealed together around the periphery to form an air-tight cushion. The top and bottom layers are connected by a plurality of ribs **14** to give the raft a flat rather than balloon shaped contour.

The bottom layer **13** is made energy absorbent on the inside of the raft by providing it with a blackened coating **15**. The exterior of the layer **13** is provided with a metalized coating, e.g., an aluminized coating **16** to make it energy reflecting. The exterior aluminized coating **16** is protected from contamination by a thin vinyl coating over the aluminum.

As shown in Figures 9.3a and 9.3b, the raft **10** may be elevated by the pair of air chambers **17, 18** which are attached to the bottom layer **13** when the air chambers **17, 18** are inflated. In the heating condition, however, the raft is lowered by deflating chambers **17, 18** as shown in Figure 9.3c so that the layer **13** is in intimate thermal contact with the water **11**. It is evident that the envelope **19** of the air chambers **17, 18** is interposed between the exterior surface **16** and the water **11**. The envelope **19** is a good thermal conductor, however, and being in intimate thermal contact with surface **16** it can be said that the surface is in thermal contact with the water.

Chambers **17, 18** and their function will be described more fully later on, but for the moment consider the heating condition wherein chambers **17, 18** are deflated as shown in Figure 9.3c and the metalized layer **16** is in thermal conductive relationship with the water **11**. During hours of significant solar radiation, i.e., daytime hours, solar energy reaches the upper layer **12** of the raft **10** from the sun.

As described earlier, the top layer **12** is transparent to thermal energy and permits the solar energy to reach the bottom layer **13** virtually unattenuated. The blackened surface **15** absorbs the thermal energy which is then conducted through layer **13** to the metallized outer surface **16**. When surface **16** is in contact with the water the thermal energy is conducted through it to the water which in turn is heated thereby.

FIGURE 9.3:  INFLATABLE RAFT

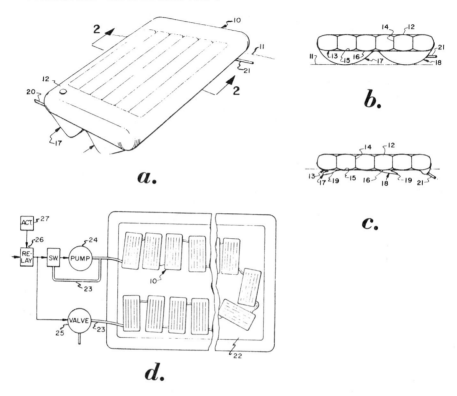

(a)    Pictorial representation, partly in section, of the heating raft
(b)    Cross sectional view
(c)    Deflated modification of Figure 9.3b
(d)    Plurality of rafts covering the surface of a pool

Source:  U.S. Patent 3,949,095

During periods of reduced solar energy impact, e.g., nighttime hours or cold days, the heated water tends to radiate energy to the cooler air and thereby lose heat.  To minimize that heat loss, and the heat which might be conducted through the raft **10** to be radiated to the air, the raft is raised above the water surface so that the metalized layer **16** now acts to reflect heat radiated from the water back to the water and eliminates heat loss by conduction through the raft.

The preferred mechanism by which the raft is raised and lowered includes the inflatable chambers **17, 18** which as stated earlier, are attached to the bottom layer **13**.  Chambers **17, 18** are not independent of each other, but air passages, not evident in the exterior views, interconnect the chambers. Chamber **17** is provided with an air input connection **20** while chamber **18** is provided with an air outlet (or exhaust) connection **21**. Two chambers attached to the periphery and to the center of the raft are used for purposes of stability in floating which might not be achieved with a single chamber. During the daytime the chambers are deflated and surface **16** is lowered into position for conducting energy to the water body, as explained earlier, through the walls **19** of chambers **17, 18** which are now collapsed and in intimate contact with surface **16**. For even better thermal conductivity the chambers may be evacuated to remove any air which might prevent direct physical contact between surface **16** and the walls **19** of chambers **17, 18**. The material of which envelope **19** of chambers **17, 18**, is made is a good thermal conductor such as that used for the top surface **12** of raft **10**. When the chambers **17, 18** are inflated the cushion **10** rises and places the metallized surface **16** in position to reflect thermal energy.

Figure 9.3d shows a plurality of rafts **10** floating in and covering a large percentage of the surface of the pool **22**. Rafts **10** are interconnected by tubing **23**, one end of which leads to an air pump **24** the other end of which leads to a solenoid actuated exhaust valve **25**. Pump **24** and solenoid valve **25** are automatically energized or deenergized through a relay **26** which is actuated by a photoelectric cell **27** so as to start pump **24** and close valve **25** in the evening and to stop pump **24** and open valve **25** in the morning. A safety pressure switch deenergizes pump **24** when pressure in the rafts **10** reaches a predetermined value and controls pump **24** to maintain that pressure.

### Floating Pan-Shaped Vessel

*R.H. Smith; U.S. Patent 3,893,443; July 8, 1975* describes a floating solar heater for swimming pools, which has side walls, end walls and a bottom forming a pan-like vessel having a shallow chamber and capable of floating on the surface of the pool. Inside surfaces of the walls and bottom are black in color and outside surfaces are lighter. Over the top of the side and end walls is a translucent cover closing the chamber in the vessel to form a substantially dead air space and sealed sufficiently at the edges to prevent water entering the chamber in a sufficient amount to sink the vessel or impair the heating action.

In the embodiment of Figure 9.4, there is shown a substantially conventional swimming pool indicated generally by the reference character **10** around which is a pool deck **11** and a coping **12** at the edge of the pool itself. In the pool and floating on the surface **13** is a plurality of units **14** consisting of floating pans, the units being distributed over a portion only of the pool surface.

The units in the chosen embodiment are rectangular although it will be appreciated that the precise geometrical perimeter may be varied to suit various conditions. It is of significance, however, that the units be of such geometrical perimeter as will allow them, when either partially or completely filling the pool, to be fitted in side-by-side or end-to-end alignment when desired and also be capable of fitting one side or another of the pool as a matter of convenience in use.

More specifically, each of the units in the chosen embodiment consists of a shallow pan formed of side walls **15** and **16** and end walls **17** and **18**. At the lower edges of the side and end walls is a bottom wall **19**, the bottom wall having a blackened surface **20** on the inside. When the pan is made of metal with good heat conducting characteristics such as aluminum, the blackened surface may be an anodized surface. When the pan is made of fiberglass reinforced plastic resin or one or another of the commercially available and expedient types of synthetic plastic resin, the blackened surface may be a film applied either by painting or by some other appropriate means compatible with the material used.

Extending over the top edges of the side and end walls is a transparent or translucent cover **21**. It has been found advantageous to provide the side and end walls with outwardly bent flanges **22** whereby to present flat areas **23** upon which outer portions of the cover may rest. By the construction described there is provided a chamber **25** which is a relatively thin dead air space in the proportions shown and described where the height of the side and end walls is about one and one quarter inches and the aggregate area of the cover is about ten square feet. It is advantageous also to have the cover in sealed engagement with the flat areas **23** thereby to provide a floating vessel which will not ship water as well as providing the chamber from which heated air cannot escape.

The material of the cover should be either of glass or preferably one of the transparent or translucent synthetic plastic resin materials of a type capable of permitting the short rays of the sun to pass through it and thereafter be absorbed by the blackened surface. In this arrangement the long rays emitted by the blackened surface under operating conditions cannot pass back out through the transparent cover. Accordingly the short rays are readily converted to heat which is then conducted through the bottom of the pan directly to the pool water surface. The structure described produces what has been frequently termed a greenhouse effect.

## FIGURE 9.4: FLOATING PAN-SHAPED VESSEL

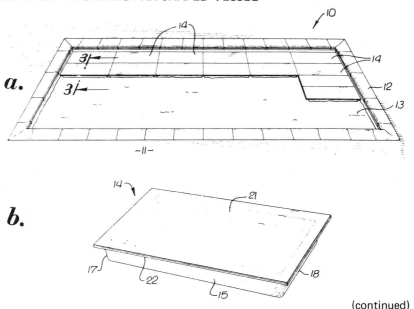

(continued)

**FIGURE 9.4:** (continued)

*c.*

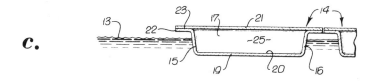

    (a)   Perspective view of pool showing a number of the devices
    (b)   Side perspective view of one unit
    (c)   Fragmentary cross-sectional view taken on line **3—3** of
           Figure 9.4a

Source:  U.S. Patent 3,893,443

Pans of the type herein described have been found by tests to be capable of absorbing and passing to the surface water of the pool about 150 Btu per hour per square foot of pan surface.  A convenient size for a rectangular pan has been found to be 2' x 5'.  Although rectangular pans which can be pushed into side-by-side or end-to-end positions have certain advantages, effective heating can be achieved by pans of perimetral configuration which do not, in fact, permit them to interfit one with another.  It is the area of pool surface covered which is instrumental in achieving the heating effect desired.

**Thermal Compartment Defined by Spacing Ribs**

A solar heating apparatus is disclosed by *M.A. Roberts; U.S. Patent 4,022,187; May 10, 1977* useful as a swimming pool cover whereby the sun's rays can penetrate the apparatus and heat the water therebeneath.  The apparatus includes a plurality of individual and separate units of a predetermined geometry which cooperate with each other to cover a given body of water.

Each unit includes an upper panel of transparent, plastic material and a bottom panel of opaque, plastic material.  The panels are joined at peripheries to provide an integral unit and spacers or ribs are provided to maintain separation between the opposing panel surfaces so that a thermal compartment is defined therebetween.

Referring to Figure 9.5a, a conventional swimming pool is illustrated in the general direction of arrow **10** which includes a rectangular coping **11** defining the perimeter of the pool which includes a body of water illustrated in general by the numeral **12**.  Disposed on the surface of the pool **12**, there is provided a plurality of individual and separate floating solar heating units such as the unit identified by numeral **13**.  The respective units are located so as to cover the entire surface of the pool and, preferably, the periphery or edge marginal regions of adjacent solar units touch or engage so that as much of the pool surface is covered as is permitted by the particular geometry or shape of the unit.

In the example, a circular solar unit **13** is illustrated.  However, it is to be understood that other predetermined configurations may be employed such as squares, rectangular shapes or the like.

FIGURE 9.5: THERMAL COMPARTMENT DEFINED BY SPACING RIBS

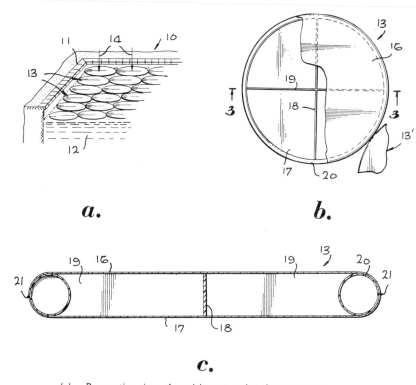

*a.*     *b.*

*c.*

(a)   Perspective view of pool incorporating the apparatus
(b)   Enlarged plan view, partially broken away, showing one unit
(c)   Transverse cross-sectional view taken in the direction of
      arrows **3—3** of Figure 9.5b

Source:   U.S. Patent 4,022,187

In this manner, a plurality of air chambers, defined by each of the separate solar heaters, are employed for retaining heat in the pool **12**. The impinging sun rays are indicated by arrows **14**.

Referring to Figure 9.5b, the solar heating unit **13** is illustrated which comprises, in general, a top panel **16** which is composed of a clear, flexible plastic material such as a polyvinyl chloride or other suitable material such as polyethylene or the like. A satisfactory construction utilizes a transparent sheet that is 0.002 to 0.005 inch thick. This same material and thickness is also used to provide a bottom panel **17** which is arranged in fixed spaced apart relationship so that the opposing surfaces of panels **16** and **17** define an air chamber therebetween.

Preferably, the internal air chamber is approximately 3¼ inches in height and adequate separation between the opposing surfaces of the panels is provided by means of a rib or spacer arrangement indicated by cross ribs **18** and **19**. Also, the entire unit is rigidized by a circular rim **20** which may be a solid tube, a hollow tube or even an inflatable tube. As illustrated, an adjacent solar heating unit **13'** is shown having its edge marginal regions touching or in engagement with the edge marginal region of the solar heating unit **13**.

In Figure 9.5c, the upper panel **16** is transparent while the bottom or lower panel **17** is opaque, or preferably black. Furthermore, if desirable, the adjacent edge marginal regions of the upper and lower panels are joined together in a seam **21** so that a unitary construction is provided rigidized by the ribs **18** and **19** as well as the rim **20**. The opposing surfaces of the upper and lower panels **16** and **17** are separated so that an adequate air chamber or space is provided therebetween so that air insulation is provided against heat transfer through the panels from the water through the ambient air. Also, the unit separates the ambient air from the surface of the water so that wind conditions cannot draw heat from the pool surface.

## ROOF-MOUNTED SYSTEMS

### Coiled Collector Panel

*T.L. Newton; U.S. Patent 4,014,314; March 29, 1977; assigned to Sunburst Solar Energy, Inc.* describes a collector panel for thermal energy emanating from the sun which comprises a coiled length of tubing arranged in a planar toroid and held in that position by a plurality of radial clamps. The tubing is continuous and carries the fluid to be heated, typically water from a swimming pool or similar container, in a spiral path in the plane of the collector. The collector is inclined at an angle to the vertical, orthogonal to the mean incidence of sunshine at the location of installation.

The fluid-bearing tubing may typically be of plastic or metal construction and range from one-half to one inch in internal diameter. The collector panel is typically several feet in diameter and presents a collecting surface, when projected onto a flat plane, of 10 square feet or more. Because the surface of the panel is composed of the upper circumference of substantially tubular flow channels, the effective collection surface is larger than the projected area of the panel.

Because of the circular, shallow spiral of the tubing forming the collector panel, the effective collection surface is independent of the angle of incident solar radiation, once the plane of the collector has been aligned with the local mean solar radiation vector, the value of which may readily be determined by reference to architectural textbooks and other sources of appropriate information. This angle of incidence will typically vary from 30° to 90° in geographic latitudes where solar energy collection is economically feasible; the above angles being referenced to the local gravitational vector of the earth.

The frontal view of Figure 9.6a shows a solar energy collector **10** which is formed by coiling an elongated piece of cylindrical tubing **12** into a toroidal shape stiffened by a plurality of radial clamps **20** and end-pieces **22**. The tubing **12** is terminated external to the circumference of the collector panel in a discharge stub **14** and an inlet **16** which extends, in substantially radial alignment, from the inner diameter of the toroid to the outer periphery.

The material of the tubing may be chosen from several plastic and metal compositions readily available; polyethylene, polyvinyl chloride, aluminum and copper compositions are included. For the plastic compositions a darkened, semiopaque finish is preferred to increase the collection efficiency for radiant heat emitted by the sun and to reduce aging from exposure to the ultraviolet end of the spectrum.

## FIGURE 9.6: COILED COLLECTOR PANEL

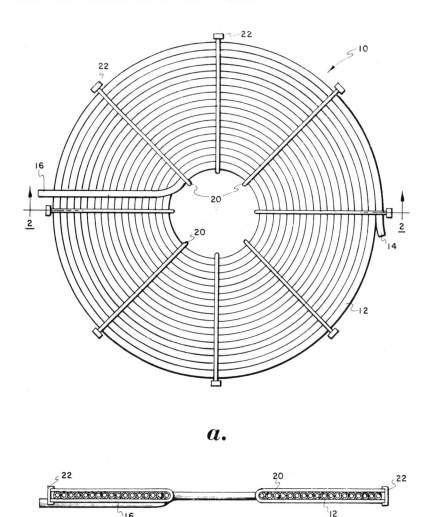

*a.*

*b.*

(continued)

FIGURE 9.6: (continued)

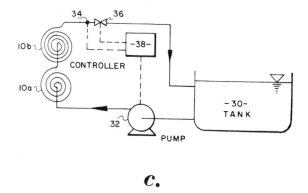

*c.*

(a)  Frontal view of collector
(b)  Transverse section
(c)  Schematic diagram of heating system employing two
      collector panels

Source: U.S. Patent 4,014,314

For metallic compositions, darkened surface finishes, typified by black-anodized aluminum, are preferred to increase the coefficient of absorption of the collector. The radial clamps **20** are rigid, elongated metal clamps, bent into U-shaped members whose internal spacing corresponds to the outer diameter of the tubing. The ends of the tines of clamps **20** are engaged by end-pieces which prevent the discharge of the tubing from the outermost winding of the collector.

Figure 9.6b indicates the manner in which the tubing **12** is closely wound to form the collector panel, adjacent turns of the spiral winding being closely packed to present a continuous absorbing surface to incident radiation.

While no supporting structure is shown in Figures 9.6a and 9.6b, an interconnecting frame may be provided, as desired, to rigidly interconnect the several clamps into a self-supporting assembly and to provide support means for inclining the collector panel at the sun-receiving angle appropriate to its geographical location. When the panel is laid directly on a planar surface, such as a roof, which is at the appropriate inclination with the mean solar vector and where one or more of the clamps may be attached to the surface, a support structure as hereinabove described is not necessary.

The panel is assembled, by preference, at the use site, the clamps and the tubing being delivered as separate items and wound into the toroidal collector immediately prior to final connection.

The collector panel **10** may be advantageously used to heat water for household use, by passing cool water through the coiled tubing **12** from inlet **16** to discharge **14** when sunlight is incident on the surface of the panel. It may also be utilized to provide heating for swimming pools and other water reservoirs which are to be maintained at a temperature above ambient.

A typical installation of the type is shown in the schematic diagram of Figure 9.6c, employing two collecting panels **10a** and **10b**. A tank **30**, suitably a swimming pool, supplies cool water to the inlet of pump **32** whence it is conveyed, under pressure, to the inlet of collector **10a**. The water is heated in the first solar heating device and then passed to the intake of a second heating panel **10b**, the discharge of which is routed back to the tank **30**.

A valve **36** governs flow through the circuit and is, itself, controlled from a controller **38**. A temperature sensing device **34** is installed near the discharge of solar collector **10b** and provides information to the controller. A temperature sensing device **34** is installed near the discharge of solar collector **19b** and provides information to the controller.

Whenever the controller senses that water at the exit of panel **10b** is at a temperature above a preset level, it opens the valve **36** and starts pump **32**, thereby causing water from the pool to circulate through the heating system. With the exception of utilizing solar heat collectors **10a** and **10b**, the pool heating system is similar to conventional devices employing gas-fired heaters or other sources of thermal energy, commonly employed in maintaining swimming pools at a temperature level comfortable for use.

### Water Circulated Between Thin Flexible Sheets

*D.H. Gerber; U.S. Patent 3,991,742; November 16, 1976; assigned to Burke Industries, Inc.* describes a heat transfer system for the heating of water by solar energy. The apparatus is especially suitable for heating large quantities of water by small temperature increments by circulating the water in repeated cycles in a thin layer between two flexible sheets of a dark colored panel.

The apparatus includes one or more large panels disposed on a sloping surface exposed to the sun. A pumping means supplies a continuous supply of water to be warmed to the upper edge of the panel. A distributor pipe, evenly distributes the water along the top edge of the panel where it flows over a member for spreading the water evenly over the entire surface area of the inside of the panel. A collector pipe collects the water at the bottom edge of the panel and a return piping system returns the warmed water to the pool of water.

The heart of the system is a large flexible panel which is made from a flexible sun- and weather-resistant elastomer. Ethylene propylene elastomer (Nordel) and chlorsulfonated polyethylene (Hypalon) are suitable for this use in that they have unusually high resistance to degradation under direct sunlight. The panel may be laid directly on asphalt shingle sloping roofs or on a suitable underlayment where the roof is constructed of thick wood shakes or tiles.

Referring to Figures 9.7a, 9.7b and 9.7c, the solar energy absorbing and heat transfer system for warming a pool of water **2** consists briefly of a solar panel **3** including a water impermeable lower member **4** and a very thin, flexible upper member **6** which has a low reflective outer surface **7** and a wettable inner surface and has high solar energy absorbing qualities; a thin, flexible spreader member **9** disposed between and in touching contact with a substantial portion of the inner surface of the upper panel member and the inner surface **11**; a distributor member **12** disposed along the upper inner edge **13** for evenly distributing fluid across substantially the entire upper edge of the panel; a collector member **14** for collecting the fluid at the lower edge **16** of the panel; supply means **17** for continuously supplying fluid to the distributor member at a relatively constant rate; and gravity discharge means **18** connected to the collector member for returning the fluid to the body of fluid such as pool **19**. Collector member **14** also prevents vacuum in the return line from pinching off and preventing discharge of fluid from the panel.

The upper member **6** of the panel **3** could be made of a rubber or plastic but because of the constant exposure to sunlight and in particular ultraviolet rays, degradation of the plastic or rubber would occur within a short period of time. One of the keys to the success of the process panel is the use of an ethylene propylene elastomer (EPE) or chlorsulfonated polyethylene (CP) as mentioned above. Since only the upper member is subject to sunlight only the upper member need be made from EPE or CP. It is probably more economical to make the entire panel from thin, flexible sheets of EPE or CP which are joined to form a container. The thickness of the sheets preferably range from 20 to 30 mils. CP in the unprocessed form is whitish but may be mixed with any color. Preferably, the panel is constructed from CP which is black in color throughout the material rather than merely black on the surface. The estimated useful life of CP is at least 20 years if the panels are properly cared for.

## FIGURE 9.7: WATER CIRCULATED BETWEEN THIN FLEXIBLE SHEETS

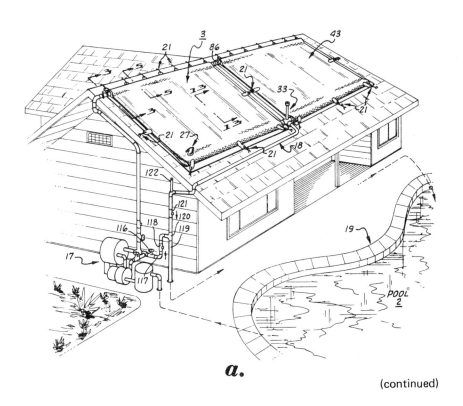

*a.*

(continued)

FIGURE 9.7: (continued)

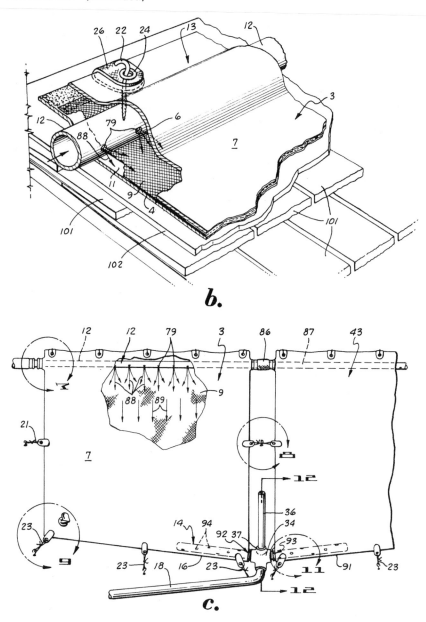

b.

c.

(a)    Perspective view of system
(b)    Perspective view of heating panel taken on line 5–5 of
        Figure 9.7a
(c)    Plan view of a portion of the system

Source:  U.S. Patent 3,991,742

One of the problems in using flexible sheet panels is the fact that water tends to flow in rivulets rather than in a thin sheet covering the entire surface of the panel.

For this reason a fluid spreader **9** is placed between the upper and lower members of the panel. The spreader may be a screen such as a layer of vinyl-coated fiberglass screening expanded plastic netting or sheeting such as Delnet or Vexar; nylon velvet, spun bonded plastic matting such as Typar; or a coarse open weave nylon or dacron cloth. A very thin, open cell, large cell polyurethane foam sheet may also be used as a spreader member.

The spreader not only serves to spread the water over the entire surface, but it also tends to separate the upper and lower layers of EPE or CP which have some tendency to stick together when exposed to the hot sun. It is not fully understood what causes the water to spread upon the screen, but it is believed that turbulence caused by the irregular spreader surface and capillary action within the spreader and between the spreader and panel plays some part in the process. The spreader is standard 18 x 16 threads per inch which is used for insect screening. The spreader is flexible so as to follow the contour taken by the flexible panel. Somewhat better spreading may be obtained by turning the spreader on the diagonal to the direction of fluid flow. Thickness of the screen is about 20 mils.

It has been found that the life of the panels is greatly extended if the EPE or CP sheets are prepared in an unvulcanized and/or not crosslinked state when placed at the particular installation. The EPE or CP is unstressed in the unvulcanized or not crosslinked state and it is believed that reduction of stress when the panels are placed on uneven surfaces such as roofs reduces deterioration due to sunlight. Vulcanization and/or crosslinking occurs slowly in the sunlight. The panels take the shape of the underlayment or roof upon which they are resting. Additional details and diagrams are included in the patent.

**Bonded Heat Exchange Panel**

Solar heating panels for swimming pools are well known. In the past a panel or series of panels has been constructed having an inlet connected to a pump for delivery of water to the panels and an outlet for delivery of water from the panels back to the pool. These panels have used relatively large cross-section straight through or serpentine passage arrangements.

The flow path through the panels and the inlet and outlet piping has been subject to leaks due to faults in the many mechanical joints and fittings. Moreover, the complexity of previously available panel assemblies and the low efficiency of heat transfer to the water flow due to the large cross-section passages rendered previous solar heaters unattractive. There is, therefore, a need for a simple, lightweight, efficient, structurally sound solar heat exchange panel, and for a simple process for fabricating the same.

The solar heating panel disclosed by *F.A. Ford, E. Armstrong and R.O. Rhodes; U.S. Patent 3,934,323; January 27, 1976; assigned to Fafco, Inc.* is a relatively thin flat sheet having multiple tubular passages running lengthwise therethrough.

The panels are cut to a predetermined length and spaced flanges are formed on the panel ends on either side of the tubular passage ends using heated dies. A pair of hollow headers are cut having a length comparable to the width of the panel, and having apertures through one side. The material of the headers and the spaced flanges is heated to the melting point and the headers and flanges are forced together under pressure creating a unitary assembly having a watertight weld between the headers and the panels when the material solidifies.

Plenum chambers are formed between the panel ends and the headers. The apertures through the sides of the hollow headers extend into the plenum chambers. An unobstructed flow path is constructed extending from an inlet to one header, through the apertures, one plenum chamber, the tubular passages, the opposite plenum chamber, the apertures in the opposite header, and through the opposite header to an outlet.

The heat exchange panel provides a continuous flow path for a fluid, a portion of the flow path being utilized to exchange heat between the fluid and the panel environment. Figure 9.8a shows a unitary heat exchange module having spaced headers **11** and **12** disposed at opposite ends of a heat exchange panel **13**.

## FIGURE 9.8: BONDED HEAT EXCHANGE PANEL

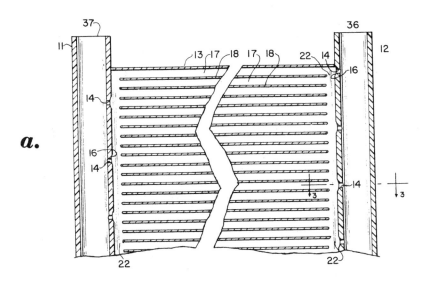

*a.*

*b.*

(continued)

FIGURE 9.8: (continued)

**c.**

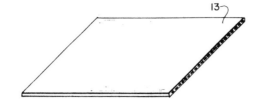

**d.**

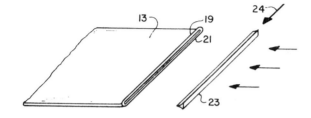

**e.**          **f.**

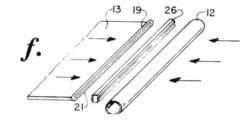

**g.**

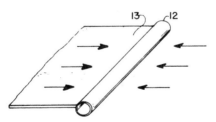

(a)   Cutaway sectional view of panel
(b)   Sectional view along the line **3–3** of Figure 9.8a
(c)   Isometric view of panel
(d)   Isometric view of panel undergoing flange formation process
(e)   Sectional view showing cross section of heating die
(f)   Isometric view of panel and hollow header undergoing
         bonding
(g)   Isometric view showing unitary assembly resulting from
         bonding process

Source:   U.S. Patent 3,934,323

Headers **11** and **12** are hollow and have along one side a line of spaced holes **14**. The holes **14** are countersunk as shown at **16** at the outer surface of headers **11** and **12**. It should be noted in Figure 9.8a that spaced holes **14** in header **11** are positioned in a staggered relationship relative to spaced holes **14** in header **12**. Multiple tubular passages **17** extend lengthwise through panel **13** and are defined by the broad outside walls of panel **13** and a plurality of partitions **18** extending therebetween.

Each end of panel **13** is subjected to a forming process. In the embodiment of Figure 9.8a, spaced flanges **19** and **21** are formed as shown in Figure 9.8b. Plenum chambers **22** are defined between the ends of panels **13**, the spaced flanges **19** and **21**, and the outer surfaces of headers **11** and **12** when the headers are joined to panel **13**. Identical plenum chambers **22** thus exist at opposite ends of panel **13**.

Heat exchange panels are cut to shape and the ends are formed as follows. Figure 9.8c shows the sheet-like member cut to a predetermined length for a heat exchange panel. Figure 9.8d shows the cut panel with spaced flanges **19** and **21** respectively formed by pressing a heated knife edge die **23** into each end of the panel. Knife edge die **23** is heated to a predetermined temperature, approximately 350°F for polyethylene panel material, and is pressed into the end of the panel at a predetermined rate.

The panel material is heated to the plastic range by die **23** thereby allowing the die to form the flanges by forcing apart the ends of panel **13** through which the tubular passages extend. The temperature and rate of advance of knife edge die **23** are important so that flanges **19** and **21** are formed while causing a predetermined reduction in cross section at the ends of tubular passages **17** without obstructing them completely.

Heated die **23** may be advanced at a lower rate during the initial stages of forming and accelerated during the latter stages to assure that the channel ends are not fully closed. Once the spaced flanges are formed, a coolant is injected about the die and the flanges as indicated by arrow **24** in Figure 9.8d so that die **23** may be removed from contact with the end of the panel without altering the shape of the flanges as formed. The coolant solidifies the material of the panel prior to removal of the die.

The headers **11** and **12** are cut to a length which is approximately the width of the panel. A line of spaced holes **14** having a countersink **16** is placed through the wall of headers **11** and **12**. The holes **14** generally have a diameter which is in a ratio of 1:16 relative to the inside diameter of headers **11** and **12**. By way of example, one-eighth inch diameter holes **14** are optimum for two inch diameter headers. The consideration is to obtain an optimum trade-off between head loss due to flow constriction and constant flow distribution throughout a plurality of panels **13**.

A heated bonding die **26** for the embodiment of Figure 9.8a has four projections **27** extending therefrom as best shown in Figure 9.8e. Projections **27** each have a planar surface on their ends shown at **28, 29, 31** and **32** in Figure 9.8e. Planar surfaces **28** and **31** are parallel and surfaces **29** and **32** are parallel.

Referring to Figure 8.9f, heated bonding die **26** is positioned between panel **13** having flanges **19** and **21** formed thereon, and hollow headers **12**. Bonding die **26** is heated to the range of 450° to 600°F for the case when the material of panel **13** and header **12** is polyethylene. Planar surface **28** contacts the face of flange **19** and planar surface **29** contacts the face of flange **21**. Surfaces **31** and **32** on die **26** contact the outside of hollow header **12** astraddle the line of holes **14**. Panel **13** and header **12** are held in contact with heated die **26** until the surface material of the panel **13** and header **11** or **12** adjacent to the planar surfaces is melted.

As soon as the surface material is melted, panel **13** and header **11** or **12** are drawn apart, die **26** is moved from between them, and the substantially parallel melted surfaces of panel **13** and header **11** or **12** are pressed together to form the unitary assembly **10**, one end of which is shown in Figure 9.8g. The material of panel **13** and headers **11** and **12** solidifies on cooling to form a fluid-impervious bond.

The type of material used for the heat exchange panel **13** and upper and lower headers **11** and **12** will dictate to some extent the process used in fabricating the unitary assembly **10**. There being no satisfactory bonding agents or solvents at the present time for polyethylene, heat forming and bonding methods are used. Use of other materials for the panel and headers or development of adhesives for bonding polyethylene may dictate the use of a particular adhesive or solvent for the bonding process. It is also advantageous to provide some ultraviolet inhibitor in the materials used in the fabrication of the solar heat exchange panel. The panel arrays may be set up on a roof top, in a field, or in any other convenient position accessible to direct sunlight.

**Flexible Collector**

The collector of *F.R. Crawford; U.S. Patent 3,859,980; January 14, 1975* consists of a pair of spaced manifolds and a plurality of tubes connected to and extending between the manifolds; these tubes may be oval in cross section rather than circular and the two outermost tubes of the unit are placed with their maximum diameters at right angles to the maximum diameters of the intermediate tubes, thus the intermediate tubes present a maximum surface to be acted on by the solar energy or heat for heating fluid flowing through them. An envelope of clear material, preferably plastic, encloses the entire unit and the two outermost tubes hold this plastic envelope in spaced relation to provide air insulating spaces both above and below the intermediate tubes in the unit, thus preventing escape of heat from the tubes into the surrounding atmosphere.

The unit is a comparatively flexible and simple solar heating unit which will utilize maximum solar energy and will prevent the convection of heat from its structure by the surrounding atmosphere or by wind.

Referring to Figure 9.9a, the unit comprises an inlet and outlet manifold **1** and a circulating manifold **2**. Tubes **3** are connected to and connect the two manifolds in a fluid circulating system which enters the inlet manifold at its inlet **4** and is directed through substantially one-half of the tubes connecting the manifolds **1** and **2** to cause the fluid to flow through the tubes into the manifold **2** and then return through the remaining tubes to the manifold **1**.

(continued)

FIGURE 9.9:  FLEXIBLE COLLECTOR

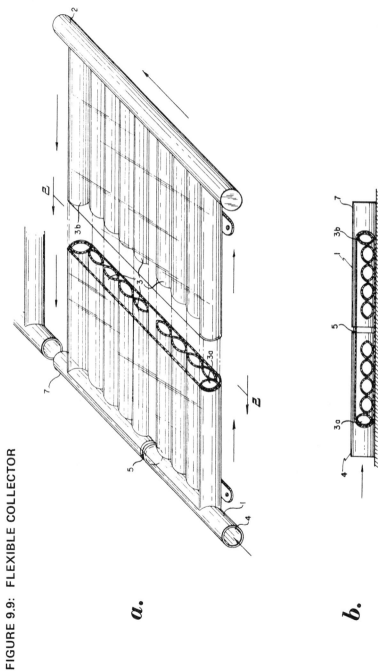

*a.*

*b.*

FIGURE 9.9: (continued)

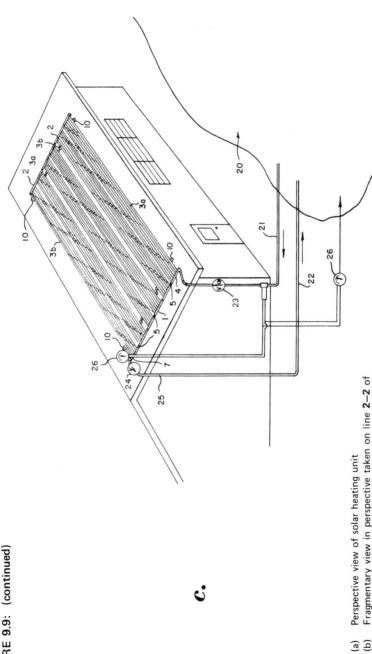

c.

(a) Perspective view of solar heating unit
(b) Fragmentary view in perspective taken on line 2–2 of Figure 9.9a
(c) View showing unit connected for heating water in swimming pool

Source: U.S. Patent 3,859,980

A partition **5** is placed at the manifold **1** substantially equidistant from its ends to cause the above flow of fluid through the unit. The tubes **3** are oval in diameter as clearly shown in Figure 9.9b and the tubes **3a** and **3b** at the outer edges of the group of tubes are placed with their maximum diameters perpendicularly while the tubes intermediate to these two tubes are placed with their maximum diameters horizontal. In other words, the maximum diameters of the two edged tubes are placed at right angles to the maximum diameters of the intermediate tubes for the purpose hereinafter specified.

The intermediate tubes having their maximum diameters positioned as above specified present a maximum surface to be acted upon by the sun or solar heat. All of the tubes may be made of black material or painted black to prevent reflection of heat from shiny surfaces and to absorb the solar heat for transmission to the fluid flowing through the tubes. The tubes and the manifolds may be made of any suitable flexible material, such as sheet plastic so that they may be folded or rolled into a compact form for transportation and for facilitating installation.

The entire unit is enclosed in a clear flexible envelope clearly shown in cross section in fragmentary Figure 9.9b, and this envelope is held spaced from the intermediate tubes **3** of the unit by the two outside tubes **3a** and **3b** to provide a space both above and below the intermediate tubes and the envelope. This space provides a sheet of air insulation which prevents the convection of heat from the tubes into the surface on which the unit is mounted and also into the atmosphere above and surrounding the unit and protecting the unit from the cooling effect of winds.

The intake manifold **1** has an inlet at one end which is connected to the source of supply of the fluid to be heated and an outlet **7** at its opposite end through which the heated fluid flows from the unit. In use the outlet **7** may be connected directly to the desired point of use of the heated water or it may be connected to the inlet of a second identical solar heating unit if one unit is unable to provide the desired heating of the fluid flowing therethrough.

It is necessary to provide sufficient force or pressure to the fluid flowing through the unit and to do this an ordinary fluid pump (not shown) together with suitable pressure regulating means (not shown) is used. The solar heating unit may be used to heat fluid, such as water or any other suitable fluid which will not chemically react with the plastic tubes.

Due to its flexibility the solar heater unit may be used or placed in any suitable place, such as on the roof of a building, on a driveway or on the ground and it has fasteners **10** attached thereto to hold it in place when installed and prevent displacement by wind, gravity or circulation of the fluid. The solar heating unit may be used for heating water for swimming pools or residential heating systems.

Figure 9.9c illustrates the use of the solar heater for heating water in a swimming pool **20**. The swimming pool is both the source of supply for water to the heater and the recipient of the heated water. A suitable pump (not shown) is provided to pump water from the swimming pool through the inlet pipe **21** to and through the heater and out of the heater through its outlet and through pipe **22** back to the pool. A check valve **23** is installed in the cool water inlet pipe **21** to prevent cool water from flowing back into the pool from the heating system when the pump is shut off and a pressure valve **24** is installed in the heated water outlet pipe **25** to maintain the desired low pressure of fluid in the heater and to prevent syphoning off water when the circulating pump is shut off.

A thermostat **26** is installed at the top of the solar heater and this thermostat may be set to turn on the circulating pump whenever the temperature reaches a predetermined reading and a second thermostat is placed in the pool and set to turn off the circulating pump whenever the temperature of the water in the pool reaches a predetermined desirable degree.

**Closed Circuit Heater**

The system of *C.W. Bouse; U.S. Patent 3,599,626; August 17, 1971* is a closed circuit solar water heater in which a sun heated fluid is gravitationally circulated to and from a heat exchanger and control unit in the form of a tank-like receptacle for heating an independent water system circulating through a pipe coil within the receptacle.

The solar heater includes coils of copper tubes leading from the bottom of the heat exchanger and control unit and disposed to be heated by sun rays, the coils receiving the fluid to be heated and then returning the heated fluid into the heat exchanger and control unit near the top thereof for gravitational circulation therethrough. Also included is a pump means controlled by the control unit for causing flow of water through the independent water system and operable only when the temperature of the sun heated fluid in the control unit is above a predetermined level.

As shown in Figures 9.10a, 9.10b and 9.10c, the solar heater, as arranged for heating the water of a swim pool, comprises a flat bottomed pan **10** across which coils of heat conductive tubing **12** are sinuously arranged for direct exposure to sun rays, each coil comprising a single tube running from a delivery manifold **14** at one side of one end **15** of the pan **10** and extending back and forth in serpentine loops over the bottom of the pan to a discharge manifold **16** at the opposite side of the one end **15** of the pan.

In the form shown, three coils are provided and the tubes thereof are disposed side-by-side on the bottom of the pan, to which they are preferably spot soldered, extending substantially the length of the pan in parallel sets connected by 180° bends at alternate ends so that each tube provides an uninterrupted passage from manifold to manifold. All of the tube sets are in a common plane except the last, which terminates at the discharge manifold **16**. This last set of three tubes is arranged to rise progressively from the bottom of the pan adjacent one end of the discharge manifold at the opposite end, so that the outlet end of the coils is at a higher level than the inlet end.

The manifolds **14** and **16** are connected directly to a control unit **20** which comprises a closed tank-like receptacle, of about 10 gallon capacity, located directly above the solar heater pan **10**, the manifold **14** being connected into the bottom of the control unit by a pipe **22** and the manifold **16** being connected to a riser pipe **24** which enters the control unit at its bottom and extends to within a short distance of its top. Thus the control unit provides a closed circuit for flow of the fluid that the solar heater is intended to handle.

# FIGURE 9.10: CLOSED CIRCUIT HEATER

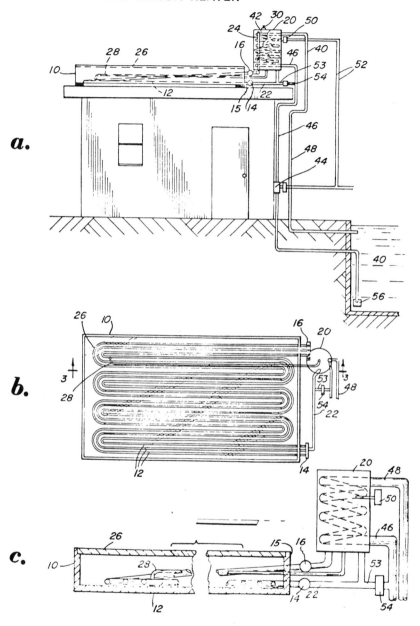

(a)   Elevational view showing solar heater mounted on roof
(b)   Plan view of solar heater
(c)   Enlarged elevational view on the line **3–3** of Figure 9.10b

Source: U.S. Patent 3,599,626

Preferably the interior of the pan **10** and the tubing therein are coated with a flat black paint to provide for maximum absorption of the solar heat and the top of the pan is covered and sealed by a plate glass panel **26** which is suitably secured so as to be water tight. Thus, when the system is filled with a suitable carrying fluid, for example, water, the sun heat will warm the fluid in the tubes **12** and it will be caused to flow upwardly into the control unit **20** and be replaced by cooler fluid from the bottom of the control unit entering the coils by way of the manifold **14**.

In order to equalize the pressure in the system and permit a free circulation of heated fluid from the heater coils **12** to the control unit **20** through the riser pipe **24**, a relatively small copper tube **28** is connected between the bottom of the control unit **20** and the heater coils at a point close to where the last set of the coil tubes begins to rise toward the manifold **16**. Also, to clear the system of air and assure its being filled with heat carrying fluid, a petcock **30** may be provided in the top of the control unit **20**.

The control unit of the solar heater system is the means by which the heat collected by the system is efficiently transferred to an associated system, where its presence is desired, in the present instance a swimming pool **40**, and to effect such heat transfer a coil **42**, of heat conducting material such as copper, is housed within the control unit **20**. Water from the associated system is forced by a pump **44** to circulate through the coil **42** in the control unit, the water entering at the bottom of the coil **42** through the return pipe **48**. As shown, the pump **44** is located in the supply pipe **46**.

Operation of the pump **44**, and hence flow of the fluid to be heated on the control unit **20**, is automatically controlled by an aquastat **50** located near the upper end of the control unit, but below the outlet end of the riser pump **24** which delivers the sun heated water to the control unit. This aquastat **50**, through the leads **52**, turns the pump on and off according to changes in temperature of the sun heated fluid flowing through the control unit. Thus the pump is operated only when sun heated water is supplied to the control unit and whenever the temperature drops below a predetermined level the pump is stopped. Thus circulation of water through the coil **42** occurs only when the fluid in the system of the control unit is sufficiently warm and circulation is automatically stopped when solar heat is not sufficiently available.

In most cases, the heat-carrying fluid filling the solar heater system will be water and when water is the fluid of the associated system, as in a swimming pool, a connection **53** containing a pressure regulator **54** is provided between the supply line **46**, from the pool **40**, and the supply pipe **22** leading from the bottom of the control unit to the manifold **14** supplying the coils **12**. This connection **53** assures the closed circuit of the solar heater system to be filled with water under a suitable pressure at all times. As shown in Figure 9.10a, a foot valve **56** is installed in the pool end of the pipe **46** so as to keep the pump **44** primed.

In a typical solar heater system for swim pools, the solar heater may be a pan 5 feet wide and 9 feet long, with depth of 7 inches, made from 16 ounce sheet copper and the heating coils **12** may be of ⅝-inch outside diameter copper tubing. The last set of coil pipes may then have a rise of 5 inches in 8 feet from the pan bottom to reach the manifold **16**. The riser **24** leading from the manifold

16 and the connection 22 leading from the control unit to the manifold 14 may each be of ¾-inch inside diameter copper tubing; and the pressure equalizing line 28 and the connection 52 between the line 46, from the pool, and the line 22 to the heater manifold 14 may be made of ¼-inch inside diameter copper tubing. The control unit may be a receptacle of about 10 to 15 gallon capacity made of a good heat conductive material.

In such a solar heater the length of each tube would be about 30 feet when arranged in four sets of tubes, as illustrated in Figure 9.10b. Thus, the relatively small diameter of the fluid stream flowing through each tube, in relation to the area of the tube surface subject to the sun heat, and the division of the total fluid volume passing to and from the control unit into a plurality of narrow streams, results in a very rapid heating of the fluid and a relatively fast flow to and from the control unit. Heater efficiency is thereby greatly enhanced and a relatively small heater area is capable of collecting enough sun heat to warm an average home-size swim pool during daylight hours of sunshine and thereby compensate for heat loss from the pool during the nighttime.

### Three Sheet Collector

A solar water heater to be engaged on an inclined roof structure is described by *W.F. Masters; U.S. Patent 3,513,828; May 26, 1970.* It comprises three superimposed sheets, there being an elongate base sheet with a heat reflecting top surface and having upper and lower ends, a black, flexible heat absorbing central sheet, and a transparent solar radiation conducting top sheet. The space between the central and the top sheets is filled with air so the top sheet is spaced from the central sheet.

Water inlet means is connected with a water supply and water is conducted between the base and central sheets at the upper end of the structure. Irrigating means is spaced longitudinally of the structure to maintain water dispersed laterally between the bottom and central sheets as it flows longitudinally therebetween and water discharge means is provided at the lower end of the structure. A pump circulates water to and from the pool as shown in Figure 9.11.

### MISCELLANEOUS SYSTEMS

### Double-Walled Inflated Structure

This process of *J.P. Kwake; U.S. Patent 4,004,380; January 25, 1977* relates to an air supported double-walled structure and a method of making same, including the preparation of a first and second plastic sheet; providing the plastic sheets with a multiplicity of predeterminedly located paired holes which determines the configuration of the final inflated structure; placing the plastic sheets opposite one another; mounting a multiplicity of grommeting means, provided with segments of cords, on the external surfaces of the plastic sheets over the holes; causing the segments of cords to extend inwardly through the holes between the plastic sheets; tying together in knots the loose ends of the cord segments, of the first sheet, with the corresponding loose ends of the cord segments of the second sheet; fusing the edges of the two sheets together; and blowing air into the thusly formed enclosure.

FIGURE 9.11: WORKING ARRANGEMENT OF THREE SHEET COLLECTOR

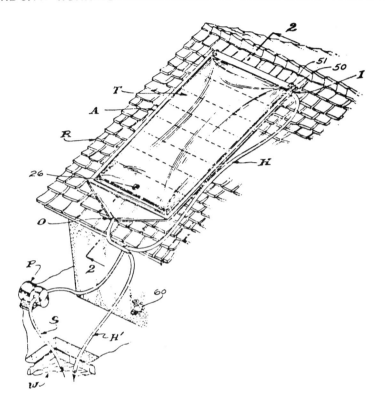

Source:  U.S. Patent 3,513,828

An alternate method of securely maintaining the cords between the two plastic sheets is described, in which gaskets are placed adhesively against the internal surface of the plastic sheets covering the areas immediately surrounding the paired holes; segments of one-piece cords are caused to extend between and pass outwardly through the paired holes of the first and second plastic sheets, respectively; the ends of the cord segments are tied in knots to prevent their slipping back through the holes, and a washer is placed between the knots and the underlying outer sheet surface to prevent tearing of the holes. The externally situated knots or grommeting means are superposed by air-tight covering means so as to prevent escape of air through the holes, in addition to improving the stability of the knots and the outward appearance of the plastic sheets.

The double-walled structure, which has an air space between a pair of plastic sheets, is found to be an excellent absorber of solar energy. If then, fluid is forced between the walls of the structure, into heat exchange contact with the air within the air space, heat transfer will readily take place whereby the fluid will be effectively heated. Since the interior of the air space in the structure is relatively unobstructed, having only cord-like elements contained therewithin for support, the fluid can pass readily downwardly over the interior surface of the structure to a low exit point. Referring to Figures 9.12a, 9.12b and 9.12c, elongated fluid supply tubes **70, 72** are placed in the double-walled inflated structure **100** at a relatively elevated point in the structure and run preferably, substantially along the length of the enclosure **100**.

## FIGURE 9.12: DOUBLE-WALLED INFLATED STRUCTURE

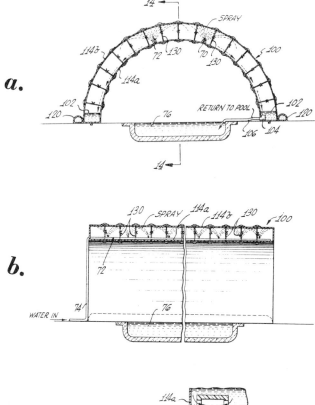

(a)  Cross-sectional view of inflated structure with solar heating modification

(b)  Cross-sectional view, taken along line **14—14** of Figure 9.12a

(c)  Enlarged cross-sectional view of ball check exit valve of Figure 9.12a

Source: U.S. Patent 4,004,380

The tubes **70, 72** are connected to an external fluid supply source, e.g., from a swimming pool **76**, via pipe **74**. Water entering tubes **70, 72** is preferably distributed, in a spray pattern, within the double walls **114a, 114b** of the enclosure **100**. The water, in spray form, thus readily picks up heat absorbed within the air space by solar energy. The heated water falls, by gravity, into a reservoir **102** at the bottom of the enclosure **100** where it can exit, via a ball check valve system **104** and exit line or pipe **106**, into the pool **76** or can be sent elsewhere for other heating purposes.

The ball check valve system **104** opens in response to the water level in reservoir **102**. As the water level in reservoir **102** overcomes the pressure exerted by spring **125**, the ball **127** unseats and allows water to flow out from enclosure **100**, via line **106**. The ball check valve system **104** could also be made temperature-responsive, if desired, and openable only when the temperature of the water in the pool was below a desired point. A temperature responsive valve means is not shown but is conventional in the art. The enclosure **100** is inflated and a water ballast system **120** is utilized.

The walls **114a, 114b** are made of plastic, the outer wall **114b** being translucent or nonopaque, and are interconnected by cord means **130**. Since the structure **100** has only interior cord-like elements **130** contained therein, the water, being heated, has relatively unobstructed passage to the interior reservoir **102**. Thus, the double-walled structure is ideally suited, in combination with a fluid supply and effluent means, as a solar water heater. The fluid may be air or water.

The double-walled structure can also serve as an efficient refrigeration space. Thus, if fluid, e.g., air or water, is circulated through the double walls **114a, 114b** as described with reference to Figures 9.12a and 9.12b, which is at a lower temperature compared to ambient, and the outer wall **114b** is heat-reflective, e.g., as by being painted with aluminized or heat-reflective paint, little heat will penetrate the air space between the double walls, and the coolant will efficiently reduce the temperature of the space enclosed by the structure. Thus, if the coolant temperature is at 60°F and the ambient temperature is 100°F, it is readily possible to reduce the temperature of the interior of the structure by 20° to 35°F or more.

## System with Automatic Temperature Control

There are many types of solar heaters available in the prior art, but many of these are unnecessarily complex and normally are designed for specific applications. Typically, a great number of commercially available solar heaters are designed to achieve relatively high temperatures for use in residential or industrial hot water heaters or environment heaters. These prior art solar heaters designed to achieve relatively high temperatures are usually insulated and protected by container devices with transparent portions in order to efficiently maintain their high temperatures. This is unnecessary for a heater designed to raise the temperature of a large body of fluid only a few degrees. These prior art high temperature heaters are generally considered to be overly complex for applications such as swimming pools.

Therefore, a need exists for a solar heater adaptable for use with relatively large bodies of liquid which is easy to install, requires little or no maintenance, is of simple design and accordingly is inexpensive to construct. Such a heater should also be capable of automatic operation wherein activation of the device is dependent upon a predetermined temperature differential between the incoming and outgoing liquid of the heater to and from the body of water being treated.

The process of *J. Pickett; U.S. Patent 3,970,069; July 20, 1976* is directed to a solar heater designed primarily to be used with large bodies of water such as swimming pools wherein it is desired to raise the temperature of a large body of liquid a few degrees above the ambient temperature. A large volume of liquid flows through the heater coils and is raised in temperature a relatively small increment generally in the range of 10° to 25°F.

This liquid flows back to the reservoir causing a small increase in temperature. As more liquid is circulated, the reservoir temperature increases above ambient temperature. There is heat lost to the atmosphere from the reservoir even as heat is added by the liquid from the heater. Equilibrium is attained when the heat losses within the system are equal to the heat gain. Where there is no heat gain by the heater, the liquid flow is terminated to prevent loss in the heater.

The solar heater of the process is indicated in Figure 9.13 generally as **10**. Heat exchanger means is indicated generally as **12** and is connected in fluid communication with the liquid reservoir as shown. The pool pump/filter system is generally indicated as **22** and can be of conventional design. Conduit means **24** passes from pool pump/filter system to the swimming pool, not shown in the drawings.

## FIGURE 9.13: SYSTEM WITH AUTOMATIC TEMPERATURE CONTROL

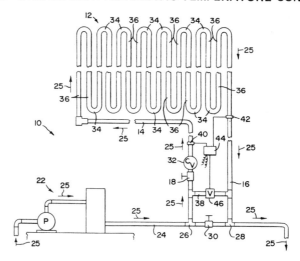

Source: U.S. Patent 3,970,069

In conduit means **24** are located first and second connector means **26** and **28** which comprise T-shaped conduits. First connector means **26** branches off of conduit means **24** and into inlet conduit means **14**. Second connector means

28 branches off of conduit means 24 downstream from first connector means 26 and into outlet conduit means 16. Fluid flow through the entire system is indicated by directional flow arrows 25. Inlet conduit means 14 passes from first connector means 26 to heat exchanger means 12. Outlet conduit means 16 passes from heat exchanger means 12 to second connector means 28.

Heat exchanger means 12 comprises substantially linear tube sections 36 connected to one another by U-shaped tube means 34. Heat exchanger means 12 comprises multiple coils of tubing in a serpentine configuration. The tubing of the heat exchanger means comprises substantially thin-walled plastic tubing.

Located in inlet conduit 14 is first valve means 18 which is operated manually. Also located in inlet conduit means 14 is check valve means 32. Check valve means 32 prevents the reverse flow of fluid through heat exchanger means 12.

In conduit means 24 is located first and second valve means 30. Second valve means 30 is substantially located between connector means 26 and 28 and serves to induce fluid flow through heat exchanger means 12. Between inlet conduit means 14 and outlet conduit means 16 is located cross conduit means 38. Cross conduit means 38 is constructed of substantially the same material as inlet conduit means 14 and outlet conduit means 16. Control valve means 46 is located at least partially within cross conduit means 38.

In the preferred embodiment, temperature differential sensing means comprises temperature sensing means 40 and 42 located on inlet conduit means 14 and outlet conduit means 16 respectively. The temperature as determined by temperature sensing means 40 and 42 is compared in temperature difference sensing means 44 which then controls automatic valve means 46.

The automatically controlled system as depicted is operated by opening first valve means 18 and closing second valve means 30. As in the manual system, this forces fluid to flow into inlet conduit means 14, heat exchanger means 12 and outlet conduit means 16. When temperature sensing means 40 and 42 indicate to temperature difference sensing means 44 that the temperature of the fluid in inlet fluid conduit means 14 is substantially equivalent to the temperature of the fluid in outlet conduit means 16, temperature differences sensing means 44 induces automatic valve means 46 to open.

The fluid seeking the course of least heat resistance, will flow through cross conduit means 38 and into the pool, thus by-passing heat exchanger means 12. However, when temperature sensing means 40 and 42 indicate to temperature difference sensing means 44 that the temperature of the fluid in inlet conduit means 14 is substantially less than the temperature of the fluid in outlet conduit means 16, temperature difference sensing means 44 induces automatic valve means 46 to close.

When automatic valve means 46 is closed the fluid is induced to flow into heat exchanger means 12 and then into the swimming pool. In the automatic configuration, the sytem functions whenever environmental conditions are such that the fluid would be warmed in the heat exchanger. In order to cool the fluid in the automatic configuration, temperature sensing means 40 and 42 are reversed such that temperature sensing means 42 is on inlet conduit means 14 and temperature sensing means 40 is on outlet conduit means 16.

## Heating System Contained in Pool Border

*A. Allocco, Jr.; U.S. Patent 3,945,059; March 23, 1976; assigned to Lawrence Peska Associates, Inc.* provides a description of a solar water heating device and construction for heating the water in a swimming pool from the heat derived from the rays of the sun. The pool is constructed with a border platform or coping around its edges with a hollow passageway under the metal top surface of the coping.

The passageway has water pipes extending therethrough and connected to the pool circulating pumps for circulating pool water through the water pipes. Heating fins are carried by the water pipes and extend into heat exchange contact with the metal top coping, which is being heated by rays from the sun. Thus the sun's rays are conducted in the form of heat into the piping water for circulation into the pool and heating its water economically.

In Figures 9.14a and 9.14b there is a swimming pool **10** with a bottom or floor wall **12**, upstanding end walls **14** and **16** and left and right side walls **18** and **20**, to receive the pool body of water **22**. The pool may have lining inner walls **24** of sheet metal or sheet plastic which is now common for lining pools and is waterproof against leakage and easily cleaned as needed.

The lining walls have top flange portions **26** which lie upon the top edges of the side walls of the pool, and with downturned end flanges as at **28** to hold them firmly in place. The walls are surmounted with a covering border or coping platform **30** which is fairly wide and extends all around the tops of the four walls of the pool, and it has a floor wall **32** formed of sheet material such as aluminum or sheet iron, and a somewhat smoothly curved or rounded top covering shell **34**.

The top covering shell **34** may be made of sheet metal such as aluminum, galvanized iron or the like which is rust resistant, and is usually coated with a baked-on enamel, paint or plastic coating **36**. There is thus formed under the outer platform or coping shell a hollow area or chamber or passageway **38**, the floor of which is the floor wall **32**, and support posts **40** are secured to the floor wall by welding, cement, bolting or the like attachment by aid of bolts **42**.

As the cover shell **34** is preferably formed in one continuous piece, it may be formed with a longitudinal channel or recess **44** to receive a snap-in filler strip molding **46** formed of sheet material such as plastic coated aluminum with side flanges **47** to snap into the receiving channel **44**. The ends of the filler strip molding **46** may be bent down to extend past the bolts **42** and have holes through which the bolts extend.

As seen in Figure 9.14b, the covering shell **34** is preferably more upraised and rounded or arched at its inner edge portion **50** to provide a hand-hold for swimmers getting out of the pool or to just hang on while resting, and there is a gutter **52** formed below the arched edge portion **50**, to skim surface debris from time to time off the top of the water as the level is raised for this purpose, the gutter being inclined for good run-off into drains along its length to aid in keeping the pool water clean.

## FIGURE 9.14: HEATING SYSTEM CONTAINED IN POOL BORDER

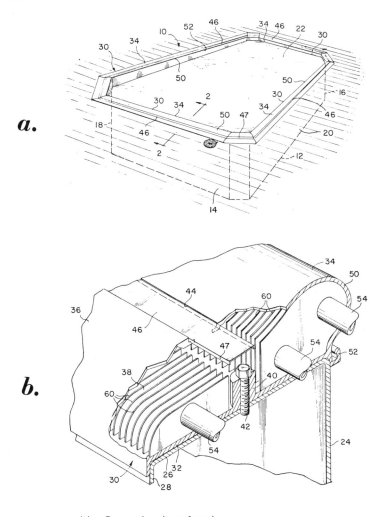

(a) Perspective view of pool
(b) Perspective view taken on plane 2–2 of Figure 9.14a

Source: U.S. Patent 3,945,059

It has been found that the metal platform or border platform coping **34** picks up a great deal of heat from the sun, even though it is coated, and is usually very hot to stand or sit on, and if colored darker it will absorb even more heat from the sun. With this process that heat is picked up and utilized to warm up the water in the pool.

For this purpose, water circulating pipes **54** are extended longitudinally through the hollow passageways or chambers **38** inside the hollow coping shell **34**, and are connected so as to pick up water from the pool from the filter outlet and usual filter pumping pump, and circulating the water from the filter outlet into the coping loop formed by the pipes **54** for three or more passes around the hollow pool border coping, and then to reenter the filter on the pump suction. Valves are used to shut off the inlet and outlet taps of this system to stop further pool water temperature gain if necessary.

The three copper tubes **54** have expanded aluminum or copper fins **60** extending out of their outer surface and made into good heat exchange contact with the tubes by soldering, welding, brazing or other means. The fins **60** are also shaped on their outer edges to fit closely against the inside of the cast or otherwise formed aluminum coping shell **34** so as to be in good heat exchange contact therewith for receiving efficiently heat therefrom and conducting it to the tubes **54**.

The heat from the border coping will be absorbed by the fins and transferred to the water circulating through the tubes **54**, and the result will be an increase in the overall pool water temperature and a decrease in the surface temperature of the coping, which is much desired. The fins will also efficiently absorb any heat which is inside the hollow channels under the coping and also transfer it to the water tubes.

### Heating System with Alternate Paths

The temperature within a confined body of water may be controlled using heating panels which are disposed in the environment surrounding the body of water. One such practical use for a system based on this principle as described by *A.C. Wright; U.S. Patent 3,906,928; September 23, 1975; assigned to Fafco Inc.*, is a system associated with a swimming pool for controlling the temperature of the water in the pool.

In the majority of instances it is desired to elevate the temperature of the water in the pool, although there are times when it may be desirable to reduce the temperature of the water in the pool. For either purpose a system associated with a swimming pool such as that shown in Figure 9.15 may be used. An inlet from the pool to the system is shown at the left, through which water is drawn by the action of a pump **11** which provides water pressure to the inlet of a filter **12**. Downstream of filter **12** two return paths may be seen. One path is a direct return path **13** in which a flow direction valve **14** is situated and an alternate path is provided by indirect return path **16** in which is positioned an array of solar heating panels **17**.

A solar heat sensor **18** is positioned so as to sense the availability of solar energy for providing heat to the array of heater panels **17**. It is usual that solar heat sensor **18** is situated proximate to heater panels **17** as indicated by dashed lines **19** so that the actual solar energy available at the location of heater panels **17** is sensed.

Solar heat sensor **18** provides an output signal or control signal which is electrically connected to a control valve **21**. A mode control switch **22** may be provided to interrupt the connection for the control signal from sensor **18**, so that the control valve **21** may be operated in either an automatic mode or a manual mode.

## FIGURE 9.15: HEATING SYSTEM WITH ALTERNATE PATHS

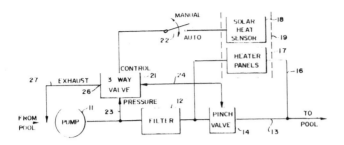

Source: U.S. Patent 3,906,928

When switch **22** is in the manual position the electrical circuit from solar heat sensor **18** to control valve **21** is open, and actuation of control valve **21** must be by manual means. Control valve **21** has the pressure at the inlet to filter **12** connected thereto through a pressure line **23**. A control line **24** is connected between control valve **21** and flow direction valve **14**. The control valve has an exhaust port **26** to which may be connected an exhaust line **27** extending to the inlet side of pump **11**. It may be seen that water leaving solar heater panels **17** or passing flow direction valve **14** continues through the remainder of indirect and direct return paths **16** and **13** respectively to the system outlet to the pool as marked at the right side of Figure 9.15.

The system controls the temperature in a confined body of water, such as that within a swimming pool, in the following fashion in one embodiment. Heater panels **17** and indirect return path **16** are elevated to some degree above direct return path **13**. Flow direction valve **14** may be of the pinch type, which operates in the following manner. Flow direction valve **14** contains a valve chamber and a pressure port for communicating pressure to the valve chamber. When pressure is introduced to the valve chamber in flow direction valve **14** a flexible member forming one wall of the valve chamber distends inwardly to block the flow through the valve.

With switch **22** in the automatic position (closed) solar heat sensor **18** is set to provide a control signal at a predetermined solar energy level which initiates flow through heating panels **17** thereby transferring heat to water flowing therethrough. The control signal is connected to control valve **21** which communicates pressure line **23** with control line **24** thereby providing pressure to the pressure port of flow direction valve **14**.

Flow direction valve **14** closes, as described above, blocking flow through direct return path **13** thereby causing the flow from filter **12** to be diverted to indirect return path **16** and through heater panels **17**. Heat transferred from heater panels **17** to the water flowing therethrough raises the temperature of the water which is subsequently returned to the pool through the remainder of indirect return path **16** and the system outlet.

When solar heat sensor **18** detects an insufficient level of solar energy for raising the water in the pool above a predetermined temperature, control valve **21** is returned to a position whereby control line **24** is placed in communication with exhaust port **26**. Pressure in the valve chamber of flow direction valve **14** is bled off through control line **24** and exhaust port **26**. Means may be provided in the form of exhaust line **27** between exhaust port **26** and the inlet side of pump **11** for positively opening flow direction valve **14** by providing a low pressure to the valve chamber, thereby positively bleeding off the pressure from the valve chamber. Flow direction valve **14** now being in an open condition, the flow from the outlet of filter **12** follows the preferred lower level direct return path **13** to the system outlet to the pool.

In the event it is desired to use the system to reduce the temperature of the pool water, switch **22** may be positioned to the manual position. Control valve **21** may now be manually positioned to communicate pressure line **23** with control line **24** closing flow direction valve **14**. As described above the flow at the output of filter **12** is diverted through indirect path **16** and heater panels **17** whereupon it is returned to the pool.

If there is insufficient solar energy available to raise the temperature of the water passing through the panels **17** above the predetermined temperature then heat exchange occurs in the opposite direction and the heater panels **17** remove heat energy from the pool water flowing therethrough and pass it to the surrounding environment. The water returns through indirect return path **16** to the pool at a temperature lower than the temperature at which it was drawn from the pool by pump **11**. In this fashion the water in the pool may be reduced in temperature to an equilibrium temperature with the environment surrounding heater panels **17**. A second embodiment of the system is included in the patent for a system in which solar heating panels are not elevated.

### Heat Exchanger of Black Matte Plastic Sheet Pairs

*E.J. Konopka and C.F. Fisher Jr.; U.S. Patent 3,868,945; March 4, 1975; assigned to Fun and Frolic Inc.* describe a heat exchanger for warming the water in a swimming pool during the day by means of solar heat and for cooling the water at night consisting of a pair of rectangular sheets of black matte finish flexible film plastic sealed together so as to form a closed perimeter having an inlet passage and an outlet passage, and a sinuous flow path consisting of a plurality of straight parallel elongated flow channels formed between the inlet and the outlet.

At a plurality of points along each straight flow channel the two plastic sections are heat-sealed together to form obstacles to the straight flow path creating zones of turbulence which enhance the efficiency of the heat exchange. A pump removes pool water from a drain, passes it through a filter and divides the filter output between one flow path back to the pool inlet and another flow path to the heat exchanger using an adjustable flow diverter consisting of a T-section having a movable tube extending up from the leg of the T into the arm.

A preferred embodiment of the heat transfer unit shown in Figure 9.16 is formed from a pair of rectangular sheets of polyvinyl chloride film **10**. Both sheets preferably are black in color. While their dimensions are not critical to the process, a typical heat exchanger will employ sheets of approximately 4' x 7'. Polyvinyl chloride film of 0.010 inch or more in thickness is suitable for the practice of the process.

# FIGURE 9.16: HEAT EXCHANGER OF BLACK MATTE PLASTIC SHEET PAIRS

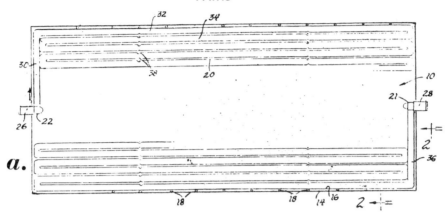

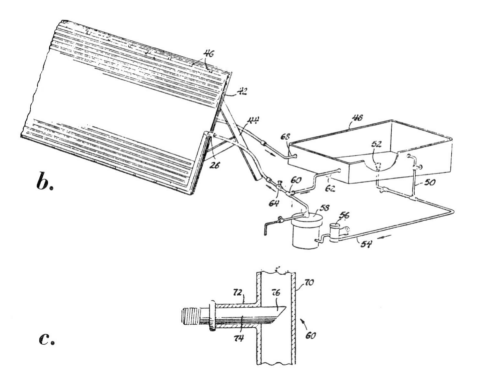

(a)  Plan view of heat exchanger
(b)  Perspective view of heat transfer system
(c)  Detailed sectional view through flow separator

Source:  U.S. Patent 3,868,945

The plastic sheets preferably have a matte or other form of nonreflective surface rather than a polished, reflective surface. The two sheets are laid adjacent to one another and are joined together along a plurality of lines by heat sealing or dielectric sealing. A pair of border lines 14 and 16, one inside the other, are formed adjacent to the edges of the sheet.

These lines may be separated from one another by approximately one inch, and may extend around the full perimeter of the device. At regular intervals of approximately 6 inches the areas between border lines 14 and 16 are heat sealed together in an annular configuration 18 having a central hole 20. The hole 20 is later removed to form grommets which may be employed to support the heat exchanger on appropriate hangers.

The areas of the sheets 10 intermediate the border lines 14 and 16 are joined together along a plurality of lines 20 so as to form a single sinuous flow path extending from inlet point 22 to output point 21. The inlet and outlet points are passages through the border areas 14 and 16 in which cylindrical plastic hose connectors 26 and 28 are inserted.

The inlet connector 26 joins to a first passage 30 which extends along one short edge of the sheets. This channel extends to one of the long ends where it connects to a flow passage 32 that runs the full length of the sheet. The flow is then directed to the next longitudinal path 34 and continues in this manner for the total width of the heat exchanger until it is returned to the outlet passage 21 via a flow section 36.

The flow channels are defined with heat sealed lines approximately one-eighth inch in thickness. In order to prevent the flow from becoming highly laminar, which would decrease the heat transfer efficiency of the device, the sealing area is widened in accordance with a predetermined pattern at regular intervals along each flow path as at 38. These protuberances extend into a pair of flow paths on the adjacent sides of the heated sealed edge. A typical flow protuberance simply consists of a smooth-edged projection which diminishes and diverts the flow area so as to create turbulence in the area of the projection.

When a fluid flow is introduced to the heat exchanger through the inlet connector 26, in a manner which will be subsequently described, the flow causes the nonsealed sections of the sheets 10 to separate to form a plurality of closed flow channels. The fluid first passes through the flow channel 30 into the flow channel 32 and from there into the flow channel 34 and continues to flow the length of the heat exchanger in a zig-zag manner until it reaches the flow channel 36 and then passes out of the heat exchanger through the outlet connector 28. The protuberances 38 tend to break up the laminar flow, as do the broad transitions in flow path which occur at the end of the channel, to provide a turbulent condition which enhances the heat transfer characteristics of the unit.

Figure 9.16b illustrates the manner in which the heat exchanger of Figure 9.16a may be supported and connected to a pool. As illustrated therein, an inclined board 42 having an area slightly in excess of the heat exchanger is supported above the ground with appropriate brackets 44. The angle of inclination of the surface of the board is chosen to be such as to extend normally to the sun's rays. The exact angle differs with various locations, seasons and times of day. The support 44 is preferably adjustable so that the angle of inclination of the board may be modified.

The heat exchanger is supported on the board by slipping the grommets **18** along one edge of the heat exchanger over hooks or screws **46** arrayed along the top edge of the board so that the heat exchanger lies along the board. Figure 9.16b also illustrates the manner in which the heat exchanger may be connected to a swimming pool **48** of the in-the-ground variety. The swimming pool is equipped with a first drain **50** located in a sidewall and a second drain **52** located in its bottom.

Both of these drains are connected to a line **54** which conveys the fluid to the intake of a suitable pump **56**, preferably of the centrifugal variety. The pump forces water through a normal swimming pool filter **58** of the diatomaceous earth or other standard variety. The outlet of the filter is divided into two sections by an adjustable flow diverter valve **60**. One portion of the flow is directed back to the pool through an inlet **62** and the balance is provided to the inlet **26** of the heat exchanger through a line which may include a shut-off valve **64**. The outlet of the heat exchanger is provided to another pool inlet **68** from the output connector **28**.

As is illustrated in Figure 9.16c, the flow diverter valve comprises a plastic T-section incorporating an arm **70** having a leg section **72** joining at right angles. A tubular insert **74** disposed within the leg sections has an open truncated end **76** which projects into the center of the arm. The far extending edge of the end terminates short of the far wall of the arm. The angle of inclination of the insert and its depth of extension within the leg may be adjusted so as to capture a controlled amount of the flow through the arm into the leg.

Assuming the flow through the arm is in an upward direction as viewed in Figure 9.16c, if the truncated section is adjusted so as to face downwardly, in the manner shown, an appreciable percentage of flow through the arm will be diverted into the leg. However, if the insert **74** is rotated so that the truncated section does not face the flow, a smaller percentage of the flow through the arm will be diverted into the leg. When the insert has been rotated through 180° so that the truncated section **76** faces upwardly, no appreciable flow from the arm will be diverted into the leg.

The flow diverter valve **60** is employed in the arrangement of Figure 9.16b to control the portion of the flow from the filter **58** that is passed through the heat transfer unit in order to control the temperature of the pool and optimize the heat transfer. For example, during daylight hours, when the water in the pool is sufficiently warm, the insert **74** is rotated so that no appreciable flow occurs through the heat exchanger, but rather the flow from the filter is passed directly back to the pool through the inlet **62**. On a sunlit day, when the water in the pool is too cool, most of the flow may be diverted through the heat exchanger; however, the flow may be diminished under these circumstances to achieve an optimum heating since an excess of flow through the heat exchanger will result in a decrease in its efficiency.

The heat exchanger may also be used at night to cool the water of a pool that has been overheated by the sunlight during the day. The accumulation of dew on the surface of the heat exchanger and its resultant condensation, aids in the cooling phenomenon.

## Heat Absorber of Sand and/or Iron Oxide

A heating system described by *G.R. Gaydos, Jr.; U.S. Patent 3,815,574; June 11, 1974* includes a fluid circuit with a pump and filter for heating water for a pool. A valved bypass circuit includes a heat absorption unit which can be included in the circuit when desired. The heat absorption unit includes a relatively shallow container of thermally nonconductive material such as wood, the interior of which is lined with a layer of foamed polystyrene.

The receptacle thus formed is lined on its interior with builder's foil and contains a relatively thick layer of sand in which is buried a continuous array of pipe either in sinuous configuration or, alternatively a plurality of parallel pipe lengths extending between headers. In either configuration an inlet and outlet connection is provided so that the pump can circulate water through all of the pipe in the absorption unit. The upper exposed surface of the sand in the unit, at least, is covered with a layer of iron oxide. Alternatively, the sand can be omitted and iron oxide can be employed to fill the entire box. Finally, a layer of crystal glass closes the upper surface of the box which is then mounted so as to receive solar radiation.

Of particular consequence in the assembly of this structure is the incorporation of a substantial layer of black sand or magnetite. For reasons which are not completely understood, the incorporation of a ferric compound and, specifically, this iron oxide compound as the upper layer of the material beneath the glass in the box vastly improves the heat absorption characteristics thereof and permits maximum utilization of that solar energy which falls upon the glass pane.

## Panel with Heat Collecting Lamina

*J.G. Gardner; U.S. Patent 3,561,425; February 9, 1971* describes a solar heater comprising a bank of panels each consisting of an inclined wooden frame supporting a heat collecting lamina and an adjacent backing surface, the lamina collecting sunlight and the backing surface having a horizontal top edge over which liquid is supplied and heated as it descends between the lamina and the backing surface.

Referring to Figure 9.17a a solar heater comprises a row of unit panels **11** erected facing the sun at an inclination of 40° to 50° to the horizontal on a supporting structure. The lower edges of the panels rest on the walls of a trough which extends along the row.

Each panel includes a rectangular wooden frame of side pieces, the top and bottom pieces **14** being 4 feet and the vertical pieces **15** being 8 feet long. The frame supports a rigid base **16** which is typically one-eighth inch plywood or other material able to withstand direct sunlight braced on the underside to prevent sagging. A sheet of polythene **17** covers this base and a sheet of PVC **18** with a matte black finish to absorb the sunlight extends across the polythene. The surface of the polythene sheet **17** is formed with bubbles or dimples **17a** so that the water flowing over it is spread across the surface.

The base has a horizontal top edge **19** which forms a weir over which water flows from a trough formed behind the base and then between the plastic sheets.

## FIGURE 9.18: PANEL WITH HEAT COLLECTING LAMINA

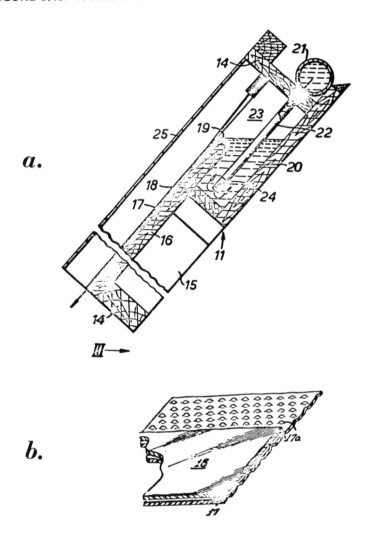

**a.**

**b.**

(a)   Vertical section of a panel
(b)   Fragmentary, partially sectioned, perspective view

Source:  U.S. Patent 3,561,425

The trough is supplied with water from a supply pipe **21** resting on the tops of the panels and having branch pipes **22** feeding the troughs.  The trough is split into compartments by baffles **23** and each compartment is fed by a branch pipe having its own valve **24** for the control of the supply.  In this way an even distribution of water flow across the top edge **19** of the base may be achieved.

The flow of water could be thermostatically controlled at the approximate rate of 100 gal/hr/panel in strong sunlight, the water being heated directly by the absorption of sunlight by the outer plastic surface **18** as it flows under gravity. The rise in temperature will of course depend upon the intensity of sunlight as well as upon the rate of water flow but it should generally be sufficient for the purpose of heating water in an open circuit for swimming pools and the like. The front of the panel has a cover of rigid glazing **25**, which may be of glass or of a transparent plastics material and the back of the panel may have an insulating layer to reduce heat losses, especially from wind.

# COMPANY INDEX

The company names listed below are given exactly as they appear in the patents, despite name changes, mergers and acquisitions which have, at times, resulted in the revision of a company name.

# INVENTOR INDEX

# U.S. PATENT NUMBER INDEX

| | | |
|---|---|---|
| 3,987,786 - 301 | 3,998,204 - 433 | 4,011,190 - 284 |
| 3,989,031 -  58 | 3,999,536 -  48 | 4,011,855 -  70 |
| 3,989,032 - 403 | 4,000,734 - 169 | 4,011,856 - 105 |
| 3,990,429 -  48 | 4,000,850 - 335 | 4,011,858 - 165 |
| 3,990,430 - 406 | 4,000,851 - 381 | 4,013,062 -  63 |
| 3,990,431 -  48 | 4,002,159 - 234 | 4,014,313 - 250 |
| 3,990,635 - 236 | 4,002,160 - 205 | 4,014,314 - 447 |
| 3,991,740 - 194 | 4,002,541 - 287 | 4,015,582 -  90 |
| 3,991,741 - 219 | 4,003,363 -  92 | 4,015,583 - 131 |
| 3,991,742 - 450 | 4,003,364 -  15 | 4,015,584 - 161 |
| 3,991,936 - 298 | 4,003,366 - 192 | 4,015,585 -  79 |
| 3,991,937 - 383 | 4,003,367 - 409 | 4,015,586 - 417 |
| 3,991,938 - 334 | 4,003,426 - 309 | 4,016,860 - 211 |
| 3,993,528 - 179 | 4,004,380 - 464 | 4,016,861 -   9 |
| 3,994,276 - 363 | 4,004,574 - 186 | 4,018,211 -  25 |
| 3,994,278 - 270 | 4,005,583 - 331 | 4,018,214 - 292 |
| 3,994,435 - 186 | 4,006,731 - 265 | 4,018,215 - 214 |
| 3,995,613 -  48 | 4,006,856 - 366 | 4,018,581 - 327 |
| 3,995,614 -  48 | 4,007,728 -  12 | 4,019,494 -   6 |
| 3,995,615 -  40 | 4,007,729 - 167 | 4,019,495 - 420 |
| 3,995,804 - 109 | 4,007,776 - 377 | 4,019,496 -   3 |
| 3,996,092 -  55 | 4,008,708 - 136 | 4,020,826 - 248 |
| 3,996,759 - 338 | 4,008,709 - 316 | 4,020,827 -  81 |
| 3,996,917 - 171 | 4,010,731 - 313 | 4,021,895 - 426 |
| 3,996,918 - 138 | 4,010,733 -  53 | 4,022,187 - 445 |
| 3,996,919 - 295 | 4,010,734 - 413 | 4,022,188 -  76 |
| 3,997,108 - 368 | | |

# NOTICE

Nothing contained in this Review shall be construed to constitute a permission or recommendation to practice any invention covered by any patent without a license from the patent owners. Further, neither the author nor the publisher assumes any liability with respect to the use of, or for damages resulting from the use of, any information, apparatus, method or process described in this Review.